BIOCHEMISTRY AND PHYSIOLOGY OF PROTOZOA

Volume III

CONTRIBUTORS TO THIS VOLUME

Eugene C. Bovee

Frank M. Child

L. G. Goodwin

T. W. Goodwin

Helene N. Guttman

Per Halldal

G. G. Holz, Jr.

S. H. Hutner

Theodore L. Jahn

R. F. Kimball

John B. Loeffer

Dorothy R. Pitelka

I. M. Rollo

Ruth Sager

Otto H. Scherbaum

Mary S. Shorb

Franklin G. Wallace

Barbara E. Wright

BIOCHEMISTRY AND PHYSIOLOGY OF PROTOZOA

Edited by

S. H. HUTNER

HASKINS LABORATORIES, NEW YORK, NEW YORK

VOLUME III

1964

ACADEMIC PRESS   New York · London

ACADEMIC PRESS INC.
111 Fifth Avenue, New York, New York 10003

United Kingdom Edition published by
ACADEMIC PRESS INC. (LONDON) LTD.
Berkeley Square House, London W.1

LIBRARY OF CONGRESS CATALOG CARD NUMBER: 51-6338

PRINTED IN THE UNITED STATES OF AMERICA

Contributors

Numbers in parentheses indicate the pages on which the authors' contributions begin.

Eugene C. Bovee, Department of Zoology, University of California, Los Angeles, California, (61)

Frank M. Child, Department of Zoology, University of Chicago, Chicago, Illinois, (131)

L. G. Goodwin,* The Wellcome Laboratories of Tropical Medicine, London, England, (495)

T. W. Goodwin, Department of Biochemistry and Agricultural Biochemistry, The University College of Wales, Aberystwyth, Wales (319)

Helene N. Guttman, Department of Biology, Haskins Laboratories, New York, New York and New York University, New York, New York, (459)

Per Halldal, Department of Plant Physiology, University of Gothenburg, Gothenburg, Sweden, (277)

G. G. Holz, Jr., Department of Microbiology, State University of New York, Upstate Medical Center, Syracuse, New York, (199)

S. H. Hutner, Haskins Laboratory, New York, New York, (1)

Theodore L. Jahn, Department of Zoology, University of California, Los Angeles, California, (61)

R. F. Kimball, Biology Division, Oak Ridge National Laboratory, Oak Ridge, Tennessee, (243)

John B. Loeffer, Office of Naval Research, Pasadena, California, and Department of Zoology, University of California, Los Angeles, California, (9)

Dorothy R. Pitelka, Cancer Research Genetics Laboratory, University of California, Berkeley, California, (131)

I. M. Rollo, Department of Pharmacology and Therapeutics, University of Manitoba Medical College, Winnepeg, Manitoba, Canada, (525)

---

* Present Address: The Nuffield Institute of Comparative Medicine, The Zoological Society of London, London, England

RUTH SAGER, Department of Zoology, Columbia University, New York, New York, (297)

OTTO H. SCHERBAUM, Department of Zoology, University of California, Los Angeles, California, (9)

MARY S. SHORB, Poultry Science Department, University of Maryland, College Park, Maryland, (383)

FRANKLIN G. WALLACE, Department of Zoology, University of Minnesota, Minneapolis, Minnesota, (459)

BARBARA E. WRIGHT, The J. Collins Warren Laboratories of the Huntington Memorial Hospital of Harvard University, at the Massachusetts General Hospital, Boston, Massachusetts, (341)

Preface

This volume of *Biochemistry and Physiology of Protozoa*—9 years after the preceding volume—is more, we hope, than an episodic Biochemical Toolmaker's Manual, Protozoological Section. As pointed out by Holz in his chapter and by myself in the Introduction, the problems get tougher and the talent is spread thinner along the expanding research perimeter. The base of talent recruitment must be broadened to include the so-called underdeveloped countries. Biochemical protozoology is expensive. How can Brazil, for instance, contribute its share of protozoological talent when it bears the burden of 5 million (estimated) cases of Chagas' disease, and its road-making crews in the hinterland are felled by drug-resistant malarias? How much can sub-Saharan Africa contribute until it casts off its burden of trypanosomiasis and malaria? A unique vicious cycle this, where the advance of protozoology ever more depends on solving large-scale life-and-death protozoological problems, yet these problems in turn require for their solution advances in protozoology and biochemistry, etc. One must hope, in all modesty, that this volume will help break the vicious cycle.

Again I thank the contributors: their inspired labors made editing more pleasure than travail. It would be presumptuous for an editor to dedicate a collective volume. Nevertheless, as this volume nears publication, we thank our colleagues in the Society of Protozoologists whose lively expectations (*nagging* is not quite the term) kept this enterprise from faltering.

I must thank my fellow editor, André Lwoff, whose vision made this series possible. And, with this third volume, it is only just to thank our friends at Academic Press for their painstaking, steadfast encouragement.

S. H. HUTNER

October 1964

Contents

CONTRIBUTORS   v

PREFACE   vii

CONTENTS OF VOLUME I   xiii

CONTENTS OF VOLUME II   xiv

Introduction

By S. H. HUTNER

Text   1

References   7

Environmentally Induced Growth Oscillations in Protozoa

by OTTO H. SCHERBAUM and JOHN B. LOEFFER

I.   Introduction   10

II.   Flagellata   10

III.   Sarcodina   18

IV.   Ciliata   19

V.   Extent of Phasing during Growth Oscillations   53

References   55

Protoplasmic Movements and Locomotion of Protozoa

by THEODORE L. JAHN and EUGENE C. BOVEE

I.   General Aspects of Structure and Energy Metabolism   62

II.   Ameboid Movement   66

III.   Shuttle Flow in Mycetozoa   77

IV.   Bidirectional Filamentous Movement   84

V.   Taxonomic Significance of Two Types of Movement in Sarcodines   88

VI.   Cilia versus Flagella   89

VII.   Movement of Flagella and of Flagellates   90

VIII.   Movement of Cilia and Ciliates   100

IX.   Other Movements of Protozoa   112

X.   Summary and Epilogue   118

References   119

The Locomotor Apparatus of Ciliates and Flagellates: Relations between Structure and Function

by DOROTHY R. PITELKA *and* FRANK M. CHILD

I.	Introduction	131
II.	The Flagellar Unit: The Kinetid	134
III.	Locomotor Systems of Flagella and Cilia	163
IV.	Reproduction and Morphogenesis	185
V.	Conclusions	190
	References	192

Nutrition and Metabolism of Ciliates

by G. G. HOLZ, JR.

I.	Introduction	199
II.	Nutrition Requirements	201
III.	Metabolic Pathways	223
IV.	Comparative Biochemistry	232
	References	233

Physiological Genetics of the Ciliates

by R. F. KIMBALL

I.	Introduction	244
II.	Cell Cycle	244
III.	Clonal Life History	253
IV.	The Immobilization Antigens	256
V.	Nuclear Differentiation	258
VI.	Genetic Control of Intracellular Symbionts	263
VII.	Other Loci	265
VIII.	Physiological Aspects of Radiation Mutagenesis	265
IX.	Conclusions	267
	References	269

Phototaxis in Protozoa

by PER HALLDAL

I.	Introduction	277
II.	Phototaxis in Flagellates	279

III. Phototaxis in *Amoeba*   291
IV. Phototaxis in Ciliates   292
 V. Phototaxis and Ecology   293
    References   295

Studies of Cell Heredity with *Chlamydomonas*

by RUTH SAGER

  I. Introduction   297
 II. Genetic Analysis   298
III. The Chloroplast as a Model Organelle   305
IV. Toward an Organelle Genetics   315
    References   316

The Plastid Pigments of Flagellates

by T. W. GOODWIN

  I. Introduction   319
 II. Chlorophylls   320
III. Carotenoids   327
IV. Biliproteins   334
 V. Pigmentation and Phylogeny of Phytoflagellates   335
VI. Nonphotosynthetic Flagellates   336
    References   337

Biochemistry of Acrasiales

by BARBARA E. WRIGHT

  I. Introduction   341
 II. The Aggregation Process   343
III. Endogenous Changes in Respiration and Substrate Levels during
     Differentiation   347
IV. Protein Synthesis   362
 V. Enzyme Activities   363
VI. Speculations on Control Mechanisms of Biochemical Differentiation in
     the Slime Mold   377
    References   379

The Physiology of Trichomonads

by MARY S. SHORB

  I. Introduction   384
 II. Carbohydrate Metabolism   385

III. Nitrogen and Lipid Metabolism 414
IV. The Chemical Composition of Trichomonads 415
V. The Nutritional Requirements of Trichomonads 419
VI. Cultural Methods 430
VII. Factors Affecting Pathogenicity 440
VIII. Immunology in Trichomonad Infections 446
IX. Antibiotics and Other Drugs as Metabolic Tools 448
X. Summary 450
References 450

Nutrition and Physiology of the Trypanosomatidae

by HELENE N. GUTTMAN *and* FRANKLIN G. WALLACE

I. Introduction 460
II. General Morphological Features of Trypanosomatids 460
III. Genera of Trypanosomatidae 462
IV. Growth in Defined Media 464
V. Growth of Trypanosomes 477
VI. Growth in Tissue Culture 484
VII. Miscellaneous Experiments 486
References 491

The Chemotherapy of Trypanosomiasis

by L. G. GOODWIN

I. Introduction 495
II. New Trypanocidal Drugs 497
III. Drug Resistance 506
IV. Trypanocides and the Metabolism of Trypanosomes 509
V. Immunity 517
References 520

The Chemotherapy of Malaria

by I. M. ROLLO

I. Introduction 525
II. Malaria and the Host 526
III. The Chemotherapy of Malaria 536
References 558

AUTHOR INDEX 563
SUBJECT INDEX 585

Contents of Volume I

Edited by S. H. HUTNER *and* ANDRÉ LWOFF

Introduction to Biochemistry of Protozoa By ANDRÉ LWOFF

The Phytoflagellates By S. H. HUTNER AND LUIGI PROVASOLI

The Nutrition of Parasitic Flagellates (Trypanosomidae, Trichomonadinae) By MARGUERITE LWOFF

Metabolism of Trypanosomidae and Bodonidae By THEODOR VON BRAND

Nutrition of Parasitic Amebae By MARGUERITE LWOFF

Biochemistry of Plasmodium and the Influence of Antimalarials By RALPH W. MCKEE

The Biochemistry of Ciliates in Pure Culture By GEORGE W. KIDDER AND VIRGINIA C. DEWEY

Contents of Volume II

Edited by S. H. HUTNER *and* ANDRÉ LWOFF

Introduction By S. H. HUTNER

Comparative Biochemistry of Flagellates By S. H. HUTNER AND LUIGI PROVASOLI

Composition and Synthesis of the Starch of *Polytomella coeca* By S. A. BARKER

The Nutrition of Ciliates By W. J. VAN WAGTENDONK

Encystment and Excystment of Protozoa By W. J. VAN WAGTENDONK

Metabolism of Free-Living Ciliates By GERALD R. SEAMAN

Mutualistic Intestinal Protozoa By R. E. HUNGATE

Developmental Physiology of the Ameboid Slime Molds By MAURICE SUSSMAN

The Chemotherapy of Malaria, Piroplasmosis, Trypanosomiasis, and Leishmaniasis By L. G. GOODWIN AND I. M. ROLLO

Comparative Studies on Amebae and Amebicides By WILLIAM BALAMUTH AND PAUL E. THOMPSON

BIOCHEMISTRY AND PHYSIOLOGY
OF PROTOZOA

Volume III

Introduction

S. H. HUTNER

Haskins Laboratories, New York, New York

Most of the work covered in this volume was done since 1955—since the publication of Volume II. To save this volume from fission, chapters on marine flagellates and on photosynthesis in flagellates had to be omitted. My colleague Dr. Provasoli discussed the main advances in his detailed chapter on phytoplankton fertility in the volume "The Sea" (1963). The photosynthesis chapter could easily have swelled into a half-book if comparable in self-sufficiency and detailed coverage to the other chapters; besides, the tempo of photosynthesis research would soon have made most of it obsolete and the publication of symposia on photosynthesis—with flagellate work usually well represented— has become very fashionable; at least one major symposium (Kettering Foundation) is in press at this writing. Much flagellate material is covered in a review on algal nutrition (Hutner and Provasoli, 1964) designed in no small part to entice plant physiologists to work with phytoflagellates, especially with *Euglena* and the newly available hardy plant-animals (voracious photosynthesizers) represented by *Ochromonas danica*.

It is hoped that the detailed treatment in this volume of some protozoa, notably of ciliates, approaches this ideal of comprehensiveness, and will sharply reduce the need to consult older literature. Since the ciliate branch of proto-zoology is now highly developed, the time seemed ripe to bring to bear on them a many-angled vision—hydrodynamics, fine structure, genetics, biochemistry— so that their value as research objects might be clearly discerned. Minor over-lappings have been retained since they help to achieve what symposia aim at and seldom do: make a subject stand out in three dimensions—the ciliate chapters amount to, I think, more than a three-blind-men-and-the-elephant job.

The expansion in protozoological research, much of it a use of protozoa by

1

workers calling themselves biochemists or biophysicists rather than protozoologists, prompts some thoughts on this situation.

Some protozoologists express dismay at designating a protozoan as a "tool" presumably applied for some distant non-protozoological purpose, and bemoan the indifference on the tool-users' part to protozoology for protozoology's sake. These protozoological purists can take heart from some truths that, however imperfectly, have guided this volume.

Truth 1. Wheeler's (1911) dictum: ". . . natural history constitutes the perennial root-stock or stolon of biological science. . . . It retains this character because it satisfies some of our most fundamental and vital interests in organisms as living organisms more or less like ourselves."

This does not contradict J. J. Thompson's familiar injunction that until a phenomenon can be measured, knowledge of it is meager and unsatisfactory.

Truth 2. "Man cannot be uplifted; he must be seduced into virtue" (Marquis, 1927). Perhaps through this volume some mechanism-minded scientists will interest themselves in studying protozoa as organisms, and morphological protozoologists will swim upstream in Helmholz fashion and interest themselves in biochemistry and biophysics.

Truth 3. The late Franklin P. Adams was a journalist turned radio performer in a program that foreran the BBC Brains Trust. Said Adams: "Everything I know I found out while looking up something else." Hence the contributors were encouraged to relate protozoological information to biochemistry, biophysics, etc., as a means of indicating how problems might be outflanked and to favor protozoological feedback to biochemistry, etc.

Protozoology and Sociology. Whence the drive for using protozoa as tools? The answer must be a blend of technology and sociology and fosters optimism about the usefulness of this volume. Protozoology registers the pressures of an increasingly research-oriented society. In the United States research now consumes 3% of the gross national product (Killian, 1963). Besides engaging in familiar practical pursuits such as finding food and antibiotics for expanding populations, biologists must cope with pollutions of air, soil, food, and water accompanying urbanization and industrialization, and with an intensification of medical research for which they must supply the biological materials—that is to say, the "systems."

This crowds biologists toward a new constraint—of demand for research pushing against the bounds of resources in talent—if not of material—even in the richest industrial societies, even with military outlays eliminated. Arithmetic foretells it: thus Robert Oppenheimer has calculated that if the *Physical Review* continues to grow at the rate developed between 1945 and 1961, it would be as big as the earth in another 100 years. The growth curve of the *Journal of Protozoology*, a fairly good index of protozoological activity (the editors have maintained a reasonably consistent ferocity in rejecting trivia and flensing blubber), shows that while the *Journal of Protozoology* is unlikely to jostle the *Physical Review* in taking over the earth, protozoology already consumes sizable resources. If one minds the world importance of malaria, trypanosomiasis, leishmaniasis, amebiasis, theileriasis, coccidiosis, and other protozoal diseases, then adds uses of protozoa in biochemical, toxicological, and cancer research, the share of research resources devoted to protozoology seems likely to increase.

Legislators—aging men and women—transmit the pressures for research, for, encouraged by past successes with infectious diseases, they demand more control over the more difficult problems of diseases of metabolism, especially cancer and aging; the cry for biological research grows as part of the "tide of rising expectations."

One way to make the most of space and materials is miniaturization, from microchemical apparatus and Warburg's micro-respirometers to transistor electronics.

The triumphs of the unity of biochemistry—a doctrine that implies that the currency of structure and metabolism is so common to all forms of life that many metabolic pathways can be studied most conveniently in protists—reinforces the drive to miniaturization and booms microbiology. Many a new nation seems to plan a microbiological institute alongside its nuclear reactor. Protozoology follows the trend; e.g., a hospital with rooms devoted to microbiological assays for vitamins (several of them based on protozoa) integrated with its clinical research and routine diagnostic service (Baker and Sobotka, 1962), if returned to rats and chicks, would have to build about half an Empire State Building, with one floor harboring a battery of statisticians and computers to smooth out animal-animal, cage-cage variability—a vanishing nuisance in microbial cultures. Attempts to extend protozoological miniaturization to pharmacology and toxicology have been outlined (Hutner, 1964).

Protozoology and Molecular Biology. Miniaturization is not enough. As genetics goes molecular, exploiting the resolution permitted in microbial systems of being able to detect one recombinant among 10^8 cells, *Drosophila* genetics looms as a grotesquery like hippopotamus genetics. Even the genetically revered eye pigments of *Drosophila*—at least the pteridines—are pursued with the *Crithidia* assay for the biopterin and related unconjugated pterines (Ziegler, 1961). This volume itself is victim of the trend from miniaturization to microminiaturization for our erstwhile editor and co-editor has been beguiled by viral genetics, and proselytizes among nonbiologists at ease with the ultramicro doings of molecules and subatoms (Lwoff, 1962).

So, conceding that protozoa are elephantine objects for much of molecular biology, what *are* they good for? This volume, taking its place among our publisher's volumes covering the protists—bacteria, viruses, algae and, in preparation, fungi—describes a few of these research tools among the flagellates, ciliates, cellular slime molds, and various pathogens, including sporozoa.

Chemists and physicists, at the outset of their ventures into biology, are mechanism- not organism-minded; when grasping a new biological tool, they need all available relevant information about the tool organism including the mundane, often loftily neglected housekeeping details of media and culture maintenance.

Public consent for this remarkable channeling of resources into biological research may come in part from a suspicion diffusing among scientists and some laymen that the complexity of life has been underestimated. We take in stride such statements in novels as: "To construct a human directly from inorganic materials is a problem of the fourth order—[i.e., entailing 10^{10} units of information]. . . ." (Hoyle, 1959). One is tempted to estimate the *hubris* implicit in this remark—what is the practicability of grading organisms on a scale of the bits of information they embody?—but the fact remains that the machinery of the simplest bacterium poses a big enough problem to use up the planet's research potential; one has to assign priorities.*

* An example: a bacterium, e.g., *Escherichia coli*, is estimated to contain at a minimum 2000 kinds of macromolecules (Lwoff, 1962). Assuming that half these have an enzymatic function, estimate that (with luck) it will take 2 years to clean each enzyme to crystallinity. *Bill:* 2000 man-years. Then to establish the active site in each enzyme may require determination of the amino acid sequence in each enzyme (0.5 year per enzyme), then piecemeal degradations checked by synthesis (say 2.5 years for each enzyme). *Bill:* 3000 man-years. Assume, too, that 100 enzymes have metal-binding prosthetic groups and so these enzymes lend themselves to a Perutz-Kendrew topological analysis, at 2 years per protein. *Bill:* 200 man-years. Then superimpose the enterprise of determining the composition of the cell-wall macromolecules and its associated endotoxin. This could easily require the attentions of 100 chemists for 20 years, since the endotoxins contain complicated amines, polysaccharides, and high-molecular lipids bound in unknown ways, probably by linkages new to science, and therefore requiring proof of structure by synthesis. (The difficulty in assembling the mitochondrion from its components is an even worse lipid problem.) *Bill:* 2000 man-years. *Escherichia coli* contains 10^7 nucleotide bases (Lwoff, 1962)—which points up the structural problem in determining the nucleotide sequences in DNA and RNA; techniques have not yet been developed for this. To this, add 1000 genetic markers to those already on hand as a start toward assigning functions to the nucleotide sequences, both in self-replication and in coding protein synthesis. It would be ridiculous at this time to try to guess the man-years required to elucidate the interactions of these systems, including identification of feedbacks controlling steady-states and growth and elucidation of the biosynthetic pathway for every kind of molecule in the cell—a task far from completed for molecules with weights <1000. To sketch the main structural-functional features of one bacterium could, then, easily soak up the world supply of biologists and chemists. Furthermore, provision of cells for analysis could well require all the capacity of tanks now devoted to antibiotic production and brewing—which would require the services of the world supply of industrial microbiologists, chemical engineers, and brewmasters. Even if the bacterium in question were only PPLO-size, matters are no better as gain in simplicity of organization may be counterbalanced by greater difficulty in rearing the organism. The simplicity of a virus such as tobacco mosaic is illusory as the virus requires the living host-plant for expression of its synthetic talents.

The slowness in accretion of fundamental knowledge of cancer warns that we must apply efficiently and to the utmost every tool at hand for understanding life, whether exemplified in bacteria or man. To justify cleaning up an enzyme, it is no longer enough to say, as did Mallory when asked why he climbed Everest: "Because it's there!" There must be a contribution to practice or theory. In medieval bestiaries and herbals, every animal and plant was supposed to have a "signature" pointing to its use for man. The singularity of protozoa likewise implies that each has a unique use; the problem is whether the investment in effort is justified by the returns—a point raised in this volume by Holz.

The strategy of research must in the long run be shaped by the suspicion that the complexity of life is being badly underestimated and that biological problems are solved more by wear-throughs (as Alfred L. Loomis puts it) than by break-throughs. The slow progress in cultivation of carnivorous protozoa and intracellular parasitic forms brings this only grudging tractability home to the protozoologist just as the slowness in cultivating differentiated cells or the problem of cancer brings this home to the man-centered biologist.

Protozoa as Research Tools. The protozoal research tools must, then, be improved and added to. Table I lists some tools, present and potential. This drive for relevance means that the role of protozoa as research tools is becoming more and more one of providing way-stations between the profusion of bacterial metabolic pathways irrelevant to human problems and the restricted array of metabolic pathways in metazoa. Protozoa are manipulable by the cheap, simple techniques of microbiology—a theme developed in preceding volumes of this series and elsewhere (Hutner, 1964, 1965). (True, some protozoa are so large one should speak of semimicrobiology.)

Needs in tool making are illustrated by the following situation. Photosynthesis of the green-plant type is increasingly studied by means of *Euglena gracilis* var. *saccharophila* (mainly Z strains). It has shortcomings: *Euglena* yet lacks the sex that permits genetic analysis of the interplay of nuclear and cytoplasmic factors in chloroplast development and drug resistance, as described in Dr. Sager's chapter, and *Chlamydomonas reinhardi* has a very limited heterotrophy. This points to the neglected aspect of protozoology: natural history or, if one likes, ecology. For all the vast knowledge of *Euglena gracilis,* its ecological niche, as noted (Hutner, 1964) is yet unknown; laboratory lore amounts to no more than hints as to how it makes a living. A specific enrichment procedure would tell a good deal. The Z strain and others were obtained by that grand natural historian, E. G. Pringsheim, by a cheese-soil-and-water enrichment. It was later selected as an object of physiological research by detailed tests on some 20 isolates. If there is some mechanism of gene recombination in the euglenoids, as suggested by the success of the group, testing for recombinants may demand cross-testing 50 or so isolates—which returns us to the need for a better enrichment procedure than Pringsheim's. The isolation

Table I

SOME USES OF PROTOZOA AS BIOCHEMICAL TOOLS

Species and problem	Unique use	Favorable	Needs development
Tetrahymena pyriformis			
Folic acid and 6 other B vitamins	No	Yes	Yes
Guanine	No	Yes	No
Thioctic acid	No	Yes	No
T. setifera			
Ethanol factor	?	?	Yes
Paramecium			
Plant-sterol requirement	Shared by guinea pig	Yes	Yes
Peranema			
Linoleic acid	?	?	Yes
Euglena			
Vitamin B_{12}	No	Yes	No
Dark-reversible chloroplast	No	Yes	No
Ochromonas malhamensis			
Vitamin B_{12}	Yes	Yes	No
O. danica			
Thiamine, biotin	No	Yes	No
Dark-reversible chloroplast	No	Yes	No
Dictyostelium			
Acrasin	?	Yes	Yes
Crithidia			
Biopterin	Yes	Yes	No
Trypanosoma mega			
Morphogenetic factor (urea?)	?	Yes	Yes
Coccolithophorids			
Calcification	No	Yes	No
Arcella			
O_2-secretion	?	Yes	Yes

problem with sexual strains of *Chlamydomonas* is simpler thanks to the discovery by Lewin (1951) that zygotes (a sign of sexuality) of *Chlamydomonas* are acetone resistant. Acetone resistance has not been fully exploited for finding a more versatile and vigorous heterotrophic, heterothallic *Chlamydomonas; C. reinhardi,* useful as it is as a research tool, is a makeshift—a hand-me-down—not a truly well designed tool, selected for the long pull from a wide assortment of candidates.

We are indebted for most of these research tools to a few old-fashioned biologists whose names appear as "isolators" in catalogs of algae and protozoa issued by type-culture collections. Such biologists, as implied by Wheeler's dictum, must not be denigrated by the new snobbery of molecular genetics. Admittedly, it is useful to take Samuel Butler's 19th century remark "a hen is an egg's way of making more eggs" and update it to "a hen is DNA's way of making more DNA"—snobberies too are updated while organism-minded biologists quietly broaden the base of that superstructure elaborately topped by molecular genetics.

This volume accordingly is divided without prejudice between molecule- and process-centered articles and organism-centered articles. For the sake of a more penetrating vision the authors invited to contribute were mainly polymaths who could shift within one chapter from one kind of vision to the other. Even the most ostensibly practical articles—those on chemotherapy—share this hoped-for three-dimensional quality.

REFERENCES

Baker, H., and Sobotka, H. (1962). *Advan. Clin. Chem.* 5, 173–235.
Hoyle, F. (1959). "Ossian's Ride." Harper, New York (original ed.); also Berkley Publ. Co., New York.
Hutner, S. H. (1964). *J. Protozool.* 11, 1–6.
Hutner, S. H., and Provasoli, L. (1964). *Ann. Rev. Plant Physiol.* 15, 37–56.
Hutner, S. H., (1965). *Developments Ind. Microbiol.*, 6, in press.
Killian, J. R., Jr. (1963). *Atlantic Monthly* No. 211, 69–72.
Lewin, R. A. (1951). *J. Gen. Microbiol.* 5, 926–929.
Lwoff, A. (1962). "Biological Order." M.I.T. Press, Cambridge, Massachusetts.
Marquis, D. (1927). "The Almost Perfect State." Doubleday, Page and Co., New York.
Provasoli, L. (1963). *In* "The Sea" (M. N. Hill, ed.), Vol. 1, pp. 165–219. Wiley, New York.
Wheeler, W. M. (1939). "Essays in Philosophical Biology." Harvard Univ. Press, Cambridge, Massachusetts.
Ziegler, I. (1961). *Advan. Genet.* 10, 349–403.

Environmentally Induced Growth Oscillations in Protozoa*,†

Otto H. Scherbaum and John B. Loefer

Department of Zoology, University of California, Los Angeles, California; and Office of Naval Research, Pasadena, California, and Department of Zoology, University of California, Los Angeles, California

		Page
I.	Introduction	10
II.	Flagellata	10
	A. Environmental Factors Inducing Growth Oscillations	10
	B. Biochemistry of Synchronized Flagellates	17
III.	Sarcodina	18
	A. General Observations	18
	B. Growth Oscillations in Clonal Cultures	18
	C. Effect of Temperature Changes on the Reproduction of Amoeba	18
IV.	Ciliata	19
	A. Factors Inducing Growth Oscillations	19
	B. Structural and Biochemical Changes during Growth Oscillations	24
	C. Effect of Radiation on Growth Oscillations	40
	D. Effect of Metabolic Inhibitors on Growth Oscillations	44
	E. Comparison of the Effect of Various Inhibitors on Growth Oscillations	52
V.	Extent of Phasing during Growth Oscillations	53
	A. General Considerations	53
	B. The Synchronization Index (SI)	53
	C. The SI in Protozoan Cultures	55
	References	55

* Work reported from the senior author's laboratory was supported by grants from the University of California Research Fund, Cancer Fund of the University of California, National Science Foundation, United States Public Health Service, and contract funds from the Office of Naval Research (NR 108–547).

† The following abbreviations are used in this chapter: HT (standard heat treatment for induction of division-synchrony); BHT (beginning of HT); EHT (end of HT); NAD (nicotinamide-adenine dinucleotide); NADP (nicotinamide-adenine dinucleotide phosphate); NTP (nucleoside triphosphate); ATP (adenosine triphosphate); GTP (guanosine triphosphate); TCA (trichloroacetic acid); DNP (dinitrophenol); PU (phenylurethane); FPA (*p*-fluorophenylalanine); SI (synchronization index).

9

I. Introduction

More than 50 years ago it was observed that some photosynthetic micro-organisms divide preferentially during certain hours of the day in their natural habitat. For example, the dinoflagellate *Ceratium fusus* divides only between 1:00 A.M. and 3:00 A.M. (Gough, 1905), and *C. tripos* only between 3:00 A.M. and 7:00 A.M. (Jörgensen, 1911). Recently similar growth oscillations, with a maximum between 9:00 A.M. and 11:00 A.M., were also noted in cultures of *Peridinium triquetrum* under natural illumination (Braarud and Pappas, 1951). In a study of photosynthetic efficiency of *Chlorella* in intermittent light, cell division occurred only during the last hour of the dark period (Tamiya *et al.,* 1953). Analysis of the cyclic transformation in *Diplococcus* following a single temperature shift led to the discovery of pronounced growth oscillations (Hotchkiss, 1954).

Interest in this field increased rapidly following the deliberate induction of synchronized cell division in a microbial population (Scherbaum and Zeuthen, 1954). Synchronized cultures provide a new approach for studying time dependent processes in the growth-duplication cycle of the cell. Results obtained on synchronized cells, however, must be interpreted with caution, since induced growth oscillations in populations cannot always be equated with metabolic events occurring within a single cell during its normal life cycle.

In this article emphasis has been placed on summarizing available data on growth oscillations in protozoa. Several reviews discuss synchronization of cell growth and division in individual systems; in them the interested reader may also find discussions of ideas concerning the underlying mechanism of synchrony (Bruce, 1957; Campbell, 1957; Zeuthen, 1958; Scherbaum, 1960; Burns, 1962). The review of the literature was completed through January 1963.

II. Flagellata

A. Environmental Factors Inducing Growth Oscillations

1. light-dark cycles

a. Growth and Reproduction in Chlamydomonas. Light-dark shifts induce growth oscillations in the green flagellate *Chlamydomonas moewusii*. In Fig. 1A the increase in cell numbers for respective cultures of a normal and a mutant paralytic strain are shown during 5 consecutive dark-light cycles. Increases in cell number occur only during the hour preceding and the hour following the dark-light transition.

Growth and reproduction of an individual cell during a 24-hr. period is depicted in Fig. 1B. At the beginning of the cycle after 1 hr. of illumination, wild-strain cells are small (134 μ^3), spherical, and motile. They increase in size; at 22 hr. the parent cell has a volume of 417 μ^3. In both strains the volume increases 3- to 4-fold during 21 hr. of the cycle, and by that time the protoplast has divided to form four daughter cells. Their liberation is restricted to a 2-hr. period at the dark-light transition (Cristofalo, 1962). At the beginning of the light period 90% of the cells in the culture are motile, toward the end of the light period only 25% exhibit movement, and only 15% are motile in the dark period. Studies on formation and utilization of high-energy phosphates might be rewarding, particularly if highly motile forms in the early light phase were compared with nonmotile forms in the dark period.

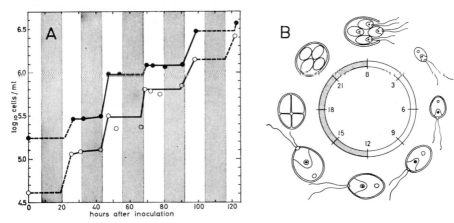

Fig. 1. Growth of *Chlamydomonas moewusii*. A. Increase in cell number in two strains as a function of light-dark cycles. Upper curve (solid circles), wild strain; lower curves (clear circles), immotile mutant strain. Shaded areas indicate dark periods of 12 hr. duration alternating with equal periods of light (8600 lux). Inorganic medium. B. Development during a 24-hr. cycle. Numbers indicate time in hours and shaded area dark period. (After Cristofalo, 1962.)

In a different strain a near 8-fold increase in cell number occurs during the first division cycle after inoculation (Bernstein, 1960), due to the fact that the parent cell characteristically gives rise to 8 flagellates. Moreover, the division burst is restricted to the last hour of the dark period, when up to 91% of the population divides.

b. Cell Division in Euglena. In 15 green species of Euglenineae mitosis was confined to the dark period of the diurnal cycle (Leedale, 1959). The first division stages generally appear about 2 hr. after the onset of darkness, and the maximum number of dividing cells (1.3–6.8%) is observed 0.5 to 2.5 hr. later. These observations on species cultured at 20°C. were extended over several months during which day length and time of onset of darkness varied. Neither the time at which division began nor the maximum percentage of cells in mitosis was affected by these variables. Mitosis did not occur, however, with day length less than 12 hr. Although these experiments show the correlation between the light-dark shift and the onset of mitosis 2 hr. later, no division or growth oscillations could be induced artificially in any species. If the natural light-dark cycle is displaced in time to such an extent that light exposure occurs during the normal dark period, the cells become quiescent and no mitosis is observed. If the light-dark cycle is reimposed on such a culture, the rhythmic reproduction characteristic of the normal light-dark cycle recurs.

The rhythmic oscillations noted when the euglenoids are in a biphasic soil-water medium disappear when the organisms are cultured in 0.2% beef extract at 20°C., and 5–10% of the cells are in division at any given time, day or night.

Data on 5 colorless species grown in biphasic medium reveal striking, but irregular bursts of mitotic activity (2–8%), with virtually no divisions occurring between these maxima. No correlations between these growth oscillations and the diurnal light changes were noted. These growth fluctuations in the colorless species continued during alternate light and dark periods, in continuous light, and in uninterrupted darkness. Transfer of the colorless *Euglena gracilis* T to beef-extract medium abolished all periodic growth rhythmicity, just as the periodic rhythmicity of the green forms is abolished by similar transfer (Leedale, 1959).

c. Selection of Light-Dark Periods for Induction of Synchrony in Euglena. A simple approach has been designed to establish light-dark periods for *Euglena gracilis*, strain Z, that does not necessarily conform to the usual 12:12-hr. pattern (Cook and James, 1960). Under continuous illumination of 130 foot-candles the generation time of this species in the medium used is 19.9 hr., and there is no evidence of growth oscillations up to 70 hr. after inoculation (Fig. 2). Transfer of the culture to darkness results in a decreased rate of multiplication, and cellular division ceases approximately 11 hr. after the light-dark shift, when maximum population density is attained.

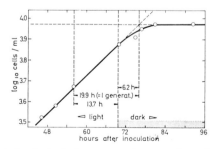

Fig. 2. Effect of a light-dark shift on growth rate of *Euglena gracilis*. At 70 hr. after inoculation the culture was transferred to darkness (shaded area). Temperature, 20°C. (After Cook and James, 1960.)

Had illumination continued, maximum population density should have been attained after only 6.2 hr., the time at which the extrapolated growth curve, as indicated by the broken line, intercepts the level of population density actually observed. Assuming that each cell in the culture has the same generation time in continuous light, it follows that the last cell which can complete division in the dark has to spend at least 13.7 hr. (19.9 minus 6.2) in the light. The light-dark ratio is therefore 13.7:6.2 or 2.2:1. Adapting the length of one cycle to 24 hr., therefore, 16 hr. light exposure followed by 8 hr. of darkness were chosen for the experiment. The results are shown in Fig. 3A.

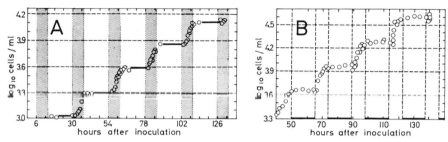

FIG. 3. Growth oscillations in flagellates. A. Increase in cell number in a culture of *Euglena gracilis* alternately exposed to 16 hr. light and 8 hr. darkness (shaded area) at 20°C. Medium (James, 1960, p. 554) supplemented with cysteine and methionine. (After Cook and James, 1960.) B. Increase in cell number in a culture of *Astasia longa* exposed to temperature cycles, each consisting of 15 hr. at 15°C. (black bars on abscissa) and 8 hr. at 25°, with 0.5-hr. transition periods. Medium 2% Proteose-peptone. (After Padilla and James, 1960.)

Increase in cell number occurs primarily during the dark period; 95% of the dividing cells complete division in a 6-hr. interval. During these division bursts the generation time is 3.9 hr. When cysteine and methionine are omitted from the growth medium, the corresponding generation time is 7.5 hr.

d. Biological Timing in Gonyaulax. Cultures of *Gonyaulax polyedra* can be maintained on a 12:12-hr. light-dark cycle (Sweeney and Hastings, 1958). At least 85% of the cells divide within 5 hr. during the latter part of the dark period and the beginning of the light period (Fig. 4A). These reproductive oscillations persist for at least 10 days if a culture primed by the light-dark cycles is transferred to continuous dim light (Fig. 4B). Temperature affects the timing of these oscillations only slightly. In a culture at 25°C. the peak of the ninth cycle occurred at about 230 hr. (upper curve), whereas, at 18.5° the ninth cyclic division peak was evident only about 15 hr. earlier (lower curve). Time between successive peaks of division is approximately 25.4 hr. at 25° and 23.9 hr. at 18.9°. The average generation time is 3.8 days at 25° versus 4.2 days at 18.5°C. Low concentrations (0.02 µg./ml.) of actinomycin D inhibit the

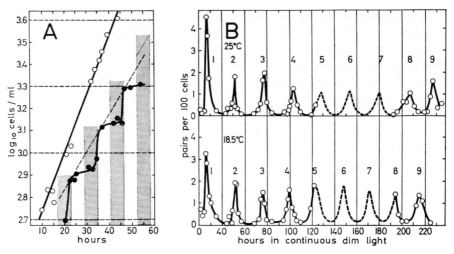

FIG. 4. Growth of *Gonyaulax polyedra* in continuous and intermittent light. A. Increase in cell number in continuous light (clear circles), and during intermittent dark (shaded areas) and light periods (solid circles). Temperature 21.5° ± 1°. Generation time in continuous light, 1 day; in light-dark, 1.5 days. B. Persistence of light-dark invoked rhythms in constant dim light. Upper curve, at 25°; lower curve, at 18.5°. A light-dark culture taken at the beginning of a light period was transferred to dim light at time zero. (After Sweeney and Hastings, 1958.)

luminescence rhythms without stopping growth (Karakashian and Hastings, 1962).

e. Circadian Rhythms. The examples of growth oscillations during the diurnal cycle described above are often paralleled by biological functions which also recur daily or with a near daily periodicity. For nonphotosynthetic protozoa, one may cite as examples of this the mating ability and response to ultraviolet light of *Paramecium,* and phototaxis, luminescence, and photosynthesis in green forms such as *Euglena* and *Gonyaulax.* Similar cyclic oscillations occur in a wide variety of algae and fungi. Since the frequency and periodicity of these functions is approximately 24 hr., they have been termed circadian rhythms (from the Latin *circa dies*). Several reviews on biological timing are available (*Cold Spring Harbor Symp.* 25, 1960; Halberg and Conner, 1961; *Ann. N.Y. Acad. Sci.* 98, 1962). As noted in the introduction, circadian growth oscillations have been known for a long time in marine dinoflagellates.

2. TEMPERATURE SHIFTS

a. Design of a Temperature Cycle (Astasia). Various parameters affect growth of *Astasia longa* (James and Padilla, 1959; Padilla and James, 1960; James, 1962, 1963). This colorless flagellate grows readily in the range of 15°

to 30°C. Elevation of the incubation temperature increases O_2 consumption and decreases generation time; dry weight per cell and cell volume also decrease. In milligrams the dry weight synthesized per microliter O_2 consumed is 1.25×10^{-3} at 15° and 2.50×10^{-3} at 25° (Table I).

Table I

DRY WEIGHT AND OXYGEN CONSUMPTION IN *Astasia longa*[a]

Incubation temperature (°C.)	Generation time (hours)	Dry weight (mg./10^6 cells)	Average cell volume (μ^3)	Q_{O_2} (μl./hr./10^6 cells)	Dry weight (mg.)[b] / Oxygen consumed (μl.)
15	33	1.12	3320	18.0	1.25×10^{-3}
20	12	0.90	2460	22.7	2.30×10^{-3}
25	11	0.94	2470	21.6	2.50×10^{-3}
30	6.5	0.50	1510	47.2	1.13×10^{-3}

[a] James and Padilla (1959).
[b] Values in last column were calculated by the method of Hutchens *et al*. (1948). If the data in columns two to five are directly used, higher values are obtained.

It is tempting to conclude that *Astasia longa* has twice as effective a synthetic capacity at the higher temperature. The authors point out that if the proportion of the cellular constituents is the same in both cases, the cold period would have to be approximately twice as long as the warm period to accomplish the same end. Certainly, this condition is not realized with respect to length of the generation times at these two temperatures (33 hr. at 15°C.; 11 hr. at 25°).

If a single shift from 25° to 15° is made in the incubation temperature, cell division does not occur for 18–20 hr. Obviously, in the design of a temperature cycle for induction of growth oscillations, the duration of incubation at 15° should not exceed 18 hr. or cell division would commence during this low temperature period. This information and considerations of relative cellular efficiency at 15° and 25° leads to design of a cycle in which a 1:2 relationship between the warm and cold periods is chosen. Alternately incubating *Astasia* at 25° for 8 hr., and for 15 hr. at 15°, with transition periods of 30 min., was very effective for inducing growth oscillations (Fig. 3B). Several hours after the onset of each warm period a consistent doubling of cell numbers was observed. The most satisfactory temperature cycle designed for *Astasia* was a 6.5-hr. period at 28.5° alternating with 17.5 hr. of incubation at 14.4°. In this cycle, the time during which almost all the cells divide is about 2.5 hr. (Blum and Padilla, 1962). According to an earlier report (Padilla and James, 1958) alternating incubation periods of 10 hr. at 5° and 14 hr. at 25° also induced growth oscillations. No cell divisions took place at $5°$ but a sharp doubling in population occurred about 6.8 hr. after the temperature shift.

The 24-hr. cycle is suitable for maintaining cultures for some time on the alternating $14.4°–28.5°$ temperature regime. To facilitate maintenance one-half of the culture is aseptically replaced by fresh medium at the beginning of each cold period. It is preferable to keep the cultures in darkness, since light inhibits multiplication (Cook, 1960).

3. NUTRITIONAL REQUIREMENTS FOR GROWTH OSCILLATIONS

a. In a Photosynthetic System (Euglena). Although growth oscillations are observed in *Euglena gracilis,* var. *bacillaris,* when grown in the basal medium alone, addition of cysteine and methionine reduces the time span for reproductions during the dark period. Assuming that doubling of cell number occurs during each dark phase of the cycle, the time required in the basal medium alone is 7.5 hr., but only 3.9 hr. in the supplemented medium. Further studies showed that cysteine and methionine: (a) reduce the variability of the generation time in mass cultures, and (b) shorten the duration of cellular fission (Cook and James, 1960).

b. In Astasia. The growth oscillations shown in Fig. 3B were obtained with a culture in 2% Proteose-peptone medium. In a Myers-Cramer medium, however, poor synchrony was observed and it could not be improved by alterations in frequency and amplitude of the temperature cycles (Padilla and James, 1960). The fission index (percent of cells in any visible stage of cytoplasmic division) differs when growth of *Astasia* from a peptone-containing medium is compared with a sampling of cells from an inorganic medium. The fission index is approximately 4-fold higher in the cultures grown in the salt medium. Since the generation times of these two cultures are almost the same, by calculation fission took 3–6 times longer in the salt medium cultures. It appears that the cells in the salt medium lacked a compound necessary for fission. As for *Euglena,* supplementation with cysteine and methionine in physiological concentrations significantly reduced the fission index and fission time in *Astasia;* the fission time, however, is not as short as in cells from the Proteose-peptone medium. The complexity of this nutritional requirement is further indicated by the finding that these two amino acids, if used individually, do not reduce the fission time to the same extent as in combination. It was reported recently (James, 1962, 1963) that thioglycolate at a concentration of $10^{-4}M$ can replace cysteine and methionine for induction of growth oscillations in *Astasia.* The rate of uptake of S^{35}-labeled thioglycolate during the division burst of synchronized *Astasia* is twice the rate recorded when no fission stages are seen in the culture. Increased thioglycolate uptake during the division period may reflect a rise in metabolic activity, and if so, this would be in contrast to many other observations reported for embryonic material and other cells (Mazia, 1961) suggesting that metabolic activity is depressed during cellular division. Radioactive thioglycolate taken up during the division period is localized in the region to which the nucleus moves prior to division (James, 1962).

B. BIOCHEMISTRY OF SYNCHRONIZED FLAGELLATES

1. CHEMICAL ANALYSES

In *Astasia* at 25° both nucleic acids double in amount when the cell count doubles (Padilla, 1960; James, 1962). Synthesis of protein, however, is not confined to a part of the 25° period, as is true for the nucleic acids. Approximately 60–70% of the protein synthesized is formed during the entire 25° phase, and the remainder is produced during a 3-hr. interval in the latter part of the 15° phase. These findings are in good agreement with the observations on maximum thioglycolate uptake during the warm period (James, 1961a). Using an improved temperature cycle treatment for induction of synchrony, additional data were obtained for *Astasia longa*. The time course of DNA, RNA, and protein synthesis was confirmed (Blum and Padilla, 1962).

2. RESPIRATION AND ENERGY REQUIREMENTS

During one complete growth oscillation *Astasia* requires the synthesis of the following, per 10^6 cells: 280 μg. protein; 30 μg. RNA and 5 μg. DNA (James, 1962). As pointed out above, both nucleic acids are synthesized during the 25° phase of the temperature cycle. It is also known that the rate of O_2 consumption per hour per 10^6 cells is 26.3 μliters and 65.6 μliters in the cold and warm periods, respectively (Wilson, 1962; Wilson and James, 1964).

It is not known exactly when, during one temperature cycle, nucleotides and amino acids are synthesized. For this reason, the energy requirements for the formation of the nucleic acids and 60–70% of the proteins are estimated only for the warm period (25°). This estimate does not include the energy requirement for nucleotide formation (James, 1962). Since approximately 18 μmoles of ATP per hour per 10^6 cells are produced during the warm period it was noted that the synthesis of protein and nucleic acids requires little more than 3% of the energy provided by O_2 consumption during the same period.

3. EFFECT OF 8-AZAGUANINE ON GROWTH OSCILLATIONS

If *Astasia* is transferred from the temperature-cycle treatment to constant 28.5°, two growth oscillations follow. Addition of 8-azaguanine to the culture 20 hr. before the transfer reduces the degree of synchrony and rate of reproduction to a great extent (Padilla and Blum, 1964).

In repetitive cycles of 14-hr. exposure to light alternating with 10 hr. of darkness cell division of *Euglena gracilis* Z is restricted to the dark period (Cook, 1964). RNA synthesis occurs at a constant rate throughout the 24-hr. duplication cycle, while DNA synthesis is limited to the light period. In another *Euglena*, strain var. *bacillaris*, synthesis of RNA occurs only in the light period (Cook, 1960).

III. Sarcodina

A. General Observations

Within a single multinucleated cell such as *Pelomyxa*, all nuclei (sometimes 1000+) divide synchronously (Kudo, 1947, 1951).

Diurnal variations in reproductive rate have been observed in *Amoeba proteus* (Liesche, 1938), *A. carolinensis* (Short, 1946), *Flamella citrensis* (Bovee, 1956a), and *Vexillifera telmathalassa* (Bovee, 1956b). In the latter two species, the growth oscillation occurs during darkness.

B. Growth Oscillations in Clonal Cultures

Growth oscillations distinguishable to a fair degree can be obtained in clonal cultures of *Chaos chaos*. Measurements of reduced weight have been obtained (Satir and Zeuthen, 1961).

C. Effect of Temperature Changes on the Reproduction of Amoeba

1. single cold shock

Increased frequency of division is obtained after cooling a culture of *Amoeba proteus* to 3–4° and then changing the temperature to 27–29° (Dawson *et al.*, 1937).

2. multiple temperature shifts

If a culture of *Amoeba proteus* is maintained for several days on a temperature cycle consisting of two equal periods at 18° and 26°C. 24 hr., the highest percentage of dividing cells is noted at the beginning of the warm period (James, 1954, 1959; Mazia and Prescott, 1954). During the 12-hr. period at 18° the average number of cells dividing per hour is 1.7% of the total population, with a maximum of 4%. After the shift to 26° the number of dividing cells increases and reaches a maximum of 20% during the fourth hour after the change. On the average 9% of the cells divide per hour during the first 9 hr. of the warm period.

IV. Ciliata

A. FACTORS INDUCING GROWTH OSCILLATIONS

1. RHYTHMIC REPRODUCTION FOLLOWING INOCULATION

The age of a stock culture used to inoculate for inoculation of is an important factor in determining the growth pattern which follows. If samples from the negative growth acceleration phase are used as an inoculum, growth oscillations are subsequently observed, but the timing of the oscillations depends on the age of the inoculum (Browning *et al.*, 1952). The fluctuations in cell number at approximately 10-min. intervals in two types of cultures are plotted in Fig. 5. Inocula for A and B were obtained, respectively, from stocks in the

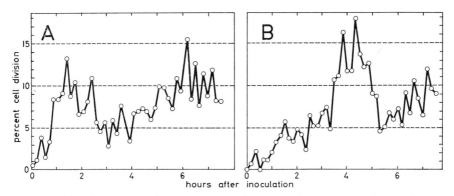

FIG. 5. *Tetrahymena pyriformis* (strain unknown). Fluctuation in the number of dividing cells in cultures started with inocula taken from early (A) and late (B) negative growth acceleration phases. (After Browning *et al.*, 1952.)

early and late negative growth acceleration phases. In A, distinct fission peaks occurred at 1.5 and 6 hr.; in B, the first division burst was observed at 3.5–4 hr. Lack of some substance which becomes available to the cells after transfer to the new medium was suggested to account for this phenomenon observed in *Tetrahymena pyriformis*.

If transfers of *Tetrahymena pyriformis* GL are made from the late negative growth acceleration phase of a peptone medium culture to physiological saline, there is also a lag period of about 3 hr. (Levy and Scherbaum, 1961). Shortly thereafter 15–20% of the cells are dividing. These workers suggest that O_2 availability may be important in connection with this phenomenon.

2. ISOLATION OF PHYSIOLOGICALLY UNIFORM CELLS

a. Control of Culture Conditions. Physiologically uniform populations of *Paramecium aurelia* were obtained by the following method (Woodward *et al.*, 1961). Since it was found that 20–23 fission generations occurred between two autogamies, a single cell was isolated after having completed 12–15 fissions. The progeny from such a culture showed a fair degree of synchronized division. After 8 fission generations of *Paramecium* isolated from this culture, dividing animals were removed and transferred to fresh medium. By this selection, the degree of synchrony was further improved to the extent that the following fission began within a 40-min. period in 90% of the selected cells (duration of interphase was 5.5–6.0 hr. at 26°). Such cultures were used for cytospectro-photometric studies on the amount of RNA, cytoplasmic and macronuclear protein, and DNA in macro- and micronuclei between two subsequent divisions (Woodward *et al.*, 1961). The results are discussed elsewhere in this volume (chapter by R. F. Kimball).

b. Centrifugation. A centrifugal force of approximately 600*g* was used to separate physiologically uniform cells from log-phase cultures of *Tetrahymena pyriformis* L1 and H (Corbett, 1963). There are seldom as many as 10% of the cells from the supernate undergoing division immediately after centrifuga-tion, although 2 hr. later 35–40% of the cells may be dividing. The method is useful for antigenicity studies and in other instances where the heat treatment is precluded.

3. CHANGES OF HYDROGEN ION CONCENTRATION IN THE MEDIUM

A sudden change in pH of the growth medium affects the rate of reproduc-tion of *Tetrahymena pyriformis* HS (Prescott, 1958). If a sterile solution of NaOH is added to a culture in the exponential phase growing at pH 5.65 to alter the pH to 7.3, three distinct effects are observed: (1) exponential multi-plication in a population growing at 28°C., with a generation time of 3.25 hr., is interrupted by a lag phase lasting 1.15 hr.; (2) the lag phase is followed by cell multiplication which is synchronized to some degree during the first two population doublings; (3) approximately 6 hr. after the pH change divisions are no longer synchronized and exponential multiplication occurs with a genera-tion time of 2.3 hr.

4. EFFECT OF TEMPERATURE CHANGES

The terms "heat" and "cold," as used in the following sections, denote tem-peratures above and below the optimum for reproduction.

a. Single Temperature Shift. The generation time of *Tetrahymena pyriformis* HS in a peptone medium is 7.3 hr. at 18.4° and 2.8 hr. at 27.7° (Prescott, 1957). After a rapid shift from 18.4° to 27.7°, the growth rate does not immediately change to the expected value for the higher temperature, but continues unaltered for 2.5 hr. After this lag the growth rate increases and temporarily exceeds the rate expected for 27.7°. An undulation in the growth curve is observed which disappears after the second oscillation, when the constant rate characteristic for 27.7° has been attained. In other words, the single temperature shift induces a transient cell division synchrony.

b. Cooling. Over a period of approximately 8 years, cultures of a number of species and strains of Tetrahymenidae were maintained at temperatures of 6° and 10° by one of us (J.B.L.) for varying periods of time. Some failed to survive successive transfers at these low temperatures in the medium used (Proteose-peptone, 1.5%; Bacto Casitone, 0.5%; yeast extract, 0.1%; plus inorganic salts). Of approximately 60 strains tested, two-thirds tolerated 10°, but only about one-third survived successive transfers at 6°. The latter included *Tetrahymena pyriformis* H, E, T, W, L3, HS, N, Y, TC, F, and one of two GL strains; *T. vorax* V_2 and TUR, *T. rostrata* NZ2; *T. corlissi;* one of three strains of *T. limacis; Colpidium campylum* C; and *Glaucoma chattoni* A. That division occurs at these low temperatures is evident since the cultures were maintained through a number of transfers. Dividing forms were rarely observed on microscopic examination, except following exposure of the cultures to a higher temperature. After 1.5–2 hr. at 25°, many cells undergo synchronous division. The maximum number of dividing cells was noted for strain T, in which 39% of the ciliates were seen dividing after 2 hr. at 25° following prolonged culture at 10°.

In other experiments (Zeuthen and Scherbaum, 1954), mass cultures of *Tetrahymena pyriformis* GL which had been maintained at 22° (optimum = 28–29°), were cooled to 7° during exponential multiplication for periods of time ranging from 2 to 16.5 hr. The number of cells in fission before the cold shift was 5–7%, and the percentage decreased to zero at 7°. Approximately 2 hr. after return of the cultures to 22°, as many as 25–30% of the cells were in the visible stages of fission. After this single oscillation induced by the temperature change, cell multiplication continues without further evidence of cycling. Additional oscillations in the division index may be obtained if the culture is returned to 7° immediately after each new division peak (Fig. 6A).

c. Single Heat Shock per Generation. The incubation temperature of a log-phase culture of *T. pyriformis* GL at time zero is changed from 27° to 33°C. and maintained at this level for 30 min. Upon return of the culture to 27° a brief period without cell division is followed by a rapid increase in population number. As many as 50% of the cells are in fission. If another heat shock is applied after the new division maximum, the growth oscillation can be repeated (Fig. 6B).

d. Repeated Heat Shocks. The standard heat treatment (HT) for induction of synchrony in *Tetrahymena pyriformis* GL employs repeated shocks of 34° for 30 min. alternating with exposure to the optimum temperature (29°) for the same period. It is desirable to begin with cultures in the exponential growth phase having a population density of 5×10^4 cells or less. After the last shift

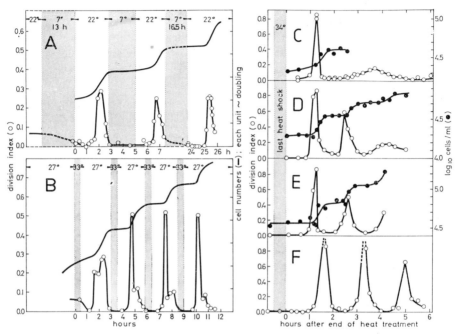

Fig. 6. *Tetrahymena pyriformis* GL. Growth oscillations after single and multiple temperature shocks.   A. Effect of 7°C. single cold shocks of 13 hr., 2 hr., and 16.5 hr. duration on cell multiplication at 22°C., as reflected in the division index (div. ind. = no. cells in fission/total no. of cells) in the lower curve, and cell number in the upper curve. (After Zeuthen and Scherbaum, 1954.)   B. Effect of single 33°C. shocks of 0.5 hr. duration on cell multiplication at 27°. (After Thormar and Zeuthen, in Zeuthen, 1958.)   C–F. Cell multiplication after the last shock of the standard heat treatment in: C, Synthetic medium at 28°C. (after Scherbaum and Zeuthen, 1954); D, Inorganic medium at 28° (after Hamburger and Zeuthen, 1957); E, Proteose-peptone medium at 28° (after Zeuthen, 1958); F, Proteose-peptone medium at 24° (after Scherbaum and Zeuthen, 1954).

to 29° a division lag or recovery period follows. Eighty minutes after EHT (the end of HT) 85% of the cells are dividing. One or more fission waves may follow, depending on factors such as chemical composition of the medium, population density, O_2 tension, etc. For successful synchrony it is important that the medium is nutritionally adequate to support growth in cell size during HT. For this reason the population density should not exceed a hundred thousand per milliliter at BHT (i.e. the beginning of HT). The results obtained by using the standard HT with slight variations in medium and temperature are shown in Fig. 6C–F.

Other modifications of the medium have been employed with the standard temperature shift. Addition of kinetin (60 μg. per liter) to a culture of *Tetrahymena pyriformis* W at EHT improves synchrony (Ron and Guttman, 1961). The poorer the synchrony in the untreated control the more effective is the addition of kinetin. For example, if only 14% of the cells divide in the control culture, addition of kinetin raises the proportion to 24%. The presence of kinetin, however, does not alter the time between EHT and the first division peak.

Tetrahymena pyriformis S responds to the same heat shock treatment as used for strains GL and W (Schuster and Vennes, 1960). When strain S is cultured on a biphasic medium (agar layer containing 1% peptone and a liquid phase with peptone) and subjected to HT, 6 successive growth oscillations are observed. The peaks of division are separated by 3.5–7.0 hr. from each other. The persistence of synchrony for 27 hr. is surprising inasmuch as there is normally considerable variability in the generation time for individual cells.

e. Are Different Temperature Treatments Required to Induce Synchrony in Different Strains? There are several basic considerations involved in the design of an effective HT for synchronizing *Tetrahymena*. Temperature levels must be chosen with respect to both optimum and sublethal ranges. The combined effect of the alternating HT must be such as to permit cell growth, but not allow cell division.

Strain WH6 requires a higher shocking temperature, 42.8° (Holz *et al.*, 1957) than the 34° shock used for strains GL, W, and S (Scherbaum and Zeuthen, 1954; Mita *et al.*, 1959; Schuster and Vennes, 1960). It is interesting to note that the sublethal temperature for GL, W, and S is one degree less than the optimum used in the HT for WH6.

f. Apparatus and Equipment for Synchronizing Cultures. For induction of growth oscillations in protozoa, equipment has been designed for automatic phase regulation of temperature, light, aeration, nutrition, and other conditions necessary for producing synchronized cultures (Scherbaum and Zeuthen, 1955; Lee, 1959; James, 1961b; Plesner *et al.*, 1963; Scherbaum and Jahn, 1964).

5. EFFECT OF REDUCED OXYGEN TENSION

Normal cultures of *Tetrahymena pyriformis* GL were subjected to two periods of anaerobiosis (oxygen tension < 0.15 mm. Hg). The exposure periods, each lasting for 50 min. were separated by 40 min. of normal aeration. After the end of the second period no increase in cell number was observed for 90 min. Cell division commenced at that time and reached a peak 140 min.

later when 60% of the cells were observed in fission (Rasmussen, 1963). The effect of anaerobiosis on heat-synchronized *Tetrahymena* will be discussed in Section IV,D,1,*d*.

B. Structural and Biochemical Changes
during Growth Oscillations

Since the first temperature-shock treatment for inducing synchronous cell division in *Tetrahymena pyriformis* was reported (Scherbaum and Zeuthen, 1954), much information has accumulated on the biochemistry and physiology of growth oscillations in microorganisms. Among the protozoa three strains of *T. pyriformis* have been used most extensively: GL, W, and WH6.

1. cell and nuclear size, weight, and respiration

When the synchronizing HT is used on strain GL, microscopic examination of the cultures reveals the following: (a) the number of cells in fission, normally 5–10%, decreases, and after the third heat shock scarcely any dividing cells are observed in the remaining period of HT (Scherbaum, 1957a); (b) cellular size increases. The normal cell size in exponential cultures is 25,000–50,000 μ^3; for cells at EHT it is 50,000–150,000 μ^3 (Scherbaum, 1956). Length and width of individual organisms increase disproportionately, the mean length increase being 30% and the mean width increase 70%.

Along with volume increase there is a gain in dry weight. The over-all rate of dry weight increase is almost linear throughout HT and continues until the first synchronized division takes place (Scherbaum *et al.*, 1959b; Hamburger and Zeuthen, 1960). More detailed studies of the dry weight increase during HT indicate that after each shift from 28° to 34° growth continues at the 28° rate for a portion of the 30-min. shock period before dry weight increase ceases. After the next temperature change from 34° to 28° the growth rate typical for 28° is resumed after a short delay (Hamburger and Zeuthen, 1960).

Between EHT and the first synchronized division a 22% gain in dry weight occurs. There is a reduction in the rate of dry weight increase during the division peak.

During the first 5 hr. after EHT the rate of dry weight increase is less than in controls at 28°C. After 5 hr., however, the heat-treated culture is similar to the control in rate of reproduction and dry weight increase (Zeuthen and Scherbaum, 1954).

No density changes (dry weight per cell volume) could be observed during HT and the growth oscillations after EHT (Scherbaum *et al.*, 1959b).

Fluctuations in O_2 consumption occur during the growth oscillation after EHT. During and immediately after this peak of cell division O_2 consumption is higher than at other times, the pattern being similar to that found in small clonal cultures. One important difference in the systems, however, is in the rate. For heat-treated *Tetrahymena* the rate is 1.5×10^{-5} μliters O_2 per cell per minute, about twice the rate of untreated cells (Zeuthen and Scherbaum, 1954).

2. MORPHOGENESIS

Certain morphogenetic changes may serve as markers for timing physiological processes and their inhibition during the recovery period (EHT to first synchronized division). These include such events as the increase in number of kinetosomes in one meridian, accumulation of kinetosomes in the anarchic

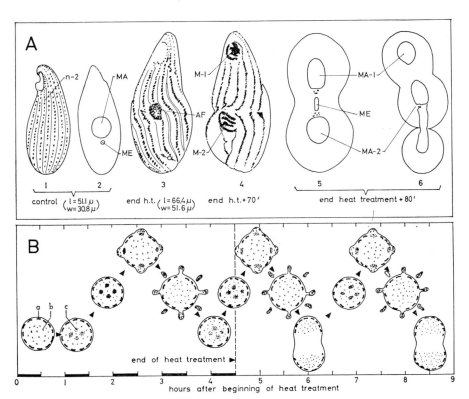

FIG. 7. Morphological changes following heat treatment (HT). A. Cortical and nuclear structures in *Tetrahymena pyriformis* GL: 1 and 2, Normal cells before HT; n-2 is the ciliary medium in which kinetosomes are counted; MA, macronucleus; ME, macronuclear extrusion. 3, Cell at end of HT; AF, anarchic field. 4, Cell 70 min. after HT; M-1 and M-2, oral apparatus. 5 and 6, Dividing cells from first division burst 80 min. after HT. (1, 3, and 4, after Williams and Scherbaum, 1959.) (2, 5, and 6, after Scherbaum *et al.*, 1958.) B. Changes in the macronucleus of *T. pyriformis* WH6 during and following HT. a, nucleolus; b, chromatin granule; c, RNA body. Black bars on abscissa show duration of heat shocks. (After Elliott *et al.*, 1962.)

field and their further development into oral organelles (Williams and Scherbaum, 1959). A comparison of the number of kinetosomes in meridian n-2 (Fig. 7A) of normal and heat-treated cells was made. The results indicate that kinetosome number at EHT is the same as in normal cells just beginning to divide. At EHT each cell in the culture also possesses an anarchic field (Fig. 7A, 3), and the cells remain at this stage of arrested morphogenesis for 50–55 min. after EHT. Approximately 70 min. after EHT, i.e., at the end of the recovery period (Fig. 7A, 4), the kinetosomes of the anarchic field become organized into four bands representing the new membranelles and the first indications of cytoplasmic division appear.

The time course of oral morphogenesis, formation of a fission line or ring, and cell division were studied during the recovery period in *Tetrahymena* (Child, 1957; Frankel, 1962). Brief exposures to high temperature (34°), low temperature (9°–11°) and *p*-fluorophenylalanine ($5 \times 10^{-5}M$ and $4 \times 10^{-3}M$) between EHT and the first synchronized division cause similar morphogenetic effects. A well defined morphological stabilization point, a developmental stage preceding that shown in Fig. 7A, 4, has been established to occur about 20 min. before the first division burst (Frankel, 1962). This is also the approximate time when a rapid change from high to low sensitivity of cells to various inhibitors occurs. This has been referred to as a physiological transition point and will be discussed in Section IV,E,2.

At the morphological stabilization point, the membranelles of the new oral primordium are fully formed and the fission line is present as a complete ring. Before that, development can be interrupted by any of the above mentioned inhibitory procedures, so the cell fails to divide and the oral membranelles are resorbed. Resumption of development culminating in cellular division occurs only after removal of the inhibitor. If applied after the stabilization point has been attained the same inhibitor may have no effect at all on later differentiation and the onset of cell division.

3. PROTEIN SYNTHESIS

a. Free Amino Acids and Peptides. The free amino acid content of non-synchronized *Tetrahymena pyriformis* GL amounts to 12.6–23.2% of the total amino acid content (Wu and Hogg, 1952; Scherbaum *et al.*, 1959a; Christensson, 1959). This percentage is not altered by the synchrony-inducing HT, nor does it change during the growth oscillations. Of the total cellular amino acids 17% occur as peptides within the cell (Wu and Hogg, 1956). Chromatograms of ethanol-soluble fractions harvested at various stages of induced synchrony reveal that changes occur in the concentration of certain ninhydrin-positive compounds, which are presumably small peptides (Scherbaum *et al.*, 1959a).

b. Incorporation of Labeled Amino Acids. Incubation of *Tetrahymena pyriformis* W for 15 min. in a peptone medium supplemented by 26.1 μC. of S^{35}-methionine in 100 ml. aliquots of culture medium taken during and after the cyclic HT shows that there is a gradual decrease in specific activity of the protein fraction. After the fourth temperature shock radioactivity is only 39% as high, and after the eighth shock only 20% as high, as that recorded from a sample of cells in the exponential growth phase. After EHT the rate of incorporation increases rapidly and 2.5 hr. later reaches 45% of the normal control (Mita *et al.*, 1959). The uptake of C^{14}-histidine by whole cells was studied in strains GL and GL-R (Hamburger and Zeuthen, 1960). Samples (25 ml. each) were removed from the synchronized culture at various times of the division cycle and 0.17 μC. C^{14}-histidine was added. Comparative results on samples incubated for 20 min. at 29°C. showed a significant drop in the rate of uptake before the first and second growth oscillations, and a minimum rate of incorporation during fission.

c. Protein Content. Cellular proteins are synthesized by strain GL during the cyclic HT (Christensson, 1959; Lee *et al.*, 1959; Scherbaum *et al.*, 1959a; Singer and Eiler, 1960). Normal cells contain $1.5-3.2 \times 10^{-3}$ μg. protein per cell (Singer and Eiler, 1960). This range in protein content is consistent with observations on cell size and dry weight reported by others. Average cell size decreases by 60% during 17 hr. of exponential multiplication when the O_2 supply is adequate (Scherbaum, 1956); decrease in size parallels decrease in dry weight (Hamburger and Zeuthen, 1960).

Interesting changes occur in two protein fractions, one soluble and the other insoluble in a mixture of 0.1M KCl and 0.011M acetic acid (Christensson, 1959). The insoluble and soluble proteins increase 2.5 and 3.2 times, respectively, over the period of HT. During HT, however, production of soluble proteins lags behind the synthesis of insoluble proteins, whereas, during the half-hour immediately after the eighth heat shock, insoluble proteins decrease by 0.5×10^{-3} μg. per cell, while soluble proteins increase by the same amount. These changes suggest a possible conversion of insoluble to soluble proteins.

The first growth oscillation after EHT in synchronized *Tetrahymena* is accompanied by a change in the total protein content. It decreases and reaches a minimum just before the first division. The rate of protein synthesis during HT is higher at the optimum temperature for growth (29°) than at the shock temperature (34°) (Christensson, 1959). These changes are not evident in Fig. 8 (Scherbaum and Levy, 1961).

Ability of heat-treated and normal *Tetrahymena* to bind the dye fast green, and thus indicate histone distribution within the cell, has been described (Scherbaum *et al.*, 1959b). Cells from maximum stationary-phase cultures bind the dye only in the nucleus. In ciliates strained during early exponential growth, however, the dye is confined to the nucleus in only 5% of the cells, while in the remaining 95% both the nucleus and the cytoplasm is stained. All heat-treated cells are deeply stained throughout. No hypothesis to account for these changes has been advanced.

4. SULFHYDRYLS

Although much attention has been focused on acid-soluble —SH in relation to synchronized cell division in marine invertebrate eggs (Mazia, 1954, 1959, 1961), only two brief reports are available on synchronized protozoa. Approximately a 50% increase per cell was found in *Tetrahymena pyriformis* W when cells at BHT and EHT were compared. An amperometric titration procedure was used to determine free —SH in acid extracts (Sugimura *et al.*, 1957). With the nitroprusside test a 3- to 4-fold increase in free —SH was observed in *T. pyriformis* GL at the same growth stages (BHT and EHT). During the recovery period (EHT to first synchronized division) a further increase in acid-soluble —SH was noted (Scherbaum *et al.*, 1960). Neither an explanation for these differences between the two reports nor for the increase in division-inhibited cells has been given.

5. NUCLEIC ACIDS AND NUCLEOPROTEINS

a. DNA Synthesis. Spectrophotometric estimates of the amount of DNA in macronuclei of *Tetrahymena pyriformis* GL suggest that DNA is synthesized in all cells during HT (Scherbaum *et al.*, 1959b). Growth of these cells in a synthetic medium containing H^3-thymidine (25 μC. per milliliter) results in labeling only 25% of the macronuclei (Scherbaum, 1960). Similarly, incubation during the recovery period in medium containing 5 μC. per milliliter H^3-thymidine also yields about 25% cells with labeled nuclei (Cerroni and Zeuthen, 1962b; Zeuthen, 1963) whether incubation is for only 4 min. at EHT or for as long as 50 min. (EHT to EHT + 50 min.), an equal number of cells is labeled (~25–30%).

If inhibitors were added to cells in inorganic medium at EHT, and followed by a brief (4-min.) incubation with H^3-thymidine either at EHT + 20 min. or at EHT + 50 min., uptake of the label was greatly reduced. Effective inhibitors were: 5-fluoro-2'-deoxyuridine ($5 \times 10^{-3}M$), deoxyadenine ($2 \times 10^{-4}M$), deoxyguanine ($2 \times 10^{-4}M$). Even in those cells with DNA synthesis taking place during the recovery period before the first synchronized division, synthesis can be inhibited without in any way affecting the first and second synchronized divisions (Cerroni and Zeuthen, 1962b; Zeuthen, 1963).

That prolonged incubation of the cells in defined medium containing H^3-thymidine (for example, during HT and EHT + 50 min.) does not label all nuclei can be partly explained by the fact that thymidine is not a required nutrient (Kidder and Dewey, 1951).

b. RNA Synthesis. RNA as well as DNA synthesis can be inhibited significantly in synchronized *Tetrahymena pyriformis* GL without affecting the following growth oscillation (Cerroni and Zeuthen, 1962a). Before the last shock, cells in Proteose-peptone medium were transferred to an inorganic medium, and at EHT + 20 min. the following inhibitors were added to separate samples: 5-fluoro-2'-deoxyuridine $(5 \times 10^{-3}M)$, deoxyguanosine $(2 \times 10^{-4}M)$, deoxyadenosine $(2 \times 10^{-4}M)$. Synthesis of RNA and DNA was followed by the incorporation of H^3-uridine and H^3-thymidine, respectively, and recorded after 6 min.; synthesis of either nucleic acid is inhibited significantly at EHT + 20 min. (inhibition from 45 to 90%), without any notable effect on the following growth oscillations. In this respect nucleic acid inhibitors differ from inhibitors of protein synthesis, since the latter prevent synchronized growth oscillations. During normal exponential multiplication of *Tetrahymena* in a medium without uracil, protein synthesis and cell division can occur without RNA synthesis for approximately two generations, but no longer (Lederberg and Mazia, 1960).

   c. *Partition of Macronuclear Material during Induced Division.* The several-fold increase of dry matter and proteins that occurs during HT, correlated with doubling of cortical structures during the same period, poses an interesting question regarding DNA synthesis: does the DNA content in *each* heat-treated cell increase beyond that in normal nonsynchronized cells before division?

   Spectrophotometrical estimation of DNA in individual cells shows clearly that in almost all heat-treated *Tetrahymena* cells DNA is synthesized in amounts greater than in normal cells entering fission (Scherbaum *et al.,* 1959b). Some of this excess DNA, found in normal as well as in heat-treated cells, is extruded during the following cellular division. Such extranuclear material was observed in 55% of the dividing cells following the first synchronized division, but in only 16% of the dividing cells in normal cultures (Scherbaum *et al.,* 1958). The mean volume of these bodies (ME, Fig. 7A, 2 and 5) in cells from normal cultures is 1.9 μ^3 and 12.2 μ^3 in cells after the first division burst. In rare instances an oversized parent cell produced by the treatment may form three or four daughter cells during the first growth oscillation (Fig. 7A, 6) and the normal time sequences of nuclear and cytoplasmic fission may be quite abnormal. In the anterior part of the cell, nuclear division may be complete, although cellular fission is only beginning; in the posterior segment of the cell cytoplasmic fission is considerably advanced relative to macronuclear division.

   d. *Transfer of Macronuclear RNA to the Cytoplasm.* Ultrastructural changes in the macronucleus of strain WH6 were observed in organisms sampled at 30-min. intervals following the HT worked out for synchronizing that strain (Holz *et al.,* 1957) and are summarized schematically in Fig. 7B (Elliott *et al.,* 1962). Cytological events concerning the formation of RNA bodies and transfer of RNA to the cytoplasm are described in four stages: (1) *Stage prior to RNA body formation.* In a stationary-phase culture (36 hr. at 35°) the macronuclear chromatin bodies are evenly distributed and the crescent-shaped nucleoli seem closely associated with the macronuclear membrane. (2) *Development of RNA bodies*. During the second heat shock after the beginning of HT (1–1.5 hr.) oval membraneless bodies appear and become clearly defined structures within an hour. These centrally located bodies appear to be fibrous structures and disappear following treatment with RNase. (3) *Disappearance of the RNA bodies*. Approximately 2.5 hr. after the beginning of HT, i.e., after the third heat shock, the RNA bodies migrate to the periphery of the nucleus and lose their identity. Simultaneously the number of chromatin bodies in the macronucleus increases. (4) *Bleb formation*. During the fourth heat shock (at 3.5 hr. after the start of HT) the number of chromatin bodies has doubled. The nucleoli have also increased in number and density. They occasionally contain RNA bodies. Blebs form on the macronuclear membrane, and subsequently appear to pinch off. This is the stage at which normal stationary phase cells not subjected to HT would divide if transferred to fresh medium.

During the fifth (and last) heat shock, newly formed RNA bodies appear and changes as described in the preceding cycle recur, excepting that nuclear and cytoplasmic fission follow approximately 1.5 hr. after EHT.

e. *Chromatographic Profiles of DNA*. That synthesis of both nucleic acids

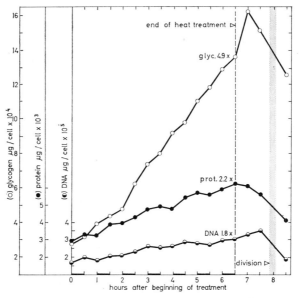

FIG. 8. Synthesis of glycogen, protein, and DNA in *Tetrahymena pyriformis* GL during and after HT. A culture in the negative growth acceleration phase was used for the HT. Black bars on abscissa show duration of heat shocks. (After Scherbaum and Levy, 1961.)

occurs during HT has been verified for *Tetrahymena pyriformis* WH6 (Harrington, 1960) and for *T. pyriformis* W (Iverson and Giese, 1957; Mita, 1958; Mita *et al.*, 1959; Kamiya, 1959), and also for strain GL (Zeuthen and Scherbaum, 1954; Scherbaum, 1957b; Scherbaum *et al.*, 1959b). Differences in the reported data on the DNA content may be partly due to the loss of Feulgen-positive material during macronuclear division. The average DNA content of the normal cell ($\sim 1.5 \times 10^{-5}$ μg.) increases almost linearly to 1.8 times this value at EHT (Fig. 8). The relative base ratios of RNA and DNA in strain GL do not change during this period (Scherbaum, 1957b). During the interval between EHT and the first synchronized division DNA synthesis continues, as shown by chemical determinations and by incorporation of H^3-thymidine into the macronucleus. Since addition of deoxyadenosine to the cultures at EHT inhibits 90% of DNA synthesis, but does not prevent the first synchronized division (Cerroni and Zeuthen, 1962a), additional DNA synthesis does not seem to be a prerequisite for division.

For fractionation of DNA, isolated and purified DNA was adsorbed onto ECTEOLA cellulose columns and eluted with NaCl of increasing concentrations and increasing pH values (Mita and Scherbaum, 1964; Table II). In the extract obtained from the cells in exponential multiplication (BHT) only 29.5% of the total DNA applied to the column is eluted by 0.5M NaCl

Table II

CHROMATOGRAPHIC FRACTIONATION OF *Tetrahymena* DEOXYRIBONUCLEIC ACID[a,b]

| | | Growth stages | | | | | |
| | | BHT | | EHT | | EHT + 1 hr. | |
Elution region	Composition of eluent	DNA (%)	c.p.m./ DNA-P	DNA (%)	c.p.m./ DNA-P	DNA (%)	c.p.m./ DNA-P
I	0.5 M NaCl; 0.01 M phosphate (pH 7)	29.5	232	78.1	713	32.1	33
II	2.0 M NaCl; 0.1 M NH₃ 0.01 M phosphate (pH 10)	56.9	271	17.2	319	57.8	16
III	2.0 M NaCl; 1.0 M NH₃ 0.01 M phosphate (pH 11)	11.9	27	3.2	166	1.3	7

[a] After Mita and Scherbaum (1964).

[b] ECTEOLA-SF columns were used. The amount of eluted DNA was estimated by absorption at 260 mμ and expressed in percent of total amount applied to the column. C.p.m./DNA-P denotes counts per minute per μg DNA phosphorus; BHT, before heat treatment, i.e., during exponential multiplication; EHT, end of heat treatment. The first growth oscillation occurred at EHT + 80 min.

at pH 7, while 56.9% of the DNA is eluted by 2M NaCl at pH 10. In the DNA extract from cells at EHT, however, the situation is reversed, i.e., 78.1% of the DNA is eluted by 0.5M NaCl at pH 7 and only 17.2% by the higher salt concentration. Differences in the rate of incorporation of P^{32} into these DNA fractions (Table II) support the view that metabolic differences exist between cells in different stages of population growth.

f. Sedimentation of Ribosomes. Intracellular incorporation of C^{14}-valine into a 70-S ribosomal fraction was studied in *Tetrahymena pyriformis* (Plesner, 1961b, 1963). Cells for the isolation of ribosomes were collected at 40 and 65 min. after EHT, respectively. The isolated ribosomes were resuspended in magnesium-free Tris buffer and their sedimentation characteristics in the analytical ultracentrifuge noted. A 70-S ribosomal fraction was found in the 65-min. sample, but not in the 40-min. sample. The 70-S fraction was incubated at 37° with ATP (5×10^{-4}M) for 30 min. and the ribosomes were removed by centrifugation. Since the ribosomal proteins were labeled with C^{14}-valine, the release of proteins from the 70-S particles could be calculated by a comparison of radioactivity in the supernate with the activity in the pellet. A significant amount of protein was released about 15 min. before synchronized division.

Ribosomes were also isolated from *Tetrahymena pyriformis* GL at three different growth stages preceding and one following the first synchronized division. Identical ribosomal peaks (125-S, 65-S, and 50-S) were observed for all growth stages (Scherbaum, 1963).

6. PYRIDINE NUCLEOTIDES

The hypothesis has been advanced that NADPH serves as a reducing agent in many synthetic pathways while NADH is more important in energy-producing systems (Klingenberg and Bücher, 1960; Lowenstein, 1961). In view of this hypothesis data on coenzyme levels can be examined in cells during growth oscillations.

Data are available on the levels of oxidized and reduced pyridine nucleotides in *Tetrahymena pyriformis* W (Kamiya and Takahashi, 1961; Takahashi *et al.*, 1964) and GL (Nishi and Scherbaum, 1962a). The levels of NADH and NADPH (0.36 and 0.46 mμmole per milligram protein respectively) in cells of the exponential growth phase of strain GL decrease, respectively, during HT, to 0.27 and 0.33. During the hour before synchronized division, a significant increase (30–43%) in NADH content was observed (Nishi and Scherbaum, 1962a). The results of two experiments are shown in Fig. 9A. In strain W, the level of oxidized pyridine nucleotides was reported to increase by 30–40% within 15 min. after EHT (Kamiya and Takahashi, 1961). This effect was not observed in strain GL (Nishi and Scherbaum, 1962a). Another difference observed between the two strains was that in exponentially growing cells of strain W the NADH:NAD ratio was 1.15, while in GL at the same growth stage it was only 0.34.

7. ATP LEVEL AND CELL DIVISION

Between EHT and the peak of the first synchronized fission of strain GL, a significant increase in the level of ATP and GTP was observed (Plesner, 1961a). Similar increases were observed with less specific methods permitting only the estimation of nucleoside triphosphates (Plesner, 1958a,b, 1961b; Bhagavan and Eiler, 1962; Scherbaum et al., 1962). If the NTP content of a cell sample taken from a normal culture before HT is compared with one from a culture after EHT, the NTP:protein ratio is virtually unchanged (Fig. 9B). However, during each half-hour shock (at 34°), the NTP:protein ratio decreases about 20–30%. A similar increase in this ratio occurs during the half-hour interval between successive heat shocks at 29°. Since the NTP pool decreases during half an hour of incubation, the effect of prolonged exposure to 34° could be studied. Although NTP content (13 mμmoles per milligram protein) decreased during the first half-hour after the temperature shift, an unexpected increase (to 16 mμmoles per milligram protein) was observed in the next 2 hr. The NTP pool remained at this level even after 24.5 hr. of continuous exposure to 34°, when cellular motility is greatly reduced. The partial pressure of O_2 in the culture medium has a profound influence on the NTP level in the cells. In cultures in which the O_2 tension is low and cell

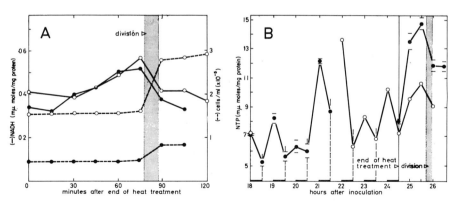

FIG. 9. Effect of standard HT on nucleotide levels in *Tetrahymena pyriformis* GL. A. NADH content before and after first synchronized division (shaded area). Two experiments are shown (clear circles and solid circles). NADH levels shown by solid lines; cell counts by broken lines. (After Nishi and Scherbaum, 1962a.) B. Nucleosidetriphosphate (NTP) content in two cultures (clear circles and solid circles). Heavy bars on abscissa indicate duration of heat shocks. Shaded area indicates time of first division burst. Each value in experiment (solid circles) is the average of two determinations shown by the horizontal bars. (After Scherbaum et al., 1962.)

multiplication has almost ceased, the NTP level (mμmoles per milligram protein) was found to be 18.4 as compared with levels ranging between 7 and 13 in exponential phase cultures in which ample O_2 is available. If the low O_2 tension-culture noted above is vigorously aerated, the NTP level increases temporarily, e.g., to 23.7, during the first hour after aeration, but after 2 hr. the level again falls to the range found in exponential cultures (Scherbaum *et al.*, 1962).

These experiments illustrate the delicate balance which exists between the formation and utilization of NTP which is partly regulated by the O_2 tension in the medium and partly by cellular capacity for utilization of NTP in synthetic reactions during growth and cell division.

8. UPTAKE AND INTRACELLULAR DISTRIBUTION OF PHOSPHORUS-32

a. Normal Population Growth. Dry weight and phosphorus content were determined for four phases of population growth (Fig. 10A; Hamburger and

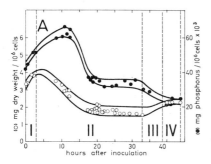 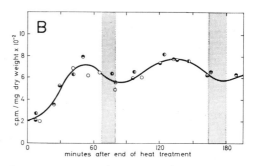

FIG. 10. Phosphorus incorporation and content in *Tetrahymena pyriformis* GL-R. A. Dry weight (clear circles) and phosphorus content (solid circles) during growth phases: I, lag; II, log ($<3 \times 10^5$ cells/ml.); III, negative growth acceleration (3×10^5–10^6 cells/ml.); IV, stationary (1×10^6 cells/ml.). B. Rate of incorporation of $P^{32}O_4$ in synchronized cells. The curve represents the combined data of 4 experiments, each shown by a different symbol. Shaded areas represent division 1 at $\sim$ 80 min. after, and division 2 at $\sim$ 170 min. after EHT. (After Hamburger and Zeuthen, 1960.)

Zeuthen, 1960). It is obvious that the greatest changes in dry weight and P content occur during exponential growth (II). During the first 10 hr. after transfer of a test tube culture to fresh medium (approximately 600 ml. in a Fernbach flask) the P content rises from 40 to 60×10^{-3} mg./10^6 cells, and 10 hr. later it has decreased to approximately 35. In the third 10-hr. period the P content remains unchanged, but it decreases during the negative growth acceleration phase (III) of the fourth 10-hr. period, and levels off again to about 25×10^{-3} mg./10^6 cells in the maximum stationary phase.

b. Effect of Temperature Treatment on the Phosphate Pool. Despite the changes in rate of assimilation of total P during HT, P distribution in various biochemical fractions is not affected by the treatment, since the same relative loss in P (23%) is observed in the following fractions: nucleic acid, acid-soluble, lipid, and protein (Hamburger and Zeuthen, 1960). In a 10-hr. culture of strain GL-R the total P content is 2% of the dry weight. It remains at this level for the next 20 hr. of exponential multiplication. If a culture in which the population density is about 50,000 per milliliter (about 25 hr. after inoculation) is subjected to HT the P-dry weight ratio decreases continuously throughout the HT, and at EHT the amount of P totals only about 1.5%.

c. Uptake of P^{32} during Growth Oscillations. Although cells which have emerged from HT have suffered only an average loss of 23% in P content (on a dry-weight basis), they take up a considerable amount of P^{32}. If small samples are removed at various times between EHT (time zero in Fig. 10B) and EHT + 190 min., and incubated for 10 min. in P^{32}-containing medium, the cells exhibit varying degrees of radioactivity. During the first 50 min. radioactivity increased about 3.5 times to a maximum preceding the first synchronized division. A second maximum is noted at approximately 130 min. after EHT. Minimum uptake of radioactivity was observed during the division bursts (Hamburger and Zeuthen, 1960).

d. Changes in the Acid-Soluble Phosphate Pool. *Tetrahymena pyriformis* GL was cultured in a Proteose-peptone medium containing P^{32}-ortho phosphate (0.3 μC. per milliliter). A control sample was removed after 16-hr. incubation at 29°C., when the standard HT was started. Additional samples for analysis were taken at EHT, before division, after division, and during the maximum stationary phase. All samples were extracted with 15% TCA. After removal of glycogen and TCA, the samples were subjected to two-dimensional chromotography and X-ray film autographs were prepared (Fig. 11). Striking changes in the pool size of certain phosphorus-containing compounds occur before, during, and after induced growth oscillation. Compounds No. 17, 18, and 19 are present only in trace amounts in cells of the exponential growth phase but are very prominent at EHT and at EHT + 60 min. (Fig. 11A). After the first synchronized division (Fig. 11B), however, no more accumulation of these particular compounds is evident (Chou and Scherbaum, 1963).

9. CARBOHYDRATES IN CELLS UNDERGOING GROWTH OSCILLATIONS

a. Total Sugars of the Acid-Soluble Fraction. TCA extracts of strain W cells were separated into two fractions by addition of barium acetate and ethanol at pH 8.2. Both supernate and precipitate were assayed for sugar content (Kamiya, 1959). Striking changes in the sugar content were observed to occur in both fractions during HT. During the interval from BHT to onset of fission, sugar

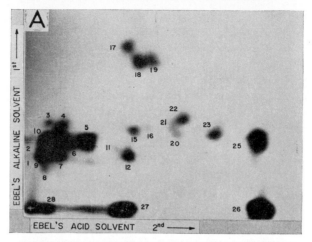

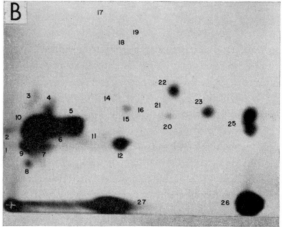

FIG. 11. Radioautographs of two-dimensional paper chromatograms of the TCA-soluble phosphate fraction of *Tetrahymena pyriformis* GL. Phosphorus (10μg.) was applied at ($+$) on each chromatogram. Numbers indicate 28 different phosphate compounds. A, 60 min. after EHT (20 min. before division 1); B, 140 min. after EHT (60 min. after division 1). (After Chou and Scherbaum, 1963.)

content per cell in the precipitate increased about 4-fold. If sugars are measured after division, the pool size is reduced about 10%, which indicates that they are utilized to some extent during the first growth oscillation. Drastic changes are also observed in the ethanol-soluble supernate. This fraction, in extracts from cells BHT, contains 25% of the total acid-soluble sugars. During HT the ethanol-soluble supernate pool is reduced to such an extent that, for cells just entering fission, it contains only 0.3% of the total acid-soluble sugar.

b. Glycogen Content. The amount of glycogen found in *Tetrahymena pyri-*

formis GL is highly variable, dependent on such factors as chemical composition of the medium, O_2 tension, and incubation temperature. During exponential multiplication in a Proteose-peptone medium without glucose, glycogen content was <4% of cellular dry weight (Scherbaum and Levy, 1961). In cultures 12 days old, glycogen content may be as high as 22% (Manners and Ryley, 1952). If 0.1% glucose is added to the medium, cellular glycogen content may be as high as 50% after 3 days of growth (Hogg, 1963).

During the cyclic HT for induction of synchronized cell division glycogen synthesis occurs at a rather constant rate. At EHT the cells have accumulated approximately 5 times the amount contained at BHT (Fig. 8).

10. ENZYME ACTIVITY

a. NADH Oxidase; NADH Cytochrome c Reductase. The oxidation of reduced NADH nicotin-amide-adenine dinucleotide added to cell homogenates of *Tetrahymena pyriformis* S is completely inhibited when the homogenates are preheated to 40°C. for 10 min. (Eichel and Rem, 1959). Heating for 5 and 10 min. at 30° inactivates the system 55% and 75%, respectively (Eichel, 1956). Since repeated heat shocks (34° or 43° for 30 min.) inhibit cell division in 5 strains of *T. pyriformis* (GL, GL-R, S, W, WH6), homogenates of strain GL were prepared before and after HT and tested for NADH oxidase activity (Nishi and Scherbaum, 1962a). The NADH oxidase activity in homogenates of cells in exponential multiplication ranged from 3.9 to 6.7 mμmoles coenzyme oxidized per minute per milligram protein. A consistent decrease in activity was found at EHT, when the cells exhibit only 42–80% of the activity in normal cells. No consistent change in activity occurred during the following hour, when the cells were preparing to divide. It is not clear, therefore, whether the NADH oxidase system is implicated as a temperature-sensitive controlling mechanism for synchrony.

The activity of NADH cytochrome *c* reductase was assayed in extracts of *Tetrahymena pyriformis* W harvested during exponential multiplication (Kamiya and Takahashi, 1961). Activity was maximum at 20°. It declined with increasing temperatures until complete and irreversible inactivation was observed at 40°.

Succinic dehydrogenase activity is discussed in Section IV,C,3 and 4.

b. The Glyoxylate Cycle. In the negative growth acceleration phase of normal cultures and during HT *Tetrahymena pyriformis* GL accumulates glycogen (Manners and Ryley, 1952; Scherbaum and Levy, 1961). Several questions relative to this phenomenon are of interest.

What substrates are utilized for glycogen synthesis in *Tetrahymena*? Besides glucose, non-sugar precursors, particularly fats, are so converted in strain E. The organisms develop the ability to convert fats to glycogen only after glucose has disappeared from the culture medium and when the growth rate has declined (Hogg and Wagner, 1956; Wagner, 1956). During exponential growth, with Proteose-peptone, glucose, and acetate in the culture medium, the cells cannot utilize lipids for glyconeogenesis (Hogg, 1959).

The obvious possibility that glycerol, aspartate, and serine are converted to glycogen has not been verified. Other than fatty acids, only phenylalanine, glucose, pyruvate, and glycine were utilized for glycogen synthesis. Pyruvate and glycine were utilized only in traces, apparently due to poor uptake. Furthermore, endogenous protein makes no net contribution to glyconeogenesis in *Tetrahymena* during the maximum stationary growth phase. It has been suggested, therefore, that all glyconeogenesis in *Tetrahymena* proceeds from fatty acids. This route can now be explained (Hogg, 1963) by the glyoxylate cycle (Fig. 12).

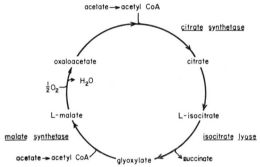

FIG. 12. The glyoxylate cycle. (After Kornberg and Krebs, 1957; Kornberg and Madsen, 1958.)

Are the enzymes of glycogen synthesis present in cells not accumulating glycogen? Despite lack of glyconeogenesis, the cells in Proteose-peptone medium (without additives) have high malate and citrate synthetase activities. Addition of glucose to the culture suppresses formation of malate synthetase. This repression is partially relieved by addition of acetate which also induces a 15- to 20-fold elevation of isocitrate lyase (Hogg and Kornberg, 1961, 1963). The same workers compared the enzyme activity in *Tetrahymena pyriformis* E during exponential multiplication (in a medium containing Proteose-peptone, glucose, and acetate) with that during the stationary phase (when glucose had disappeared from the medium). Log-phase cells, despite their inability to synthesize glycogen, did contain isocitrate lyase and malate synthetase, the key enzymes of the glyoxylate cycle. There is evidence that these enzymes are associated with a specific cytological structure, the "glyoxylate granules." It has been suggested that these granules may constitute one of at least two types of mitochondria. They are found in the No. 1 fraction (Table III). The No. 1 fraction of stationary phase cells has higher glyoxylate enzyme activity than the same fraction from log-phase cells. In the latter, which are incapable of glyconeogenesis,

Table III

SPECIFIC ACTIVITY OF GLYOXYLATE CYCLE ENZYMES IN TWO INTRACELLULAR FRACTIONS
OF *Tetrahymena pyriformis* E

Enzyme	Log-phase cell homogenate fractions[b]			Stationary-phase cell homogenate fractions[b]		
	No. 1	No. 2	S	No. 1	No. 2	S
Isocitrate lyase	0.86	0.69	0.20	3.7	<0.01	0.4
Malate synthetase	0.48	<0.01	0.80	4.8	<0.01	<0.01
Citrate synthetase	4.5	14.6	0.66	8.3	14.7	<0.01

[a] Data from Hogg and Kornberg (1963).

[b] Washed cell suspensions were chilled and homogenized by passage through a fritted glass filter before centrifugation at 2000g for 10 min. No 1 was a jelly-like sediment containing homogeneous glyoxylate granules; No. 2 a more tightly packed pellet containing heterogeneous particles. S was a supernatant liquid layer. Specific activity of extracts of these fractions is given in μmoles substrate transformed per milligram soluble protein per hour.

isocitrate lyase activity is considerably higher in fraction No. 2 than in the No. 2 fraction of stationary-phase cells. There is also a substantial increase in malate synthetase activity in the supernate of the log-phase sample as compared with activity in the supernate from a stationary-phase sample. Evidence that the glyoxylate cycle enzymes are spatially separated from sites of oxidation has been obtained from studies on the utilization of C^{14}-glutamine in *Tetrahymena* cells grown with acetate (Hogg and Kornberg, 1963).

In synchronized cells, isocitrate lyase may have a controlling function for glyconeogenesis via the glyoxylate cycle, since this enzyme occurs at a much lower level than does malate synthetase. During HT, however, the specific activity of the isocitrate lyase does not show the increase which could be expected on the basis of the increasing glyconeogenesis during HT (Fig. 8). The specific activity of this enzyme BHT (0.3–0.4 μmoles per hour per milligram protein) is nevertheless greater than the maximal rate of glyconeogenesis during HT (0.2 μmoles glucose per hour per milligram protein). A 10-fold increase of isocitrate lyase activity is observed in cells entering the stationary phase (Hogg, 1963).

c. Oxidative Phosphorylation; Cytology of Mitochondria. Although the nucleoside triphosphate:protein ratio is strikingly similar in exponentially growing and in synchronized *Tetrahymena* after HT, significant changes have been observed in phosphorylation activity in these two phases of growth (Nishi and Scherbaum, 1962b). The rate of phosphorylation in homogenates prepared from cells harvested in exponential growth is 0.1–0.2 μmoles per milligram protein per 30 min. at 23°C. In cells at EHT the rate is only 50% as high, although phosphorylation activity rises to normal during the hour preceding the first growth oscillation. The rate decreases again during the following division.

Simultaneous assays for oxidation of β-hydroxybutyrate in whole homogenates show no significant changes during the cycle of induced growth oscillation. Consequently, the phosphorus-acetoacetate ratio (P:AA) follows the pattern of phosphorylation activity of the system. These results suggest that phosphorylation activity in *Tetrahymena* is rather sensitive to temperature changes. The observed decline in rate of phosphorylation that occurs during HT and division is in accord with the findings reported by others showing low P^{32} incorporation rates for strain GL during the corresponding period (Hamburger and Zeuthen, 1960). In the studies mentioned above whole cell homogenates were used. For a determination of phosphorus-oxygen (P:O) ratios particulate fractions were isolated and tested with different substrates (Eiler *et al.*, 1956; Eichel and Rem, 1961; Nishi and Scherbaum, 1962b). The P:O ratios usually found were around 1.0 although they have been reported to be as high as 2.5 (Eiler *et al.*, 1956). Some evidence has been presented that a fatty acid (possibly a lysophosphatide) acts as an uncoupling agent contributing somehow to the low P:O ratios (Eichel and Rem, 1961).

During the exponential phase of multiplication of strain WH6 (Elliott, 1961) and strain W (Sato, 1960) most mitochondria (which number 35–40 per 100 μ^2 of cell surface) are localized in the ectoplasm near the pellicle. A daughter cell contains 600–800 mitochondria, and the number doubles before the next division. In synchronized cells their shape changes from oval to thread-like about 30 min. before the first synchronized cell division. This morphological change occurs at the approximate transition point noted in the inhibitor studies to be discussed in Section IV,D.

d. Acid Phosphatase. Using starch gel electrophoresis, several acid phosphatases were demonstrated in homogenates of *Tetrahymena pyriformis* W. Total acid phosphatase activity between EHT and EHT + 80 min. is only 55% of the activity of the nonsynchronized control culture. Values increase to 80% at EHT + 120 min., but decrease to 60% at EHT + 140 min. (Klamer and Fennell, 1963).

C. EFFECT OF RADIATIONS ON GROWTH OSCILLATIONS

Three aspects of the irradiation effect on cells in various growth stages will be discussed: effect on division delay; inhibition of nucleic acid synthesis; and effect on specific enzyme systems.

1. DIVISION DELAY FOLLOWING ULTRAVIOLET TREATMENT

Cultures of *Tetrahymena pyriformis* W were irradiated at different periods (Iverson and Giese, 1957). Samples taken BHT, at EHT, and during the final stage of the first synchronized division were removed, washed, and suspended in water and given different irradiation dosages at 226 mμ or 265 mμ. Results for 3 dosages at 265 mμ (Fig. 13A, B, and C) show that the dosage which caused the longest division delay was 15 × 10¹³ quanta per square millimeter (= 1122 ergs per mm.²); the effects of this dosage are discussed below.

Whether the cells are irradiated BHT or at EHT, the first division is delayed approximately 25 hr. The second division is delayed only 30 hr. following irradiation at EHT, but irradiation BHT delays the division for about 100 hr. (Fig. 13A). The third division in the same experiment was delayed approximately 450 hr. whether irradiation treatment was given at BHT or EHT (Fig. 13B).

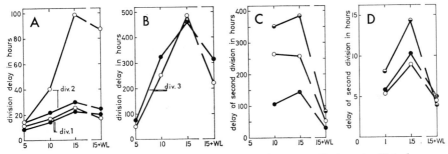

FIG. 13. Delay of induced growth oscillations by UV radiations in *Tetrahymena pyriformis* W. Division time delay is plotted on the ordinate against the following dosages on the abscissa: 1, 1.5, 5, 10, and 15 × 10¹³ quanta per square millimeter. The last value beyond the break on each chart shows the photoreversal effect of white light (WL). Cells were irradiated at the following growth stages: BHT (clear circles), EHT (solid circles), during late first division stage (◗). Wavelengths of 265 mμ were used in A, B, and C; and of 226 mμ in D. (After Iverson and Giese, 1957.)

In other experiments (Fig. 13C) the second division delays were longer than those shown in Fig. 13A, but they confirm that cells irradiated BHT are more sensitive than those irradiated at EHT. The extreme sensitivity of cells irradiated during the terminal stages of the first synchronized division is shown by the second division's being delayed 380 hr.

In contrast to the pronounced ultraviolet (UV) radiation effects with wavelength 265 mμ administered at different growth stages, irradiation at 226 mμ shows none of these division-delaying effects, although cells treated during the terminal stage of the first fission are somewhat more sensitive in this respect than others (Fig. 13D). Irradiation at 226 mμ (but not at 265 mμ) immobilizes the ciliates.

The photoreversal effect of white light is shown (Fig. 13A–D) on the UV injury caused by the dosage of 15 × 10¹³ quanta per square millimeter. In almost all cases the division delay that follows UV treatment is counteracted.

The division delays effected by irradiation are interpreted as being due to inter-ference with DNA synthesis.

2. DNA SYNTHESIS AFTER ULTRAVIOLET RADIATION

The effect of 254 mμ UV irradiation on synchronized *Tetrahymena pyri-formis* WH6 was observed (Harrington, 1960). Cultures in which division 1 had just occurred were exposed 30 and 60 sec., respectively, and each was transferred to fresh defined medium containing tritiated thymidine (50 mC. per milliliter). Samples were removed from each culture at 10-min. intervals for radioauto-graphy. As shown on the abscissa (Fig. 14A,B), the UV exposures were made 7

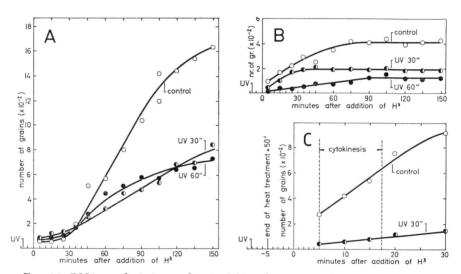

Fig. 14. DNA synthesis in synchronized *Tetrahymena pyriformis* WH6 after UV irradiation at 254 mμ for 30 and 60 sec. At time 0 tritiated thymidine (H³) was added to the culture. Numbers on the ordinate designate the number of reduced silver grains counted on the autoradiograms. Control received no irradiation. A and B. Immediately after the first division cells were irradiated at the time indicated by "UV" on the abscissa. Incorporation of H³ into the macronucleus is shown in A, and into the micronucleus in B. C. DNA synthesis in the micronucleus during and shortly after division 1. As indicated on the abscissa, UV irradiation took place 47 min. after the end of HT, i.e., 13 min. before the onset of cytokinesis. (After Harrington, 1960.)

min. before the beginning of incubation with H³-thymidine at time zero. In-crease in average number of silver grains above each nucleus was the measure of DNA synthesis. Data were obtained for synthesis in macro- and micronucleus.

a. Macronuclear DNA. Synthesis of DNA in the macronucleus began ap-proximately 35 min. after the first synchronized cell division in control and irradiated cells, and continued throughout the observed period of 150 min. Irradiation for either 30 or 60 sec. reduced both the rate of synthesis and the final amount of DNA produced in the macronucleus (Fig. 14A).

b. Micronuclear DNA. Synthesis of DNA in the micronucleus, on the other hand, shows no initial delay either in controls or in cultures which received 30 sec. irradiation, and continues linearly for about 70 min. (Fig. 14B). Hence, the period of DNA synthesis is much shorter in the micronucleus than in the macronucleus. Irradiation for either 30 or 60 sec. reduces DNA synthesis considerably, so that only about half the normal amount is synthesized.

At EHT + 47 min. an aliquot of the control culture was exposed to UV irradiation for 30 sec. (Fig. 14C, point "UV"). At this stage the micronuclei are still arrested in an "anaphase-like" configuration (Holz *et al.*, 1957). At EHT + 50 min. (time −5 in Fig. 14C) micronuclear division occurred; 5 min. later time zero) the cells were transferred to the tritiated thymidine medium. Cytokinesis began 5 min. later (EHT + 55) and was completed in about 12 min. Synthesis of DNA in the micronucleus as shown by the uptake of labeled thymidine continues linearly during cellular fission (Fig. 14C). It is evident that irradiation for 30 sec. about 13 min. before the beginning of cytokinesis reduces DNA synthesis to about one-fifth the control rate.

3. ALTERATION OF SUCCINIC DEHYDROGENASE ACTIVITY BY ULTRAVIOLET RADIATION

Succinic dehydrogenase activity in strain GL was determined colorimetrically for 3 stages (BHT, EHT, and during division 1) of the synchrony cycle (Sullivan and Sparks, 1961). In nonirradiated cultures subjected to HT, samples of the last two stages showed about a 50% reduction in enzyme activity as compared to the controls (BHT).

If comparable samples are exposed to UV radiations (254 mμ, for 2.5 min.) before the determinations, no differences are apparent.

Organisms taken at EHT from nonirradiated cultures flourish after transfer to fresh medium; similar samples from irradiated cultures die after 2–3 days.

4. EFFECT OF X-RADIATION

a. Inhibition of DNA Synthesis and Cell Division. Division in exponential cultures of *Tetrahymena pyriformis* W is inhibited by X-radiations (60 kr. for 30 min.). This dosage induces a division lag of 2.75–3 hr. at 25°C. Synchronized cultures, whether irradiated before the first division, or between the first and second growth oscillations, are inhibited to the same extent. Since the rates of DNA formation are known to differ at the several synchronized growth stages tested, it appears that the division delay caused by X-irradiation is not due to inhibition of DNA synthesis (Ducoff, 1956).

b. Succinic Dehydrogenase Activity. A significant decrease in the activity of succinic dehydrogenase, as measured by the Thunberg method, is observed in *Tetrahymena pyriformis* GL at EHT and during the first synchronized division. X-radiation with 120 kr. causes a restoration of enzyme activity at these two stages to the extent that significant decreases no longer exist. The obliteration of this decrease in dehydrogenase activity by the X-ray treatment does not affect cellular viability or modify subsequent growth in fresh medium (Sullivan and Boyle, 1961).

c. Fumarase Activity. Purified enzyme was prepared from *Tetrahymena pyriformis* GL and its activity was determined spectrophotometrically (Sullivan and Snyder, 1962). It appears that enzyme activity in nonirradiated cultures is decreased at EHT, EHT + 90 min., and EHT + 150 min., when the cultures are passing through the first two growth oscillations. X-radiation (180 kr.) causes a considerable reduction of fumarase activity at all stages studied.

D. Effect of Metabolic Inhibitors on Growth Oscillations

Tetrahymena exposed to the synchrony-inducing HT attain 2–4 times their normal size. Transfer of these cells to an inorganic medium at EHT does not interfere with the following growth oscillations (Hamburger and Zeuthen, 1957). The increase in cellular mass and the sequence of preparatory steps leading to division have apparently been dissociated in time (Scherbaum, 1957a, 1960). Consequently, effects of drug action can be studied on either of these phenomena.

1. inhibition of intermediary metabolism

a. Dinitrophenol (DNP). Oxygen uptake at 28°C. decreases after transfer of *Tetrahymena pyriformis* GL from Proteose-peptone to an inorganic medium. Two hours after transfer the endogenous respiration is only 30% of that for

Table IV

Oxygen Uptake by Heat-Treated and Nonsynchronized *Tetrahymena pyriformis* GL[a]

	O_2 uptake in μl. per 10^6 cells per min. in		Rate of uptake in B vs. A (%)
Cellular material	A. Proteose-peptone medium	B. Washed cells in inorganic medium	
Exponential phase cells	4.8	1.4	29
Synchronized cells (just before division)	15.2	4.6	30
Rate increase for synchronized cells	217%	228%	—

[a] Data from Hamburger and Zeuthen (1957).

cells in the organic medium. Similar decreases are observed in cells from exponential growth phase cultures as well as in synchronized cells (Table IV). The rate of O_2 uptake for synchronized cells just before division is more than 3 times the rate for exponential phase cells.

Maximum stimulation of respiration in inorganic medium follows exposure to DNP ($3 \times 10^{-4}M$ at pH 7.3). Approximately 2 hr. after removal of the drug, respiration is 2.4 times that in cultures without added DNP. The same has been observed in normal and synchronized cells. This higher rate, however, is only 73–76% of the rate for cells growing in a Proteose-peptone medium. When cells in Proteose-peptone medium were given 2-hr. treatments of DNP (0.15–1.0 mM), inhibition of respiration was observed in all cases (Hamburger and Zeuthen, 1957).

Addition of DNP ($2 \times 10^{-4}M$, pH 7.3) to heat-treated and washed cells 30–40 min. before the first synchronized division suppresses all following growth oscillations for at least 5–8 hr. after exposure to the drug. Cell multiplication was suppressed at a lower concentration of drug than that which maximally stimulated respiration (2 versus $3 \times 10^{-4}M$).

Cells from a Proteose-peptone culture washed and transferred to inorganic medium before or at EHT will divide synchronously. If such cells are exposed to DNP ($5 \times 10^{-5}M$, pH 6.0) at any time after EHT, division will be delayed (Fig. 15A; Hamburger and Zeuthen, 1957). Intervals after EHT when the cells were transferred to the drug are shown on the abscissa. Time of exposure (20 min.) has been subtracted in all cases, and the remaining delay shown on the ordinate. Therefore a delay of zero means that the development toward division was "frozen" for 20 min. The slope of the curve shows an increasing delay as the cells approach fission with the maximum delay of about 40 min. around EHT $+$ 50 min. for the first division and at EHT $+$ 135 min. for the second division. Each maximum is followed by an interval of about 15 min. during which the drug causes little or no significant division delay.

b. Fluoride, Fluoroacetate, and Azide. (1) Phosphatase inhibition by fluoride. ATP added to neutralized acid extracts of *Tetrahymena pyriformis* GL is rapidly hydrolyzed. Addition of NaF ($4 \times 10^{-2}M$) reduces the amount of inorganic P to 25% of the amount formed in the control (incubation at 26° for 30 min.). Trapping the added ATP with the hexokinase system greatly reduces phosphatase activity. With glucose-6-phosphate as a substrate, phosphatase action is completely blocked at a concentration of $2 \times 10^{-2}M$ NaF (Nishi and Scherbaum, 1962b). This system made it possible to study oxidative phosphorylation (Section IV,B,10,*c*). (2) Delay of growth oscillations by fluoride, fluoroacetate, and azide. Heat-synchronized cells of strains GL and GL-R were treated with inhibitors for 30-min. periods at various times between EHT and the second growth oscillation, and the first and second division delays in each case were observed (Hamburger, 1962). The delaying effects for three

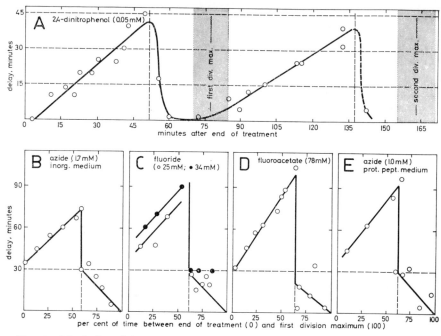

Fig. 15. Metabolic inhibitor effects on growth oscillations in *Tetrahymena pyriformis* GL. A. At various times after EHT, cells in inorganic medium were exposed to dinitrophenol (DNP) for 20 min. Treatments during the first 80 min. delay division 1; subsequent exposures delay division 2. (After Hamburger and Zeuthen, 1957.) B, C, D, and E. Synchronized cells were treated for 30 min. with respective inhibitors shown. The medium was Proteose-peptone, except in B. Note that percent of time, rather than actual time, is plotted on abscissa. (After Hamburger, 1962.)

inhibitors on the first division are shown in Fig. 15. In experiment B, the cells were transferred from Proteose-peptone to inorganic medium prior to the last heat shock; in C, D, and E, the culture medium was Proteose-peptone throughout the experiment. Since the cells in all experiments were exposed to the inhibitor for 30 min., this time delay is indicated by the horizontal line in Fig. 15B–E. It indicates that during this period the cells were arrested or "frozen" in their preparation for division. Values above this line show an "excess" time delay, that is in addition to the 30 min. of exposure to the drug (Zeuthen, 1958; Thormar, 1959). The results clearly demonstrate that if exposures are made at increasingly longer intervals after EHT, the delay time for synchronized division gradually increases to a maximum. Maximum delays are observed at 60–65% of the time interval between EHT and the first growth oscillation, regardless of which of the three inhibitors is added. After these periods of maximum delay, the effect of each drug in arresting the following synchronized division declines and becomes zero during cell division. This is shown by the parts of the curves below the broken horizontal line (Fig. 15B–E). That the nature of the medium in which the drug is applied has no effect on inhibition may be noted by comparing curves B and E.

  c. *Phenylurethane* (*PU*). (1) Effect on normal cells. As noted in Table IV, the rate of endogenous respiration of normal *Tetrahymena* cells suspended in an inorganic medium is 29% of the rate of cells in nutrient medium. It is not changed by addition of PU in concentrations ranging from 0.001 to $1 \times 10^{-3}M$. In cultures in nutrient medium, however, respiration is inhibited by addition of PU in direct proportion to the concentration of the drug (range 0.1 to $1.0 \times 10^{-3}M$). The lack of respiratory stimulation strongly suggests absence of an uncoupling effect (Eiler, 1962).

  The effects of PU and reduced O_2 pressure on growth and respiration of nonsynchronized *Tetrahymena* in nutrient medium are shown in Table V. In-

Table V

Effect of Phenylurethane (PU) and Reduced Oxygen Pressure on Normal Growth and Respiration of *Tetrahymena tyriformis* GL in Nutrient Medium[a]

Treatment	Respiration (% of control)	Growth (increase in mass)
1×10^{-3} M PU	70	Almost completely blocked
51 mm. Hg pO_2	70	50% of maximum rate
12 mm. Hg pO_2	30	33% of maximum rate
12 mm. Hg $pO_2 + 1 \times 10^{-3}$ M PU	30	Completely blocked

[a] Data from Eiler (1962).

terestingly, $1 \times 10^{-3}M$ PU has the same inhibitory effect on respiration as 51 mm. pO_2, i.e., respiration is reduced to 70% of the control in both cases. Phenylurethane blocks growth completely, although partial O_2 pressure equal to 51 mm. Hg only reduces it to 50%. At 12 mm. pO_2, respiration and growth are reduced to 30% and 33%, respectively. Addition of PU to such a culture does not affect respiration, but blocks growth completely (cf. last column, Table V). The view has been advanced that the effect of PU goes beyond depression of respiration, possibly inhibiting some synthetic process necessary for cell division (Eiler, 1962).

  (2) Phenylurethane effect on synchronized cells. No cell division takes place during the 8 hr. of the standard HT. In the course of 5.5 hr. after EHT, three growth oscillations are observed. This is a period of division and synthesis. The effect of PU and reduced O_2 pressure when applied during and after HT is shown in Table VI. The presence of $1 \times 10^{-3}M$ PU in a culture during and after HT reduces growth, as measured by the amount of protein formed, to 74% and the increase in cell number to 30% of the control (line 2, in Table

Table VI

THE EFFECT OF PHENYLURETHANE AND REDUCED OXYGEN PRESSURE
ON SYNCHRONIZED *Tetrahymena pyriformis* GL[a]

Growth conditions during periods		Comparative increases from EHT to EHT + 5.5 hr. in	
A. BHT to EHT B. EHT to EHT + 5.5 hr.		Protein (%)	Number of cells (%)
1. Control. No drug present during A or B; normal O₂ pressure[b]		2-fold (= 100)	6-fold (= 100)
Normal oxygen pressure during A and B			
2. PU present[c]	PU Present	74	30
3. No drug	PU present	—	35
4. PU present	No drug	100	40
No drug present during A or B			
5. Normal O₂	Reduced O₂[d]	67	30
6. Reduced O₂	Normal O₂	—	100

[a] Data from Eiler (1962).

[b] Pressure = 152 mm. Hg.

[c] 1×10^{-3} M concentration used in all tests.

[d] Pressure = 51 mm. Hg.

VI). Addition of PU at EHT suppresses cell division to the same extent as if the drug were present during HT (line 3). Conversely, if the drug is present only during HT and removed at EHT (by transfer of the cells to fresh medium) cell division is blocked to almost the same extent as if the drug were present during the period following EHT (line 4 versus line 3). Protein synthesis, however, is not affected. A partial pressure of O_2 equal to 51 mm. Hg does not affect the yield in cell number (line 6), although low pO_2 applied after EHT inhibits increase in cell number to 30% of the control (line 5). Almost the same yield in cell number is obtained by exposure to PU during HT, after HT, or continuously (cf. lines 4, 3, and 2 in Table VI).

The effects of PU and reduced pO_2 on growth and division are interpreted as follows (Eiler, 1962): (a) A major effect of the narcotic is to inhibit the formation of a precursor of a substance which is rate-determining for the onset of division; (b) the depression of respiration by PU might inhibit macromolecular synthesis, mediated by reduction in oxidative phosphorylation (Eiler and McEwen, 1949) but not by uncoupling (Mehta and Eiler, 1964).

d. Anaerobiosis. If synchronized *Tetrahymena pyriformis* GL are subjected to anaerobiosis (<0.15 mm. Hg) for 60 min. between EHT and EHT + 90 min., the first synchronized division is delayed (Rasmussen, 1963). The degree of this delay is a function of the time when the treatment is carried out. The delay is least if anaerobiosis is applied immediately after the end of the last shock, but the delay increases gradually if applications are made at later periods, until a maximum is obtained at EHT + 55 min.; shortly thereafter the delay is minimal. This brief period between maximum and minimum delay is the "transition point." A quite similar response was observed after treatment with heat shocks (34°C.) or exposure to 2,4-dinitrophenol (Rasmussen and Zeuthen, 1962).

2. AMINO-ACID ANALOGS AND OTHER INHIBITORS OF PROTEIN SYNTHESIS

Ethionine, β-thionylalanine, canavarine, chloramphenicol, and puromycin show delay effects on synchronized cell division similar to those shown by p-fluorophenylalanine (Zeuthen, 1961a,b; Holz *et al.*, 1964).

a. p-Fluorophenylalanine (FPA). The general procedure for determining long incubation effects is as follows. After a HT consisting of six standard shocks the cells are washed and transferred to an inorganic medium. At various times during the period from EHT to EHT + 180 min., cell samples are transferred to 0.8 mM DL-p-fluorophenylalanine (FPA) and observed at frequent intervals over a period of about 5 hr. to note the time of occurrence of the first and second synchronized division peaks (Rasmussen and Zeuthen, 1962). The results are shown in Fig. 16. The two growth oscillations in the control culture

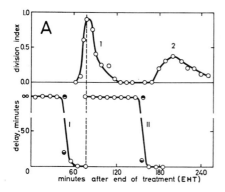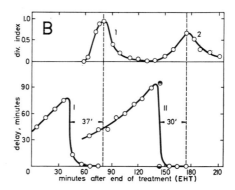

FIG. 16. Effect of p-fluorophenylalanine on growth oscillations of *Tetrahymena pyriformis* GL. A. Continuous incubation with 0.8 mM FPA. Upper curve indicates the first two division peaks (1, 2) after EHT in the control culture; lower curves: I shows delay of division peak 1, and II delay of division peak 2. At two rather restricted time periods (around 50 min. in curve I, and at about 160 min. in curve II) there is a heterogeneous response to the drug. Some of the cells fail to divide subsequently (◖), while division is only slightly delayed in others (◗). B. Exposure to same drug as in A for only 20 min. Upper curve, as in A, shows two division peaks in the control cultures. Lower curves I and II: delays of division 1 and 2, respectively, are plotted on the ordinate against time after EHT on abscissa when treatment with the drug was initiated. As with continuous exposure in A, at specific periods, there is a heterogeneous response to the drug. (After Rasmussen and Zeuthen, 1962)

are denoted by the division index (upper curve of A). In the lower curves, each point indicates a time after EHT when samples of the cells are transferred to the drug. The delays of first and second divisions are given on the ordinate (I and II). The infinity sign (∞) indicates that the first division (left curve) or second division (right curve) was not observed during the 5-hr. period after EHT. Delay curve I shows clearly that contact with the drug up to EHT + 45 min. completely inhibits division 1. Drug exposure between 45 and 85 min., however, has only a very slight, if any, delaying effect on the timing of division 1. The second division is delayed if the drug is applied during the 70-min. interval between the first division maximum (at EHT + 80) and EHT + 150.

If FPA is added any time after EHT, it inhibits all cells up to EHT + 45 min. During a brief period thereafter, however, some cells in all samples tested (◒ in Fig. 16A) are released from the drug inhibition, and go through the first synchronized division quite on schedule, while other cells in each sample (◐) remain inhibited. If the drug is added to the culture any time between EHT + 80 min. and EHT + 150 min., a similar all-or-none effect occurs. Although all of the "drug-released" cells underwent division 1 simultaneously with the control, none underwent division 2. Inhibition of division is abolished competitively by L-phenylalanine (Rasmussen and Zeuthen, 1962).

For the brief incubation treatment, cells were prepared in the same manner as for continuous incubation excepting that they were exposed to FPA for 20 min. only at successive time intervals after EHT (Fig. 16B). The upper curve indicates the fission waves or growth oscillations in a control culture. Each point on the two curves below indicates the time when a 20-min. exposure to the drug started. An increase in division-delay time is observed up to EHT + 45 min. Later exposure to the drug delays the first division only slightly or not at all. The second division, however, is delayed, and maximum delay occurs when the drug is applied at EHT + 140 min. A comparison of A and B (Fig. 16) reveals transition points during the preparation for division, when high susceptibility to the drug (causing the longest delay) changes to a refractive state, during which exposure causes little or no division delay. The period of total drug inhibition (the "all effect" when division is prevented) during continuous exposure (cf. Fig. 16A, I and II) corresponds to a period of progressive delay when temporary exposure to the inhibitor is given (cf. Fig. 16B, I and II). The hypothesis that the cells must synthesize a "division protein" prior to fission is based primarily on these findings (Rasmussen and Zeuthen, 1962).

b. Chloramphenicol. Continuous exposure of washed, synchronized *Tetrahymena* to chloramphenicol (3.0 mM) delays the first division. This delay amounts to 30 min. if addition is at EHT + 5, and to 12 min. if it is added at EHT + 45 (Rasmussen and Zeuthen, 1962).

A lower concentration of chloramphenicol (2.0 mM) apparently does not inhibit cell division but does affect growth (Lee *et al.,* 1959). When this amount is added to a culture in nutrient medium at BHT, cellular protein increases only 30% as much as in control cultures, in which the increase is 3-fold. In nutrient control cultures, cellular counts increased 6 times in the 5.5 hr. after EHT; with chloramphenicol the increase was only 3.5 times. If cells were transferred to inorganic medium at EHT, 5.5 hr. later the count tripled regardless of whether chloramphenicol has been added. It is clear from these experiments that the drug does not prevent cell division, but inhibits protein synthesis during and after the HT.

3. BASE ANALOGS AND INHIBITORS OF NUCLEIC ACID SYNTHESIS

The following compounds added to washed cells in inorganic medium at any time between EHT and the first growth oscillation induce no division delay: azathymine, 5-bromouracil, 5-fluoro-2'-deoxyuridine, adenopterin, 5-fluoro-uracil. Two base analogs inhibited: 8-azaguanine ($0.7–4.0 \times 10^{-4}M$) and 6-methylpurine ($1.6 \times 10^{-3}M$) block the first synchronized division in washed cells only if added within 70 min. after EHT. Guanine, guanosine, adenine, and adenosine antagonized the inhibition by 8-azaguanine; adenine and adenosine, but not guanine, antagonized 6-methylpurine (Zeuthen, 1961a).

It has been suggested that base analogs probably interfere with the metabolism of nucleotides (Rasmussen and Zeuthen, 1962; Hamburger and Zeuthen, 1960). Azaserine ($4.5 \times 10^{-5}M$) exposure at the start of HT does not interfere with the 3-fold increase in protein that occurs during HT (Lee et al., 1959). If, however, washed cells are transferred at EHT to the same concentration of the drug in organic medium, almost complete blockage of cell division is observed at EHT + 5.5 hr.

4. INHIBITORS OF LIPID SYNTHESIS

Seventeen inhibitors of steroid synthesis were tested for effect on synchronized cell division and on normal growth of exponentially growing cultures of *Tetrahymena pyriformis* GL. All 17 compounds inhibited synchronized cell division in inorganic medium, and normal multiplication of exponentially growing cultures in chemically defined medium as well (Holz et al., 1964).

If triparanol citrate is applied to samples of *Tetrahymena pyriformis* GL in inorganic medium between EHT and the first growth oscillation, division delay (inhibition) is observed. With 0.01 mM triparanol at pH 7.0 and 28°C., the ensuing delay is a function of time of application. Addition (and subsequent continuous exposure) between EHT and EHT + 15 min. causes a delay of 90 min. A maximum delay of 180 min. is observed following treatment with triparanol between EHT + 35 and EHT + 45 min. After EHT + 45 min., the period of delay decreases rapidly; at EHT + 65 min., the drug was no longer effective in blocking the first growth oscillation, which occurred as usual at EHT + 80 min.

The effect of triparanol was greatly reduced or abolished if palmitic acid or any one of several oleic acid-containing compounds was added simultaneously. A number of other fatty acids, sterols, sterol precursors, and phospholipids were inactive. Since inhibition of the first synchronized division by triparanol is prevented by a variety of oleic acid-containing compounds but not by sterols, the authors conclude that sterol synthesis may not be necessary prior to synchronized division (Holz, 1962; Holz *et al.*, 1962), although sterol synthesis does occur in *Tetrahymena pyriformis* W (Castrejon and Hamilton, 1962; Mallory *et al.*, 1963).

E. Comparison of the Effect of Various Inhibitors on Growth Oscillations

1. continuous exposure

Synchronized *Tetrahymena* in a Proteose-peptone medium at EHT were transferred to inorganic medium containing the inhibitor. Delay of the first synchronized division (which occurs at EHT + 85 min. in controls) is taken as a measure of inhibitor effect. In this way, the effect of 10 purine, 14 pyrimidine, and 12 amino acid analogs, 2 specific inhibitors of protein synthesis and 17 supposed inhibitors of steroid synthesis were tested (Holz *et al.*, 1964). The results indicate (1) that synchronized cell division is supported by accumulated nucleic acids not present in cells of the normal exponential growth phase and (2) that synthesis of specific proteins and long-chain unsaturated fatty acids must take place before the first synchronized growth oscillation.

2. temporary exposure

For these experiments the test system was modified so that the cells are exposed to various inhibitory treatments for short periods at different times from EHT + 5 min. to EHT + 75 min. (Nachtwey, 1961; Rasmussen and Zeuthen, 1962). A summary of the effect of various treatments follows: (a) FPA applied for 30 min. causes the longest delay in division when applied at EHT + 35 min.; no delay is observed if treatment is carried out at EHT + 55 min. (b) The longest delay caused by a heat shock (34° for 45 min.) is observed when the heat shock is applied at EHT + 45 min.; a short delay (about 10% of the maximum) occurs when the heat shock is applied just 10 min. later, at EHT + 55 min. (c) Oxygen lack for 15 min. (cells in nutrient medium) causes a maximum delay at EHT + 45 min. and a delay of ∼50% of the maximum at EHT + 55 min. or later. (d) The longest delay, 58 min., is caused by DNP (0.05 mM) added to the culture at EHT + 45 min. and removed 20 min. later.

It was concluded that temporary application of FPA, DNP, heat, and anaerobiosis to cells after EHT and undergoing preparation for division causes a comparable response; specifically, as time progresses during the 80-min. period from EHT to division 1, the cells become increasingly "sensitive" to inhibitory treatment. In other words division delay time increases to a maximum at EHT + 45 min. This period of maximum sensitivity is followed by one of low sensitivity—a shift referred to as the physiological transition point (Rasmussen and Zeuthen, 1962).

V. Extent of Phasing during Growth Oscillations

A. General Considerations

Ways to express degree of synchrony in microbial populations have been explored (Zeuthen, 1958; Scherbaum, 1959; James, 1960; Engelberg, 1961; Spencer et al., 1961; Blum and Padilla, 1962; Blumenthal and Zahler, 1962; Burns, 1962; Smith and Dendy, 1962); one approach to the problem (Scherbaum, 1962) is outlined here.

Any degree of cell division synchrony is reflected in the population growth curve. The straight line obtained by plotting the logarithm of cell number of an exponentially growing population (ordinate) versus time (abscissa) is altered as reproductive rates change. Fluctuations in cell number between periods of little or no division and phases of high division activity constitute growth oscillations. Theoretically, the highest degree of synchrony would be achieved in a culture in which all cells complete fission simultaneously, grow for one generation, and divide in unison again. Were this true a sharp stepwise growth curve without undulations would be observed. To understand the problem several factors must be considered: (1) number of cells (percent of total population) participating in the synchronous division, (2) time span for synchronous division, (3) generation time, average population doubling time, or the length of a complete cycle.

B. The Synchronization Index (SI)

On the basis of these factors, and taking into consideration the geometrical relationship between the growth curves for normal and phased cultures, the following equation has been derived:

$$SI = 1 - \frac{t + gt(2 - n)}{1.12\ gt}$$

in which: $n = \dfrac{\text{number of cells in synchronous division}}{\text{total number of cells}} + 1$

t = time in minutes during which synchronous division is observed

gt = generation time of the population

Table VII

Synchronization Index (SI) in Protozoan Cultures

No.	Organism	Generation time (gt)	Environmental changes inducing growth oscillations	Duration of synchronous division burst	Percent cells in synchrony	SI	Reference
	Flagellata						
1.	Chlamydomonas moewusii[a]	24 hr.	Light (12 hr.)-dark (12 hr.)	1.0 hr.	91	0.88	Bernstein (1960).
2.	C. moewusii (wild-type)[a]	24 hr.	Light (12 hr.)-dark (12 hr.)	4.4 hr.	79	0.65	Cristofalo (1962).
3.	Gonyaulax polyedra	36 hr.	Light (12 hr.)-dark (12 hr.)	4.0 hr.	37	0.34	Sweeney and Hastings (1958).
4.	Euglena gracilis[b]	24 hr.	Light (16 hr.)-dark (8 hr.)	9.5 hr.	100	0.65	Cook and James (1960).
5.	Euglena gracilis[c]	24 hr.	Light (16 hr.)-dark (8 hr.)	6.0 hr.	86	0.65	Cook and James (1960).
6.	Astasia longa[d]	11.5 hr.	15°C., 15.5 hr.; 25° 8.5 hr.	1.1 hr.	100	0.92	Padilla and James (1960).
7.	Astasia longa[e]	13.0 hr.	15°C., 15.5 hr.; 25°, 8.5 hr.	2.0 hr.	100	0.86	Padilla and James (1960).
	Sarcodina						
8.	Amoeba proteus	24.0 hr.	Light (12 hr.)-dark (12 hr.)	9.0 hr.	80	0.49	James (1959).
	Ciliata						
9.	Tetrahymena pyriformis HS	135 min.	pH shift (5.65-7.30)	50 min.	67	0.37	Prescott (1958).
10.	Tetrahymena pyriformis GL	140 min.	7 Heat shocks, 34°, 30 min.	22 min.	82	0.70	Scherbaum and Zeuthen (1954).
11.	Tetrahymena pyriformis GL	160 min.	Single heat shock, 32° 3.5 hr.	20 min.	35	0.31	Zeuthen and Scherbaum (1954).
12.	Tetrahymena pyriformis HS	168 min.	Single temperature shift 18.4°-27.7°C	35 min.	40	0.28	Prescott (1957).
13.	Tetrahymena pyriformis GL	175 min.	Single cold shock, 7°, 2 hr.	25 min.	30	0.25	Zeuthen and Scherbaum (1954).
14.	Paramecium aurelia	6 hr.	Selection and nutritional change	40 min.	90	—	Woodward et al. (1961).

[a] No. 1, 2: In these photosynthetic systems normally 4 to 8 cells are formed from one parent cell during the 24-hr. cycle. In the computation of the SI, therefore, a 4- or 8-fold increase during gt has been assumed.
[b] No. 4: From a culture in medium lacking cysteine and methionine.
[c] No. 5: From a culture in medium containing cysteine and methionine.
[d] No. 6: In 2% Proteose-peptone medium, without cysteine and methionine.
[e] No. 7: In Myers-Cramer medium containing cysteine and methionine.

C. The SI in Protozoan Cultures

Table VII shows the relationship between the generation time, duration of synchrony, percent cells in synchrony, and the SI for several free-living protozoa. These parameters vary considerably depending on the species and condition of the culture system. The SI should serve only as a guide to aid in evaluation of physiological and biochemical information obtained from protozoan cultures undergoing growth oscillations.

References

Bernstein, F. (1960). *Science* 131, 1528. Personal Communication.

Bhagavan, N. Y., and Eiler, J. J. (1962).

Blum, J. J., and Padilla, G. M. (1962). *Exptl. Cell Res.* 28, 512.

Blumenthal, L. K., and Zahler, S. A. (1962). *Science* 135, 724.

Bovee, E. C. (1956a). *J. Protozool.* 3, 151.

Bovee, E. C. (1956b). *J. Protozool.* 3, 155.

Braarud, T., and Pappas, J. (1951). *Avhandl. Norske Videnskaps-Akad. Oslo I. Mat.-Naturv. Kl.* 2, 1.

Browning, I., Brittain, M. S., and Bergendahl, J. C. (1952). *Texas Rept. Biol. Med.* 10, 794.

Bruce, V. G. (1957). *In* "The Influence of Temperature on Biological Systems" (J. H. Johnson, ed.), p. 127. Am. Physiol. Soc., Washington, D.C.

Burns, V. W. (1962). *Prog. Biophys. and Biophys. Chem.* 12, 1.

Campbell, A. (1957). *Bacteriol. Rev.* 21, 263.

Castrejon, R. N., and Hamilton, J. G. (1962). *Federation Proc.* 21, No. 2, 300 (abstr.)

Cerroni, R. E., and Zeuthen, E. (1962a). *Exptl. Cell Res.* 26, 604.

Cerroni, R. E., and Zeuthen, E. (1962b). *Compt. Rend. Trav. Lab. Carlsberg* 32, 499.

Child, F. M. (1957). *J. Protozool.* 4, Suppl., 12.

Chou, S. C., and Scherbaum, O. H. (1963). *Biochim. Biophys. Acta* 71, 221.

Christensson, E. (1959). *Acta Physiol. Scand.* 45, 339.

Cook, J. R. (1960). Ph.D. Thesis. Univ. California, Los Angeles, California.

Cook, J. R. (1964). In preparation.

Cook, J. R., and James, T. W. (1960). *Exptl. Cell Res.* 21, 583.

Corbett, J. J. (1963). Personal communication.

Cristofalo, V. J. (1962). Ph.D. Thesis. Univ. Delaware, Newark, Delaware.

Dawson, J. A., Kessler, W. R., and Silberstein, T. K. (1937). *Biol. Bull.* 72, 125.

Ducoff, H. S. (1956). *Exptl. Cell Res.* 11, 218.

Eichel, H. J. (1956). *J. Biol. Chem.* 222, 137.

Eichel, H. J., and Rem. L. T. (1959). *Arch. Biochem. Biophys.* 82, 484.

Eichel, H. J., and Rem. L. T. (1961). *Proc. 1st Intern. Conf. Protozool., Prague, 1961* p. 44.

Eiler, J. J. (1962). *Proc. 22nd Intern. Congr. Intern. Union Physiol. Sci., Leiden, 1962* p. 783.

Eiler, J. J., and McEwen, W. K. (1949). *Arch. Biochem.* 20, 163.

Eiler, J. J., Krezanoski, J. Z., and Lee, K. H. (1956). *Federation Proc.* 15, 247.

Elliott, A. M. (1961). Personal communication.

Elliott, A. M., Kennedy, J. R., Jr., and Bak, I. J. (1962). *J. Cell Biol.* 12, 515.

Engelberg, J. (1961). *Exptl. Cell Res.* **23**, 218.

Frankel, J. (1962). *Compt. Rend. Trav. Lab. Carlsberg* **33**, 1.

Gough, L. H. (1905). *Dept. Marine Biol. Assoc. U.K., Intern. Fishery Invest., 1902–1903* pp. 325–377.

Halberg, F., and Conner, R. L. (1961). *Proc. Minn. Acad. Sci.* **29**, 227.

Hamburger, K. (1962). *Compt. Rend. Trav. Lab. Carlsberg* **32**, 359.

Hamburger, K., and Zeuthen, E. (1957). *Exptl. Cell Res.* **13**, 443.

Hamburger, K., and Zeuthen, E. (1960). *Compt. Rend. Trav. Lab. Carlsberg* **32**, 1.

Harrington, J. D. (1960). Ph.D. Thesis. Catholic Univ. America Press, Washington, D.C.

Hogg, J. F. (1959). *Federation Proc.* **18**, 247.

Hogg, J. F. (1963). Personal communication.

Hogg, J. F., and Kornberg, H. L. (1961). *Biochem. J.* **81**, 17.

Hogg, J. F., and Kornberg, H. L. (1963). *Biochem. J.* **86**, 462.

Hogg, J. F., and Wagner, C. (1956). *Federation Proc.* **15**, 275.

Holz, G. G., Jr. (1962). *Proc. 22nd Intern. Congr. Intern. Union Physiol. Sci., Leiden, 1962* p. 792.

Holz, G. G., Jr., Scherbaum, O. H., and Williams, N. (1957). *Exptl. Cell Res.* **13**, 618.

Holz, G. G., Jr., Erwin, J., Rosenbaum, N., and Aaronson, S. (1962). *Arch. Biochem. Biophys.* **98**, 312.

Holz, G. G., Jr., Rasmussen, L., and Zeuthen, E. (1964). *Compt. Rend. Trav. Lab. Carlsberg.* in press.

Hotchkiss, R. D. (1954). *Proc. Natl. Acad. Sci. U.S.* **40**, 49.

Hutchens, J. O., Podolsky, B., and Morales, M. F. (1948). *J. Cellular Comp. Physiol.* **32**, 117.

Iverson, R. M., and Giese, A. C. (1957). *Exptl. Cell Res.* **13**, 213.

James, T. W. (1954). Ph.D. Thesis. Univ. California, Berkeley, California.

James, T. W. (1959). *Ann. N.Y. Acad. Sci.* **78**, 501.

James, T. W. (1960). *Ann. N.Y. Acad. Sci.* **90**, 550.

James, T. W. (1961a). *Pathol. Biol., Semaine Hop.* **9**, 510.

James, T. W. (1961b). Personal communication.

James, T. W. (1962). *Proc. 22nd Intern. Congr. Intern. Union Physiol. Sci., Leiden, 1962* p. 788.

James, T. W. (1963). *In* "Cell Growth and Cell Division" (R. J. C. Harris, ed.), p. 9. Academic Press, New York.

James, T. W., and Padilla, G. M. (1959). *Proc. 1st Natl. Biophys. Conf., Columbus, Ohio, 1957* p. 694.

Jörgensen, E. (1911). *Intern. Rev. Ges. Hydrobiol., Biol. Suppl. Ser.* **2**, 1–124.

Kamiya, T. (1959). *J. Biochem. (Tokyo)* **46**, 1187.

Kamiya, T., and Takahashi, T. (1961). *J. Biochem. (Tokyo)* **50**, 227.

Karakashian, M. W., and Hastings, J. W. (1962). *Proc. Natl. Acad. Sci. U.S.* **48**, 2130.

Kidder, G. W., and Dewey, V. C. (1951). *In* "Biochemistry and Physiology of Protozoa" (A. Lwoff, ed.), Vol. 1, p. 324. Academic Press, New York.

Klamer, B., and Fennell, R. A. (1963). *Exptl. Cell Res.* **29**, 166.

Klingenberg, M., and Bücher, T. (1960). *Ann. Rev. Biochem.* **29**, 669.

Kornberg, H. L., and Krebs, H. A. (1957). *Nature* **179**, 988.

Kornberg, H. L., and Madsen, N. B. (1958). *Biochem. J.* **68**, 549.

Kudo, R. R. (1947). *J. Morphol.* **80**, 93.

Kudo, R. R. (1951). *J. Morphol.* **88**, 145.

Lederberg, S., and Mazia, D. (1960). *Exptl. Cell Res.* **21**, 590.

Lee, K. H. (1959). *J. Am. Pharm. Assoc., Pract. Pharm. Ed.* **48**, 468.

Lee, K. H., Yuzuriha, Y. O., and Eiler, J. J. (1959). *J. Am. Pharm. Assoc., Pract. Pharm. Ed.* **48**, 470.

Leedale, G. F. (1959). *Biol. Bull.* **116**, 162.

Levy, M., and Scherbaum, O. H. (1961). Unpublished data.

Liesche, W. (1938). *Arch. Protistenk.* **91**, 135.

Lowenstein, J. M. (1961). *J. Theoret. Biol.* **1**, 121.

McDonald, B. B. (1958). *Biol. Bull.* **114**, 71.

Mallory, F. B., Gordon, J. T., and Conner, R. L. (1963). *J. Am. Chem. Soc.* **85**, 1362.

Manners, D. J., and Ryley, J. F. (1952). *Biochem. J.* **52**, 480.

Mazia, D. (1954). *In* "Glutathione" (S. Colowick *et al.*, eds.), p. 209. Academic Press, New York.

Mazia, D. (1959). *In* "Sulfur in Proteins" (R. Benesch *et al.*, eds.), p. 367. Academic Press, New York.

Mazia, D. (1961). *In* "The Cell" (J. Brachet and A. E. Mirsky, eds.), Vol. 3, p. 77. Academic Press, New York.

Mazia, D., and Prescott, D. M. (1954). *Science* **120**, 120.

Mehta, R. K., and Eiler, J. J. (1964). To be published.

Mita, T. (1958). *Zool. Mag. (Tokyo)* **67**, 20 (in Japanese).

Mita, T. and Scherbaum, O. H. (1964). In preparation.

Mita, T., Ono, T., and Sugimura, T. (1959). *Zool. Mag. (Tokyo)* **68**, 65 (in Japanese).

Nachtwey, D. S. (1961). *In* "Progress in Protozoology" (J. Ludvik *et al.*, eds), p. 224. Academic Press, New York.

Nishi, A., and Scherbaum, O. H. (1962a). *Biochim. Biophys. Acta* **65**, 411.

Nishi, A., and Scherbaum, O. H. (1962b). *Biochim. Biophys. Acta* **65**, 419.

Padilla, G. M. (1960). Ph.D. Thesis. *Univ. California, Los Angeles, California.*

Padilla, G. M., and Blum, J. J. (1964). In preparation.

Padilla, G. M., and James, T. W. (1958) *J. Protozool.* **5**, Suppl., 22 (abstr.).

Padilla, G. M., and James, T. W. (1960). *Exptl. Cell Res.* **20**, 401.

Plesner, P. (1958a). *Biochim. Biophys. Acta* **29**, 462.

Plesner, P. (1958b). *Intern. Abstr. Biol. Sci. (Suppl., 4th Intern. Congr. Biochem., Vienna, 1958)* p. 79.

Plesner, P. (1961a). Cited in Mazia (1961), p. 146.

Plesner, P. (1961b). *Cold Spring Harbor Symp. Quant. Biol.* **26**, 159.

Plesner, P. (1963). *In* "Cell Growth and Cell Division" (R. J. C. Harris, ed.), p. 77. Academic Press, New York.

Plesner, P., Rasmussen, L., and Zeuthen, E. (1963). *In* "Synchrony in Cell Division and Growth" (E. Zeuthen, ed.). Wiley (Interscience), New York. In preparation.

Prescott, D. M. (1957). *J. Protozool.* **4**, 252.

Prescott, D. M. (1958). *Physiol. Zool.* **31**, 111.

Rasmussen, L. (1963). *Compt. Rend. Trav. Lab. Carlsberg* **33**, 53.

Rasmussen, L., and Zeuthen, E. (1962). *Compt. Rend. Trav. Lab. Carlsberg* **32**, 333.

Ron, A., and Guttman, R. (1961). *Exptl. Cell Res.* **25**, 176.

Roth, L. E., and Minick, O. T. (1961). *J. Protozool.* **8**, 12.

Satir, P., and Zeuthen, E. (1961). *Compt. Rend. Trav. Lab. Carlsberg* **32**, 241.

Sato, H. (1960). *Anat. Record* 138, 381.

Scherbaum, O. H. (1956). *Exptl. Cell Res.* 11, 464.

Scherbaum, O. H. (1957a). *Exptl. Cell Res.* 13, 11.

Scherbaum, O. H. (1957b). *Exptl. Cell Res.* 13, 24.

Scherbaum, O. H. (1959). *J. Protozool.* 6, Suppl., 17 (abstr.).

Scherbaum, O. H. (1960). *Ann. Rev. Microbiol.* 14, 283.

Scherbaum, O. H. (1962). *J. Protozool.* 9, 61.

Scherbaum, O. H. (1963). *In* "The Cell in Mitosis (L. Levine, ed.), p. 125. Academic Press, New York.

Scherbaum, O. H., and Jahn, T. L. (1964). *Exptl. Cell Res.* 33, 99.

Scherbaum, O. H., and Levy, M. (1961). *Pathol. Biol., Semaine Hop.* 9, 514.

Scherbaum, O. H., Louderback A. L., and Jahn, T. L. (1958). *Biol. Bull.* 115, 269.

Scherbaum, O. H., and Zeuthen, E. (1954). *Exptl. Cell Res.* 6, 221.

Scherbaum, O. H., and Zeuthen, E. (1955). *Exptl. Cell Res., Suppl.* 3, 312.

Scherbaum, O. H., James, T. W., and Jahn, T. L. (1959a). *J. Cellular Comp. Physiol.* 53, 119.

Scherbaum, O. H., Louderback, A., and Jahn, T. L. (1959b). *Exptl. Cell Res.* 18, 150.

Scherbaum, O. H., Louderback, A. L., and Brown, A. (1960). *J. Protozool.* 7, Suppl., 25.

Scherbaum, O. H., Chou, S. C., Seraydarian, K. H., and Byfield, J. E. (1962). *Can. J. Microbiol.* 8, 753.

Schuster, G. L., and Vennes, J. W. (1960). *Proc. N. Dakota Acad. Sci.* 14, 1.

Short, R. B. (1946). *Biol. Bull.* 90, 8.

Singer, W., and Eiler, J. J. (1960). *J. Am. Pharm. Assoc., Sci. Ed.* 49, 669.

Singer, W., Lee, K. H., and Eiler, J. J. (1960). *J. Am. Pharm. Assoc., Sci. Ed.* 49, 90.

Smith, C. L., and Dendy, P. O. (1962). *Nature* 193, 555.

Spencer, H. T., Schmidt, R. R., Kramer, C. Y., Moore, W. E. C., and King, K. W. (1961). *Exptl. Cell Res.* 25, 485.

Sugimura, T., Ono, T., and Mita, T. (1957). *J. Japan. Biochem. Soc.* 27, 714 (in Japanese).

Sullivan, W. D., and Boyle, J. V. (1961). Rev. Broteria Sér. Ciencias Nat. 30, 77.

Sullivan, W. D., and Snyder, R. L. (1962). *Exptl. Cell Res.* 28, 239.

Sullivan, W. D., and Sparks, J. T. (1961). *Exptl. Cell Res.* 23, 536.

Sweeney, B. M., and Hastings, J. W. (1958). *J. Protozool.* 5, 217.

Takahashi, T., Kamiya, T., and Kikuchi, S. (1964). in press.

Tamiya, H., Iwamura, T., Shibata, K., Hase, E., and Nihei, T. (1953). *Biochim. Biophys. Acta* 12, 23.

Thormar, H. (1959). *Compt. Rend. Trav. Lab. Carlsberg* 31, 207.

Thormar, H., and Zeuthen, E. (1958). Cited in Zeuthen (1958).

Wagner, C. (1956). Ph.D. Thesis. Univ. Michigan, Ann Arbor, Michigan.

Williams, N. E., and Scherbaum, O. H. (1959). *J. Embryol. Exptl. Morphol.* 7, 241.

Wilson, B. W. (1962). Ph.D. Thesis. Univ. California, Los Angeles, California.

Wilson, B. W., and James, T. W. (1964). in press.

Woodward, J., Gelber, B., and Swift, H. (1961). *Exptl. Cell Res.* 23, 258.

Wu, C., and Hogg, J. F. (1952). *J. Biol. Chem.* 198, 753.

Wu, C. and Hogg, J. F. (1956). *Arch. Biochem. Biophys.* 62, 70.

Zeuthen, E. (1958). *Advan. Biol. Med. Phys.* 6, 37.

Zeuthen, E. (1961a). *In* "Growth in Living Systems" (M. X. Zarrow, ed.), p. 135. Basic Books, New York.

Zeuthen, E. (1961b). *In* "Biological Structure and Function" (T. W. Goodwin and O. Lindberg, eds.), Vol. 2, p. 537. Academic Press, New York.

Zeuthen, E. (1963). *In* "Cell Growth and Cell Division" (R. J. C. Harris, ed.), p. 1. Academic Press, New York.

Zeuthen, E., and Scherbaum, O. H. (1954). *Proc. Symp. Colston Res. Soc.* 7, 141.

Protoplasmic Movements and Locomotion of Protozoa*

THEODORE L. JAHN AND EUGENE C. BOVEE

Department of Zoology, University of California, Los Angeles, California

	Page
I. General Aspects of Structure and Energy Metabolism	62
A. Assumptions of Muscle-Like Movement in Protozoa	62
B. Fibrillar ATP-Actomyosin-Like Proteins in Protozoa	63
II. Ameboid Movement	66
A. Theories of "Gel-Sol" Mechanics in Ameboid Movement in *Amoeba proteus*	66
B. Other Factors in Ameboid Movement	70
C. Other Forms of Ameboid Movement	70
D. Aggregate Ameboid Movement	72
III. Shuttle Flow in Mycetozoa	77
A. Importance of the Rhythmic Shuttle Flow	77
B. Theories of "Gel-Sol" Mechanics in Shuttle Flow	78
C. Explanation of Shuttle Flow as a Contraction-Hydraulic System	78
D. Other Theories	81
E. Rhythmic Shuttle-Flow Movement and Net Unidirectional Advance	81
F. Environmental Factors Affecting the Movement	82
G. Unexplained Phenomena	83
IV. Bidirectional Filamentous Movement	84
A. Occurrence	84
B. Bidirectional Movement in Foraminiferans	84
C. Importance of Bidirectional Shear in Flow Mechanisms	86
D. Bidirectional Protoplasmic Movements in Other Protozoa	86

* Based partly on experimental work supported by NIH grants #6462, 8611, and E-1158, and by ONR Task NR-304-502, Contract Nonr-233(65).

Page

V. Taxonomic Significance of Two Types of Movement in Sarco-
dines 88
  A. The Distinctiveness of the Two Types 88
  B. Revision of Higher Taxa 88
  C. The Major Defect of the Old System 89
VI. Cilia versus Flagella 89
  A. Evidence for Essential Similarities 89
VII. Movement of Flagella and of Flagellates 90
  A. Classification of Flagellar Movements 90
  B. Longitudinal Base-to-Tip Movements 91
  C. Longitudinal Tip-to-Base Movements 93
  D. Lateroposterior Movements 95
  E. Multiple Movements of Flagella in One Organism . . . 97
  F. Rotary Drive of Dinoflagellate Transverse Flagellum . . . 97
  G. Comparison to Sperm Flagella 97
  H. Theories of Internal Flagellar Mechanisms 98
  I. Hydrodynamic Factors Involved in Flagellar Movement . . 99
VIII. Movement of Cilia and Ciliates 100
  A. The Nature of the Ciliary Beat 100
  B. "Kinetodesmal" Subpellicular Interciliary Fibrils . . . 102
  C. A Hydrodynamic Theory of Metachrony 105
  D. Ciliary Reversal 106
  E. Pattern Swimming by Ciliates 110
IX. Other Movements of Protozoa 112
  A. A List of Poorly Understood Movements 112
  B. Cyclosis 112
  C. Myoneme Movements 112
  D. Trichocyst Extrusion 113
  E. "Metabolic" Movements of Euglenids 114
  F. Gliding Movements 114
  G. "Peristaltic" Movements of Gregarines 115
  H. Swimming of Sporozoan Trophozoites 115
  I. Suctorian Movements 116
X. Summary and Epilogue 118
References 119

FUNDAMENTAL LAWS OF THE UNIVERSE

*All inanimate objects and all living organisms which do not have a central
nervous system and are completely devoid of the power of reason behave in a
completely logical manner.*   T.L.J.

I. General Aspects of Structure and Energy Metabolism

A. ASSUMPTIONS OF MUSCLE-LIKE MOVEMENT IN PROTOZOA

The tacit assumption of certain early protozoologists that movements and
locomotion of protozoa were due to contractions of the body or its organelles,

somewhat analogous to muscle (Dujardin, 1835; Sharpey, 1835; Ehrenberg, 1838; Schulze, 1875) has never been entirely discarded, although the manner in which the contractions are evoked has continued to be the subject of much debate.

In recent years, studies in biochemistry and physical chemistry have elucidated considerably the nature of the energy-storing nucleotides and the fibrillar protein complexes with which they interact to cause contraction in vertebrate muscle (see reviews, Szent-Györgyi, 1953; Weber, 1958; Perry, 1960). The discovery of actin, and of its role with myosin, adenosine triphosphate (ATP), and various cations, especially Ca^{++}, Mg^{++}, and K^+ (Szent-Györgyi, 1945, 1949, 1953), in the contraction of glycerin-extracted actomyosin models, caused prompt attempts to apply such biochemical events to protozoan motility, initially to ameboid movements (Goldacre and Lorch, 1950; Bovee, 1952), although the normal existence of ATP-actomyosin-like protein systems in protozoa was then only theoretical.

B. Fibrillar ATP-Actomyosin-Like Proteins in Protozoa

1. fibrillar components in locomotor mechanisms

The inevitable search for such systems in protozoa (as well as other organisms) followed. It is now evident that fibrillar organization, revealed by electron microscopy, is present in the presumably contractile gel of the mycetozoon *Physarum polycephalum* (Terada, 1962; Wohlfarth-Bottermann, 1962), and of amebae (Lehman, 1958; Wohlfarth-Bottermann, 1960), in the filopods of the foraminiferan *Allogromia laticollaris* (Wohlfarth-Bottermann, 1961), and the axopods of heliozoa (Wohlfarth-Bottermann and Kruger, 1954; Wohlfarth-Bottermann, 1959, 1964; E. Anderson and Beams, 1960; Kitching, 1964).

Cilia and flagella, metazoan or protozoan, are now generally known to be fibrillar, in a pattern of nine peripheral doublets and two central fibrils, attached to a basal plate imbedded in peripheral cytoplasm, often with accessory fibrils (for reviews, see Fawcett, 1961; Pitelka, 1963). Ciliate myonemes (Randall and Jackson, 1958) and spasmonemes (Fauré-Fremiet *et al.*, 1956) are also fibrillar in organization, as are certain ciliate trichocysts, too, when extruded (Jakus and Hall, 1946). The tentacles and stalks of suctorians are also clearly fibrous (Rudzinska and Porter, 1954; Roullier *et al.*, 1956). Pitelka (1963) considers the most unique feature of protozoan ultrastructure to be the extent to which fibrous components are present in their cytoplasmic organelles and organelle systems.

Roth (1962, 1964) postulates that individual fibrillar components of cilioflagellar organelles, mitotic apparatus, and subpellicular filaments in protozoa have a "standard" dimensional diameter of 15 mμ. He claims this unit filament has much to do with filament functions, organelle replication, and division synchrony.

2. ATP-ACTOMYOSIN-LIKE PROTEIN ORGANIZATION

The research on the biochemical materials of the fibrils, as data accumulate, indicates the general presence of an actomyosin-like mechanochemical system in these fibrillar complexes in protozoa. When ATP is injected into living amebae it affects locomotion (Kriszat, 1949, 1954; Goldacre and Lorch, 1950), viscosity, and gel strength (Zimmerman et al., 1958). Similarly, ATP applied to the surface of or injected into the mycetozöon, Physarum, accelerates the rate of protoplasmic flow (Ts'O et al., 1956; Kamiya et al., 1957), increases the motive force (Takata, 1957), and may initiate contraction (Jahn et al., 1964b). "Live" flagella, broken from the flagellate body, will swim in ATP solutions (Brokaw, 1961). Glycerinated models of amebae (Hoffmann-Berling, 1953; Simard-Duquesne and Couillard, 1962a) contract and relax as ATP concentration is varied in the solution; and glycerinated models of flagellates (Hoffmann-Berling, 1954, 1955) and of cilia, flagella, and vorticellid spasmonemes contract rhythmically when ATP is applied to them (for review, see Hoffmann-Berling, 1960). Cytoplasmic movements in suctoria and rate of flow of prey-cytoplasm through the tentacles are also accelerated by ATP (Hull, 1961b).

That these contractile fibrillar complexes of protozoa are some variety of actomyosin is indicated by chemical analyses as well. The myomyosin extracted from Physarum (Loewy, 1952) is of a molecular size and functional character almost identical to vertebrate myosin-B (Ts'O et al., 1956b; Nakajima, 1956, 1960, 1963; Oosawa, 1963). It reacts with vertebrate ATP (Takeuichi and Hatano, 1955, 1956) and normally exists with an ATP of its own which, in extracts, elicits contraction by models of vertebrate myosin-B (Takeuichi and Hatano, 1956). Amoeba proteus also contains an actomyosin-like protein with ATPase activity (Simard-Duquesne and Couillard, 1962b), and Acanthamoeba has an ATP-ADP-ATPase system (R. L. Klein, 1961). From Paramecium aurelia an ATPase protein complex has been extracted (van Wagtendonk and Vloedman, 1951); and the flagella of Polytoma (Tibbs, 1957) and Chlamydomonas (Jones and Lewin, 1959), and the cilia of Tetrahymena (Child, 1959, 1961; M. R. Watson and Hopkins, 1962) contain fibrillar proteins which behave, when chemically extracted, like actomyosin. These fibrillar proteins of cilia and flagella also have ATPase activity, as do actomyosins.

3. GENERALITY OF ATP-USING SYSTEMS IN PROTOPLASMIC MOVEMENT

Meantime, it has been shown that in plant cells, too, protoplasmic movement is accelerated, in Acetabularia, for example, by ATP (Takata, 1958); and undulatory and sliding fibrous proteins are present in Nitella (for review, see Kamiya, 1959). Similarities between the two-dimensional movements of plant protoplasm and that of certain protozoa have been suggested (Jarosch, 1958,

1964; Jahn and Rinaldi, 1959; Jahn *et al.,* 1960; Jahn and Bovee, 1964). The weight of evidence indicates that protozoa, as well as other living things, rely on ATP-actomyosin-like protein mechanochemical systems for motion, as succinctly expressed by Weber (1955, 1958, 1960), Kamiya (1959, 1964a), Hoffmann-Berling (1960, 1964), and Oosawa (1963). The predictions of Hill (1926) that there was then some evidence to suggest that the movements of all living organisms are based on the same fundamental process, and of Schaeffer (1920) that the general features of protoplasmic streaming are similar and caused by the same fundamental process, wherever they occur, have thus been generally accepted.

4. MULTIPLE FUNCTIONS OF ATP-ACTOMYOSIN-LIKE SYSTEMS

The roles of ATP and the actomyosin in protozoa may not always be contraction, however. The presence and, particularly, the amount of ATP present are important, as are the ionic balances, and the local concentration of anions and cations, especially Ca^{++}, Mg^{++}, K^+, and Na^+ (Szent-Györgyi, 1949, 1953; Bovee, 1952; Bingley and Thompson, 1962; Simard-Duquesne and Couillard, 1962b). Salisbury (1962) assigns to Ca^{++} a role in triggering flagellar motility.

Hoffmann-Berling (1960) suggests at least five roles for ATP: (1) contractions driven by ATP-splitting; (2) elongation caused by ATP-binding; (3) relaxation caused by ATP; (4) inhibition of elongation by ATP; (5) movements reversed by ATP. He contends that ATP is primarily a relaxing agent, the only physiological one known; and that it loads the protein complexes with energy, which when released by cationic triggers, drives the motion of the proteins. Pautard (1962) claims for ATP the dual role of relaxation at low electrolyte and high (i.e., alkaline) pH and high nucleotide concentration, and contraction in high electrolyte, low (i.e., acid) pH, and low nucleotide concentration.

Hence, that protozoan motility is due to proteins which change orientation and form, releasing energy from ATP, is agreed upon by most. There is, however, little agreement as to the details of the machinery so far as its functioning in the protozoan is concerned, and certainly no agreement that all movement involves contraction. Much theory and debate exists, despite considerable experimental and observational data, concerning the applications of the mechanism, whether the movement considered is ameboid, filamentous, ciliary, flagellar, or cyclotic.

II. Ameboid Movement

A. Theories of "Gel-Sol" Mechanics in Ameboid Movement in *Amoeba proteus*

Most observations and theories for ameboid movements are based on studies of *Amoeba proteus* or some related laboratory ameba, and may only in part or scarcely at all explain the movements of many other amebas (Bovee, 1959, 1960a, 1963a,b, 1964; Abé, 1961, 1962, 1963, 1964).

1. CONTRACTION-HYDRAULIC THEORY

The current theories all agree that there is a cyclic development involving a fibrous protein complex which forms a semirigid ectoplasmic tube ("gel"). According to the contraction-hydraulic theory the gel contracts at the posterior end, causing the less fibrous endoplasm ("sol") to flow forward, diverting it peripherally at the anterior end to add to the gel tube by conversion to gel. Simultaneously, shortening at the rear and dissolution of fibrous gel into more fluid sol occurs at the inner posterior-gel margin, at an equivalent rate. The visible events are well documented by Mast (1926). The principal debate concerns the site of major contraction and, therefore, of motive force. Most explanations assume that the physiologically and chronologically older ectoplasm contracts, placing pressure on more fluid endoplasm, driving it forward against an anterior hyaline cap (Mast, 1926, 1941; Lewis, 1951; Bovee, 1952; Goldacre, 1952, 1961a,b, 1964; Allen and Roslansky, 1959; Jahn, 1964a; Rinaldi and Jahn, 1962, 1963). This has recently been termed a contraction-hydraulic mechanism (Jahn *et al.*, 1960; Jahn and Bovee, 1964; Rinaldi and Jahn, 1963; Jahn, 1964a) to emphasize the nature of the motive force. Figures 1A and 1B (Jahn, 1964a) show a recent concept of movements of sol and gel.

2. "FOUNTAIN-ZONE" FRONTAL-EVERSION THEORY

Another theory, voluminously championed by its progenitor (Allen, 1960, 1961a,b,c, 1962), but not seriously considered likely by most other investigators of ameboid movement, proposes that the major site of contraction is at the anterior zone where the fibrous gel originates, that also being the site of the motive force. Called a "fountain-zone" theory by its author, it might better be called a frontal-eversion contraction system. Peripheral pressure is assumed to be absent and posterior pressure is assumed to be negative in the system, the ameba maintaining form by the rigidity of the ectoplasmic tube, developing a "pseudoplastic plug" of endoplasm which is everted to make the ectoplasmic tube. The concept is derived mainly from observations that fibrils form and stream cyclically in ameboid endoplasm which has been ejected from the ameba into oil, and that analogous movements appear to occur in amebas

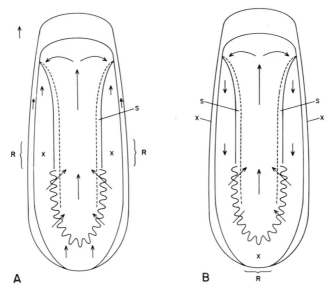

A   **B**

FIG. 1A. Diagram of relative movement of protoplasm in an ameba which is attached to the substrate near the middle of its body. Outer zone between solid lines represents hyaline ectoplasm. Inner zone bounded by solid lines represents gelated contractile granular tube. Wavy line indicates area of solation. Dotted line represents boundary of solated granular endoplasm. R is the region of attachment. X is the stationary protoplasm. S is the shear zone between the gel tube and the solated endoplasm. Arrows indicate the directions of movement of protoplasm and of the ameba.

     B. Diagram of relative movement of an ameba attached at its rear end. It does not locomote; and the pattern of movement of its protoplasmic organization produces the so-called "fountain-streaming." (After Jahn, 1964a.)

trapped in capillaries, or those which are floating, or are attached only at the rear end (Allen *et al.*, 1960; Allen, 1961a,b). Also, the idea relies upon the erroneous assumption of the theorist that the proponents and supporters of the contraction-hydraulic explanation believe and require that the sol be a Newtonian fluid (Allen, 1960, 1961a; also see Rinaldi and Jahn, 1963), whereas it has long been known to be thixotropic (Mast, 1926; Heilbrunn, 1958; Jahn, 1964a).

There seems little else to support the "frontal contraction" idea, but since the major site of contraction in the ectoplasmic tube is yet to be metabolically determined, the idea cannot be proven entirely false.

3. OTHER THEORIES

Two other recent proposals exist. One (Kavanau, 1962, 1963a,b) proposes that an endoplasmic reticulum (ER) equated with the ER of electron microscopy is the fibrous protein. It is presumed to stream forward against a counter current of "matrix" jetted cyclically toward the rear by the pumping contractions of the endoplasm and their continued contractions as they associate into and become part of the ectoplasmic tube. The concept, while ingenious, is completely untestable experimentally and seems to merit little consideration for the present. The second new proposal assumes that because a gradient of difference in electrical potential has been found from anterior to posterior of the ameba, the motive force is caused by a current flow which in its turn is presumed to be due to active transport of ions across the plasma membrane (Bingley and Thompson, 1962). The authors admit this to be only one possible role of the bioelectrical gradient and that another likely role (more likely in our estimation) is that it reflects the activity of a triggering mechanism which is associated with a mechanochemical system of streaming, contractility, and protoplasmic change of phase. Furthermore, the causal relationship between ion transport and electromotive force which is ordinarily assumed, on the basis of some very elaborate and interesting experiments, to exist in frog skin (Ussing and Zerahn, 1951; Ussing, 1957) and therefore in other biological materials, has no logical basis in terms of Kirchhoff's laws of electrical circuits (Marsh and Jahn, 1964).

4. EVIDENCE FOR THE CONTRACTION-HYDRAULIC MECHANISM

The bulk of experimental and observational data is more readily explained by and assimilated into the contraction-hydraulic hypothesis than into any of the other three, including the data purported to support the others (Bovee, 1964; Jahn, 1964a; Goldacre, 1964; Marsland, 1964). Posterior contraction is heavily supported by observations that: (1) Protein is densest at the rear of the locomoting ameba (Allen and Roslansky, 1959). (2) A retracting pseudopod contracts with a measured force of 10^3 dynes/cm.^{2} (Goldacre, 1961a). (3) The pressure generated by the posterior end of the ameba in locomotion is equivalent to about that of a 1-cm. column of water, and the locomotion can be stopped by a counter pressure of that degree (Kamiya, 1964b). (4) Protein stained by neutral red dye (which inhibits solation) continues to contract and becomes denser, accumulating at the rear of the locomoting ameba (Goldacre, 1952; Noland, 1957). (5) The chemical rupture of the ATP bond may be expected to generate an electric current (Szent-Györygi, 1960; Jahn, 1961), causing actomyosin contraction, i.e., the more ATP broken, the more contraction, and the more current generated; and there are measurements which show higher current production in the contracting rear of an ameba than further forward, with a gradient of increase of 1 volt per centimeter of length (Bingley and Thompson, 1962). (6) Both the bioelectric gradient and the differential gradient in protein concentration fade and cease when locomotion slows and stops, and are presumably therefore a consequence of locomotion. The latter was considered by the observers at the time of observation to support a posterior site of major contraction (Allen and Roslansky, 1959). (7) A puncture through the gel tube into the streaming endoplasm of the ameba in locomotion, even at the rear, results in an outflow of endoplasm through the hole (Goldacre, 1961a), indicating the presence of a positive peripheral and posterior pressure. (8) Electric current imposed on a cathodally directed ameba inhibits gel formation at the anterior end, causes contraction at the posterior end, and increases the rate of locomotion (Mast, 1931; Hahnert, 1932). (9) Sudden increases in illumination may cause reversal of flow in advancing pseudopods while posterior pressure and forward flow continue to go on at the rear, so that the central region of the body may become greatly distended by the effects of the counter pressures (Mast, 1931, 1932). (10) Fine granules, observable with darkfield, move forward through the gel and sometimes in the hyaline ectoplasm (Rinaldi and Jahn, 1962, 1963). (11) The ridges of the pseudopods of *A. proteus* and *Chaos carolinensis* are formed by posterior sol breaking through the *side* of the gel tube and flowing forward between the gel tube and the plasmalemma (Schaeffer, 1920; Mast, 1926). (12) In newly forming pseudopods *all* of the granules, i.e., throughout any whole cross section, are moving forward (Jahn and Rinaldi, 1963). (13) The anterior portion of the gel tube is stretched forward as if by hydraulic pressure (Rinaldi and Jahn, 1963), where as frontal-eversion theory demands either no movement of it, or contraction of it toward the rear. (14) The data on the effects of high hydrostatic pressure demonstrate a close relationship between contraction and solation (Landau, 1959), whereas the frontal contraction theory requires a close relationship between contraction and gelation.

In spite of the wide variety of new evidence concerning the mechanism of ameboid movement, some of which may be equivocal and all of which has led to much discussion and will lead to much more, the simplest, clearest, and therefore the most devastating evidence against the frontal-eversion theory (and in favor of the contraction-hydraulic theory) consists of the old data of Mast and Hahnert, cited in items 8 and 9 above and discussed by Jahn (1964a). These data, incidentally, were not obtained for the purpose of evaluating theories of ameboid movement but were part of a study of the fundamental effects of light and electricity, 30 years before the frontal-eversion theory was proposed.

As assessment of the presently available data indicates that the general description of the events in ameboid movement given by Mast (1926) is essentially correct, and that pressure generated at the rear forces the more fluid endoplasm forward, establishing a contraction-hydraulic flow system (Jahn, 1964a). Bovee (1952) and Landau (1959) discuss the general role of the

ATP-actomyosin-like protein, its dynamic equilibrium as promoting the gel-sol conversions, and the nature and locale of the propulsive force. The latter author gives a detailed discussion of much supporting data.

B. OTHER FACTORS IN AMEBOID MOVEMENT

The perhaps intricate roles of cell surface (Schaeffer, 1920; Bovee, 1960a; Goldacre, 1961a; Bell, 1963) and nucleus (Schaeffer, 1920; Goldacre, 1958; Landau, 1959; Bovee, 1964) must be considered. According to Goldacre (1961a), the membrane must be in contact with the ameboid cortical ecto-plasm (i.e., the gel) before contraction may ensue. He interprets this relation-ship to indicate the possible presence in the membrane of an ATPase necessary to trigger the contraction.

The multiple role of the nucleus (Hirshfield, 1959; Landau, 1959) is little understood; but according to Sells *et al.* (1961) it is involved with the rate of ATPase activity, perhaps indicating an important nuclear role in the bio-chemistry of locomotion.

That the entire length of the gel tube is structurally oriented is evident from the following observations, among others: (1) There are gradients of protein density and gel strength (Allen and Roslansky, 1959), and bioelectrical potential (Bingley and Thompson, 1962) from anterior to posterior. (2) Birefringence is significantly detectable only in the denser cortical material of the ameba; none is present in the streaming endoplasm (Mitchison, 1950). (3) The medial portion of the gel tube is virtually stationary, indicating there a nearly isometric contractile state (Bovee, 1952), but near the anterior end granules move forward as the tube is stretched (Rinaldi and Jahn, 1963; Jahn, 1964a).

C. OTHER FORMS OF AMEBOID MOVEMENT

It should be remembered, however, that the theories discussed above apply specifically to the movements and locomotion of *Amoeba proteus* and closely related species. Although it is probable that in general the contraction-hydrau-lic system may serve in most amebae, there may be many variations in the applications of the general ATP-actomyosin-like system necessary to explain pseudopodal formations and movements in other species (Bovee, 1959, 1960a,b,c, 1963a,b, 1964; Abé, 1961, 1962, 1963, 1964).

1. MOVEMENT OF *Thecamoeba striata*

Abé (1962), who analyzed motion pictures of *Thecamoeba striata*, contends that the plasmalemma of such species moves essentially as a rolling sac-like sheath, as Jennings (1904) first contended, but that there is a fenestral open-ing at the rear, permanently maintained, which precludes a pressure-flow sys-tem. Although Abé postulates parallel longitudinal endoplasmic gel piers as

the cause of the dorsal ridges of *striata* amebae in locomotion, he denies any
active shearing flow of solated endoplasm along them. He assumes, instead, an
anterior pull of fibrous hyaline gel in the anterior margin, converting the sol
to gel and everting the organism forward within its own plasmalemma (Fig.
2A,B,C,D). This proposal is very similar to but independent of the frontal-

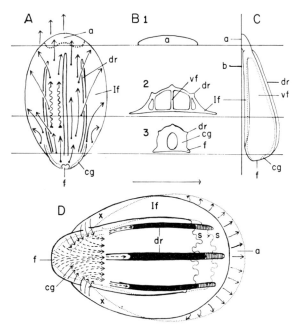

Fig. 2. Protoplasmic movements in *Thecamoeba striata;* semidiagrammatic. (After
Abé, 1961, 1962.)

A. Movements of granules during locomotion. Solid arrows at front indicate
direction and extent of advance during indicated granular movements. Solid non-wavy
arrows on the ameba indicate the direction and extent of movement of granules attached to the surface at various points. Wavy arrows, movements of granules in the
internal granular endoplasm. KEY TO LABELING: a, area of anterior attachment to the
substrate; dr, dorsal ridge, lf, lateral fin; cg, contractile gelated ectoplasm; f, fenestral
posterior area.

B. Transverse sections through the ameba. 1. Through the anterior area of attachment to the substrate. 2. Near the mid-region of the body. 3. Near the rear end
of the body. vf, vertical gel fibers between dorsal ridge and ventral gel.

C. Median longitudinal section through the body. b, surface along which the
ameba moves.

D. Areas of conversion of sol to gel and vice-versa during locomotion. Solid areas
indicate movements of gel. Dashed arrows indicate conversion of gel to sol. Solid
black areas of dorsal ridges indicate stationary gel; white area of dorsal ridges, area
of gel to sol change; cross-lined, area of new anterior gel of dorsal ridges. s, advance
of serrated margin of solated endoplasm; x, area of lateral fin which converts from
gel to sol and flows forward.

eversion theory of Allen (1961a,b,c). Later Abé (1963) made the same suggestion for a verrucosa type ameba.

2. MOVEMENT OF *Vannella miroides*

For the fan-shaped flabellulid ameba, *Vannella miroides,* cinematographic analyses show (Bovee, 1963b, 1964) that currents of hyaline solated endoplasm are driven forward under pressure, apparently from the main body mass, into the mid-region of the clear anterior fan-shaped border where they solidify to form coalesced gel-islands. These drift laterally, to left or right borders of the margin, becoming smaller and denser, contracting together as they then move medially and ventrally into the main granular mass (Fig. 3A,B,C). There appears to be a contraction-hydraulic mechanism operative.

3. MOVEMENT OF SOIL AMEBAE

Bovee (1963a) also describes a burrowing movement by *Acanthamoeba castellani* in culture on soft agar, involving a contraction-hydraulic system which drives a series of hemispherical pseudopods into the agar ahead of the ameba, extending the tunnel into the agar and enabling the ameba to move forward into it (Fig. 4A,B,C,D).

D. AGGREGATE AMEBOID MOVEMENT

1. IN SOIL AMEBAE

Certain small species of hartmanellid amebae (e.g., *Hartmannella astronyxis* and *Acanthamoeba castellani*) exhibit an aggregate movement in mass culture with bacteria on agar, described as a "wave-front" movement (Ray and Hayes, 1954; Bovee, 1963a). The amebae crawl over one another so that the mass, made up of hundreds of individuals, rolls slowly forward. The mass movement is due to the aggregate of individual progressions of the amebae; yet the advancing speed of the wave-front is about four times that of any single ameba in the group (Ray and Hayes, 1954). *Hartmannella astronyxis,* in less crowded cultures, also forms aggregate groups after the replete feeding which precedes encystment, the amebae congregating into clumps of several hundred, forming an irregular adhesive rolling ball which promptly ceases movement as the amebae encyst (Ray and Hayes, 1954); and *Acanthamoeba castellani* forms layered plaques by congregation of amebae which then encyst as food runs out (Bovee, 1963a).

The latter movement resembles the more widely known aggregation of "cellular slime mold" amebulae (for review, see Bonner, 1959) which are morphologically very similar to the hartmannellid amebae. In fact, some mutant strains of the cellular slime molds aggregate into clumps resembling those described for *H. astronyxis* but do not migrate or form "fruiting bodies"; other mutants

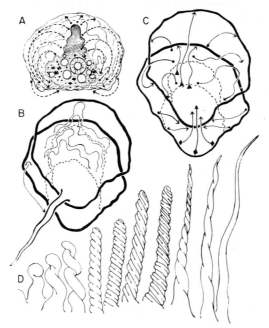

Fig. 3. Protoplasmic movements of the flabellulid ameba, *Vannella miroides*. (After Bovee, 1964.)

A. A tracing of the ameba from a phase-contrast motion picture frame. Wavy solid lines indicate margins of gelated areas in the fan-shaped anterior wave. Cross-lined area indicates flow of sol into the anterior area which gelates to form new gel islands. Dashed lines and arrows indicate movements of gel islands from front to rear as they contract. Dotted area indicates granular solated endoplasm containing nucleus, vacuoles, crystals, and granules.

B. Successive stages of advance of a tongue of sol, under pressure, into the anterior gelated wave, traced from 400 frames of a motion picture film photographed at 8 frames per second, showing positions at each 100th frame. Arrow indicates the site of formation of a tapering pseudopod and its movement to the rear.

C. Movements of protoplasm. Round dots and their arrows indicate the movements of single gel islands during the 400 frames of motion picture. Triangles indicate areas of sol and their forward movements under pressure. Diamonds indicate areas of posterior gel converted to sol, entering the granular endoplasm.

D. Stages in the formation of a long, tapering pseudopod like that in Fig. 2B, plotted from 3000 frames of motion picture film, photographed by phase contrast at 14 frames per second, showing the state at about each 300th frame. Note that the pseudopod begins formation as a hemispheric bulge, elongating as a twisted digitate structure, showing then increased torsion and tapering, becoming nearly straight when fully formed.

do not aggregate at all (Sussman, 1954). Bonner (1959) and others believe that the cellular slime molds are closely related to and probably have a common origin with the free-living hartmannellid amebae.

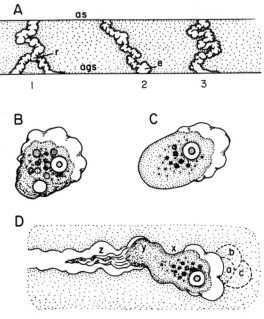

FIG. 4. Movements of *Acanthamoeba castellani*. (After Bovee, 1963a.)

A. Tunnels made by amebae burrowing in agar, 1, 2, 3; as, agar surface; ags, agar and glass interface. In tunnel 1, the ameba burrowed to the glass, and then retreated to r, and burrowed again to the glass; then moved off between the glass and the agar. In tunnel 2, the ameba burrowed to the glass and encysted at e. In tunnel 3, burrowing was continuous from agar to glass, and the ameba moved off immediately between agar and glass.

B. The form of the ameba moving in fluid on the agar surface, seen from above.

C. The form of the ameba moving between agar and glass, somewhat flattened, seen from above.

D. The form of the ameba burrowing in the agar, a, b, c—positions of subsequent, newly extruded pseudopods pushed into the agar; x, area of attachment to the agar tunnel; y, area of contraction and shortening of the gel tube; z, area of further shortening and contraction of the "tail."

2. IN ACRASID SLIME-MOLD "SOCIAL" AMEBAE

The locomotion mechanism of the individual slime mold amebula in the feeding, nonaggregative state differs but little from the progression of the hartmannellid and entamebid amebae. A variety of forms of pseudopods may be extended (i.e., both filose and eruptive-lobose, the latter being locomotor organelles), but the general contraction-hydraulic mechanism seems to apply. However, Shaffer (1964) dissents and suggests that movement is by means of membranous ripples similar to those postulated for movements of tissue-cultured cells (for review, see Ambrose, 1961). Speed of locomotion is apparently related to frequency of pseudopod formation (Samuel, 1961).

a. Physiological States Involved in Aggregation. The aggregation and migration of slime mold amebulae in the form of an aggregate "slug" (i.e., the pseudoplasmode) are very complex unsolved phenomena on the mechanics of protoplasmic movement. Five principal states of the physiology of the amebulae appear to be related to aggregative pattern in the life cycle (Shaffer, 1957): (1) the active feeding state, unoriented to light and heat, and unresponsive to and incapable of secreting the chemotactic aggregation-promoting substances ("acrasin"); (2) the state capable of reacting to and secreting the acrasin, but not yet doing so, and capable of orientation, but unoriented; (3) the locomotive and extended state, anteriorly sensitive to and oriented toward acrasin, while posteriorly secreting but inactive to acrasin, being adhesive, migrating singly or in streams of individuals toward a center of aggregation; (4) similar sensitive, secreting, and oriented cells already in the aggregation center or locomotive slug, but more rounded physically and more pseudopodially active, adhesive, and interdigitated, oriented and sensitive toward light and heat; (5) a state of differentiation in the fruiting body, no longer locomotive.

b. Aggregation. Any of the amebulae in stage 2 may begin the secretion of acrasin in "bursts" or waves which are quickly depleted, apparently by an accompanying hydrolyzing enzyme (Shaffer, 1961). Specialized, genetically distinct "initiator" cells (Sussman and Ennis, 1959) apparently do not exist (Konijn and Raper, 1961); but any stage 2 cell may become a "founder" cell (Shaffer, 1957). In *Polysphondylium violaceum* such "founders" may be noted in a group of feeding amebulae since they are more rounded, granular, adhesive, and stationary than their neighbors (Shaffer, 1961). Removal of the "founders" can prevent aggregation. "Starter" cells of *Dictyostelium discoideum* are *not* visibly distinguishable (Konijn and Raper, 1961). Food depletion and exposure to light, particularly in combination, may trigger the origin and activity of "founder" cells whereas darkness and confinement between agar and glass, particularly in combination, inhibit them (Shaffer, 1961). Presumably the "founder" or "starter" cells reach a critical state sooner than their neighbors. When a "founder" cell secretes acrasin, others "in range" of the burst turn and move toward the "founder." As they begin to move after orientation, they also secrete bursts of acrasin at the rear, attracting still others. The acrasin is presumed to be quickly degraded by enzymes (Bonner, 1959) and no permanent gradient is set up; but as the secreting amebulae congregate around the "founder" and continue to secrete, they establish a functional gradient.

Such aggregating amebulae adhere in advancing rows, head to tail. The acrasin-secreting rear of each attracts the front half of others. Amebulae joining the columns frequently enter by fastening to the rear end of an amebula already in the advancing stream, squeezing between it and its follower (Shaffer, 1964). The displaced follower attaches to the rear of the entrant.

The chemical identity of acrasin is not yet known, but it is dialyzable (Shaffer, 1956a,b), and is made up of three components necessary in combination of definite ratio for activation (Sussman *et al.*, 1958). It is unstable in raw state at room temperature; but stable when quick-frozen or when separated from an accompanying protein partner by dialysis. Acrasin diffuses over and is active within shorter distances in light than in darkness. It is presumed that the protein which is separated from it by dialysis is a hydrolyzing enzyme for the acrasin. An aggregative stimulus equal to that of acrasin for the amebulae is also provided by estradiol, progesterone, or testosterone (Wright, 1958); but whether the acrasin is itself a similar steroid is not known.

c. Movement of the Aggregate "Slug." The aggregate of amebulae, once collected, forms a migratory "slug" which, if large, moves faster than any individual amebula, or if small, moves less rapidly than a single amebula (Samuel, 1961). As the slug advances, it secretes a slime sheath through which it progresses and which it leaves behind, along with certain amebulae which move too slowly to keep up. Larger, faster moving amebulae in the slug advance to and remain in front; and smaller slower ones lag and accumulate at the rear (Bonner and Adams, 1958; Bonner, 1959). After locomoting for a time the slug stops; the anterior cells form a stalk up which the slower posterior ones crawl to group at the top as a sorus of encysted individual amebulae. In some species the "spores" are identical with microcysts formed by individual unaggregated amebulae left behind in the slime track; in other species the spores are smaller and distinctive in shape from the microcysts (Bonner, 1959).

Adhesion of cells in aggregation, and the slime secretion, may be due to antigen-antibody relationships. Species-specific antigens appear in the feeding, nonaggregative amebulae (J. H. Gregg, 1956); but a general nonsurface antigen appears in the amebulae at the time of aggregation (Gregg, 1956; Takeuichi, 1961). The anterior and posterior regions of the migrating slug may also be antigenically different (Gregg, 1961; Takeuichi, 1961). In general, different strains and even different species of amebulae may aggregate together to form a migratory slug; but the respective cells sort themselves out from one another in the locomotive slug, to form distinct sori when the slug ceases locomotion and differentiation occurs (Bonner, 1959).

d. External Factors and Aggregation. While aggregation may occur under water, or on a wet surface from 80 to 100% humidity, sorus formation occurs mainly between 96 and 99% humidity, with a slowly decreasing humidity favoring sorus production. Both aggregation and fruiting occur in a wide pH range (4.5 to 8.7), with an optimum at pH 6.5. Minimal temperatures for aggregation extend below 10°C., but the optimum is a much warmer

30°. The migratory slug is highly thermo- and light-sensitive. It will orient and move toward a source of heat which may cause an anteroposterior gradient of as little as 0.0005 °C. along the length of the slug; and it will move toward as dim a light as that produced by a colony of phosphorescent bacteria (Bonner and Adams, 1958).

Recent studies (Whittingham and Raper, 1957) show that some simpler nitrogenous food sources (e.g., certain amino acids) favor aggregation whereas more complex ones (e.g., peptone and tryptone) and carbohydrates may inhibit aggregation.

According to Konijn and Raper (1962) constant light favors aggregation, migration, and fruiting more than does constant darkness. Illumination after 6–8 hr. of darkness causes a sharp increase in aggregation activity; but longer periods of darkness delay it. Transfer from light to darkness just prior to the "dark time" for aggregation also accelerates aggregation. Strangely, some but not all species or strains require light for aggregation, and some not only do not require light but are not stimulated to aggregate by transfer from darkness to light (Shaffer, 1958).

Ethylenediaminetetraacetate (EDTA) will prevent aggregation; and in 5 mM concentration it causes already formed aggregates to dissociate (DeHaan, 1959). The effects of EDTA are blocked by equimolar $CaCl_2$ and are reversible when the EDTA-containing solution is replaced by Bonner's salt solution. Since EDTA acts as a chelating agent, it perhaps interferes with membrane activities dependent on the monovalent:divalent cation ratios on the membrane (i.e., Gibbs-Donnan equilibria).

III. Shuttle Flow in Mycetozoa

A. Importance of the Rhythmic Shuttle Flow

Reversals of flow and complex patterns of flow in mycetozoan plasmodia have long been known (DeBary, 1884; Vouk, 1910, 1913), and the importance of rhythmic shuttle flow with net advance in one direction was stressed by Seifriz (1942, 1943, 1952). The elegant studies of Kamiya and his co-workers (for review, see Kamiya, 1959), and contributions by Camp (1936, 1937), Kitching and Pirenne (1940), Price and Allen (1942), Loewy (1949, 1950, 1952), J. D. Anderson (1951, 1964), Andresen and Pollack (1952), Tauc (1953), Ts'O and his co-workers (1956a,b, 1957a,b), Stewart and Stewart (1959) and Stewart (1964), among numerous others, have contributed much valuable data. However, Noland (1957) reviewed the subject and stated that the rhythmicity of the shuttle flow, and the net advance, had not yet been explained.

B. Theories of "Gel-Sol" Mechanics in Shuttle Flow

1. CONTRACTION-HYDRAULIC THEORY

Most of the experimental and observational data accumulated for the mycetozoa indicate that a contraction-hydraulic system of movement is present
which involves numerous and variable centers of contractile force. This results
in a shuttle flow of the more liquid endoplasm through a polytubular ectoplasmic gel, with an aggregate of advance of the whole plasmodium in one
direction (for reviews, see Kamiya, 1959, 1960).

2. DIFFUSION-DRAG THEORY

A recent revival of the diffusion-drag hypothesis which Rashevsky (1948)
devised to explain cytokinesis has been invoked to explain mycetozoan shuttle
flow (Stewart and Stewart, 1959). A still more recent assessment of the diffusion-drag hypothesis in relation to mycetozoan locomotion is given by Jahn
(1964b). The Rashevsky diffusion-drag forces, if they really exist, *must* act
centrifugally from the sites of their generation. Jahn (1964b) has demonstrated
that the mathematical formulas for the theoretical diffusion-drag force were
substituted (by Rashevsky) in an integral equation denoting the three-dimensional geometry of an elongating cell, and that the signs of some of the terms
in the equations were changed to conform with the facts of cell elongation.
However, when the substitutions were made in these equations it became implicit that the diffusion-drag force had to act centrifugally along one main
axis, but *centripetally* along the other two. This is impossible, and the equations as derived are purely empirical and therefore incapable of explaining cell
movements (Jahn, 1964b). Rashevsky (1952) also indicates other difficulties
in applying diffusion-drag hypothesis to cell movements. Furthermore, it is
highly doubtful that a diffusion-drag force really exists.

C. Explanation of Shuttle Flow
as a Contraction-Hydraulic System

1. "ORIGINS" OF MOVEMENT AND THEIR FUNCTIONS

A fairly complete explanation of flow in *Physarum* has been proposed by
Jahn (1964b) who assumes, as have several of the earlier workers, that the
plasmodium is a very complicated hydraulic system with elastic tubes, of various diameters, under hydrostatic pressure, and with many contracting areas
designated as "origins." These contracting areas operate with various periods
and therefore are usually out of phase. The pressure at any one given point
is the algebraic summation of that transmitted from all contracting areas, but
reduced in accordance with the pressure drop caused by viscosity losses (Hagen-

Poiseuille law). The pressure in any tube will vary from moment to moment. As the phase relationships of the various contracting areas change, the direction of flow in any given tube may also change, as described by Kamiya (for review, see 1959).

The shift from contraction to distention (relaxation) at any given contracting area may be caused by solation of the gel wall from the inside toward

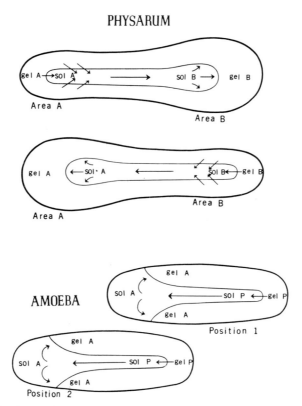

FIG. 5. Sol-gel transformation in *Physarum* and *Amoeba*, and the relationship of rhythmic flow to sol-gel transformation, diagrammatic. (After Jahn, 1964b.)

Physarum. At area A, top, gel contracts and becomes thinner by solation, while at B gel expands and becomes thicker by added gelation of sol. Then the gel area at B contracts and grows thinner by solation while at area A, gel expands, growing thicker by added gelation of sol. This repetitive process is the basis of rhythmicity in *Physarum*.

Amoeba. At the anterior end, gel A increases by added gelation of sol onto the end of the gel tube. This gel remains in position and eventually becomes gel P as the posterior end moves forward from position 1 to position 2. At the posterior end gel contracts and decreases in volume because of solation. The walls replace the rear end continuously, but at a more forward position. This process forms the basis of locomotion in *Amoeba*. The anterior gel may also be stretched forward as shown in Fig. 1.

the outside. Since contraction is necessarily followed by solation (Landau, 1959), the contracting portion of the wall becomes thin. As the wall thins it reaches a state where it no longer can overcome the hydraulic pressure against which it is working. It then begins to become stretched by the inflowing sol, and the sol becomes gel, thereby thickening and strengthening the wall while it is distended.

Figure 5 (Jahn, 1964b) shows a comparison of the flow in *Amoeba* and in *Physarum*.

2. PHENOMENA OF SHUTTLE FLOW TO BE EXPLAINED

Stewart and Stewart (1959) discuss various patterns of flow, including upstream and downstream reversals of flow, differences of flow rate in adjacent channels, effects of blockage of flow, movements of individual particles independently of general flow, lack of peristaltic systematic contractile movements of tube walls, low energy used in flow compared to total amount expended, fluctuation of motive force periodically whether flow is permitted or not, insignificant change in viscosity of flowing protoplasm, fluctuating electrical potential gradients which continue when flow is impossible, the parabolic velocity profile of flow in a single channel with maximal velocity along the axis, the role of ATP-sensitive myxomyosin in flow. They contend these phenomena cannot be satisfactorily explained in terms of contraction of the gel posterior to flow. However, Jahn (1964b) points out that these are easily explainable on the basis of a contraction-hydraulic system and gives a detailed explanation for each.

3. ROLE OF THE ATP-MYXOMYOSIN MECHANISM

In regard to the source of energy for the gelation-contraction-solation cycle, the only assumptions needed are that the numerous and uniformly scattered mitochondria produce adenosine triphosphate (ATP) continuously, that it be used in contraction, and that the amount of ATP present controls the viscosity, as in actomyosin or myxomyosin solutions *in vitro* (Szent-Györgyi, 1953; Loewy, 1952; Nakajima, 1956).

The fundamental mechanism resembles that of ameboid movement in having a cyclic relationship of gel formation followed by solation. There is evidence that this depends upon ATP and an actomyosin-like protein complex named myxomyosin (Loewy, 1952) with a chemistry almost identical to that of myosin-B (Ts'O *et al.*, 1956b, 1957a,b; Kamiya *et al.*, 1957; Nakajima, 1956, 1960, 1963; Oosawa, 1963; Takeuichi and Hatano, 1955, 1956). There is present a cortical ectoplasm which is a contractile protein gel mesh, and a non-Newtonian more-or-less solated endoplasm which streams. A contraction-hydraulic system produces the shuttle flow (for review, see Kamiya, 1959; Jahn, 1964b). ATP injected at any site, or applied externally, initially causes a lessened amplitude of flow and of pressure oscillations until assimilated; then it causes a rise in pressure with greater amplitude, period, and polarity of the rhythmic contraction and relaxation which results in flow (Kamiya et al., 1957). External application of ATP solution may also initiate a contraction at that site (Jahn et al., 1964b).

A recent electronic analysis of the locale of heat production by contraction of mycetozoan tubules (Allen et al., 1963) indicates the site of energy utilization and propulsive force to be the contracting region of the tubule wall designated by Jahn (1964b) as an "origin."

D. Other Theories

Other theories of flow in mycetozoa suggest surface-tension changes (Ewart, 1903); contraction and relaxation of polypeptide chains (Hosoi, 1937; Frey-Wyssling, 1949, 1952) or of fibrous proteins at a shear interface (Loewy, 1949); electrostriction (Osterhout, 1952); a shearing propulsion based on actively motile gel filaments with opposite displacement forces (Gimesi and Pozsár, 1956; Jarosch, 1957, 1958); and an endoplasmic-reticulum jet-propulsion idea (Kavanau, 1963b). However, none of these offers a serious challenge to the abundant evidence supporting a contraction-hydraulic system.

Although the above theories, especially the newer version of the contraction-hydraulic theory (Jahn, 1964b), explain the causes of motive force, of the complexity of flow, and of the polyrhythmic movements which wax and wane in the plasmodium, the theories so far presented do not explain completely the net advance of a whole plasmodium in a given direction.

E. Rhythmic Shuttle-Flow Movements and Net Unidirectional Advance

1. Assumptions of Stewart

Recently Stewart (1964), apparently discarding the diffusion-drag hypothesis he previously championed (Stewart and Stewart, 1959), presented four assumptions he says are needed to explain the polyrhythmic movements: (1) The nonstreaming gel meshwork is under tension, and puts hydrostatic pressure on the more fluid streaming endoplasm. (2) The gel meshwork may relax at any point, largely converting to semifluidity, becoming weaker, permitting flow into the region. (3) The weakening is reversible, the gel meshwork regains its organization and strength, and inflow of endoplasm ceases. (4) Waves of local weakening spread from the site of occurrence, and the resulting waves of weakening and strengthening produce shuttle streaming.

Stewart (1964) says that net locomotion of the plasmodium results from the interaction of the following factors: (1) the detailed wave forms of the waves of weakening; (2) the pattern they follow as they spread over the plasmodium; (3) the location of their sources. Any point may act as such a source, but he postulates regions which "normally" so act. He also assumes a net stability of rhythm, and an unexplained "integrative control system."

2. FACTORS PROMOTING RHYTHMICITY AND UNIDIRECTIONAL ADVANCE

However, the net rhythmicity of the whole plasmodium is explainable as due in major part to several factors: (1) The older gel is more rigid (Mast, 1926), more contractile (Jahn, 1964b), and solates less easily under pressure (Landau et al., 1954) than does younger gel. (2) The rate and volume of flow and the hydrostatic pressure are greater in the older tubules of larger diameter (Kamiya, 1959). (3) The gel is thicker, and of greater relative volume in larger tubules. (4) The oldest, largest, most efficient tubules are at the rear of the plasmodium. (5) Since viscosity losses vary inversely with the square of the radius (Hagen-Poiseuille law) the larger tubes are inherently more efficient as producers and transmitters of a hydraulic pressure. (6) The front of the plasmodium is a sheet of the newest gel, permeated by many fine channels of sol which has been pumped out of the smallest and weakest tubules. The fringe, therefore, is without tubular organization and of low contractile efficiency. The smallest tubules intermediate in position between the fringe and the larger tubules also exert some of their force backward toward the larger tubules, but this is easily overcome by the greater force of the large tubules. Furthermore, the magnitude of this backward pumping is decreased by the greater internal resistance of the small tubules in which it is generated.

Therefore the net effect of the activity of the origins of old regions of the plasmodium versus the counter-effects of origins in the newer regions is a surging of greater net pressure and flow from old toward new, since the additive effects of the stronger older regions overcome those of the new areas. Locomotion would unavoidably be in the direction of the newer regions.

The integrative system assumed by Stewart (1964) does not seem to be separately necessary, but seems to be an inherent part of the hydrodynamics of the intricate contractile system. Since there are many nuclei, however, and their roles in locomotion are unknown, the possibility of an over-all regulating mechanism must be considered.

F. ENVIRONMENTAL FACTORS AFFECTING THE MOVEMENT

The direction of the net movement supposedly can be determined by any of several environmental factors, none of which have been seriously investigated. However, obvious possibilities are light, temperature, humidity, pH gradients, and gravity. Light in the visible range apparently has minimal effects on plasmodial migration so long as it is well fed and the humidity is high. According to Kamiya (for review, see 1959) older observations on light effects have been confused with heat effects, and are unreliable. He found (Kamiya, 1953) little detectable effect of visible light. However, a starved plasmodium of *Physarum,* which moves much more rapidly than a well fed one, will quickly cease locomotion if exposed to light, and sporulates soon thereafter (Guttes *et al.,* 1961); and it requires light to sporulate, continuing to move rapidly and shrinking in size if kept in the dark. Other species do not require light to sporulate, although some are stimulated by light to do so, while others are not (W. D. Gray, 1938).

Short wavelengths of radiation beyond the visible range (e.g., X-ray, radium rays, ultraviolet) usually injure the plasmodium, the injury being preceded by a shock-reaction slowing of protoplasmic movements, followed by a temporary acceleration of flow (Loquin, 1949; for review, see Kamiya, 1959); and β-rays from radium in "proper" intensity accelerate streaming in the mycetozoan plasmodium (Loquin, 1949).

Heat, distinct from and unaccompanied by light, has a measurable effect on plasmodial movements (Kamiya, 1953). An increase of temperature from 15° to 25°C. causes increase of frequency of the contractile rhythm in *Physarum polycephalum* (i.e., a decrease in period, from 2.6 sec. to 1.6 sec. per cycle) accompanied by a decrease in amplitude of the waves apparent in a dynoplasmogram, and a 20% decrease in the strength of motive force.

There is little detectable effect of a pH gradient on the rhythm and streaming of the plasmodium, within a range of 5.0 to 9.0 (Nakajima, cited by Kamiya, 1959).

Although no critical studies appear to have been made on the phenomenon, locomotion of the plasmodium tends to be away from a gravitational force (Camp, 1937; McManus, 1961; J. D. Anderson, 1964), particularly when the plasmodium is about to sporulate, the last report being an effect perhaps partly assignable to decreased humidity. Humidity changes, however, do not lead directly to sporulation, since the plasmodium, if not ready to sporulate, will stop locomotion and form a nonsporular sclerotium as humidity decreases (Camp, 1937; and many others).

G. UNEXPLAINED PHENOMENA

One other observation should be made. The mechanics of mycetozoan locomotion discussed here apply to the plasmodium on a moist flat surface. Practically nothing is known of how the mycetozoön can, and does, propel itself through the xylem tubules of rotting logs in nature. Any discussion of this would be pure speculation. Another unanswered question is how to account for the complete cessation of locomotion and shuttle flow during synchronous mitotic division of nuclei in *Physarum polycephalum* (Guttes and Guttes, 1963).

IV. Bidirectional Filamentous Movement

A. Occurrence

Bidirectional movement of protoplasm has long been known in foraminiferans (Schultze, 1865; Leidy, 1879; Sandon, 1934; Jepps, 1942, 1956; Jahn and Rinaldi, 1959; Allen, 1964); in heliozoa (Leidy, 1879; Jahn *et al.*, 1960; Jahn and Bovee, 1964); radiolarians (Hertwig, 1879; Schewiakoff, 1894, 1926; Schneider, 1906); certain so-called testacean amebae with filose pseudopods (Leidy, 1879; Bělař, 1921; Berrend, 1959, 1964); and in certain so-called proteomyxans (Leidy, 1879; Nauss, 1949).

B. Bidirectional Movement in Foraminiferans

1. evidence for and similarity to other types of bidirectional movement

Most of the attempts to study bidirectional flow in protozoa have been with the foraminifera. Sandon (1934) showed that the bidirectional movement of granules along all filaments, reported in beautiful descriptive detail by Leidy (1879), cannot be explained by a tubular gel-sol conversion system. Noland (1957) indicated the need of "molecules that can orient themselves on any solid surface while others crawl forward on the backs of the first layer" as a means of bidirectional flow. The theories of Frey-Wyssling (1949), Loewy (1949), and Jarosch (1957, 1964) suggest that protein filaments in plant cells stream against stationary gel or against oppositely moving filaments in a similar bidirectional type of movement; and Jarosch (1958) suggested an application of such streaming concepts to ciliary and axopodial movements. There is a similarity also to the proposed opposite movements of actively sliding filaments in muscle (H. E. Huxley and Hanson, 1954; A. F. Huxley and Niedergerke, 1954).

In muscle such a sliding movement has been postulated by Weber (1958) as employing ATP energy to shift bonds of active acid groups on actin along a series of —SH, phenolic, and alcoholic —OH groups; and Hoffmann-Berling (1960) suggests that active elongation of spindle fibers of cells, and other fibrous movements in protoplasm similarly use ATP energy, particularly in extension movements.

2. shearing flow theory

Jahn and Rinaldi (1959) suggest that a sliding action similar to that proposed for plant protoplasmic movements (Jarosch, 1957, 1958) or for muscle may propel the filamentous pseudopods of foraminiferans. They envision the smallest filopods as composed of a single gel filament bent back on itself so that it crawls against itself, producing bidirectional movement, and the rhizo-podial network as composed of bundles and interweavings of these filaments, each individually active. Bonds sequentially made and broken as Weber (1958) suggests for muscle might provide the motive power for each filament. They assume the filament has no separate membrane, the gel surface so serving, thereby avoiding some of the problems involved in multiple shearing of sur-faces and filaments.

According to Jahn and Rinaldi (1959), the pseudopods of *Allogromia laticollaris* when first formed may reach a length of several hundred microns while being only 1 μ in diameter, and they may extend in straight lines out into the fluid in any direction. Later, the pseudopods branch, and the branches anastomose, eventually forming a large network. At all times granules 2–4 μ in size can be seen moving distally on one side of the pseudopod and basally on the other, and turning around at the tip. These granules pass through the nodes of the net in a single file. In broad pseudopods (up to 10 μ diameter) many rows of moving granules may be seen, with some of the adjacent rows going in *opposite* directions. In brief, the granules seem to be loosely attached to ex-tremely thin (less than 0.5 μ in diameter) moving filaments which are com-pletely hyaline. One very obvious characteristic of these pseudopods is that the granules are always moving, and that in retracting pseudopods, movement is in both directions. Furthermore, small fragments of pseudopods as short as 40 μ in length may become organized as minute organisms ("satellites") which may have several pseudopods, *all* with bidirectional streaming. Another interesting feature is that the *surface* of the pseudopod moves in both directions, as demon-strable by means of attached dye particles, even when the particles are many times the diameter of the pseudopod. Most of the above observations have been confirmed by Allen (1964) on a different species of *Allogromia*.

No evidence is yet available for the presence of an ATP-actomyosin-like system in foraminiferan protoplasm, but the universal findings of such com-plexes in protoplasm when they have been sought indicates they are probably present.

3. "FRONTAL-CONTRACTION" THEORY

Allen (1964) assumes that each foraminiferan filopod is tubular, basing his assumption on electron microscope studies by Wohlfarth-Bottermann (1961) who concludes that each such filament has a surface membrane surrounding bundles of oriented fibrils in a groundplasm matrix. Both contend that the presence of a typical "unit membrane" invalidates the Jahn-Rinaldi idea and the type of shearing movement they postulate.

Allen substitutes for their theory a modification of his "frontal-contraction" theory of ameboid movement (Allen, 1961a, 1964), assuming that motive force is applied at the tips of the filopods as they turn back on themselves, with assistance from contractile centers in substrate-contact points nearby. He does not attempt to explain how these contractile "centers" overcome the probable drag of the apposed surfaces of membranes around the filaments.

4. HELICAL TENSION THEORY

Jarosch (1964) has elaborated further his earlier (1957, 1958) theory of protoplasmic streaming by assuming that all protoplasmic filaments are helical structures. By ingenious use of wire models he concludes that helical fibrils of varying pitches are wound together in complex fibers of larger diameter. Tensions placed on the helical fibers singly and differentially or in groups may then cause a wave of contraction to progress away from or toward the anchorage of the fibrils. Thus almost any protoplasmic movement is explainable, he postulates, depending upon tensions developed locally or along the entire length of fibrils, singly or in groups. The fibrils would not then necessarily have to move from a relatively fixed situation; and waves of motion generated along them could propel objects (e.g., granules) which might be associated with or adherent to them or to the membranes surrounding them. Cole (1963) offers a generalized theory for protoplasmic movements based on contraction and extension of helical molecules associated, side to side, with fibrous ones.

C. IMPORTANCE OF BIDIRECTIONAL SHEAR IN FLOW MECHANISMS

At present there is no doubt that an active sliding system is present in *Allogromia*, as pointed out by Jahn and Rinaldi (1959). The only question is how it works, and we have exactly the same question in numerous other protozoa, in muscle, in plant cells such as *Tradescantia* hair cells, *Chara*, *Nitella*, and in many other biological materials. It is interesting (if rather disconcerting) that although bidirectional movement and cyclosis have been known to exist for more than 100 years, it is only during the past decade that the necessity (and possibility) for an active shearing system has been realized (muscle, H. E. Huxley and Hanson, 1955; *Chara*, Jarosch, 1957; *Nitella*, Kamiya, 1959; foraminifera and other protozoa, Jahn and Rinaldi, 1959; Jarosch, 1958). It was previously assumed that all movement must be caused by contraction. This old assumption may or may not be true at the molecular level, but if so, there is no evidence of it at the visual level of information. Whatever the mechanism of bidirectional protoplasmic movement may be, it is a universal and important phenomenon, well worthy of considerable research effort.

D. BIDIRECTIONAL PROTOPLASMIC MOVEMENTS IN OTHER PROTOZOA

1. HELIOZOANS

Other observed movements exist in ameboid organisms for which no theories have yet been offered. Axopods of heliozoans (and certain radiolarians) have axial filamentous bundles which may be extended or shortened (Kitching, 1964), or folded into groups and retracted (Bovee, 1960b; Bovee and Wilson, 1961). These fibers resemble those of cilia except that they are arranged in two interposed spirals, instead of a ring within which there are two central fibers (Kitching, 1964). The movements of the fibrils may be very rapid, almost explosive, in extension in the helioflagellate *Dimorpha floridanis* during transition from the flagellate form to the heliozoan form (Bovee, 1960b), the transition being triggered by increase in the salt ions of the water. Folding, shortening, and assumption of the flagellate state is in response to a dilution of the salts with fresh or distilled water. It is also known that heliozoa swim by vibrational movements of the axopods (Leidy, 1879; Penard, 1904), "jump" from a substrate with them, or roll over and over on the tips of the axopods (Penard, 1904). We have some recent cinephotomicrographs of these activities, but offer no theories as yet.

2. RADIOLARIANS

In acantharian radiolarians, bidirectional flow in the peripheral protoplasmic network is known (Hertwig, 1879; Schewiakoff, 1926; Jepps, 1956), as well as in the radiating filopods and the axopods. The central fibrils of the axopods, as in the heliozoa, may be rapidly extended or withdrawn. Crawling movements by means of the filopodial networks when the animal is in contact with the substrate have also been described (Schewiakoff, 1926). Similarities to the movements of foraminiferan pseudopods are evident; and probably similar mechanisms are present, but no recent studies are available.

3. PROTEOMYXANS

For the so-called proteomyxans (a diverse group of little real mutual relationship) little is known, except for Leidy's (1879) accurate description of movements of *Biomyxa vagans* (which he rightly considered closely allied to the foraminiferans), and *Reticulomyxa filosa* (Nauss, 1949) which is also, perhaps, similarly related.

4. FILOSE TESTACEANS

For the so-called filose testacean rhizopods older studies on *Euglypha* (Leidy, 1879; Verworn, 1889, 1930), *Pamphagus* (Bĕlař, 1921), and others (DeSaedeleer, 1932, 1934), as well as more recent ones on *Cyphoderia* (Berrend, 1959, 1964), and taxonomic considerations (Bovee and Jahn, 1960, 1964) indicate that the mechanism of flow in the filopods is bidirectional and much similar in interpretation to that of foraminiferans. Berrend (1959) contends each filopod has a gelated axial "core," over which a less gelated (but only slightly more fluid) slender stream advances. The core is assumed to be contractile and retractile; and it bends or coils during retraction.

V. Taxonomic Significance of Two Types of Movement in Sarcodines

A. THE DISTINCTIVENESS OF THE TWO TYPES

The two types of movement discussed above, namely, the two-way shearing and contraction-hydraulic systems, appear to be mutually exclusive as locomotor mechanisms in the sarcodines. Furthermore, the differences in the mechanisms are visibly distinctive, both morphologically and physiologically. Therefore, it has been suggested that this distinction be used as a taxonomic character in separating the two major groups of the Sarcodina (Jahn and Rinaldi, 1959; Jahn *et al.*, 1960).

B. REVISION OF HIGHER TAXA

Jahn and Bovee (1964) have formally proposed that the existence of either of these two types of movement be used as the criterion for separating the Subphylum Sarcodina into two classes as follows: (1) Class Autotractea—with slender filamentous pseudopods in which two-way active shearing flow is evident; and (2) Class Hydraulea—with tubular or polytubular pseudopods or body in which contraction of the gel tubes drives the more fluid inner contents. Since this dichotomy cuts across previous systematic categories for the Sarcodina, a revision of other suprafamily groups is also indicated (Bovee and Jahn, 1960, 1964).

Within the Class Autotractea they suggest a dichotomy into two subclasses: (1) Subclass Actinopodia—with axopods, containing the groups (a) Order Heliozoida—having axopods extended from a central granule or peripheral nuclei; and (b) Order Acantharida—having axopods extended from the center of the body penetrating an internal membrane; and (2) Subclass Filoreticulosia —with filoreticulopods but no axopods, containing the groups (a) Order Hyporadiolarida—having radiating, rarely anastomosing filoreticulopods; (b) Order Radiolarida—having peripherally radiating, basally anastomosing, distinctly granular filoreticulopods; (c) Order Granuloreticulida—having filoreticulopods as a mobile anastomosing network around the body; and (d) Order Filida—having finely granular filoreticulopods which rarely branch and anastomose.

The Class Hydraulea is considered to be composed of two subclasses: (1) Subclass Cyclia—with ameboid generally unidirectional cyclic flow in steady locomotion, containing the groups (a) Order Lobida—having pseudopods digitate or as hemispherical eruptive waves, or as a clear border formed by protoplasmic flow; and (b) Order Acrasida—having amebulae which aggregate to form a motile slug-like pseudoplasmode; and (2) Subclass Alternatia—with a polytubular plasmodial body in which cytoplasm moves by shuttle flow with net unidirectional advance, containing the groups (a) Order Mycetozoida—

having amebulae which grow to become the plasmode of interconnected gel tubes; and (b) Order Xenophyophorida—poorly understood marine organisms with polytubular chitinoid structure and granular internal protoplasm.

C. The Major Defect of the Old System

Previous separation of the Sarcodina into Actinopodea and Rhizopodea was based on the presence or absence of axopodia (Calkins, 1909). However, the true Radiolaria, previously always placed in the Actinopodea, do not possess axopods (Trégouboff, 1953). This is only one of the major defects of the old system, which are discussed in detail by Bovee and Jahn (1960, 1964). Furthermore, the new system, in spite of the radical nature of the changes proposed, does not violate any of the laws of priority.

VI. Cilia versus Flagella

A. Evidence for Essential Similarities

Arbitrary distinctions between cilia and flagella may be found in many textbooks, and some of these were valid on the basis of evidence extant at the time the books were written. However, within recent years new evidence based on electron micrographs, biochemical data, and high-speed cinematographs demonstrate that these distinctions are no longer tenable on either morphological or physiological grounds.

1. ELECTRON MICROSCOPE OBSERVATIONS

Electron micrographs have revealed the fundamental and universal presence in all cilia and flagella, wherever found, except in bacteria, of an organization of nine peripheral doublet fibrils and two central ones extended from an attachment at a basal plate (for reviews, see Afzelius, 1961; Fawcett, 1961; Grimstone, 1961; Sleigh, 1962). Pitelka (1963) says "cilia are one of several varieties of flagella." There is also a similarity in biochemistry, i.e., the presence of the ATP-actomyosin-like protein complex (Hoffmann-Berling, 1960; Child, 1961; Tibbs, 1958, 1962; M. R. Watson and Hopkins, 1962). Presumably some series of tensions and contractions in the fibrils, using ATP energy, is involved in their movements.

Histochemical reactions show a concentration of phosphate reserves at the inner ends of ciliary and flagellar peripheral fibrils (Hunter, 1951, 1959) where, with the basal plate, they form the basal body of the cilium (or flagellum), variously also called a basal granule, blepharoplast, kinetoplast, or kinetosome. ATP and ATPase are also to be found along the length of the actomyosin-like fibrils (Nelson, 1954, 1958, 1962); and glycerinated models, under some circumstances, show a coordinated rhythmic activity in the presence of ATP (Bishop, 1958; Brokaw, 1961, 1962a,b). Antigenic reactions suggest that the actin-like component forms the "hollow" tubular nine peripheral doublet fibrils, with the myosin-like fraction making up the core of each such doublet tubelet (Nelson and Plowman, 1963).

Isolated, mildly glycerinated flagella without basal bodies, obtained from normal strains of *Chlamydomonas moewusii* and *Polytoma uvella* swim in ATP solutions, but those of the paralyzed mutant strain of *C. moewusii* (Lewin, 1952b) do not (Brokaw, 1960), and isolated cilia and flagella have long been known to show spontaneous movement (Bütschli, 1882; Erhard, 1910).

Acetylcholinesterase has been reported in *Tetrahymena* (Seaman and Houlihan, 1951) and this is sometimes assumed to be evidence of a "neurohumor," thereby indicating the presence of a "neuroid" system. However, acetylcholinesterase is found in many biological systems, including vertebrate red blood cells (Zajicek and Datta, 1953) and the plasmodium of *Physarum polycephalum* (Nakajima and Hatano, 1962), where no neuroid function seems probable.

VII. Movement of Flagella and of Flagellates

It is generally assumed that the difference between the movement of flagella and cilia is that flagella beat with an undulatory or helical movement and push water distally (Lowndes, 1941, 1943, 1944; Sleigh, 1962), while cilia beat sideways and push water laterally (Sleigh, 1962). However, recent high-speed cinephotomicrographs by Jahn and his co-workers (cf. below), of various flagellates in locomotion, show that flagella may move in a variety of ways.

A. CLASSIFICATION OF FLAGELLAR MOVEMENTS

Some of the types of flagellar movement based on geometry of the wave, with typical examples, are (Jahn *et al.*, 1964e):

1. PLANAR SINUSOIDAL WAVES

a. Wave distally directed, exerting a locomotor force *toward* the base, i.e., a pushing force, e.g., posterior flagellum of *Ceratium* (Jahn *et al.*, 1964a) and many sperm.

b. Wave basally directed, exerting a locomotor force *away* from the base, i.e., a pulling force, e.g., Trypanosomidae (Jahn and Fonseca, 1963).

c. Wave distally directed, exerting a locomotor force *away* from the base, i.e., a pulling force. Known so far only for the pantonematic flagellum of chrysomonads (Jahn *et al.*, 1964a,e).

2. HELICAL WAVES

a. Wave distally directed, exerting a pushing locomotor force *toward* the base, e.g., *Euglena*, which is pushed at the front end by an anteriorly attached but posteriorly directed flagellum with a helical wave (Lowndes, 1941), or *Rhabdomonas*, where the flagellum and wave are tangential to the circumference of gyration of the body, and do not produce a forwardly directed component (Lowndes, 1941).

b. Wave basally directed, exerting a *pulling* force on the organism, e.g., *Mastigamoeba* (Bovee *et al.*, 1963).

c. Wave directed circumferentially in a groove of the body, more or less at right angles to the resulting forward component and therefore to the direction of locomotion; a true rotary drive, e.g., the transverse flagellum of *Ceratium* (Jahn *et al.*, 1961b, 1963a).

3. LATERO-POSTERIOR BEAT, SIMILAR TO THAT OF CILIA

Force exerted at right angles to the beating position of the flagellum, e.g., *Peranema, Petalomonas, Entosiphon* (Jahn *et al.*, 1963b), *Trichomonas* (Sleigh, 1962; Bovee and Telford, 1964; Jahn and Fonseca, 1964, unpublished), *Chlamydomonas* and *Polytoma* (Lewin, 1952a), and *Mastigamoeba setosa* moving on a surface (Bovee *et al.*, 1963).

The above seven types of flagellar movement do not include all of those which occur, and we expect more to be described in the near future, some of which will introduce other principles of hydrodynamics new to microbiology.

Types 1a, 1b, and 1c are shown in Fig. 6 and type 2c in Fig. 8 (see Section VII,F). The existence of such a variety of flagellar locomotor mechanisms, especially type 3, of course precludes any functional distinction between cilia and flagella (cf. Sleigh, 1962).

Flagella also may be classified on the basis of the relationship of the wave to the body, as in sections B to F below.

B. LONGITUDINAL BASE-TO-TIP MOVEMENTS

1. DINOFLAGELLATES, POSTERIOR FLAGELLUM

The posterior flagellum of *Ceratium* beats in the manner often described in textbooks as standard for all flagella (Jahn *et al.*, 1961b, 1963a). In brief, the flagellum is attached posteriorly and is directed posteriorly; and the wave is planar, is distally directed, pushes water backward, and therefore pushes the organism forward (Fig. 6c). This type of movement certainly is not universal for flagellates, and it actually is quite unusual in its occurrence among the flagellate orders. Furthermore, it was recognized by Lowndes (1941) that this

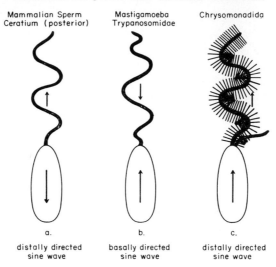

FIG. 6. Planar sinusoidal movements of flagella.

a. Distally directed sine wave, pushes the cell in the direction opposite to the movement of the wave, employed by mammalian sperm and by the posterior flagellum of dinoflagellates, especially *Ceratium*.

b. Basally directed sine wave, pulls the cell in the direction opposite to the movement of the wave, employed by certain trypanosomes and by mastigamoebae, in which the wave may be helical.

c. Distally directed sine wave, flagellum with stiff mastigonemes, pulls the cell in the same direction as the movement of the wave, employed by certain chrysomonads.

type of movement is hydrodynamically stable only for slowly moving organisms. He stated that rapidly moving organisms should gyrate with the end to which the flagellum is attached going foremost, and he described this type of gyration with reversal of ends for *Euglena*. Apparently the only reason this type of movement seems to be stable in rapidly moving dinoflagellates is that it occurs in combination with a true rotary drive (see Section VII,F).

2. *Euglena, Astasia, Rhabdomonas*

Many flagellates (e.g., *Euglena, Astasia, Rhabdomonas*) gyrate as they swim, but the functional significance of the gyration is not often realized. It was first pointed out by Lowndes (1941, 1943, 1944; see also Jahn, 1947; Jahn and Jahn, 1949; Brown, 1945) that the gyrations cause the body to act as a rotary inclined plane, i.e., a one-bladed propeller. This is obvious in *Euglena* in which the flagellum, attached anteriorly, beats with a posteriorly directed helical wave, producing a forward component, a lateral component, and a torque. The result of these forces is to push the organism forward along a gyrating pathway, at about one gyration per second. As the organism gyrates, the anterior end sweeps out a much larger circle than the posterior end, and the body, regardless of shape, acts like a rotary inclined plane. The inclined plane effect is even more obvious in *Rhabdomonas* because, according to Lowndes (1941), the flagellum beats at right angles to the path of locomotion, thereby having *no forward component*. However, the flagellum beats tangentially to the anterior circumference of the gyrating pathway, and serves *only* to cause the gyration. The gyration, then, through the mechanism of the inclined plane, produces movement in the forward direction.

3. CHRYSOMONADS, ANTERIOR FLAGELLUM

In a marine chrysomonad, *Chromulina* sp., and also in *Ochromonas malhamensis* and *O. danica,* the flagellar wave is planar and moves from base to tip, as it is usually assumed a flagellum "should" beat, but the flagellum is held forward, and the body also *moves forward* (Jahn *et al.,* 1964a,c). This movement, which is in the reverse direction to what would "normally" be expected, is attributed to the presence of the stiff brush-like array of mastigonemes on the flagellum (Manton, 1952; Pitelka and Schooley, 1955; Fig. 6C). These cause the flagellum to behave as a rough-surfaced, flexible, undulating cylinder, which, according to the hydrodynamic computations of G. I. Taylor (1952), may drive the organism in the direction of the undulating wave along the cylinder, because the backward push of the flagellar shaft is overcome by the opposite thrust of the rough surface, i.e., the mastigonemes.

It can be seen (Fig. 7) that as the sine wave moves distally, each mastigoneme will push backward as it passes over the peak of the sine wave, or more exactly as the peak of the sine wave passes through the region to which the mastigoneme is attached. Figure 7 shows two mastigonemes which pass through positions A, B, and C. Under these conditions the axial body of the flagellum will create a distally directed current of water while the mastigonemes create a basally directed current. The direction of the net locomotor force will depend upon the dimensions, number, and stiffness of the mastigonemes.

C. LONGITUDINAL TIP-TO-BASE MOVEMENTS

1. IN TRYPANOSOMES, PLANAR SINE WAVES

Jahn and Fonseca (1963) find that during normal swimming of *Trypanosoma lewisi,* the single flagellum with its undulating membrane beats from *tip* to *basal body* in a planar sine wave, with an increasing amplitude which is damped by the body of the organism and which does not extend posteriorly beyond the basal body. Moreover, the body of the organism also undulates in unison with the flagellum so that the organism swims in a snake-like fashion, with flagellum foremost and with a high amplitude. In specimens which are attached to the slide the flagellar wave may be helical and there may also be

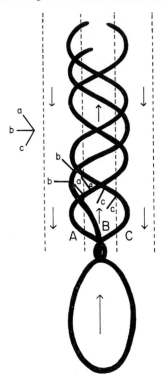

FIG. 7. Effects of stiff mastigonemes on the flagellar movements of chrysomonads. As planar sine waves move distally through positions A, B, and C the mastigonemes indicated move through positions a, b, and c. Each mastigoneme, as it passes the crest of the sine wave, exerts force toward the cell body. The main axis of the flagellum exerts force away from the cell body.

accompanying body undulations in the opposite direction. Since trypanosomes are usually attached to the slide this is the confused state of affairs usually observed in microscope slides of living trypanosomes. Actual swimming is rather rare, for undetermined reasons. Leptomonad forms of *Trypanosoma cruzi* (Jahn and Fonseca, 1963) normally move in one direction by means of a planar sine wave from tip to base of the flagellum, but may also reverse the direction of the wave on the flagellum and simultaneously the direction of movement of the body for short intervals of time. The existence of basally directed waves and also waves of reversal was reported by Pipkin (1962) in attached specimens of *Trypanosoma cruzi,* on the basis of cinematographs taken at normal speed. It was Pipkin's pictures which stimulated Jahn and Fonseca (1963) to make the above described observations at 600 frames per second in order to obviate beat frequency effects which might appear as reversals, and also to extend the observations.

2. IN MASTIGAMEBAE WITH HELICAL SINE WAVES

Bovee *et al.* (1963) observed in mastigamebae (e.g., *Mastigamoeba steinii*, *M. setosa*, and *Mastigamoeba* spp. unidentified) that attached and swimming organisms usually generated a helical wave but sometimes a planar wave, both of which move from tip to basal body of the flagellum.

For *Mastigamoeba steinii*, a large ameboflagellate, and for several other small unidentified *Mastigamoeba* spp., frame by frame analysis of cinematographic records (Bovee *et al.*, 1963) shows that as the long lone flagellum begins its beat, helical waves progress, one after another, more and more rapidly, from tip to base of the flagellum, each wave increasing in amplitude until it is damped out at the basal body of the flagellum. Visual observation indicates that the still larger *Mastigamoeba setosa* has a similar flagellar action in swimming. The body of the mastigameba is tipped and thrown into gyration by the beating of the flagellum, so that the anterior end of the body describes a circle greater in diameter than that described by the rear end, i.e., the body moves as an inclined plane, screwing its way forward in the water. This forward component, plus the forward component exerted by the tractile action of the tip-to-base undulations of the helically active flagellum, cause the animal to swim forward. The number of gyrations of the body per second (about 2 to 6) seems to be related to the number of waves progressing sequentially along the flagellum—i.e., the more waves, the more gyrations per second. Each wave progresses from tip to base of the flagellum in about $\frac{1}{5}$ to $\frac{1}{10}$ sec., and there may be as many as 10–12 waves progressing separately and sequentially along the single flagellum.

In the trypanosomes and also the mastigamebae there is no doubt that the wave starts at the tip and progresses basally and even exhibits an increase of amplitude in the process. This is rather disconcerting to investigators who endow the basal body, under a variety of names, with the sole power to initiate a wave of bending in the flagellum. If this supposed function of the basal body should be proven true, we will then need an explanation of how the stimulus goes from the basal body to the tip—possibly by way of the two central fibrils? The problem is further complicated by the fact that in *Mastigamoeba* sp. (Bovee *et al.*, 1963) nearly a dozen waves may be simultaneously and sequentially inbound along the flagellum.

D. LATEROPOSTERIOR MOVEMENTS

1. TRACTELLAR FLAGELLUM OF *Peranema*, *Mastigamoeba*, AND *Entosiphon*

The lateroposterior type of beat has been described (Jahn *et al.*, 1963b) for *Peranema*, *Petalomonas*, and *Entosiphon* during the gliding type of locomotion on a substrate. In *Peranema* and *Petalomonas* the flagellum is held forward, as is well known, but the organism pulls itself forward by snapping beats, toward the body, of the anterior 30–35% of the flagellar length. The forward sliding is smooth and continuous, possibly due to some unknown additional component of forward motion. These observations obviate Sleigh's (1962) assertion for the correctness of Lowndes' (1941) contention for a bent-back undulatory tip of the flagellum in *Peranema* presumed to act as a pusillum, and also for Lowndes' contention that all flagella push. A similar beat of the anterior 20–25% of its flagellar length is performed by *Mastigamoeba setosa* on a smooth substrate with added propulsive components of a simultaneous ameboid flow of the body and a tight, tractile helical wave that runs from the beating tip of the flagellum to its basal body (Bovee *et al.*, 1963).

Entosiphon sulcatum, another euglenid flagellate, uses a similar cilium-like action of the anterior flagellum, bending 80 to 90% of its length laterally and positively in a power stroke, with the anteriorly directed recovery stroke overlapping the power stroke. Its heavy posterior flagellum trails under the body, acting as a skid, motionless during locomotion; and the body wobbles from side to side in synchrony with the flagellar beat (Jahn *et al.*, 1963b).

2. "BREAST-STROKE" MOVEMENTS OF FLAGELLA OF TRICHOMONADS AND CERTAIN PHYTOFLAGELLATES

The same type of flagellar movement occurs in *Monocercomonas* spp. (Bovee and Telford, 1964) *Tritrichomonas foetus* (Jahn and Fonseca, 1964) and *Trichomonas termopsidis* (Sleigh, 1962), in which the three anterior flagella move in unison, analogous to a human swimmer's breast stroke. Lewin (1952a) described a similar "breast stroke" beat for the two anterior flagella of *Chlamydomonas* and *Polytoma;* and Jahn and Fonseca (1964) have also observed similar movements in certain colonial phytomonads, except that the two flagella of any given cell beat parallel to each other rather than at 180° as described by Lewin.

3. REINSTATEMENT OF THE TERM TRACTELLUM

It is clear that Lowndes (1944) was premature in his assumption that all flagella are pusillary and that the term "tractellum" should be abolished. Plainly, the term tractellum should be reinstated (Jahn *et al.*, 1964a,e) and used whenever a term to designate a pulling flagellum is needed. It is also evident that there are several types of tractella which may be typified as: (1) the trypanosome type, 1b above; (2) the chrysomonad type, 1c above; (3) the *Mastigamoeba* type, 2b above; and (4) the *Peranema* type, 3 above. All of these definitely pull the organisms and therefore are tractella, and possibly there are still other types.

E. Multiple Movements of Flagella in One Organism

An individual flagellum may not be limited to one type of movement as outlined above. For example Krijgsman (1925) described several types of movement for *Monas,* some of which were confirmed by Lowndes (1944). In the high-speed cinematographs of Jahn and co-workers of the above-mentioned peranemids, trypanosomes, and mastigamebae, lashing movements, each a single powerful helical or planar sine wave from base to tip of the flagellum, usually complete before a second is begun, may occur intermittently during the tractile type of locomotion. The waves push toward the base, usually obliquely, thereby causing reorientation of the anterior end of the body so that further locomotion, upon resumption of the normal locomotor beat from the tip, is in a new direction.

F. Rotary Drive of Dinoflagellate Transverse Flagellum

Jahn *et al.* (1961b, 1963a) have demonstrated that in the dinoflagellate *Ceratium* and presumably in other dinoflagellates with a ribbon-shaped transverse flagellum in a girdle, the transverse flagellum beats with an irrotational traveling helical wave of such amplitude that half of each cycle is out of the girdle. The outside portion pushes tangentially to the helix, and posteriorly as far as the organism is concerned, while the inside portion is more or less in contact with the inner surface of the girdle, which acts like a bearing. Therefore, each half wavelength serves as a mechanical couple, with any section momentarily farthest from the body pushing backward on the water and two other sections, each a half wavelength in either direction, pushing forward on the inner surface of the anterior flange of the girdle, thereby driving the organism forward (Fig. 8).

Ceratium may move forward either by means of the distally directed planar sine wave of the posterior flagellum, or by means of the transverse flagellum, or by both methods simultaneously, as shown in Fig. 8. The transverse flagellum also produces a component along the axis of the helix, i.e., circumferential to the organism, which may cause rotation of the organism on its long axis, but some species, e.g., *Ceratium furca,* ordinarily do not rotate.

G. Comparison to Sperm Flagella

The above observations indicate that there is a much greater variety of types of movement known for protozoan flagellates than for animal sperm, in which the movement consists of either plane or helical sine waves. Earlier sperm motility studies (J. Gray, 1928) indicated that the normal flagellar beat of sperm is a planar sine wave from basal body (or distal centriole) to the flagellar tip, acting as a pusillum, with motion of the body opposite to that of the

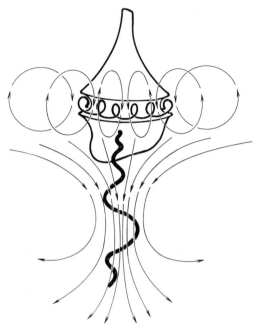

FIG. 8. Movements of the flagella of *Ceratium*. Helical waves along the transverse flagellum in the girdle push to the rear and the posterior flagellum with a distally directed planar sine wave movement also pushes toward the rear. Either or both movements may drive the organism forward. Arrows indicate the paths of polystyrene spheres in the water pushed by the movements of the flagella, indicating that the driving force on the water is toward the rear.

flagellar wave (J. Gray, 1955). There is also evidence that the wave is helical (Rikmenspoel, 1962; Rothschild, 1961, 1962); and the planar wave, in sperm, has been called "pathologic" (Rikmenspoel, 1962). Astbury *et al.* (1955), assume that the wave is helical, and propose theories of flagellar movement based on that assumption. However, some plant sperm (e.g., *Fucus*) have pantonematic flagella and swim with the flagellum held forward, as in the chrysomonads (Manton, 1952).

H. THEORIES OF INTERNAL FLAGELLAR MECHANISMS

How a flagellate modifies the beat of the flagellum in response to various circumstances is not known, although certain physical factors and chemicals bring about such variations (Mast, 1941; Lee, 1954a,b; Kinosita, 1936; Okajima, 1953; Naitoh, 1958; Borgers and Kitching, 1956; for reviews, see Rivera, 1962; Salisbury, 1962; Brokaw, 1962a,b); but how the factors operate, and whether the site is the basal body, is not known.

Theories of a flagellar stimulus, assuming a commutator action on peripheral fibrils via the basal body (Bradfield, 1955), or by way of a stimulatory wave up the central fibrils from the basal body (Astbury *et al.*, 1955; Hodge, 1949; Brown, 1945; Wolken, 1961) explain the base-to-tip progression. However, they do not explain the tip-to-base progression of movement, nor do they show how flagella of the same or different organisms, on approaching one another will change phase to beat together in synchrony. Therefore, the general assumption that the site of the stimulus for flagellar action is always the basal body is open to question. According to Sleigh (1962), the synchronous beat is probably due to the viscosity of the water bringing about damping effects of the wave movements of each flagellum on those of each adjacent one, tending to bring them into phase with one another (J. Gray, 1955). This would seem to imply that a feedback from the activity of the flagellum to the basal body (or directly to the other flagellum) may be involved. As J. Gray (1962) points out, it is difficult to think that anything comparable with conducted nervous impulses is fundamentally concerned here.

I. Hydrodynamic Factors Involved in flagellar Movement

The hydrodynamics of flagellar movement has attracted increasing attention in the past quarter century, especially in the locomotion of sperm. The mathematical computations presented by J. Gray (1928, 1931, 1955), Hancock (1953), G. I. Taylor (1951, 1952), Machin (1958), and others, and the use of models (Lowndes, 1943, 1944; G. I. Taylor, 1952) indicate several important factors affecting flagellate swimming. Among these are: (1) The flagellum bends actively (J. Gray, 1955), and it *must* do so in order to produce the various patterns and the amplitudes known to exist (Machin, 1958). (2) The rate of locomotion varies directly with the amplitude of the waves in the flagellum (Hancock, 1953). (3) The Reynolds' number (ratio of inertial to viscous resistance to movement) is about 10^{-2} for the body and 10^{-4} or less for the flagellum. This means that inertial resistance is negligible and that viscosity of the medium is the main resistance to be overcome (G. I. Taylor, 1951). (4) An asymmetrical helical wave along the flagellum may generate a pulsating torque strong enough to rotate the body of the flagellate even if the flagellum itself does not rotate (J. Gray, 1955). (5) The flagellate is not able to swim unless its body resists the torque produced by helical flagellar undulation (Hancock, 1953). (6) In sperm the body, because of its small size, causes little resistance to the viscosity of the medium; whereas the tangential viscous drag on the length of the flagellum causes most of the resistance. However, this apparently is not true for flagellates. (7) In flagellates the body, acting as an inclined plane, may screw its way through the water (e.g., *Rhabdomonas incurvum;* see Lowndes, 1941) with force, but not forward thrust, provided by flagellar action; or the body may swim with some forward push from the flagellum combined with inclined propeller action, yielding greater forward speeds (e.g.,

Euglena viridis; see Lowndes, 1941). (8) The roughness of a swimming cylinder may exert a force opposite to and greater than the force exerted by the body of the cylinder, so that the net force is in the direction opposite to that normally expected (G. I. Taylor, 1952). This theory can explain the action of stiff fixed mastigonemes (Jahn *et al.,* 1964c) of chrysomonads. (9) In general, the various physical and hydrodynamic factors affecting the path of movement approximately cancel one another's tendency to change the pathway of locomotion, so that a steady beating of the flagellum usually results in a gyration of the flagellate body along a helical path of advance, the axis of which is a straight line through the center of a cylinder which fits the diameter of the helix.

VIII. Movement of Cilia and Ciliates

A. The Nature of the Ciliary Beat

Whereas studies on the mechanics of protozoan flagella have been sparse until very recently, there is a wealth of data based on studies of the form, composition, and activity of protozoan cilia and their compound organelles, particularly for *Paramecium, Stentor, Tetrahymena,* and *Opalina*—the latter a protozoan with both ciliate and flagellate affinities, having its organelles in rows as do the ciliates.

1. THE PATH OF THE BEAT

While it has been assumed that the beat of a cilium is pendular (J. Gray, 1928), and presumably different therefore from the undulatory beat of flagella, that distinction is abrogated by the observations on flagellates cited above.

It has been claimed that metazoan cilia beat in a plane perpendicular to a line connecting the two central fibrils (Fawcett and Porter, 1954). This can not be completely true for protozoan cilia which are not limited to movement in one plane. There are many observations that protozoan cilia move in a funnel-shaped three-dimensional pattern (Ulehla, 1911; Párducz, 1953, 1954, 1957). Also the power stroke is not directed straight backward, but at an angle (Jennings, 1904) resembling a segment of a helical wave rather than a linear beat from front to rear. Sleigh (1962) contends, probably correctly, that the ciliary beat in protozoa is a modification of the flagellar function, and Pitelka (1963) considers a cilium to be a type of flagellum. Some reports suggest that there is a continuously functional intrinsic rotary movement of the cilium about its base (Ulehla, 1911), evidenced when the cilium is separated from its neighbors (Verworn, 1889) or is partly anesthetized so that the "stronger" aspect of the power stroke ceases (Alverdes, 1922). Pitelka (1963) deems it a primary movement related to the simplest form of beat in a flagellum.

2. DISCONTINUOUS ACTIVITY

It has long been contended that some metazoan cilia are perhaps normally continuously active (Bidder, 1923; J. Gray, 1928; Thompson, 1945). This continuous activity may not be entirely true of cilia in protozoa, since visible functioning may cease under certain conditions normally encountered in which the ciliate is not moribund and is fully responsive, e.g., the cessation of movement of ventral cirri of hypotrichs, and of cilia of *Paramecium* on contact with a surface, e.g., the so-called "thigmotactic response" (Jennings, 1931), which also occurs with flagella, e.g., *Chlamydomonas* and *Trypanosoma* (Jahn and Fonseca, 1964), or as the result of "inhibition" e.g., *Stentor* (Sleigh, 1962).

3. THEORIES OF POWER AND RETURN STROKES

a. Inadequacy of a Rigid Ciliary Shaft. Ludwig (1930), in a lengthy mathematical analysis of hydrodynamic principles applied to ciliary movements, concluded that the shape and motion of the cilium produced the greatest possible efficiency for such an organelle. He also concluded that because of the very low Reynolds' number of an individual cilium (about 10^{-4}) it is not possible for cilia to drive a ciliate unless the cilia are bent on the return stroke. In other words, if the cilia were straight rods, hinged at the base, moving with different velocities in the two directions, they would not be able to exert a net locomotor force for a complete ciliary cycle.

b. Turgidity Changes. To what degree the cilium changes state in the cycle of movement is not known. Earlier theories—and some recent ones—have assumed it alternately becomes stiff on the power stroke and limp or flaccid on the return by gain and loss of turgidity due to fluid volume increases and decreases (Schäfer, 1910; Ludwig, 1930). Later ideas assume that fibrillar components stiffen or relax (Carter, 1924; Astbury *et al.*, 1955; J. Gray, 1955) perhaps also with gain and loss of turgidity. In the latter case the central fibrils have been assumed to provide the elastic rigidity and the peripheral fibrils the contractile component.

c. Continuous Turgor and Active Fibrillar Changes. Harris (1961) calculates by means of the formula for a bending couple, that no biological material composing the central fibrils of the cilium could be rigid enough to resist the bending and concludes that the central fibrils could not, therefore, be the principal supporting structures of the cilium. He suggests there is a continuous turgor in the cilium which lends the ciliary membrane enough rigidity to cope with the force of the bending couple. Sleigh (1962) suggests that the principal rigidity is in the peripheral fibrils, each of which, except when using ATP energy, is a semirigid elastic tube. At any rate, the entire length of the cilium appears to be rigid in the power stroke and more flexible during the return stroke (Carter, 1924); but is also reported as being actively flexible during the return stroke rather than limp (Sleigh, 1962).

d. Presumed Roles of Ciliary Fibrils. Most recent theories assume that the peripheral fibrils of the cilium are contractile, and the central ones supporting (Bradfield, 1955; Sleigh, 1960) and perhaps conducting (Bradfield, 1955; Astbury *et al.*, 1955). Inoué (1959) diverges, however, by considering the two central fibrils to be the contractile ones. However, in order to produce a helical wave at least four linear contractile fibers seem necessary.

B. "Kinetodesmal" Subpellicular Interciliary Fibrils

1. assumption of a neuroid function

As early as the turn of the century (Schuberg, 1905), it was suggested that the subpellicular interciliary fibrils conducted impulses responsible for metachrony. It has since been widely proposed—mainly on the *prima facie* morphological evidence, with uncritical acceptance—that the fibrils and cilia constitute a "neuromotor" system.

a. The General Theory. As in the case of flagella, most of the theories also assume that excitation of the cilium "almost certainly starts in the basal body" (Sleigh, 1962; cf. flagella, Section VII, above). The morphology of the cilium and the arrangement of them, in ciliated protozoa, in connected rows with interciliary fibrils has led to the general acceptance by ciliophorologists and many other biologists of such terms as "kinetosome" for the basal body, and "kinetodesmose" or "kinety" for the connecting fibrils (e.g., Corliss, 1961; Pitelka, 1963); this has also led to the assumption that the basal bodies are sequentially "fired" by stimuli relayed along the interciliary fibrils.

b. Application to Ciliate Membranelles. Sleigh (1957, 1962) has recently presented a version of the "neuroid" transmission of interciliary fibrils, assuming that the metachronal beat in each ciliary row of a membranelle in the adoral ring thereof in *Stentor* is begun at a "pacemaker" cilium, presumably the "first in any row"; and that if the pacemaker cannot perform its role for some lack of communication, any other in the row which physically or functionally becomes first in the row then becomes "pacemaker." Each cilium is assumed to transmit a stimulus, hypothetically one way to the next in the row, presumably over a fibril. Sleigh (1957) also assumes the viscous drag of the medium to be the initial source of stimulus, but does not explain how or why the "pacemaker" may be the more sensitive of the cilia to that stimulus.

2. morphological position of the fibrils

The electron microscope investigations (for reviews, see Fawcett, 1961; Pitelka, 1963) do demonstrate, as had earlier silver-staining techniques (B. M. Klein, 1926; von Gelei, 1932; Lund, 1933; Chatton and Lwoff, 1930, 1935; Corliss, 1953) an intricate subpellicular fibrillar system in ciliates to which the basal bodies of cilia are connected. It is also evident that the major fibrils parallel the rows of cilia along which metachronal waves of ciliary movement progress. In most ciliates the fibril is to the (ciliate's) right of the basal bodies—the so-called "rule of desmodexy" (Chatton and Lwoff, 1935).

3. MICRODISSECTION OF THE FIBRILS, AND PRESUMED "NEUROID" EVIDENCE

Microdissection studies on ciliates (Rees, 1922; Chambers and Dawson, 1925; C. V. Taylor, 1920; Worley, 1934; Lund, 1941; Sleigh, 1957) have resulted in the disturbance of metachronal waves or other coordinated ciliary movements on one or both sides of a cut through a ciliary row and its parallel or connected fibrils or through a membranelle. These observations have been proposed as *a priori* evidence of the conductile function of the fibrils.

4. CILIARY REVERSAL STUDIES AND PRESUMED "NEUROID" EVIDENCE

However, in such studies the physiological effects of cutting the cell surface (obviously unavoidable), and the relation of the cut to electrostatic and electrochemical potentials have been largely ignored. So, also, have observations that although the metachronal wave may be disturbed by the cutting, the reversal response of the cilia is not, e.g., in either *Opalina* (Okajima, 1954) or *Paramecium* (Doroszewski, 1958). The reversal response has also often been included in the *a priori* evidence for the presumed neuromotor system, since contact of the anterior cilia with an object or chemicals in the water which the ciliate enters provokes the response (Jennings, 1904; and many others).

5. ARGUMENTS AND COMMENTS AGAINST "NEUROID" TRANSMISSON

Worley (1934) concluded, as a result of microdissection experiments, that the conduction of the stimulus for metachronally coordinated ciliary action is a phenomenon of the *surface* parallel to the fibrils of the "silverline system" being perhaps slowed, not facilitated by them. Hammond (1935) asserts that none of the fibrillar systems of *Paramecium* can account for the coordination of its cilia, whether of the gullet, the oral groove, or the general body surface; and Seravin (1962) denies the role of any morphological system in ciliary coordination, assuming instead an ectoplasmic physiological gradient.

Wichterman (1953) while assuming the fibrils as of prime importance in conduction of metachronal impulses, considers the reversal impulses to be transmitted at the surface. He warns that

> "very few interpretations concerning the functions of the subpellicular fibrils have been made upon experimental evidence. It must be frankly admitted that the specific function or functions are not known. To ascribe functions to the various fibrils without experimen-

tation is incompatible with sound scientific principles. Some of the interpretations of the functions of the ciliate fibrillar systems are so unsound scientifically that (they) remind one of Ehrenberg's fallacious theories in which he claimed identity of organs in the infusoria to those common in higher animals."

Wichterman's criticisms are still valid.

Sometime proposals for a "motorium" (C. V. Taylor, 1920; Rosenberg, 1937) or "neuromotorium" (Lund, 1933), based largely on morphological position of silver-stained lumps in the fibrillar network, are not supported by any detectable differentiation of fibrillar organization when the sites of the lumps are examined by electron microscopy. Roth (1956, 1957) found only intertwined fibrils, for example, where C. V. Taylor (1920) postulated a "motorium" for *Euplotes*.

Pitelka (1963), in discussing the ultrafine morphological details of the rows of basal bodies of ciliate cilia and their associated fibrils, says (p. 170) that:

"Many functions have been ascribed to these various structures, including those implied by the terms neuromotor and neuroformative. We shall see that the evidence does not yet justify any general conclusions in this regard."

and (pp. 226–27):

"It is certain that no fibrillar system described for *Opalina, Paramecium* and the tetrahymenids could, by its distribution, be held responsible for either normal metachrony or ciliary responses to stimuli over the general body surface."

and also (p. 217):

"At the moment the only known function for the silverline system is to aid the protozoologist in identification and developmental studies of his cells, but presumably the ciliate has some less altruistic reason for preserving it."

In *Opalina* the metachronal wave changes direction spontaneously and also in response to K^+ ions or cathodal current. This change may be gradual, increasing slowly from $0°$ up to $180°$, and reversing repeatedly, either spontaneously or in response to ionic or electrical changes (Okajima, 1953; Naitoh, 1958). If this type of change in the directional pattern is under control of neuromotor fibrils, it seems as if not only the fibrils, but something comparable to a central nervous system would also be necessary. A similar statement might be made about *Nyctotherus*, in which reversal of the metachronal waves sometimes starts as a small vortex which increases in diameter and eventually includes a large area of the organism before becoming a typical longitudinal reverse metachronal wave (Rosenberg, 1937).

6. OTHER POSSIBLE FUNCTIONS OF THE FIBRILS

It would be as reasonable to assume a supportive (von Gelei, 1932; Jacobsen, 1931) or contractile function for the so-called "kinetodesma" as a neuroid one, particularly in such contractile ciliates as *Spirostomum* and *Condylostoma* where the presumed "myonemes" have been shown by electron microscopy to be probably identical with the "kinetodesma" (see review, Pitelka, 1963). There is, however, no sound evidence for either a neuroid or contractile function for the fibrils. Even so, Roth (1958) has postulated a possible contractile function for the ciliary rootlet fibrils, based on his electron microscope studies of them, and Rosenberg (1937) considered ciliary rows responsible for body contractions in *Nyctotherus*.

7. SOME COMPLICATIONS OF THE PROBLEM

The question as to the cause of coordinated movements of cilia is still an unsolved one. A whole ciliate is coordinated in its movements; but so are experimentally newly cut anterior and posterior halves and fragments of *Paramecium* (Jennings and Jamieson, 1902), the cilia of the pellicular "hulls" of ciliates with cilia intact (Lepşi, 1926), small segments of *Dileptus* (Doroszewski, 1961) or *Spirostomum* (Clark, 1946), and ectoplasmic pellicular fragments cut from living ciliates (Worley, 1934). All show normal ciliary beat, reversal of beat, metachrony, and spiral swimming. To what degree the ciliary coordination is due to "regulation" by the ciliate there is no evidence. There appears to be interaction between cilia due to the hydrodynamic relationship of a cilium to its neighbors, but the full relationships are unclear. The metachrony of a single row and isochrony of adjacent rows of cilia on the basis of a "neuromotor" system is still only suppositional, even if possible, and even though the possibility may exist.

C. A Hydrodynamic Theory of Metachrony

The hydrodynamic approach to metachrony and isochrony is much more fruitful. It takes into account the fluid medium, which must be considered, avoids the assumption of intracellular "brains" and transmission pathways, and provides explanations for phenomena otherwise not possible—except via fantastic additional and unfounded functional assumptions to be assigned to a "neuromotor" system.

If each cilium be considered a separately energized independent oscillator its compressional wave should be semicircular. Such oscillators, beating with nearly the same, but flexible, period, will become synchronized in the phase of beat. This is due to the effect of the component of the pressure wave of one cilium on the next. The pressure waves would have a stronger effect on those next to them in the direction of the power stroke than upon those next to them in the opposite direction because of the stronger component of pressure in the direction of the power stroke of the cilium.

Lack of complete synchrony is probably due, mainly if not entirely, to delay in establishing the minimal pressure necessary to affect the next cilium in the row. The minimal pressure would have to be generated during the acceleration of the cilium from zero velocity to the minimal critical velocity necessary to generate the minimal pressure component. The delay could not be due to conduction of the pressure wave through the fluid because the distance covered by a pressure wave during one ciliary cycle is many times the length of the whole ciliate. The difference in the velocity of the power and return strokes, about 5 to 1 (Kraft, 1890; Wichterman, 1950) causes generation of the directional pressure, which in turn causes the transmissional delay and the resultant metachrony. Because of bending, little directional pressure is assumed to be generated during the return stroke (see Ludwig, 1930).

Assuming the above to be the cause of metachrony, isochrony of adjacent rows is a function thereof. The anterior cilium in each row is about the same radial distance from the approximately parallel cilia in adjacent rows as from the next posterior cilium in its own row. Hence the pressure wave generated by the anterior cilium in any row would affect the nearest neighbors in adjacent rows as well as in its own row. The additive and interacting effects are ultimately such as to bring *all* rows into approximate synchrony, and laterally adjacent cilia in two separate rows (and others) would be therefore isochronic. A detailed explanation of this purely physical theory of metachrony will soon be published by Jahn. (Jahn, 1964c).

That such a physical theory of metachrony is more reasonable than some "neuroid" explanation is supported by the observation of perfect metachrony of movements by the many spirochaetes attached to the body surface of certain symbiotic trichomonad flagellates of termites (Cleveland, 1963; Cleveland and Grimstone, 1964; Jahn, 1964c).

It is also possible to predict hydrodynamically, that increases in temperature will cause an increase in frequency of ciliary beat, as noted by Sleigh (1956), and that an increase of viscosity of the fluid medium causes an increase of metachronal wavelength, as reported by Gosselin (1958). Still other phenomena, as yet unexplained, or unknown, may be revealed by further hydrodynamic applications.

D. CILIARY REVERSAL

1. BY DIRECT ELECTRICAL CURRENT; THE LUDLOFF PHENOMENON

a. Description of the Phenomenon. It has long been known that cathodal electric current reverses the ciliary beat (Verworn, 1889; Ludloff, 1895; Kamada,

1931; Kinosita, 1936, 1954; Okajima, 1953; Watanabe, 1955; Naitoh, 1958),
resulting also in the "Ludloff phenomenon" (i.e., when the current is closed,
cilia on the surface toward the cathode are reversed; but if the organism is
obliquely across the path of the current, cilia on all sides of the body nearest
the cathode reverse in relationship to a plane at right angles through the body
to the direction of current; and that the stronger the current the greater
the portion of the body affected up to about 60%). Reversal is also promoted
by various chemicals, e.g., monovalent cations, barium and manganese ions,
oxalate, CO_2, and Novocain (Bancroft, 1905; Kamada, 1929; Worley, 1934;
Oliphant, 1938, 1942); and the chemical reversal can be rereversed by current
(Kamada, 1931). The Ludloff phenomenon has been assumed to be caused by
a "neuromotor" system (Mast, 1941), but without evidence.

b. Core-Conductor Explanation. Jahn (1961) has recently re-analyzed the
data relative to the effects of electric current on ciliates, and has demonstrated
that all of the natural and experimental reversal phenomena may be explained
on the basis of the depolarization of the cell membrane, provided that the
ciliate is regarded as a core-conductor immersed in a volume conductor, thus
indicating that a "neuromotor" system is not required to explain the phe-

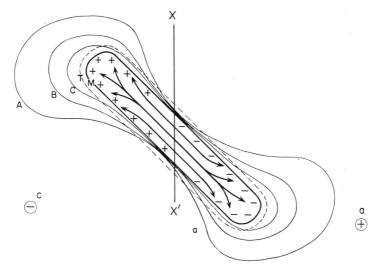

FIG. 9. Current density (or degree of polarization near anode and depolarization
near cathode) for any given applied current strength plotted as function of position
on a cylindrical representation of the body of a *Paramecium*. A, strong current; B,
weaker current; C, still weaker current; M, membrane of the body; T, the threshold
for reversal. The electric field is assumed to be uniform with cathode on left and
anode on right. Magnitude of current density is denoted by perpendicular distance
between line M and lines A, B, or C. Reversal is assumed to occur whenever the line
which represents current density (A, B, or C) is farther from line M than the line T
which represents the threshold. A uniform threshold is assumed over the entire
surface.

nomena. The core-conductor theory used is exactly the same as that customarily applied to the stimulation of nerve or muscle. However, it is much more meaningful in *Paramecium* because the conductivity of the "core" (i.e., *Paramecium* cytoplasm) is about ten times that of the "volume conductor" (i.e., the external medium, e.g., pond water) whereas in nerve and muscle they are the same. The principles of the theory are shown in Fig. 9. The current passes through the organism more or less lengthwise if the animal is at a 45° angle to the electric field. The current density is shown as a function of position on the organism at three current strengths in curves A, B, and C, and the dash line represents the threshold for reversal. As the current strength is increased more cilia will be reversed, and the topological distribution of the reversed cilia will be exactly that noted in the Ludloff phenomenon.

2. REVERSAL BY CHEMICALS; CATION RATIOS

a. Statement of the Problem. Kamada and Kinosita (1940) performed a very excellent and detailed series of experiments on the effect of the ratio of the concentrations of K and Ca on the duration of reversal of the ciliary beat. These investigators found that the maximal duration of reversal was not related to any one value of [K]:[Ca], but that the ratio of [K]:[Ca] for greatest duration increased with dilution from 3:1 at 0.1M to 63:1 at 0.0016M. No explanation of this effect was offered.

b. Application of the Gibbs-Donnan Ratio. Jahn (1962b) found that at the maximal reversal of ciliary beat, using the data of Kamada and Kinosita, the Gibbs-Donnan ratio (i.e., $[K^+]:\sqrt{[Ca^{++}]}$) was the same, regardless of dilution of the solutions employed. The constancy of the ratio is shown in Fig. 10, which includes curves for three experiments. The reversal time is plotted against the $[K]:\sqrt{[Ca]}$ ratio and each group of twelve curves represents twelve series of transfers from a given adaptation medium into various $[K]:\sqrt{[Ca]}$ ratios, but differing in total concentration from 0.1M to 0.0016M Each of the three experiments involved organisms from a given adaptation medium. The $[K]:\sqrt{[Ca]}$ ratios for the adaptation media were 0.0, 0.0007, and 0.00142, and the ratios showing maximal reversal were 0.40, 0.63, and 0.86. The constancy of this ratio for each set of conditions denotes several things, one of which is that calcium must be bound divalently. Jahn (1961) suggests that reversal is related to the removal of a critical amount of divalently bound ion from the cell membrane. This explains how oxalate (which binds calcium) and barium and manganese ions (which compete with calcium for binding sites, but bind monovalently because of the size of the barium and the bond angle of manganese) also can trigger reversal of the ciliary beat by changing the ratio of monovalently to divalently bound ions on the membrane. Magnesium and strontium ions do not cause reversal because they, having approximately the same size and bond angle as calcium, bind certain critically

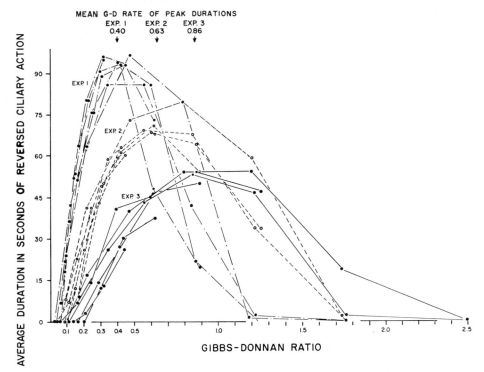

FIG. 10. Data from three experiments when duration of reversed swimming is plotted against $[K^+]:\sqrt{[Ca^{++}]}$, the Gibbs-Donnan ratio, for the seven test solutions. There is a single maximum for each of three experiments. (From Jahn, 1962b; data of Kamada and Kinosita, 1940.)

spaced carboxyl groups divalently, and therefore have the same effect as calcium.

(1) The Role of Divalent Ions on the Cell Membrane. The reason why a critical ratio of monovalent to the square root of appropriate (i.e., divalently bindable) ions is needed *in the solution* is that this is the ratio which, regardless of total concentration, will give a critical ratio of monovalent to appropriate divalent ions *on the membrane*. This principle, although known for 25 years (Danielli, 1937) is generally unrecognized. However, it may serve as a key to the general problem of monovalent–divalent ion antagonism, especially when combined with the use of ion size and bond angle, and its usefulness is by no means limited to ciliary reversal.

The usual explanation of why a given ratio of monovalent to divalent ions is needed on the membrane is that they bind two carboxyl groups together for structural (i.e., morphological) reasons. Jahn (1962a) suggested that the divalently bound ion may also be needed to conduct electrons between the two carboxyl groups to which each ion is attached. Another related explanation can be derived from the Ling (1960) association-induction theory, according to which the divalent ion, if bound to a "cardinal site" will bring about a shift in the electron distribution of the molecule, thereby changing the "c-values" of individual ionic (both cationic and anionic) binding sites. According to the Ling (1962) theory the c-values directly control the dissociation constants of all binding groups, and indirectly the type of ion bound (e.g., K^+ versus Na^+) and even the sign of the electromotive force of the membrane to which the ions are bound. The Ling theory thereby proposes a mechanism by which shifts in the electron distribution pattern of the protein molecules on the surface can be brought about by the presence of acceptable divalent ions at certain cardinal sites. The effects of these shifts can be far-reaching without much if any actual electronic flow through the attached ion, but mostly by induction. This theory, therefore, is not incompatible with the Jahn (1962a) theory of electron conduction.

(2) Interrelationship of Electrical and Chemical Reversals. A highly probable link between the effect of electric current and of ions on ciliary reversal was proposed by Jahn (1962b) in that electric current causes calcium to leave the membrane 20% faster at the cathodal end of the ciliate than sodium, thereby almost immediately changing the monovalent to divalent cation ratio to the triggering level for reversal. This linkage of effects is compatible with the Ling (1962) association-induction theory.

Furthermore, any local change in the membrane (e.g., cutting it) which critically changes the Gibbs-Donnan ratio at that or at nearby points would disturb ciliary functions there, regardless of whether any such internal structures as fibrils presumed to be conductive were interfered with.

E. Pattern Swimming by Ciliates

1. description of the phenomenon

Another feature of ciliate and flagellate movement is the tendency of large populations of ciliates and flagellates to form patterns of swimming in which a critical number of individuals (a minimum of about 150,000/ml.) take part in shallow (1.5 to 2.0 mm. deep) solutions (Loefer and Mefferd, 1952; Robbins, 1952). Under optimal conditions patterns may be formed in less than 10 sec. The accumulative force of the mass of moving organisms has been presumed to interact with their individual movements, so that they tend to move in phase (Nettleton *et al.*, 1953).

2. hydrodynamic linkage

These movements in *Tetrahymena* have been interpreted by Jahn and Brown (1961) as being caused by the fact that any two swimming ciliates tend to turn toward one another hydrodynamically because of the nonuniform field flow caused by the complex velocity profile in the adjacent medium. The pattern is initially set up by organisms approaching one another in culture. This is calculated to be some 7% per second, for organisms approaching others at a solid posterior angle of 90°, in a randomly distributed culture. Each organism produces a turbulent vortex ring, resulting from Newton's third law of motion, despite a low Reynolds' number (about 10^{-2}). Any organism entering the vortex ring is hydrodynamically linked to the organism producing the ring and therefore follows it. Dead organisms will join the pattern (Jahn *et al.*, 1961a, 1962), but tend to accumulate on the bottom at nodes of the polygons of the pattern, and to a lesser extent under the lines between nodes of the polygons.

3. THE EFFECT OF GRAVITY AND CENTRIFUGAL FORCE

This proposed mechanism for the phenomenon involves a geotactic response. If true, the patterns should disperse under conditions of zero gravity, with the patterns reforming as the gravitational state is reintroduced. Preliminary experiments rendering a population of pattern-swimming *Tetrahymena pyriformis* weightless for 12–15 sec. by means of parabolic flight in an airplane (Jahn *et al.*, 1964f) demonstrate that the pattern breaks up during the weightless period and reforms in less than half a minute on return to the effect of the gravitational field. Under the influence of centrifugal force, up to three times gravity, the patterns are formed more rapidly.

4. FACTORS AFFECTING PATTERN FORMATION

Factors which adversely affect motility of individuals also affect the speed with which the pattern is formed, as well as the distinctness of the pattern. These factors include low temperatures, high osmotic pressure, anaerobic conditions, ultraviolet rays, parathion, methylcellulose, and age of the culture, with the older culture developing less distinct patterns (Loefer and Mefferd, 1952). Phenanthraquinone may stimulate pattern formation (Jones and Baker, 1946). Either atmospheric carbon dioxide or ammonia causes the organisms to move downward in the solution, leaving a thin clear area of the solution beneath the surface and above the pattern (Jahn *et al.*, 1961a). This results in a doubling of columns moving horizontally, and also of those moving vertically at the polygonal nodes, with the horizontal columns being separated by a clear space, and the center of the node also being clear (Jahn *et al.*, 1961a).

IX. Other Movements of Protozoa

A. A List of Poorly Understood Movements

Besides the more often studied ameboid and cilio-flagellar movements, there are many other expressions of protoplasmic movements demonstrated in and by protozoa and by their organelles of movement. While generally known to protozoologists and to some other biologists, these are but poorly understood. Among them are: (1) Internal cyclosis of protoplasm in ciliates. (2) The extrusion of ciliate trichocysts. (3) The movement of myonemes and spasmonemes in ciliates. (4) Saltatory movement of certain ciliates with heavy body cirri (e.g., *Halteria, Cyclidium*). (5) Movements of contractile-vacuolar canals in ciliates (e.g., *Paramecium, Haptophyra*). (6) So-called "metabolic" movements of euglenid flagellates. (7) The swimming of colonial flagellates of various sorts. (8) The extension and retraction of heliozoan and helioflagellate axopods. (9) Swimming, rolling, and jumping movements of heliozoan axopods. (10) Swimming and crawling movements of radiolarians. (11) Gliding movement, "peristaltic" movements, and syzygial rotation of gregarines. (12) Oscillatory "churning" movements in the cytoplasm of certain gregarines. (13) Locomotion of the sporozoites of gregarines; and (14) of the sporozoites, merozoites, or other trophozoitic forms of any other of the sporozoa. (15) The sucking action of the tentacles of suctorian protozoa. A detailed list of such not-understood movements in protozoa would be voluminous, and only fragmentary information of such movements is available, in widely scattered sources, so that assessment of material is difficult.

B. Cyclosis

It seems possible that the mechanics of cyclosis in ciliates may be the same as or similar to that for plant cells, in which an active shearing mechanism of undetermined nature exists between the motile sol and nonmotile gel. This idea is supported by observations made by Jahn (1964) from cinematographs of *Paramecium*, that the highest velocity is just within the cortical layer which contains the trichocysts, and that the velocity profile through the body of the animal is the type one would expect from an active shearing mechanism in this region. In brief, the velocity profile of *Paramecium* cytoplasm is similar to that found by Kamiya and Kuroda (1956) for *Nitella*.

C. Myoneme Movements

1. PERITRICH STALK SPASMONEMES

The contractile fibrils in the stalks of certain peritrichs (e.g., the "spasmonemes" of *Vorticella*), as glycerinated models, will undergo a rhythmic cycle of contraction and relaxation (i.e., extension) in the presence of calcium ions and ATP (Hoffmann-Berling, 1960). However, Ca^{++} triggers the *contraction* (Levine, 1956; Hoffmann-Berling, 1958); and ATP induces a temporary relaxation, but *not* contraction in the spasmoneme (Hoffmann-Berling, 1960). It is assumed that the ATP promotes the relaxation of the spasmonene, loading it with energy prior to contraction, which is then triggered by calcium ions (Hoffmann-Berling, 1960). The action of calcium suggests the possible importance of a Gibbs-Donnan equilibrium in spasmoneme function.

2. BODY MYONEMES

Little is known of the functioning of ciliate body myonemes. Some contractile ciliates (e.g., *Spirostomum* and *Condylostoma*) have no myonemes which are detectable by electron micrographs (for review, see Pitelka, 1963), the presumed myonemes being identical to the "kinetodesma." Even for the much studied body myonemes of *Stentor* spp. there are no reports yet concerning possible ATP-actomyosin-like components in the body myonemes based either on chemical analyses and reactions, or on studies of glycerinated models. It is known that *Stentor* contracts violently in curare (a contraction antagonized by physostigmine), and contracts more or less normally in weak strychnine sulfate solutions (Neresheimer, 1903). It is completely unable to contract, however, in a mixed solution of the two (Parisis, 1956), but the cilia beat. Calcium chloride (Dierks, 1926) and caffeine (Neresheimer, 1903) stimulate contraction, while morphine hydrochloride and nicotine anesthetize. Potassium chloride also anesthetizes and is mutually antagonistic to calcium chloride which stimulates (Dierks, 1926). Sodium sulfate (Dierks, 1926) and 1% KI or NaI completely anesthetize the contraction of the myonemes (Tartar, 1957), so that the animal may be cut in two without contractile response. The *Stentor* will still then contract, however, in fixing agents. Tartar (1961) says that the myonemal contraction is the last vital function to persist in moribund animals, even to the moment of death. The implication of a possible ATP-actomyosin-like system may be conjectured, but much more analysis and experiment is needed for even a partial confirmation.

D. TRICHOCYST EXTRUSION

1. PRESUMED TRICHOCYST FUNCTIONS

Trichocyst functions in ciliates are debated, being presumably secretory (Penard, 1922), or holdfasts for *Paramecium* (Saunders, 1925; Cloyd and Jones, 1951), or toxic organs of attack in *Dileptus* (Visscher, 1923), or defense in *Paramecium* (see Wichterman, 1953), or osmoregulatory structures (Wohlfarth-Bottermann, 1953). They are clear, light refractile, and birefringent before expulsion, and the tip remains birefringent after extrusion (Schmidt, 1939). Those of *Paramecium,* when extended, are cross-striated, probably tubular proteinaceous structures (Jakus and Hall, 1946; Wohlfarth-Bottermann, 1953). The trichocysts are "fired" by pressure or mechanical shock, electric shock, ultraviolet rays, chemicals (especially those which shift pH), food, etc. It is presumed that they extrude *via* the hydration of proteins in the trichocyst capsule (Brodsky, 1924; Jakus and Hall, 1946; Prosser and Brown, 1961).

2. ATP-USING SYSTEM OF *Paramecium* TRICHOCYSTS

The trichocysts of *Paramecium* extrude explosively in the presence of Ca or Sr ions, NH_4 ions, or in the presence of invert soaps (e.g., cetyltrimethylammonium chloride); but Mg ions do not trigger extrusion. There is an ATPase present in *Paramecium* trichocysts; and ATP inhibits projection, but not as a Ca binder (Hoffmann-Berling, 1960). Salgyran (an —SH and ATPase inhibitor) will not easily block Ca^{++}-triggered extrusion of the trichocysts unless ATP is present; then it blocks in much lower concentrations. The Salgyran inhibition remains when both the ATP and Salgyran are removed. It is presumed here, also, that ATP acts as the relaxing energy-loading substance (Hoffmann-Berling, 1960).

E. "METABOLIC" MOVEMENTS OF EUGLENIDS

The anteroposterior contractions and extensions of the bodies of various species of *Euglena, Astasia, Peranema, Heteronema,* and *Distigma,* referred to as "metabolie" (Klebs, 1883), have often been seen, but rarely studied. Klebs (1883) assumed them to be due to internal cytoplasmic movements. More recently Diskus (1955) concludes that the metabolic movements are due to the layer of protoplasm adjacent to the pellicle. The presence of fibrils paralleling the pellicular ridges of *Euglena* (Gibbs, 1960; deHaller, 1960) and *Peranema* (Roth, 1959) suggest that a myoneme-like action is perhaps involved. If so, the fibrils may constitute the layer suggested by Diskus (1955) and the motile cytoplasm suggested by Klebs (1883). There is as yet no evidence as to the actual function of the fibrils beyond supposition. Kamiya (1939) found the metabolic movements of *Euglena* ordinarily arhythmic; but in acid solutions or other unfavorable conditions, the movements became almost perfectly rhythmic. He considered the rhythmic oscillations to be pathologic. These rhythmic movements may be, at least under certain conditions, greatly increased by acetate (Jahn and McKibben, 1937).

F. GLIDING MOVEMENTS

1. OF EUGLENIDS

Gliding movements of euglenids have been presumed, as for gregarines (cf. below) to be variously due to pellicular movements, slime production (Günther,

1927), or to protoplasmic shearing movements at the interface between the pellicle and the mucous trail (Jarosch, 1958, 1960, 1962).

2. OF GREGARINES

The movements of gregarine trophozoites have also been called a "gliding" locomotion. It early was thought due to slime secretion (Schewiakoff, 1894), or to be caused by the action of myonemes at or beneath the pellicle (Crawley, 1902; M. Watson, 1916). However, myonemes are present in some gregarines, but not others (Beams *et al.*, 1959; Kümmel, 1958). Therefore, since gliding is common to all gregarines, it cannot be caused by myonemes. Mühl (1921) proposed three types of movements by various gregarines; i.e., "peristaltic," "passive" (i.e., the gliding), and "flexing." Prell (1921) considered the gliding movement to be due to contractions of the cytoplasm or to myonemes. Jarosch (1958, 1962) has more recently modernized an old theory of Schultze (1865) which suggested external protoplasmic flow in the gliding movements. Jarosch (1962) proposes a shearing action between external protoplasmic fibrils and the secreted mucous track, drawing the organism in a direction opposite to the movement of the fibrils. The theory also requires a shearing movement of fibrils against the pellicular surface. Richter (1959) assumes ripples of movements in the pellicle set up by the protoplasmic fibrils of molecular dimensions adjacent to the pellicle.

Indication that the gregarine pellicle and its adjacent materials definitely are involved in gliding has been demonstrated by Jahn and Kozloff (1963) in cinephotomicrographs which show that the gliding movement of the pellicle may continue after puncture of the pellicle and leakage of most of the cytoplasm into the external medium.

G. "PERISTALTIC" MOVEMENTS OF GREGARINES

So-called peristaltic or churning movements have been investigated cine-photomicrographically by Watters (1963) in the gregarine *Urospora* sp., depicting unidirectional contractile waves from front to rear accompanied by 90° torsion of the body. Carmine particles are swept the length of the body. Watters (1963) reports birefringence in the cortical areas of *Urospora* sp. which is not due to any resolvable myonemes.

H. SWIMMING OF SPOROZOAN TROPHOZOITES

That the trophozoites other than gregarines also move has long been known, but little study has been made of them. Koch (1902) described a spiral forward movement by *Sarcocystis muris;* and Manwell and Drobeck (1953) have described rotary, saltatory, and spiral-swimming movements by *Toxoplasma* without attempting to explain them. The newly hatched sporozoites of *Gregarina rigida* swim with a "slow lateral motion similar to that of certain nematodes" (Allegre, 1948). Doran *et al.* (1962) found by cinephotomicrography that sporozoites of *Eimeria* spp. swim in spurts along helical paths. The authors assume the presence of an irrotational sine wave progressing from anterior to posterior, $90°$ out of phase with a second one, together producing a helical wave. The animal probably rotates as it swims because it has no way of resisting torque. At least four longitudinal and one circumferential contractile components must be present to produce the observed locomotion. It seems as if *Toxoplasma* and *Sarcocystis* move in a similar manner.

I. SUCTORIAN MOVEMENTS

It has been long known that the tentacles of suctorian protozoa contract and extend during and after sucking or upon mechanical stimulus (Claparède and Lachmann, 1858; Hertwig, 1876; Kitching, 1952). Noble (1932) observed that the tentacles contract spirally, becoming shorter and thicker. It was early suggested that such contractions were analogous to those of muscle (Maupas, 1881).

Structurally the cylindrical sucking tentacles contain fibrils, arranged somewhat like the peripheral fibrils of cilia. The central fibrils are absent, and the peripheral fibrils more numerous than those of cilia (Pottage, 1959). The tapering prehensile tentacles of *Ephelota* also contain fibrils, but in bundles of 20–30 fibrils, each bundle being isolated by septa in one of 5 to 7 compartments within the tentacle (Rouillier *et al.*, 1956).

Little is known of the contractile mechanism of the tentacles, except that it involves Ca ions. Injection of ATP into the suctorian causes some dilation of the tentacle, but no contraction resulting from it was recorded (Hull, 1961b). Okajima (1957) obtained rhythmic contractions and extensions of tentacles of *Acineta* during its adaptation to artificial sea water; and also observed sustained contraction to one-tenth the original lengths in 0.1M $CaCl_2$. When rewashed in sea water the tentacles extended within 10 min., and the $CaCl_2$-triggered contraction could be repeated, several times over, by alternate washings and exposures. Similar effects were achieved with Ba^{++} and Sr^{++} ions but not with Mg^{++}, or any of the monovalent cations. Adaptation to Ca-free solutions, with Ca absent or bound by citrate, resulted in loss of contractility. The Ca-triggered contractions resemble those of vorticellid spasmonemes. The data also suggest an involvement of the $[K]:\sqrt{[Ca]}$ ratio at the membrane (i.e., the Gibbs-Donnan equilibrium). Hull (1961b) reports that adherence of the tentacles to prey is similarly affected by cations, being less effective in reduced free cations, the adherence being restored by divalent, but not by monovalent cations. The active extension of tentacles and pushing away of debris by them (Penard, 1920) remains unexplained.

It is probable that suctoria really suck the protoplasm out of their prey (Kitching, 1952; 1957), most likely by physically and actively developing a negative internal pressure through self-expansion of the body (Penard, 1920; Kitching, 1952; Canella, 1957; Hull, 1961b). The claims that contractile-vacuolar pumping (Eismond, 1890), peristalsis of (Collin, 1912) or the active pumping by contraction and expansion of tentacles (Plate, 1886), or an active retreat of cytoplasm from the central tube of the tentacles (Kormos, 1938) might cause the aspirative action have recently been denied (Canella, 1957; Hull, 1961a,b). The suggestion (Kahl, 1933) of an increased turgor pressure in the prey due to enzymes of the suctorian acting on prey cytoplasm, thus driving it into the suctorian, has also been rejected (Canella, 1957).

Kitching (1952) reported an active wrinkling of surface membrane of *Podophrya* which he deemed responsible for the suction by causing a change of shape toward the spherical with an increase in body volume of 100% or more. Hull (1961b) found that a nearly instantaneous change of shape from pyriform toward the spherical in *Podophrya collini* upon attachment to prey was followed by a rapid increase in diameter of tentacles (to 2×) and a flow of suctorian cytoplasm into the tentacle as it expanded. The tentacles did not shorten, however, as they expanded. Hull (1961b) observed no peristaltic or pumping actions of the tentacles, and attributed the suction entirely to expansion of body and tentacles. He reports an expansion of the body of 10% in volume due solely to the change toward spherical shape, with at least another 10% of increase due to rapid active expansion of the body upon contact of tentacles with the prey.

Hull (1961b) attributes these movements of suctoria to biochemical processes similar to those involved in other protoplasmic movements (i.e., those involving actomyosin-like protein complexes utilizing ATP as an energy source); and he reports that 1% ATP solution injected into a feeding suctorian accelerates rate of flow of prey cytoplasm into it, as well as the respiratory and contractile-vacuolar rates of the suctorian. When 1% ATP is injected into a nonfeeding suctorian (Hull, 1961b), there is an immediate change toward the spherical shape, a rapid increase in body volume (to 2×), and agitation and disappearance of subpellicular granules. These changes are nearly identical to those which occur in a normally feeding organism upon adherence to a prey animal. Also, there is a burst of increased respiratory activity (Hull, 1961b) and more rapid rate of pumping of the contractile vacuole upon contact with prey (Kitching, 1952) throughout the first 8 to 12 min. of feeding, during which change of shape, enlargement of the body, and early ingestion of prey cytoplasm occur, indicating the utilization of the total biochemical machinery of the suctorian in the processes (Canella, 1957; Hull, 1961b).

X. Summary and Epilogue

Currently the study of protozoan locomotion, which had been in a quiescent stage for some time, is a very active field of research, and this new interest in the protozoa is correlated with increased interest in cell biology in general.

Gradually, it has become more clear that the untested early assumptions of the generality of "muscle-like" movement in all protoplasm is both partly factual and partly fatuous. Biochemically the evidence accumulates that some sort of ATP-energized actomyosin-like protein molecules are involved in most, if not all, protoplasmic movements. The evidence accumulated, however, also indicates that muscle is a highly specialized form of the protoplasmic motile mechanism; and that there are several other, perhaps many other, specializations of the basic machinery.

Two systems of protoplasmic movement are now recognized. Several others have been proposed, and these have contributed interest to discussions of the subject and also have stimulated valuable observations and experimental research. The existence of a contraction-hydraulic system, known for many years, and recently questioned, is now confirmed for amebae and mycetozoans. Perhaps the most striking advance in the study of protoplasmic movement in recent years is recognition of the existence of an active shearing mechanism in plant cells, striated muscle, foraminifera and other protozoans, and wherever cyclosis occurs. Possibly the next major advance will be elucidation of the nature of this mechanism, now a popular subject of conjecture. Furthermore, the existence of two visibly different systems of movement (contraction-hydraulic and active shearing) offers an opportunity to use these systems in providing a long needed rational reclassification of the Sarcodina.

Progress has also been made in the study of movement of small amebae, in which the mechanisms of movement are probably either one of the two discussed above, but the criteria for identification of the mechanism are not so obvious, mostly because of the small size of the organisms and the inadequacy of the patience of many observers.

In the protozoa, as in all aquatic organisms, movements are always subject to the laws of hydrodynamics. Hence, any explanations which have any ultimate demonstrable relation to fact must employ hydrodynamic principles to elucidate the theory. Structures, real or hypothetical, must, positionally and operationally, meet the hydrodynamic tests; and this applies whether the structures are temporary or permanent, external or internal. The principles of hydrodynamics recently have been applied more intensively to the study of movement of amebae and mycetozoans and have aided greatly in our understanding of these phenomena.

Furthermore, the movements of cilia and flagella have been studied from the viewpoint of hydrodynamics and have been found to be theoretically and actually much more complex than previously assumed. Flagella can move in a great variety of patterns, not all of which have yet been described. Some of these flagellar movements are the same as those of individual cilia. Therefore the supposed differences between cilia and flagella, under question for some time on the basis of the similarity of electron micrographs, are also questionable on the basis of movement; and the terms "cilium" and "flagellum," although still useful for separating the two ends of morphological and physiological spectra, do not necessarily denote how an individual organelle moves or even that its structure differs from those that move differently.

The effects of chemical substances, especially ions, and of electric current on ciliary action have been investigated for many years, but available interpretations have, until recently, been vague and confusing. However, through application of general laws of ionic equilibria, ionic and membrane structure, and core and volume electrical conductors, it has been possible to systematize most of the available knowledge, so that future experiments can be planned more purposefully, to elucidate other principles which are still unrecognized.

Supposition and theory are necessary to the ultimate understanding of protozoan movements; and critical experimental work still is, as it always has been, the principal route to the facts, provided that data are obtained in a manner which permits rational interpretation. More of the facts are beginning to emerge.

REFERENCES

Abé, T. H. (1961). *Cytologia (Tokyo)* **26**, 378–407.

Abé, T. H. (1962). *Cytologia (Tokyo)* 27, 111–139.

Abé, T. H. (1963). *J. Protozool.* **10**, 94–101.

Abé, T. H. (1964). *In* "Primitive Motile Systems in Cell Biology" (R. D. Allen and N. Kamiya, eds.), pp. 221–236. Academic Press, New York.

Afzelius, B. A. (1961). *In* "Biological Structure and Function" (T. W. Goodwin and O. Lindberg, eds.), Vol. 2, pp. 557–567. Academic Press, New York.

Allegre, C. F. (1948). *Trans. Am. Microscop. Soc.* 67, 211–226.

Allen, R. D. (1960). *J. Biophys. Biochem. Cytol.* **8**, 379–397.

Allen, R. D. (1961a). *Exptl. Cell Res., Suppl.* **8**, 17–31.

Allen, R. D. (1961b). *In* "The Cell" (J. Brachet and A. E. Mirsky, eds.), Vol. 2, pp. 135–216. Academic Press, New York.

Allen, R. D. (1961c). *In* "Biological Structure and Function" (T. W. Goodwin and O. Lindberg, eds.), Vol. 2, pp. 549–556. Academic Press, New York.

Allen, R. D. (1962). *Sci. Am.* **206**, 112–122.

Allen, R. D. (1964). *In* "Primitive Motile Systems in Cell Biology" (R. D. Allen and N. Kamiya, eds.), pp. 407–432. Academic Press, New York.

Allen, R. D., and Roslansky, J. D. (1959). *J. Biophys. Biochem. Cytol.* **4**, 517–524.

Allen, R. D., Cooledge, J. W., and Hall, P. J. (1960). *Nature* **187**, 896–899.

Allen, R. D., Pitts, W. R. Jr., Speir, D., and Brault, J. (1963). *Science* **142**, 1485–1487.

Alverdes, F. (1922). *Arch. Ges. Physiol.* 195, 227–244.

Ambrose, E. J. (1961). *Exptl. Cell Res., Suppl.* 8, 54–73.

Anderson, E., and Beams, H. W. (1960). *J. Protozool.* 7, 190–199.

Anderson, J. D. (1951). *J. Gen. Physiol.* 35, 1–16.

Anderson, J. D. (1964). *In* "Primitive Motile Systems in Cell Biology" (R. D. Allen and N. Kamiya, eds.), pp. 125–134. Academic Press, New York.

Andresen, N., and Pollack, B. M. (1952). *Compt. Rend. Trav. Lab. Carlsberg, Sér. Chim.* 28, 247–264.

Astbury, W. T., Beighton, E., and Weibull, C. (1955). *Symp. Soc. Exptl. Biol.* 9, 282–305.

Bancroft, F. W. (1905). *Arch. Ges. Physiol.* 107, 535–556.

Beams, H. W., Tahmisian, T. N., Devine, R. L., and Anderson, E. (1959). *J. Protozool.* 6, 136–146.

Bělař, K. (1921). *Arch. Protistenk.* 43, 287–354.

Bell, L. G. E. (1963). *New Scientist* 18, 103–105.

Berrend, R. E. (1959). Ph.D. Thesis, unpublished. University of Wisconsin, Madison.

Berrend, R. E. (1964). *In* "Primitive Motile Systems in Cell Biology" (R. D. Allen and N. Kamiya, eds.), pp. 433–444. Academic Press, New York.

Bidder, G. P. (1923). *Quart. J. Microscop. Sci.* 67, 293–323.

Bingley, M. S., and Thompson, C. M. (1962). *J. Theoret. Biol.* 2, 16–32.

Bishop, D. W. (1958). *Nature* 182, 1638–1640.

Bonner, J. T. (1959). "The Cellular Slime Molds." Princeton Univ. Press, Princeton, New Jersey.

Bonner, J. T., and Adams, M. S. (1958). *J. Embryol. Exptl. Morphol.* 6, 346–356.

Borgers, J. A., and Kitching, J. A. (1956). *Proc. Roy. Soc.* B144, 507–519.

Bovee, E. C. (1952). *Proc. Iowa Acad. Sci.* 59, 428–434.

Bovee, E. C. (1959). *J. Protozool.* 6, 69–75.

Bovee, E. C. (1960a). *Am. Midland Naturalist* 63, 257–269.

Bovee, E. C. (1960b). *Arch. Protistenk.* 104, 503–514.

Bovee, E. C. (1960c). *J. Protozool.* 7, 55–60.

Bovee, E. C. (1963a). *Am. Midland Naturalist* 66, 173–181.

Bovee, E. C. (1963b). *J. Protozool.* 10 [Suppl.], 10–11.

Bovee, E. C. (1964). *In* "Primitive Motile Systems in Cell Biology" (R. D. Allen and N. Kamiya, eds.), pp. 189–220. Academic Press, New York.

Bovee, E. C., and Jahn, T. L. (1960). *J. Protozool.* 7 [Suppl.], 8.

Bovee, E. C., and Jahn, T. L. (1964). *Am. Midland Naturalist* 72 (in press).

Bovee, E. C., and Telford, S. R., Jr. (1964). *Trans. Am. Microscop. Soc.* 83 (in press).

Bovee, E. C., and Wilson, D. E. (1961). *Am. Zool.* 1, 345.

Bovee, E. C., Jahn, T. L., Fonseca, J. R. C., and Landman, M. (1963). *Abstr. 7th Ann. Meeting Biophys. Soc., 1963* MD2.

Bradfield, J. R. G. (1955). *Symp. Soc. Exptl. Biol.* 9, 306–334.

Brodsky, A. (1924). *Arch. Russ. Protistol.* 3, 23–37.

Brokaw, C. J. (1960). *Exptl. Cell Res.* 19, 430–432.

Brokaw, C. J. (1961). *Exptl. Cell Res.* 22, 151–162.

Brokaw, C. J. (1962a). *In* "Sperm Motility" (D. W. Bishop, ed.), pp. 269–278. Am. Assoc. Advance. Sci., Washington, D.C.

Brokaw, C. J. (1962b). *In* "Physiology and Biochemistry of Algae" (R. A. Lewin, ed.), pp. 595–602. Academic Press, New York.

Brown, H. P. (1945). *Ohio J. Sci.* 45, 247–301.

Bütschli, O. (1882). In "Klassung und Ordnung des Thierreichs" (H. G. Bronn, ed.), Vol. I, Part 1, pp. 1–1097. Winter, Leipzig.

Calkins, G. N. (1909). "Protozoology." Lea & Febiger, Philadelphia, Pennsylvania.

Camp, W. G. (1936). Bull. Torrey Botan. Club 63, 205–210.

Camp, W. G. (1937). Bull. Torrey Botan. Club 64, 307–335.

Canella, M. F. (1957). Ann. Univ. Ferrara, Sez. 3 1, 1–716.

Carter, G. S. (1924). Proc. Roy. Soc. B96, 115–122.

Chambers, R., and Dawson, J. A. (1925). Biol. Bull. 48, 240–242.

Chatton, E., and Lwoff, A. (1930). Compt. Rend. Soc. Biol. 104, 834–836.

Chatton, E., and Lwoff, A. (1935). Compt. Rend. Soc. Biol. 118, 1068–1072.

Child, F. M. (1959). Exptl. Cell Res. 18, 258–267.

Child, F. M. (1961). Exptl. Cell Res., Suppl. 8, 47–53.

Claparède, E., and Lachmann, J. (1858). "Études sur les Infusoires et les Rhizopodes." Vaney, Geneva.

Clark, A. M. (1946). J. Exptl. Biol. 22, 88–94.

Cleveland, L. R. (1963). J. Protozool. 10 [Suppl.], 6.

Cleveland, L.R. and Grimstone, A.V. (1964). Proc. Roy. Soc. (in press).

Cloyd, W. J., and Jones, A. W. (1951). J. Tenn. Acad. Sci. 26, 148–49.

Cole, A. (1963). Abstr. 7th Ann. Meeting Biophys. Soc., 1963 MF6.

Collin, B. (1912). Arch. Zool. Exptl. Gen. 51, 1–457.

Corliss, J. O. (1953). Stain Technol. 28, 97–100.

Corliss, J. O. (1961). "The Ciliated Protozoa." Pergamon Press, New York.

Crawley, H. (1902). Proc. Acad. Nat. Sci. Phila. 54, 4–20.

Danielli, J. F. (1937). Proc. Roy. Soc. B122, 155–174.

DeBary, A. (1884). "Die Mycetozoen," rev. ed. Engelmann, Leipzig.

DeHaan, R. L. (1959). J. Embryol. Exptl. Morphol. 7, 335–343.

DeHaller, G. (1960). Verhandl. 4. Intern. Kongr. Elektronenmikroskopie, Berlin, 1958 2, 517–520.

DeSaedeleer, H. (1932). Arch. Zool. Exptl. Gen. 74, 597–626.

DeSaedeleer, H. (1934). Mem. Mus. Hist. Nat. Belg. 60, 1–112.

Dierks, K. (1926). Zool. Anz. 67, 207–218.

Diskus, A. (1955). Protoplasma 45, 460–477.

Doran, D. J., Jahn, T. L., and Rinaldi, R. A. (1962). J. Parasitol. 48, 32–33.

Doroszewski, M. (1958). Acta Biol. Exptl., Polish Acad. Sci. 18, 69–88.

Doroszweski, M. (1961). Acta Biol. Exptl., Polish Acad. Sci. 21, 15–34.

Dujardin, F. (1835). Ann. Sci. Nat. Zool. 4, 343–377.

Ehrenberg, C. G. (1838). "Die Infusionsthierchen als volkommene Organismen." Voss, Leipzig.

Eismond, J. (1890). Zool. Anz. 13, 721–723.

Erhard, H. (1910). Arch. Zellforsch. 4, 309–442.

Ewart, J. A. (1903). "On the Physics and Physiology of Protoplasmic Streaming in Plants." Oxford Univ. Press, London and New York.

Fauré-Fremiet, E., Rouiller, C., and Gauchery, M. (1956). Arch. Anat. Microscop. Morphol. Exptl. 45, 139–161.

Fawcett, D. W. (1961). In "The Cell" (J. Brachet and A. E. Mirsky, eds.), Vol. 2, pp. 217–297. Academic Press, New York.

Fawcett, D. W., and Porter, K. R. (1954). J. Morphol. 94, 221–282.

Frey-Wyssling, A. (1949). Exptl. Cell Res., Suppl. 1, 33–42.

Frey-Wyssling, A. (1952). "Submicroscopic Morphology of Protoplasm." Elsevier, Amsterdam.

Gibbs, S. P. (1960). *J. Ultrastruct. Res.* 4, 127–148.

Gimesi, N. I., and Pozsár, B. I. (1956). *Acta Biol. Acad. Sci. Hung.* 8, 113-132.

Goldacre, R. J. (1952). *Intern. Rev. Cytol* 1, 135–164.

Goldacre, R. J. (1958). *Proc. 1st Intern. Congr. Cybernetics, Namur (Belg.), 1956,* pp. 715-725.

Goldacre, R. J. (1961a). *Exptl. Cell Res., Suppl.* 8, 1–16.

Goldacre, R. J. (1961b). *In* "Biological Structure and Function" (T. W. Goodwin and O. Lindberg, eds.), Vol. 2, pp. 633–643. Academic Press, New York.

Goldacre, R. J. (1964). *In* "Primitive Motile Systems in Cell Biology" (R. D. Allen and N. Kamiya, eds.), pp. 237–256. Academic Press, New York (in press).

Goldacre, R. J., and Lorch, I. J. (1950). *Nature* 166, 497–500.

Gosselin, R. E. (1958). *Federation Proc.* 17, 372.

Gray, J. (1928). "Ciliary Movement." Cambridge Univ. Press, London and New York.

Gray, J. (1931). "A Textbook of Experimental Cytology." Cambridge Univ. Press, London and New York.

Gray, J. (1955). *J. Exptl. Biol.* 32, 775–801.

Gray, J. (1962). *In* "Spermatozoan Motility" (D. W. Bishop, ed.), pp. 1–12. Am. Assoc. Advance. Sci., Washington, D.C.

Gray, W. D. (1938). *Am. J. Botany* 25, 511–522.

Gregg, J. H. (1956). *J. Gen. Physiol.* 39, 813–820.

Gregg, J. H. (1961). *Develop. Biol.* 3, 757–766.

Grimstone, A. V. (1961). *Biol. Rev. Cambridge Phil. Soc.* 36, 97–150.

Günther, F. (1927). *Arch. Protistenk.* 60, 511–590.

Guttes, E., and Guttes, S. (1963). *Exptl. Cell Res.* 30, 242–244.

Guttes, E., Guttes, S., and Rusch, H. P. (1961). *Develop. Biol.* 3, 588–614.

Hahnert, W. F. (1932). *Physiol. Zool.* 5, 491–526.

Hammond, J. C. (1935). *Ohio J. Sci.* 35, 304–306.

Hancock, G. J. (1953). *Proc. Roy. Soc.* A217, 96–121.

Harris, J. E. (1961). *In* "The Cell and the Organism" (J. A. Ramsay and V. B. Wigglesworth, eds.), pp. 22–36. Cambridge Univ. Press, London and New York.

Heilbrunn, L. V. (1958). *Protoplasmatologia* 2, 1–109.

Hertwig, R. (1876). *Morphol. Jahrb.* 1, 20–82.

Hertwig, R. (1879). "Der Organismus der Radiolarien." Fischer, Jena.

Hill, A. V. (1926). *Proc. Roy. Soc.* B100, 87–108.

Hirschfield, H. I. (1959). *Ann. N.Y. Acad. Sci.* 78, 647–654.

Hodge, A. J. (1949). *Australian J. Sci. Res.* B2, 368–378.

Hoffmann-Berling, H. (1953). *Biochim. Biophys. Acta* 10, 628–633.

Hoffmann-Berling, H. (1954). *Biochim. Biophys. Acta* 15, 332–339.

Hoffmann-Berling, H. (1955). *Biochim. Biophys. Acta* 16, 146–154.

Hoffmann-Berling, H. (1958). *Biochim. Biophys. Acta* 27, 247–255.

Hoffmann-Berling, H. (1960). *In* "Comparative Biochemistry" (M. Florkin and H. S. Mason, eds.), Vol. 2, pp. 341–370. Academic Press, New York.

Hoffmann-Berling, H. (1964). *In* "Primitive Motile Systems in Cell Biology" (R. D. Allen and N. Kamiya, eds.), pp. 365–376. Academic Press, New York.

Hosoi, T. (1937). *J. Fac. Sci., Imp. Univ. Tokyo Sect. IV* 4, 299–305.

Hull, R. W. (1961a). *J. Protozool.* 8, 343–350.

Hull, R. W. (1961b). *J. Protozool.* 8, 351–359.

Hunter, N. W. (1951). *Proc. Am. Soc. Protozool,* 2, 15

Hunter, N. W. (1959). *J. Protozool.* 6, 100–104.

Huxley, A. F., and Niedergerke, R. (1954). *Nature* 173, 971–973.

Huxley, H. E., and Hanson, J. (1954). *Nature* 173, 973–976.
Huxley, H. E., and Hanson, J. (1955). *Symp. Soc. Exptl. Biol.* 9, 228–264.
Inoué, S. (1959). *Rev. Mod. Phys.* 31, 402–408.
Jacobsen, I. (1931). *Arch. Protinstenk.* 75, 31–100.
Jahn, T. L. (1947). *Quart. Rev. Biol.* 21, 264–274.
Jahn, T. L. (1961). *J. Protozool.* 8, 369–380.
Jahn, T. L. (1962a). *J. Theoret. Biol.* 2, 129–138.
Jahn, T. L. (1962b). *J. Cellular Comp. Physiol.* 60, 217–228.
Jahn, T. L. (1964a). *In* "Primitive Motile Systems in Cell Biology" (R. D. Allen and N. Kamiya, eds.), pp. 270–372. Academic Press, New York.
Jahn, T. L. (1964b). *Biorheology* (to be published).
Jahn, T. L. (1964c). *Abst. 8th Meeting Biophys. Soc.* 1964, FE 13.
Jahn T. L. (1964d). Unpublished data.
Jahn, T. L., and Jahn, F. F. (1949). "How To Know the Protozoa." W. C. Brown, Dubuque, Iowa.
Jahn, T. L., and Brown, M. (1961). *Am. Zool.* 1, 454.
Jahn, T. L., and Fonseca, J. R. C. (1963). *J. Protozool.* 10 [Suppl.], 11.
Jahn, T. L., and Bovee, E. C. (1964). *Am. Midland Naturalist* 72 (in press.).
Jahn, T. L., and Fonseca, J. R. C. (1964). Unpublished data.
Jahn, T. L., and Kosloff, E. (1963). Unpublished data.
Jahn, T. L., and McKibben, W. R. (1937). *Trans. Am. Microscop. Soc.* 56, 48–54.
Jahn, T. L., and Rinaldi, R. A. (1959). *Biol. Bull.* 117, 100–118.
Jahn, T. L., and Rinaldi, R. A. (1963). *Abstr. 7th Ann. Meeting Biophys. Soc., 1963* MD2.
Jahn, T. L., Bovee, E. C., and Small, E. B. (1960). *J. Protozool.* 7 [Suppl.], 8.
Jahn, T. L., Brown, M., and Winet, H. (1961a). *Am Zool.* 1, 454.
Jahn, T. L., Harmon, W., and Landman, M. (1961b). *J. Protozool.* 8 [Suppl.], 7.
Jahn, T. L., Brown, M., and Winet, H. (1962). *22nd Intern. Union Physiol. Sci. Hague Excerpta Med.* 48, 628.
Jahn, T. L., Fonseca, J. R. C., and Landman, M. (1964a). (To be published.)
Jahn, T. L., Rinaldi, R. A., and Brown, M. (1964b). *Biorheology* (in press).
Jahn, T. L., Harmon, W., and Landman, M. (1963a). *J. Protozool.* 10, 358–363.
Jahn, T. L., Fonseca, J. R. C., and Landman M. (1963b). *J. Protozool.* 10 [Suppl.], 11.
Jahn, T. L., Landman, M., and Fonseca, J. R. C. (1964c). *Proc. 16th Intern. Congr. Zool., Washington, D.C., 1963* 2, 192.
Jahn, T. L., Brown, M., and Winet, H. (1964d). Unpublished data.
Jahn, T. L., Bovee, E. C., Fonseca, J. R. C., and Landman, M. (1964e). *Symp. 10th Botan. Congr., Edinburgh, 1964* (to be published).
Jahn, T. L., Brown, M., and Winet, H. (1964f). Unpublished data.
Jakus, M. A., and Hall, C. E. (1946). *Biol. Bull.* 91, 141–144.
Jarosch, R. (1957). *Biochim. Biophys. Acta* 25, 204–205.
Jarosch, R. (1958). *Protoplasma* 50, 277–289.
Jarosch, R. (1960). *Phyton (Buenos Aires)* 15, 43–66.
Jarosch, R. (1962). *In* "Physiology and Biochemistry of Algae" (R. A. Lewin, ed.), pp. 573–581. Academic Press, New York.
Jarosch, R. (1964). *In* "Primitive Motile Systems in Cell Biology" (R. D. Allen and N. Kamiya, eds.), pp. 599–622. Academic Press, New York.
Jennings, H. S. (1904). *Carnegie Inst. Wash. Publ.* 16, 1–256.
Jennings, H. S. (1931). "Behavior of Lower Organisms." Columbia Univ. Press, New York.

Jennings, H. S., and Jamieson, C. (1902). *Biol. Bull.* 3, 225–234.

Jepps, M. W. (1942). *J. Marine Biol. Assoc. U.K.* 25, 607–666.

Jepps, M. W. (1956). "The Protozoa, Sarcodia." Oliver & Boyd, Edinburgh and London.

Jones, P. F., and Baker, H. G. (1946). *Nature* 157, 554.

Jones, P. F., and Lewin, R. A. (1959). *Exptl. Cell. Res.* 19, 408–410.

Kahl, A. (1933). *Arch. Protistenk.* 80, 64–71.

Kamada, T. (1929). *J. Fac. Sci., Imp. Univ. Tokyo Sect. IV* 2, 123–139.

Kamada, T. (1931). *J. Fac. Sci., Imp. Univ. Tokyo Sect. IV* 2, 299–307.

Kamada, T., and Kinosita, H. (1940). *Proc. Imp. Acad. (Tokyo)* 16, 125–130.

Kamiya, N. (1939). *Ber. Deut. Botan. Ges.* 57, 231–240.

Kamiya, N. (1953). *Ann. Rept. Sci. Works, Fac. Sci., Osaka Univ.* 1, 53–83.

Kamiya, N. (1959). *Protoplasmatologia* 8, 1–199.

Kamiya, N. (1960). *Ann. Rept. Sci. Works, Fac. Sci., Osaka Univ.* 8, 13–41.

Kamiya, N. (1964a). *In* "Non-Muscular Contractions in Biological Systems" (T. Hayashi, ed.). Academic Press, New York (in press).

Kamiya, N. (1964b). *In* "Primitive Motile Systems in Cell Biology" (R. D. Allen and N. Kamiya, eds.), pp. 257–278. Academic Press, New York.

Kamiya, N., and Kuroda, K. (1956). *Botan. Mag. (Tokyo)* 69, 544–554.

Kamiya, N., Nakajima, H., and Abé, S. (1957). *Protoplasma* 48, 95–112.

Kavanau, J. L. (1962). *Science* 136, 652–653.

Kavanau, J. L. (1963a). *J. Theoret. Biol.* 4, 124–141.

Kavanau, J. L. (1963b). *Develop. Biol.* 7, 22–37.

Kinosita, H. (1936). *J. Fac. Sci., Imp. Univ. Tokyo Sect. IV* 4, 155–161.

Kinosita, H. (1954). *J. Fac. Sci., Univ. Tokyo Sect. IV* 7, 1–14.

Kitching, J. A. (1952). *J. Exptl. Biol.* 29, 255–266.

Kitching, J. A. (1957). *Proc. Symp. Colston Res. Soc.* 7, 197–203.

Kitching, J. A. (1964). *In* "Primitive Motile Systems in Cell Biology" (R. D. Allen and N. Kamiya, eds.), pp. 445–456. Academic Press, New York.

Kitching, J. A., and Pirenne, M. H. (1940). *J. Cellular Comp. Physiol.* 16, 131–133.

Klebs, G. (1883). *Untersuch. Botan. Inst. Tübingen* 1, 1–13.

Klein, B. M. (1926). *Arch. Protistenk.* 56, 243–279.

Klein, R. L. (1961). *Exptl. Cell Res.* 25, 571–584.

Koch, M. (1902). *Verhandl. V. Zool. Vongr.* 5, 674–684.

Konijn, T. M., and Raper, K. B. (1961). *Develop. Biol.* 3, 725–756.

Konijn, T. M., and Raper, K. B. (1962). *Am. J. Botany* 49, 667.

Kormos, J. (1938). *Allattani Kozlemenyek* 35, 130–153.

Kraft, H. (1890). *Arch. Ges. Physiol.* 47, 196–235.

Krijgsman, B. J. (1925). *Arch. Protistenk.* 52, 478–487.

Kriszat, G. (1949). *Arkiv Zool.* 1, 81–86.

Kriszat, G. (1954). *Arkiv Zool.* 6, 195–201.

Kümmel, G. (1958). *Arch. Protistenk.* 102, 501–522.

Landau, J. V. (1959). *Ann. N.Y. Acad. Sci.* 78, 487–500.

Landau, J. V. Zimmerman, A. M., and Marsland, D. A. (1954). *J. Cellular Comp. Physiol.* 44, 211–232.

Lee, J. W. (1954a). *Physiol. Zool.* 27, 272–275.

Lee, J. W. (1954b). *Physiol. Zool.* 27, 276–280.

Lehman, F. E. (1959). *Ergeb. Biol.* 21, 88–127.

Leidy, J. (1879). *U.S., Geol. Surv. Rept.* 12, 1–324.

Lepsi, J. (1926). *Mikrokosmos* 20, 54–66.

Levine, L. (1956). *Biol. Bull.* 111, 319.

Lewin, R. A. (1952a). *Biol. Bull.* 103, 74–79.

Lewin, R. A. (1952b). *J. Gen. Microbiol.* 6, 233–248.

Lewis, W. H. (1951). *Science* 113, 473.

Ling, G. N. (1960). *J. Gen. Physiol.* 43, 149–174.

Ling, G. N. (1962). "A Physical Theory of the Living State." Random House (Blaisdell), New York.

Loefer, J. B., and Mefferd, R. B., Jr. (1952). *Am. Naturalist* 86, 325–329.

Loewy, A. G. (1949). *Proc. Am. Phil. Soc.* 93, 326–329.

Loewy, A. G. (1950). *J. Cellular Comp. Physiol.* 35, 151–153.

Loewy, A. G. (1952). *J. Cellular Comp. Physiol.* 40, 127–156.

Loquin, M. (1949). *Trav. Botan. Algiers* 2, 209–214.

Lowndes, A. G. (1941). *Proc. Zool. Soc. (London)* A111, 111–134.

Lowndes, A. G. (1943). *Proc. Zool. Soc. (London)* A113, 99–107.

Lowndes, A. G. (1944). *Proc. Zool. Soc. (London)* A114, 325–338.

Ludloff, K. (1895). *Arch. Ges. Physiol.* 59, 525–554.

Ludwig, W. (1930). *Z. Vergleich. Physiol.* 13, 397–504.

Lund, E. E. (1933). *Univ. Calif. (Berkeley), Publ. Zool.* 39, 35–76.

Lund, E. E. (1941). *J. Morphol.* 69, 563–573.

McManus, M. A. (1958). *Am. J. Botany* 48, 502–588.

Machin, K. E. (1958). *J. Exptl. Biol.* 35, 796–806.

Manton, I. (1952). *Symp. Soc. Exptl. Biol.* 6, 306–319.

Manwell, R. D., and Drobeck, H. P. (1953). *J. Parasitol.* 39, 577–584.

Marsh, G., and Jahn, T. L. (1964). *Abst. 8th. Ann. Meeting Biophys. Soc.* 1964, FG12.

Marsland, D. A. (1964). *In* "Primitive Motile Systems in Cell Biology" (R. D. Allen and N. Kamiya, eds.), pp. 173–188. Academic Press, New York.

Mast, S. O. (1926). *J. Morphol. Physiol.* 41, 347–425.

Mast, S. O. (1931). *Z. Vergleich. Physiol.* 15, 309–328.

Mast, S. O. (1932). *Physiol. Zool.* 1, 1–15.

Mast, S. O. (1941). *In* "Protozoa in Biological Research" (G. N. Calkins and F. M. Summers, eds.), pp. 271–351. Columbia Univ. Press, New York.

Maupas, E. (1881). *Arch. Zool. Exptl. Gen.* 9, 299–368.

Mitchison, J. M. (1950). *Nature* 166, 313–314.

Mühl, D. (1921). *Arch. Protistenk.* 43, 361–414.

Naitoh, Y. (1958). *Annotationes Zool. Japon.* 31, 59–73.

Nakajima, H. (1956). *Seitai No Kagaku* 7, 256–259.

Nakajima, H. (1960). *Protoplasma* 52, 413–436.

Nakajima, H. (1963). *In* "Non-Muscular Contractions in Biological Systems" (T. Hayashi, ed.). Academic Press, New York (in press).

Nakajima, H., and Hatano, S. (1962). *J. Cellular Comp. Physiol.* 59, 259–263.

Nauss, R. N. (1949). *Bull. Torrey. Botan. Club* 76, 161–173.

Nelson, L. (1954). *Biochim. Biophys. Acta* 14, 312–320.

Nelson, L. (1958). *Biol. Bull.* 115, 326–327.

Nelson, L. (1962). *In* "Spermatozoan Motility" (D. W. Bishop, ed.), pp. 171–187. Am. Assoc. Advance. Sci., Washington, D.C.

Nelson, L. and Plowman, K. (1963). *Abst 7th Ann. Meeting Biophys. Soc.* 1963. MD4.

Neresheimer, E. R. (1903). *Arch. Protistenk.* 2, 305-324.

Nettleton, R. M., Jr., Mefferd, R. B., Jr., and Loefer, J. B. (1953). *Am. Naturalist* 67, 117–118.

Noble, A. E. (1932). *Univ. Calif. (Berkeley), Publ. Zool.* 37, 477–520.

Noland, L. E. (1957). *J. Protozool.* 4, 1–6.

Okajima, A. (1953). *Japan J. Zool.* 11, 87–100.

Okajima, A. (1954). *Annotationes Zool. Japon.* 27, 46–51.

Okajima, A. (1957). *Annotationes Zool. Japon.* 30, 51–62.

Oliphant, J. F. (1938). *Physiol. Zool.* 11, 19–30.

Oliphant, J. F. (1942). *Physiol. Zool.* 15, 443–452.

Oosawa, F. (1963). *In* "Non-Muscular Contractions in Biological Systems" (T. Hayashi, ed.). Academic Press, New York (in press).

Osterhout, W. J. V. (1952). *J. Gen. Physiol.* 35, 519–527.

Párducz, B. (1953). *Acta Biol. Acad. Sci. Hung.* 4, 177–220.

Párducz, B. (1954). *Acta Biol. Acad. Sci. Hung.* 5, 169–212.

Párducz, B. (1957). *Acta Biol. Acad. Sci. Hung.* 8, 219–251.

Parisis, N. G. (1956). Cited in Tartar (1960).

Pautard, F. G. E. (1962). *In* "Spermatozoan Motility" (D. W. Bishop, ed.), pp. 189–232. Am. Assoc. Advance. Sci., Washington, D.C.

Penard, E. (1904). "Les Héliozoaires d'Eau douce." Kündig, Geneva.

Penard, E. (1920). *Mem. Soc. Phys. Hist. Nat. Geneve* 39, 131–229.

Penard, E. (1922). "Étude sur les Infusoires d'Eau douce." Kündig, Geneva.

Perry, S. V. (1960). *In* "Comparative Biochemistry" (M. Florkin and H. S. Mason, eds.), Vol. 2, pp. 245–340. Academic Press, New York.

Pipkin, A. C. (1962). *J. Parasitol.* 48, 50.

Pitelka, D. R. (1963). "Electron-microscopic Structure of Protozoa." Macmillan (Pergamon), New York.

Pitelka, D. R., and Schooley, C. N. (1955). *Univ. Calif. (Berkeley), Publ. Zool.* 61, 79–128.

Plate, L. (1886). *Z. Wiss. Zool. Abt. A.* 43, 175–241.

Pottage, R. H. (1959). *Proc. 15th Intern. Congr. Zool., London, 1958* pp. 472–473.

Prell, H. (1921). *Arch. Protistenk.* 42, 99–175.

Price, W., and Allen, P. (1942). *Am. J. Botany* 29, 15–16.

Prosser, C. L., and Brown, F. A., Jr. (1961). "Comparative Animal Physiology," 2nd ed. Saunders, Philadelphia, Pennsylvania.

Randall, J. T., and Jackson, S. F. (1958). *J. Biophys. Biochem. Cytol.* 4, 807–830.

Rashevsky, N. (1948). "Mathematical Biophysics: Physicomathematical Foundations of Biology," rev. ed. Univ. of Chicago Press, Chicago, Illinois.

Rashevsky, N. (1952). *Bull. Math. Biophys.* 14, 293–305.

Ray, D. L., and Hayes, R. E. (1954). *J. Morphol.* 95, 159–188.

Rees, C. W. (1922). *Univ. Calif. (Berkeley), Publ. Zool.* 20, 333–365.

Richter, J. E. (1959). *Protoplasma* 51, 197–241.

Rikmenspoel, R. (1962). *In* "Spermatozoan Motility" (D. W. Bishop, ed.), pp. 31–54. Am. Assoc. Advance. Sci., Washington, D.C.

Rinaldi, R. A., and Jahn, T. L. (1962). *J. Protozool.* 9 [Suppl.], 16.

Rinaldi, R. A., and Jahn, T. L. (1963). *J. Protozool.* 10, 344–358.

Rivera, J. A. (1962). "Cilia, Ciliated Epithelium and Ciliary Activity." Pergamon Press, New York.

Robbins, W. J. (1952). *Bull. Torrey Botan. Club* 79, 107–109.

Rosenberg, L. E. (1937). *Univ. Calif. (Berkeley), Publ. Zool.* 41, 249–276.

Roth, L. E. (1956). *J. Biophys. Biochem. Cytol.* 2 [Suppl], 235–240.

Roth, L. E. (1957). *J. Biophys. Biochem. Cytol.* 3, 985–1000.

Roth, L. E. (1958). *Exptl. Cell Res., Suppl.* 5, 573–585.

Roth, L. E. (1959). *J. Protozool.* 6, 107–116.

Roth, L. E. (1962). *Abstr. 2nd Meeting Am. Soc. Cell Biologists, 1962, San Francisco.* P. 158.

Roth, L. E. (1964). *In* "Primitive Motile Systems in Cell Biology." (R. D. Allen and N. Kamiya, eds.), pp. 527–548. Academic Press, New York.

Rothschild, L. (1961). *In* "The Cell and the Organism" (J. A. Ramsay and V. B. Wigglesworth, eds.), pp. 9–21. Cambridge Univ. Press, London and New York.

Rothschild, L. (1962). *In* "Spermatozoan Motility" (D. W. Bishop ed.), pp. 13–29. Am. Assoc. Advance. Sci., Washington, D.C.

Rouiller, C., Fauré-Fremiet, E., and Gauchery, M. (1956). *J. Protozool.* 3, 194–200.

Rudzinska, M. A., and Porter, K. R. (1954). *Experientia* 10, 460–462.

Salisbury, G. W. (1962). *In* "Spermatozoan Motility" (D. W. Bishop, ed.), pp. 59–87. Am. Assoc. Advance. Sci., Washington, D.C.

Samuel, E. M. (1961). *Develop. Biol.* 3, 317–335.

Sandon, H. (1934). *Nature* 133, 761–762.

Saunders, J. T. (1925). *Biol. Rev. Cambridge Phil. Soc.* 1, 249–269.

Schaeffer, A. A. (1920). "Ameboid Movement." Princeton Univ. Press, Princeton, New Jersey.

Schäfer, E. A. (1910). *Quart. J. Exptl. Physiol.* 3, 285–288.

Schewiakoff, W. (1894). *Z. Wiss. Zool. Abt. A.* 58, 340–354.

Schewiakoff, W. (1926). *Fauna Flora Naples* 37, 1–755.

Schmidt, W. J. (1939). *Arch. Protistenk.* 92, 527–536.

Schneider, K. C. (1906). *Arch. Zool. Inst. Wien* 16, 99–118.

Schuberg, A. (1905). *Arch. Protistenk.* 6, 61–110.

Schultze, M. (1865). *Arch. Mikroskop. Anat.* 1, 376–402.

Schulze, F. E. (1875). *Arch. Mikroskop. Anat.* 11, 329–353.

Seaman, G. R., and Houlihan, R. K. (1951). *J. Cellular Comp. Physiol.* 37, 309–321.

Seifriz, W. ed. (1942). "The Structure of Protoplasm," pp. 245–264. Iowa State Univ. Press, Ames, Iowa.

Seifriz, W. (1943). *Botan. Rev.* 9, 49–123.

Seifriz, W. (1952). *In* "Deformation and Flow Systems" (A. Frey-Wyssling, ed.), pp. 3–156. Elsevier, Amsterdam.

Sells, B. H., Six, N., and Brachet, J. (1961). *Exptl. Cell Res.* 22, 246–256.

Seravin, L. N. (1962). *Tsitologiya* 4, 545–554.

Shaffer, B. M. (1956a). *Science* 123, 1173–1175.

Shaffer, B. M. (1956b). *J. Exptl. Biol.* 33, 645–657.

Shaffer, B. M. (1957). *Am. Naturalist* 91, 19–35.

Shaffer, B. M. (1958). *Quart. J. Microscop. Sci.* 99, 103–121.

Shaffer, B. M. (1961). *J. Exptl. Biol.* 38, 833–849.

Shaffer, B. M. (1964). *In* "Primitive Motile Systems in Cell Biology" (R. D. Allen and N. Kamiya, eds.), pp. 387–406. Academic Press, New York.

Sharpey, W. (1835). *In* "Todd's Cyclopaedia of Anatomy and Physiology," Vol. I, pp. 606–636. Longmans, Green, New York.

Simard-Duquesne, N., and Couillard, P. (1962a). *Exptl. Cell Res.* 28, 85–91.

Simard-Duquesne, N., and Couillard, P. (1962b). *Exptl. Cell Res.* 28, 92–98.

Sleigh, M. A. (1956). *J. Exptl. Biol.* 33, 15–28.

Sleigh, M. A. (1957). *J. Exptl. Biol.* 34, 106–115.

Sleigh, M. A. (1960). *J. Explt. Biol.* 37, 1–10.
Sleigh, M. A. (1962). "The Biology of Cilia and Flagella." Pergamon Press, New York.
Stewart, P. A. (1964). *In* "Primitive Motile Systems in Cell Biology" (R. D. Allen and N. Kamiya, eds.), pp. 69–78. Academic Press, New York.
Stewart, P. A., and Stewart, B. T. (1959). *Exptl. Cell Res.* 17, 44–58.
Sussman, M. (1954). *J. Gen. Microbiol.* 10, 110–120.
Sussman, M., and Ennis, H. L. (1959). *Biol. Bull.* 116, 304–317.
Sussman, R. R., Sussman, M., and Fu, F. L. (1958). Cited in Bonner (1959).
Szent-Györgyi, A. (1945). "Studies on Muscle." Norstedt, Stockholm.
Szent-Györgyi, A. (1949). *Science* 110, 411–413.
Szent-Györgyi, A. (1953). "Chemical Physiology of Contraction in Body and Heart Muscle." Academic Press, New York.
Szent-Györgyi, A. (1960). "Introduction to a Submolecular Biology." Academic Press, New York.
Takata, M. (1957). Cited in Kamiya (1959).
Takata, M. (1958). *Kagaku To Kogyo (Osaka)* 28, 142.
Takeuichi, I. (1961). *Am. J. Botany* 48, 530–531.
Takeuichi, I., and Hatano, S. (1955). Cited in Kamiya (1959).
Takeuichi, I., and Hatano, S. (1956). Cited in Kamiya (1959).
Tartar, V. (1957). *Exptl. Cell Res.* 13, 317–332.
Tartar, V. (1961). "The Biology of Stentor." Pergamon Press, New York.
Tauc, L. (1953). *J. Physiol. (London)* 45, 232–233.
Taylor, C. V. (1920). *Univ. Calif. (Berkeley), Publ. Zool.* 19, 403–471.
Taylor, G. I. (1951). *Proc. Roy. Soc.* A209, 447–461.
Taylor, G. I. (1952). *Proc. Roy. Soc.* A211, 225–239.
Terada, T. (1962). *Ann. Rept. Sci. Works, Fac. Sci., Osaka Univ.* 10, 47–58.
Thompson, D'A. W. (1945). "On Growth and Form." Macmillan, New York.
Tibbs, J. (1957). *Biochim. Biophys. Acta* 23, 275–288.
Tibbs, J. (1958). *Biochim. Biophys. Acta* 28, 636–637.
Tibbs, J. (1962). *In* "Spermatozoan Motility." (D. W. Bishop, ed.), pp. 233–250. Am. Assoc. Advance Sci., Washington, D.C.
Trégouboff, G. (1953). *In* "Traité de Zoologie," Vol. I, Part 2 (P.-P. Grassé, ed.), pp. 267–490. Masson, Paris.
Ts'O, P. O. P., Bonner, J., Eggman, L., and Vinograd, J. (1956a). *J. Gen. Physiol.* 39, 325–347.
Ts'O, P. O. P., Eggman, L., and Vinograd, J. (1956b). *J. Gen. Physiol.* 39, 801–812.
Ts'O, P. O. P., Eggman, L., and Vinograd, J. (1957a). *Arch. Biochem. Biophys.* 66, 64–70.
Ts'O, P. O. P., Eggman, L., and Vinograd, J. (1957b). *Biochim. Biophys. Acta* 25, 532–542.
Ulehla, V. (1911). *Biol. Zentr.* 31, 645 and 721–731.
Ussing, H. H. (1957). *In* "Metabolic Aspects of Transport Across Cell Membranes" (Q. R. Murphy, ed.), pp. 39–56. Univ. of Wisconsin Press, Madison, Wisconsin.
Ussing, H. H., and Zerahn, K. (1951). *Acta Physiol. Scand.* 23, 110–127.
van Wagtendonk, W. J., and Vloedman, D. A., Jr. (1951). *Biochim. Biophys. Acta* 7, 335–336.
Verworn, M. (1889). "Psycho-physiologische Protistenstudien." Fischer, Jena.
Verworn, M. (1930). "Allgemeine Physiologie," 4th ed. Fischer, Jena.
Visscher, J. P. (1923). *Biol. Bull.* 45, 113–143.

von Gelei, J. (1932). *Arch. Protistenk.* 77, 152–174.

Vouk, V. (1910). *Sitzber. Akad. Wiss. Wien, Math. Naturw. Kl.* 119, 853–876.

Vouk, V. (1913). *Denkschr. Akad. Wiss. Wien, Math. Naturw. Kl.* 88, 652–692.

Watanabe, I. (1955). *Zool. Mag. (Tokyo)* 64, 334–337.

Watters, C. D. (1963). *Abstr. 7th Ann. Meeting Biophys. Soc., 1963* MD3.

Watson, M. (1916). *Univ. Illinois Biol. Monogr.* 2, 211–468.

Watson, M. R., and Hopkins, J. M. (1962). *Exptl. Cell Res.* 28, 280–295.

Weber, H. H. (1955). *Symp. Soc. Exptl. Biol.* 9, 271–281.

Weber, H. H. (1958). "Motility in Muscle and Cells." Harvard Univ. Press, Cambridge, Massachusetts.

Weber, H. H. (1960). *In* "Molecular Biology" (D. Nachmansohn, ed.), pp. 25–36. Academic Press, New York.

Whittingham, W. F., and Raper, K. B. (1957). *Am. J. Botany* 44, 619–627.

Wichterman, R. (1950). *Biol. Bull.* 99, 366–367.

Wichterman, R. (1953). "The Biology of Paramecium." McGraw-Hill (Blakiston), New York.

Wohlfarth-Bottermann, K. E. (1953). *Arch. Protistenk.* 98, 169–226.

Wohlfarth-Bottermann, K. E. (1959). *Zool. Anz.* 162, 1–10.

Wohlfarth-Bottermann, K. E. (1960). *Protoplasma* 52, 58–107.

Wohlfarth-Bottermann, K. E. (1961). *Protoplasma* 54, 1–26.

Wohlfarth-Bottermann, K. E. (1962). *Protoplasma* 54, 514–539.

Wohlfarth-Bottermann, K. E. (1964). *In* "Primitive Motile Systems in Cell Biology" (R. D. Allen and N. Kamiya, eds.) pp. 79–110. Academic Press, New York.

Wohlfarth-Bottermann, K. E., and Kruger, F. (1954). *Protoplasma* 44, 177–191.

Wolken, J. J. (1961). "Euglena." Rutgers Univ. Press, New Brunswick, New Jersey.

Worley, L. G. (1934). *J. Cellular Comp. Physiol.* 5, 53–72.

Wright, B. E. (1958). Cited in Bonner (1959).

Zajicek, J., and Datta, N. (1953). *Acta Haematol.* 9, 115–121.

Zimmerman, A. M., Landau, J. V., and Marsland, D. A. (1958). *Exptl. Cell Res.* 15, 484–495.

The Locomotor Apparatus of Ciliates and Flagellates: Relations between Structure and Function

DOROTHY R. PITELKA AND FRANK M. CHILD

*Cancer Research Genetics Laboratory, University of California, Berkeley, California
and Department of Zoology, University of Chicago, Chicago, Illinois*

		Page
I.	Introduction	131
II.	The Flagellar Unit: the Kinetid	134
	A. Morphology	134
	B. Chemistry and Physiology of Isolated Flagella and Cilia	147
	C. Movements of Flagella and Cilia	155
	D. Genetic Aspects of Flagellar Motility	162
III.	Locomotor Systems of Flagella and Cilia	163
	A. Introduction to the Facts of Coordination	163
	B. Protozoan Fibrillar Systems	165
	C. Mechanisms of Coordination	172
IV.	Reproduction and Morphogenesis	185
	A. Kinetosome Reproduction	186
	B. Growth of Flagella and Cilia	188
	C. Growth of Intracellular Fibrils	189
V.	Conclusions	190
	References	192

I. Introduction

For almost as long as their existence has been known, flagella and cilia have compelled the inquisitive biologist to wonder how anything so small can be designed to wiggle so actively and so methodically. Their primary function—to make a fluid move past a cell's surface or vice versa—has never been in question, but how they do it remains one of the tantalizing enigmas of biology. Because they operate at the surface, flagella and cilia permit a cell or a sheet of cells to do mechanical work without itself undergoing changes of shape; and because, given fuel, they do not fatigue, their work can be incessant throughout a lifetime, or many lifetimes. The flagellum was probably among the first specialized organelles evolved by eucellular protists, and in all the ages since, no organism has discovered a more effective means for doing what it does.

Whether all flagella, sperm tails, and cilia are fundamentally similar was a matter of debate until the middle of this century. Electron microscopy has answered the question decisively. Not only are they similar, but their axial structure is identical despite the enormous phylogenetic diversity of the organisms that bear them.

The ubiquity of a morphological pattern that, as will be seen, is by no means a simple or self-explanatory one suggests strongly that the elemental contractile mechanism, operating at the level of individual subunits within the axial complex, is the same in all flagella and cilia. Thus any model proposed to explain the mechanics or mechanism of their motility must be flexible enough to accommodate the simplified, formalized, repetitive movement of a vertebrate epithelial cilium, the frenetic undulation of a spermatozoon, the versatile gymnastics of a protozoan flagellum, and all variations within this gamut.

In agreement with most modern students of evolution (see Hyman, 1940; Grassé, 1952), we assume that the first organisms to perfect a flagellar apparatus were primitive eucellular algae (the much simpler filamentous appendages of bacteria, also called flagella, are not considered in this discussion). The inheritors of this innovation became in time widely diversified and gave rise to all of the known lines of eucellular protists (except probably the Rhodophyta) and through them to the land plants and the animals. While retaining with scrupulous faithfulness the details of axial morphology, the flagellum underwent many modifications—all presumably associated with new ancillary functions or with new demands for mechanical efficiency associated with new body sizes and shapes.

Among these modifications was the introduction of paraxial structures and superficial elaborations of various sorts, now largely restricted to the phyto- and zooflagellates and spermatozoa and often strikingly characteristic of particular phylogenetic lines. Another obvious modification consisted of multiplication of the flagellar unit within the cell. This occurred repeatedly and always imposed on the cell the necessity of preventing mutual interference by two or more flagella. Extreme development of the flagellar apparatus along these lines is represented by the fields of short flagella covering the surfaces of opalinid and ciliate protozoa and metazoan epithelial cells. Here the individual versatility of flagellar movement has been progressively subjugated to the requirement for effective cooperation among them. Thus cilia are one of several modifications of flagella; they justify a separate name only because their activity is always specialized for this cooperative function.

Among the protozoa (including phytoflagellates) are to be found the most extreme and dramatic modifications of structure and behavior in motile flagella, as well as the most nearly primitive ones in existence. While all of the major protozoan groups include forms with flagellate stages in their life cycles, the Mastigophora and Ciliophora consist of organisms in which the flagellar apparatus is the dominant feature.

It is our purpose to assemble pertinent information on structure and behavior of the flagellar apparatus in the flagellates and ciliates and to examine in this light current hypotheses of flagellar motility. Obviously, two lines of inquiry must be followed. One concerns the fine structure and activity of an individual flagellum or cilium, the other the behavior of coordinated fields of cilia and any structural patterns that conceivably may be related to the phenomenon of coordination. The two lines are not entirely separable, but it will be convenient to consider them in sequence.

A review emphasizing locomotor activities in protozoa is possible in this chapter only because several other recent reviews of broader scope survey a wealth of relevant detail in related areas.* Fawcett (1961) and Fauré-Fremiet (1961a,b) analyze metazoan as well as protozoan flagellar systems, including those that have become primarily sensory. The functioning of mammalian ciliated epithelia is reviewed by Rivera (1962). Grimstone (1961) and Pitelka (1963a) consider the structure of various kinds of protozoan locomotor apparatus in relation to the detailed morphology of the whole cell. Most of these works have discussed as one of many considerations the locomotor function of the flagellar apparatus that is our primary concern here. We intend to consider in more detail a selection of examples for which extensive information is at hand and which represent a variety of flagellar types, without attempting redundantly to summarize all of the related data.

Ultrastructure research on the flagellar apparatus has known two major developmental phases. The first began with the exploration of biological uses of electron microscopy in the 1940's and progressed rapidly during the 1950's as methods of fixation and thin sectioning were developed. In this phase the existence and the marvelous uniformity of the now familiar 9 + 2 pattern were discovered, and many remarkable features of the intracellular components of the apparatus were discerned. The second phase may be said to have begun with the application of a new osmium fixative to sea-urchin spermatozoa by Afzelius (1959), revealing a new depth of morphological detail. Since then, improved fixation and (especially) embedding methods, higher microscope resolution, and

---

* While this manuscript was being completed, publication was announced of an important book, "The Biology of Cilia and Flagella" by M. Sleigh (Pergamon Press, Oxford). Sleigh's earlier experimental work figures significantly in our discussion, and we are familiar with some of his views, but we have not been able to refer to his new book in preparing the present review.

inspired choices of subjects have enabled several electron microscopists to scrutinize the flagellar apparatus with an intensity not previously possible. Technical progress thus renders obsolete many works that were models of achievement only a few years ago, and the finer details of the pictures that emerged then must now be reexamined.

II. The Flagellar Unit: the Kinetid

A. MORPHOLOGY

A flagellum is only the externally conspicuous part of a unit that includes in addition the *kinetosome* from which it arises and—almost always—intracellular fibers originating at the kinetosome. For this unit Edouard Chatton in 1924 proposed the term *kinetid;* with subsequent expansion of his comparative studies and concepts he and his colleagues developed a comprehensive and convenient terminology. Although prior designations (e.g., basal body, blepharoplast for kinetosome; mastigont for kinetid) are widely used and may be particularly apt for some variants, the consistent French terminology is applicable to all flagellated and ciliated cells and quite remarkably accommodates the discoveries of ultrastructure research. The assembly of kinetids in any one cell is the *kinetome*. A chain of ontogenetically related kinetids is a *kinety*. A fiber that lies to the right of each kinety in many ciliates is the *kinetodesmos* (Chatton, 1924, 1931; Chatton and Lwoff, 1935a; Lwoff, 1950; Fauré-Fremiet, 1961a). Names proposed for other kinetosome-linked fibers can be applied in the context of ultrastructure research in some instances, but identities are not yet certain enough to justify general classification.

1. THE KINETOSOME

Of the parts of the kinetid, all may be transitory except the kinetosome— the center about which the other elements are organized. With the first wave of electron-microscope studies it became apparent that the kinetosome is a hollow cylinder of 9 equally spaced fibrils; it averages about 500 mμ in length and about 150 mμ in over-all diameter. Kinetosomes in metazoan ciliated epithelia often are markedly curved and may taper to a closed tip basally; the fibrils in their walls may be embedded in a dense matrix (Fawcett and Porter, 1954; Bradfield, 1955). In protozoa and in many metazoan cells the kinetosome is straight and constant, or nearly so, in diameter, and is only exceptionally closed basally by the application of some other material against it.

Recent high-resolution studies include, most prominently, an intensive examination of kinetids in *Trichonympha* and related hypermastigote flagellates by Gibbons and Grimstone (1960), and a number of excellent reports on metazoan kinetids, or parts of them, by other workers (sea-urchin sperm tails,

Afzelius, 1959; ctenophore swimming-plate cilia, Afzelius, 1961; lepidopteran sperm tails, André, 1961; snail-sperm centrioles, Gall, 1961; gill cilia in the mollusc, *Anodonta,* Gibbons, 1961c; coronal cilia of a rotifer, Lansing and Lamy, 1961). These provide standards with which previously published and more recent data may be compared. Since *Paramecium* has so frequently been

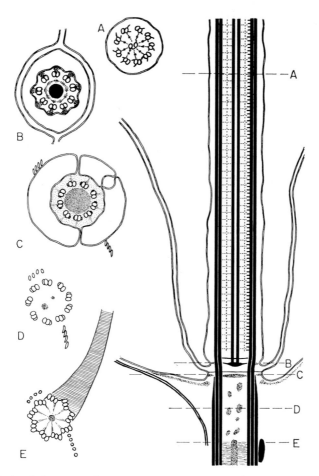

Fig. 1. Idealized diagrams of a *Paramecium* kinetid. At the right is shown a longitudinal section through the base of the cilium and the kinetosome, with adjoining parts of the cell membranes and membranes of the pellicular alveoli. At the left are cross sections at the levels indicated by the letters and broken lines. A. Free cilium.   B. Cilium at level of axosome.   C. Kinetosome at level of terminal plate, surrounded by a pair of alveoli; parasomal sac adjacent to kinetosome, at right; anterolateral and posterior tubular fibrils shown.   D. Kinetosome at about its middle level, with anterolateral and posterior tubular fibrils.   E. Base of kinetosome with cartwheel structure, kinetodesmal fibril attachment, and tubular fibrils.

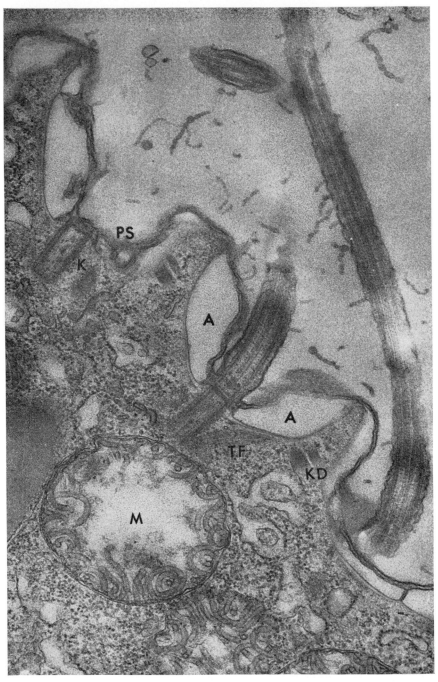

Fig. 2. Electron micrograph of section of *Paramecium multimicronucleatum* fixed in osmium tetroxide, embedded in Epon 812, and stained with lead hydroxide. Sec-

employed in experimental studies of locomotion to be discussed, the present description will use *Paramecium multimicronucleatum* (Pitelka, 1963b) as a model (for earlier accounts of *Paramecium*, see Ehret and Powers, 1959; Sedar and Porter, 1955; Metz *et al.*, 1953). More completely documented descriptions of other protozoan types that will be mentioned here may be found in a recent review (Pitelka, 1963a).

The *Paramecium* kinetosome (Figs. 1, 2, 3) stands approximately perpendicular to the cell surface. Basally it is open, its lumen apparently in communication with the substance of the surrounding cytoplasm. Each of the 9 fibrils in its wall is composed of a row of 3 subfibrils that are tubular in appearance, having dense peripheries and low-density centers. Where the subfibrils adjoin, they share a common wall; hence they are probably not individually complete units. In cross section the composite fibril measures about 24 by 50 to 60 mμ and its longer axis is not tangential to the circle of 9, but is sharply skewed inward in a clockwise (when viewed from the base distally) direction. The 3 subfibrils are designated A, B, and C, A being the innermost, most clockwise one (Gibbons and Grimstone, 1960).

Proximally, the cavity of the kinetosome contains a cartwheel-like structure consisting of fine filaments swirling inward from the 9 fibrils toward a central hub. Additional filaments connect subfibrils A and C of adjacent fibrils. In Gibbons and Grimstone's beautifully clear micrographs of hypermastigote kinetosomes still other filaments in rather consistent patterns are evident. The cartwheel extends only about one-third the length of the kinetosome in *Paramecium;* in other organisms this length varies, or the cartwheel may be entirely absent [but it is present in such diverse protozoa as *Trichonympha* (Gibbons and Grimstone, 1960), *Naegleria* (Schuster, 1963), and *Colpidium* (Pitelka, 1963b)]. Above the cartwheel the kinetosome lumen in *Paramecium multimicronucleatum* contains scattered small granules of moderate density.

At some level above the middle of the kinetosome the subfibrils C all taper to an end, and the degree of skewing of the remaining doublets is reduced. In *Paramecium* and the hypermastigotes, the final termination of the C-subfibrils is at the upper extremity of the kinetosome. In the mollusc *Anodonta* (Gibbons, 1961c), and in the small zooflagellate *Bodo* (Pitelka, 1961b, 1963b), it is about one-third the distance from the top. From the limited number of examples avail-

---

tion perpendicular to the cell surface and cutting slightly diagonally across three kineties. Ectoplasmic ridges, continuous external membrane, and pellicular alveoli of the silverline mosaic are apparent. A ciliated kinetosome is cut longitudinally in the center of the picture; a nonciliated one at left above. Note terminal plates on both kinetosomes, axosome, and central fibrils in cilium. A group of posterior tubular fibrils appears to the right of the lower kinetosome. A,A, pair of alveoli surrounding kinetid; K, nonciliated kinetosome; KD, kinetodesmal fibrils cross-sectioned in ectoplasmic ridge; M, mitochondrion; PS, parasomal sac; TF, group of tubular fibrils. Magnification: ×33,000.

able, it appears that it is at this level that the flagellum-bearing kinetosome usually establishes a precise association with the cell membrane. Above this level the kinetosome in *Bodo* and *Anodonta* contains doublet fibrils only and protrudes above the cytoplasmic surface, surrounded by the membrane.

At the top of the kinetosome its lumen is closed off by a flat plug or plate of variably dense material. In *Paramecium* it is about 30 mμ thick and is topped by a second, very thin, transverse septum. This *terminal plate* is distinct from the axial granule or axosome to be described below, but is identical in some instances with what has been called the basal plate of the flagellum; it probably is present in all kinetosomes.

When a kinetosome bears a flagellum, the continuity of the two is undeniable and the definition of the top of the kinetosome is only a semantic one. But very often kinetosomes do not bear flagella for short or prolonged periods in the life of the cell. When *Paramecium* is caused by chemical treatment to shed its cilia (Pitelka and Párducz, 1962), the kinetosome that remains is always complete up to and including the terminal plate. We know that cilia can be regenerated from such blind kinetosomes, hence it seems likely that this entire structure, shaped rather like an inverted tumbler, represents the functional organizational center of the kinetid. Micrographs of conjugating *Paramecium caudatum* (Vivier and André, 1961; André and Vivier, 1962) clearly show terminal plates in kinetosomes in the contact zone, where cilia have been lost by natural means. Most other published observations on resting kinetosomes are inconclusive for technical reasons, but in *Epistylis* (Fauré-Fremiet *et al.*, 1962) a thickened annulus caps the resting kinetosome, corresponding in position to the apical septum (terminal plate) present in ciliated ones.

In every respect except possibly the presence of a terminal plate, the kinetosome resembles the animal centriole where the fine structure of the latter is resolved (Bernhard and de Harven, 1960; Gall, 1961). Triplet fibrils, a central cartwheel, and interconnecting fine filaments are clear in snail spermatocyte centrioles pictured by Gall (1961, Figs. 28, 42).

Gibbons and Grimstone first recognized in *Trichonympha* a consistent relationship between the asymmetry of the kinetosome and its polarity. They found that the inward skewing of the triplet fibrils is clockwise when the kinetosome is viewed from the base distally. Gibbons (1961a,b) reported the same orientation in several other kinds of kinetids, including those of *Paramecium*. The relationship is very easily demonstrated in this ciliate, where a kinetodesmal fibril, known to arise at the anterior right edge of the kinetosome, provides an unmistakable landmark. Gall (1961) found evidence of the same consistency in asymmetry and polarity of spermatocyte centrioles as judged by the position of daughter procentrioles always near one end of the mother and by the probable direction of growth of flagella. It appears, as Gibbons first suggested (1961b), that one of the most important features of a kinetid—its conspicuous polarity—

is built into the kinetosome, and clockwise skewing may prove to be a universal characteristic.

The flagellum-bearing kinetid emerges from the cell surface at or below the level of the terminal plate; as mentioned above, this emergence usually coincides with the termination of the C-subfibrils. The point of emergence in many cells is at the base of a deep invagination (for example, the profound flagellar grooves of *Trichonympha* or the reservoir of euglenoids and trypanosomes). But wherever it is, the emergent flagellum is wrapped in an extension of the plasma membrane at the surface of the cell. In *Paramecium* and other ciliates that have a mosaic of membrane-bounded pellicular alveoli lying beneath the surface membrane, it is the membranes of two adjacent alveoli that establish this first connection with the kinetid at the level of the terminal plate, and the cell surface membrane replaces them a short distance distally. The enveloping membrane, which fits rather loosely, like a sleeve, over most of the flagellum, usually constricts to form a short, precise bracelet at the level of the terminal plate. Often the latter bears a raised rim extending either distally or proximally just within the circle of peripheral fibrils. Outside of the fibrils a shelf of material resembling the terminal plate reaches, in *Paramecium*, to the adjacent membrane, with denser strands extending from each doublet to the membrane. Fine filaments extending from the ends of the C-subfibrils to the surface membrane are reported for the hypermastigotes and for *Anodonta*.

2. THE AXONEME

The narrow transition zone between the terminal plate of the kinetosome and the point where the flagellum assumes its characteristic morphology is undoubtedly a critically important one both morphogenetically and functionally. It is here, as noted above, that autotomy of the flagellum most commonly occurs. Shortly above the terminal plate, a number of consistently observed structural modifications appear. Most conspicuously, two single fibrils appear in the center of the flagellum. These are about 24 mμ in diameter and 35 mμ apart, center to center. In *Paramecium* (Figs. 1, 2, 3 inset a, 4) and many other organisms, they originate in a small, dense, lens-shaped body called the axial granule or *axosome*. In *Trichonympha* the axosome is asymmetric; in *Anodonta* and *Bodo* it apparently is absent. A curved septum cradles the axosome of *Paramecium*, and another transverse septum appears immediately above it. Nine densities occur between the fibrils and the surrounding membrane, which has a regularly scalloped profile at this level.

At or somewhat distal to the level where the central fibrils originate, several other new elements are added. The doublet peripheral fibrils are now only slightly skewed and each acquires, evenly spaced along its length, paired short arms protruding from subfibril A in the general direction of the next fibril. Poorly defined strands of material extend from each of the 9 fibrils toward the central pair. Cross sections frequently reveal densities on these strands about midway between central and peripheral fibrils and these may represent tenuous secondary filaments extending longitudinally through the flagellum. The central pair of fibrils may appear to be enclosed in a delicate sheath, or, in *Paramecium*, short arms appear on one or both of the central fibrils. In heavily stained specimens, subfibril A of each peripheral fibril may appear denser centrally than subfibril B. Several bits of evidence suggest that the central fibril walls may contain or consist of a helical component.

This 9 + 2 complex of fibrils and filaments, together with the low density matrix that embeds them, constitute the *axoneme* of the motile flagellum. Many examples are known of cilia that are not motile, and from these the central fibril pair typically is missing. Whether arms, spokes, and secondary filaments are present is not known.

At the tapering distal end of the flagellum, the axoneme loses its geometric integrity; arms, spokes, and secondary filaments disappear first, the spacing of the 9 + 2 fibrils becomes irregular, and individual subfibrils end apparently at random (Gibbons and Grimstone, 1960). In some algae, flagella bear long, fine whip ends, and these are formed by an extraordinary prolongation of the two central fibrils beyond the termination of the 9 peripheral ones (Manton, 1959a).

The geometry of the axoneme led Manton and her colleagues as long ago as 1952 (Manton and Clarke, 1952, 1956; Manton, 1955b, 1959b) to suggest a plane of symmetry passing between the two central fibrils and bisecting one of the peripheral ones. Although its detailed configuration renders the axoneme asymmetric, the superficial bilateral arrangement is still apparent, and several authors have suggested that it is related to the plane of beat of metazoan epithelial cilia and many spermatozoa. Fawcett and Porter (1954) noted that in a mollusc gill epithelium the plane of ciliary beat was perpendicular to a plane uniting the two central fibrils, hence parallel to Manton's plane of symmetry, and Gibbons (1961c) confirms this observation.

Afzelius (1959) proposed a useful system of numbering the peripheral fibrils starting with the fibril bisected by Manton's plane and proceeding clockwise. He was the first to note the presence of a bridge, formed by an extra pair of arms projecting anticlockwise from subfibril B of fibril 6 and meeting the usual pair from fibril 5. Several workers have subsequently noted bridges in metazoan cilia, but none have reported them in protozoa. Theories on the significance of the bridge and of Manton's plane will be discussed in Section II,C, but it should be noted here that protozoan flagella are capable of beating in many different directions, and the normal beat of individual ciliate cilia includes a bending out of the plane of the effective stroke.

Axoneme structure in motile flagella is strikingly constant throughout the living world. Only one normal exception has been noted. In the spermatozoon of the flatworm, *Haematoloechus* (Shapiro *et al.*, 1961), the occurrence of a unique central fibril is reported and illustrated. Two reports of obvious ab-normalities have been published, one (Satir, 1962) involving extra fibrils in one cilium from a mollusc gill, and the other (Pitelka, 1962), deletion of one or two fibrils, with a segment of matrix, from several cilia in the mouth of *Paramecium* (Fig. 3, inset b). In neither of these instances was the author able to examine sections of the kinetosomes of these specific kinetids, nor was it possible to assume that the affected cilia were motile. These two examples prove that anomalies can occur, presumably in development, and suggest, as Satir points out, that the remarkable consistency of axoneme structure is the result of constant selection pressure in its favor, rather than of any immutable geo-metric property of the underlying morphogenetic mechanism.

3. THE SHEATH

If all axonemes are constructed after the same blueprint, the sheaths that surround them are not. The multiple uses to which flagella may be put is reflected in part by the multiplicity of accessories to flagellar structure. Among the first of these to be recognized were the lateral filaments, or *mastigonemes*, that embellish the flagella of many kinds of phytoflagellates. They have been classified and discussed by Manton (1956), Pitelka (1949, 1963a), and Pitelka and Schooley (1955). They occur in different sizes and configurations, but in all instances they are filamentous projections, inserted possibly on the flagellar membrane but more probably, according to Manton *et al.* (1953), beneath it on or between specific fibrils of the axoneme. In euglenoid flagellates they are very long and slender and under normal conditions are wrapped around the flagellar surface. In chrysomonads they are shorter and probably rigidly ex-tended in life. The best guess one can hazard as to their significance is that they serve to increase the mechanically effective surface of a beating flagellum.

Quite different from the mastigonemes are minute villiform projections of the surface membrane commonly observed in protozoan cilia. They are often seen in groups of cilia that beat coherently as membranelles or cirri, and Roth (1956) suggested that they might interweave to hold the active cilia together. However, they may also be present on normal body cilia of *Paramecium* (Figs. 2, 3, 4). To what extent they may represent artifacts of handling is uncertain.

Other external decorations include spines on the flagella of certain brown algal spermatozoa (Manton *et al.*, 1953), possibly functioning in mating, and minute scales arrayed over the surface of the flagellum as well as the body of *Micromonas squamata* (Manton and Parke, 1960). Some euglenoid flagellates have, in addition to mastigonemes, ribbons of striated material that flank the flagellum, apparently outside the usual surface membrane (Pitelka, 1949; Pitelka and Schooley, 1955; Roth, 1959).

A peculiar variation on this theme is found in the elastic stalks of some peritrichs (Fauré-Fremiet *et al.*, 1962; Randall and Hopkins, 1962). Here

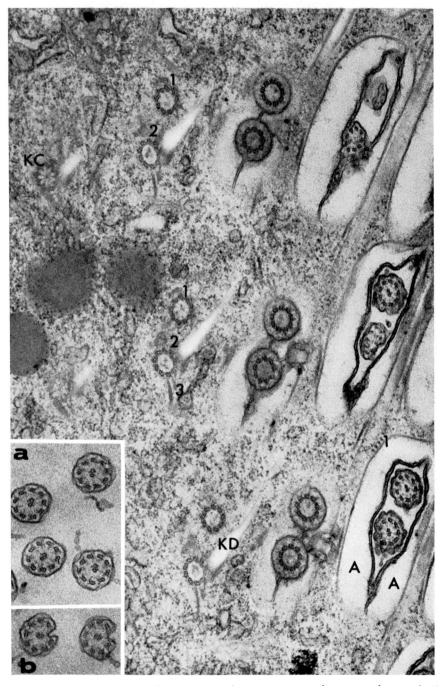

FIG. 3. Electron micrograph of section of *Paramecium multimicronucleatum* fixed in osmium tetroxide, embedded in Epon 812, and stained with lead hydroxide.

kinetosomes occur within the ciliate body at the membrane-limited junction between it and the stalk. Abortive cilia, lacking the two central fibrils, project for a short distance into the stalk. Outside of their membranes the stubs are ensheathed by cylinders or nine bundles of striated fibrillar material that continue posteriad through the stalk and provide mechanical support and elasticity.

Between the axoneme and the flagellar membrane, accessory rods of dense material are present in a variety of phyto- and zooflagellates. These paraxial rods have been found in flagella (e.g., of trichomonads and trypanosomes) that are active in spite of adhering to the cell surface, or in exceptionally long, free-swinging flagella (e.g., *Peranema, Bodo*), and a function in mechanical strengthening of the organelle seems likely. In other instances, a paraxial swelling, consisting of a mass of amorphous material, is enclosed within the flagellar membrane adjacent to a stigma or eyespot (*Euglena,* Gibbs, 1960). Its function is not known.

4. INTRACELLULAR FIBROUS STRUCTURES

In his definition of the kinetid, Chatton (1924, 1931), recognized two kinds of internal fibrils of common occurrence: a root fibril, often linking the kinetosome with the nucleus (in which case it is generally called a *rhizoplast*), and a *parabasal fibril* linking the kinetosome with the parabasal body (Golgi apparatus). Electron microscopy confirms the existence of these and demonstrates a bewildering array of other fibrillar appendages, generally divisible into three classes.

a. Striated Fibrils. Unfortunately no one has yet published an intensive, high-resolution study of the locomotor apparatus of a phytoflagellate. Abundant evidence shows, however, that root fibrils exist in most of the species that have been studied. Rhizoplasts are evident, for example, in electron micrographs of *Synura caroliniana* by Manton (1955a), and of *Chromulina psammobia* by Rouiller and Fauré-Fremiet (1958). They are obliquely striated ribbons closely applied at their origin against one side of the kinetosome, passing to the apex

---

Tangential section at cell surface. Kineties run from lower left to upper right. Kinetosomes and cilia are cross-sectioned at various levels. The three pairs of kinetosomes slightly to the left of center show origins of kinetodesmal fibrils (incompletely penetrated by embedding medium and appearing empty here), and of the three sets of tubular fibrils, all sectioned obliquely. Numbers 1, 2, and 3 are placed immediately to the right of the fibrils they designate: 1, anterolateral tubular fibrils of anterior kinetosome; 2, anterolateral tubular fibrils of posterior kinetosome; 3, posterior tubular fibrils, present only on posterior kinetosome; A,A, pair of alveoli surrounding a pair of cilia; KC, kinetosome with cartwheel structure in its lumen; KD, kinetodesmal fibril. Magnification: ×33,000. Inset a. Cross sections of four cila from the buccal cavity. Magnification: ×40,000. Inset b. Cross sections of two abnormal cilia. Each lacks one peripheral fibril and a wedge-shaped section of matrix. Magnification: × 40,000.

of the nucleus, and then turning and running along the outer membrane of the nuclear envelope. More than one rhizoplast may arise from a single kinetosome; where two kinetosomes are present rhizoplasts may originate at one or both. The rhizoplast(s) may branch and form a plexus along the nuclear surface. Very often, the Golgi apparatus is found in a constant position alongside the rhizoplast; in this case the rhizoplast is also a parabasal fibril. Similar root fibrils that do not appear to be associated with either nucleus or Golgi body are seen in some other phytoflagellates; their termini may appear near the cell membrane, at the stigma, or free in the cytoplasm.

Striated root fibrils thus are seen in the phylogenetically simplest kinetids that have been studied. They are to be found again in zooflagellates, ciliates, and metazoa. In the amebo-flagellate, *Naegleria gruberi* (Schuster, 1963), a striking, heavy rhizoplast extends from the cluster of anterior kinetosomes, making contact with more than one of them, and back toward the nuclear surface, but contact with the nuclear membrane may be transitory. This rhizoplast is always flanked by rows of mitochondria. *Tritrichomonas muris* (Anderson and Beams, 1959, 1961) has a slender, striated parabasal fibril and in addition a heavy, striated rod called the costa extending from one of the four anterior kinetosomes posteriad beneath the attachment of the undulating membrane. Striated parabasal fibrils exist in several other zooflagellates, including the extravagantly complex *Trichonympha* (Pitelka and Schooley, 1958), where they take origin, not from the kinetosomes of any flagella, but at a dense anterior zone that is identified by light microscopy as the centriole (Cleveland, 1960). According to Grimstone (1961), a kinetosome–centriole of conventional structure is recognizable in Cleveland's centriolar zone.

In the ciliates, striated ciliary roots are never associated with the nucleus or with Golgi bodies. In *Paramecium* (Figs. 1, 3, 4) and related hymenostomes, one banded kinetodesmal fibril arises at the right anterior margin near the base of each kinetosome (or one of each pair) and passes to the right and anteriad, close under the cell surface, to taper to an end after 5 to 20 μ.

Well developed striated root fibrils are characteristic of kinetids of most metazoan ciliated epithelia; some kinds of mammalian epithelia have them (Fredericsson and Björkman, 1962) but others lack them (Fawcett, 1961). They resemble the fibrils seen in phytoflagellates in that they arise laterally on the kinetosome and pass medially, usually around and beyond the nucleus. There may be one or two per kinetosome.

Observations on ciliated or flagellated cells in the lower invertebrates are relatively few, but distinct striated roots are present, for example, in the acontia of a sea anemone (Westfall, 1963), in the flagellated epithelium of a coral (Goreau and Philpott, 1956), in the flame cell of a flatworm (Kümmel, 1958), and in rotifer coronal cilia (Lansing and Lamy, 1961).

All of the banded fibrils, when examined in sufficient detail, display a composite repeating pattern, with secondary stripes. The length of the period varies, even within a single fibril. They appear either to be solid or, more probably, to be coherent bundles of close-packed, very fine filaments. Their general morphological resemblance to collagen and circumstantial evidence suggesting an anchoring and supporting function are discussed by Fawcett (1961), with whose conclusions we agree.

b. Tubular Fibrils. A second type of root fibril found in some flagellates appears tubular, with a dense periphery and low density center; it resembles a central fibril or a subfibril of the axoneme but is somewhat finer (around 20 mμ in diameter), and is never continuous with kinetosomal fibrils. Its most conspicuous characteristic is the precision with which it is aligned with others of the same kind in rows or bundles. In *Euglena gracilis* (Roth, 1958a), small groups of such fibrils originate at the kinetosomes and pass anteriad to join a system of parallel fibrils underlying the pellicle of the reservoir. In *Bodo*, similar groups arise from kinetosomes and likewise extend under the surface membrane in a precise and complex arrangement (Pitelka, 1963b). In *Naegleria*, a scoop-shaped band of tubular fibrils departs from each kinetosome and passes toward the cell surface (Schuster, 1963).

All ciliates that have been examined in detail prove to have systems of tubular fibrils, often of preposterous complexity, associated with at least some of their kinetosomes. Kinetids of *Paramecium multimicronucleatum* occur in pairs over much of the body surface. Commonly, both kinetosomes of the pair are ciliated, but only the posterior one gives rise to a kinetodesmal fibril from its right anterior margin. At the right posterior margin of the same kinetosome an oblique row of tubular fibrils arises, passing up to the surface of the ectoplasm and posteriad under the limiting membrane. From the left anterior margins of both kinetosomes of the pair, tangential rows of tubular fibrils arise and likewise pass toward the cell surface (Figs. 1–4). In the specialized buccal kinetids, kinetodesmal fibrils are absent but the oblique rows of tubular fibrils are unusually long and extend for some distance beneath the nonciliated buccal wall. Very similar systems of diverging, nonanastomosing tubular fibrils are present in *Colpidium* and related tetrahymenids (Pitelka, 1961a).

A prominent characteristic of these tubular-fibril structures, as stressed above, is their precise alignment. When seen in cross section, they are evenly spaced in at least one dimension, and in longitudinal section they appear fairly straight and parallel. This arrangement seems to have no counterpart in metazoan cells yet studied, except in some spermatozoa (Christensen, 1961; Nicander, 1962; Shapiro *et al.*, 1961). Tubular fibrils that usually are more slender and are considerably less orderly in arrangement are represented by the spindle and astral fibrils of the animal mitotic figure (e.g., P. Harris, 1961, 1962). Gibbons (1961c) has also found fine tubular fibrils, with no discernible pattern of arrangement, diverging from kinetosomes in the *Anodonta* gill.

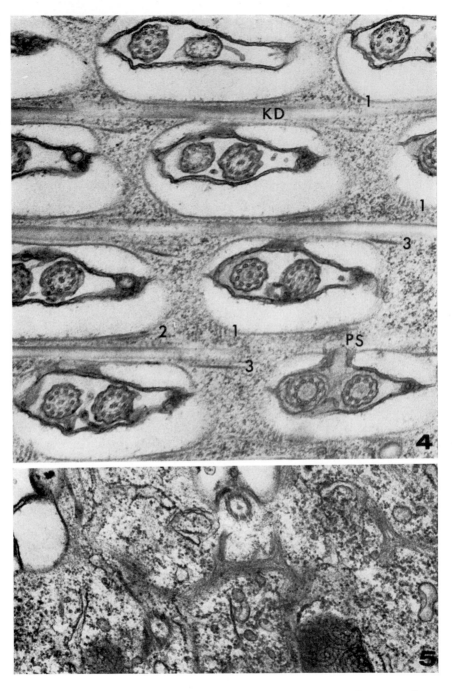

FIGS. 4 and 5. Electron micrographs of sections of *Paramecium multimicronucleatum* fixed in osmium tetroxide, embedded in Epon 812, and stained with lead hydroxide.

c. Fine Filaments. A third general category of kinetosome-associated fibrous structures in protozoa embraces a variety of finely filamentous tracts observed sporadically, and rarely at high resolution. Some of these are seen as fibrous bridges interconnecting kinetosomes in organelles made up of multiple cilia. *Paramecium* has a system of filamentous tracts forming a roughly polygonal lattice in the deep ectoplasm (Fig. 5). Kinetosomes generally appear in the interstices of this lattice, but some branches of it make contact with them at least occasionally. Also in *Paramecium*, a loose reticulum of very fine filaments with denser nodes surrounds much of the buccal cavity, and similar filaments are associated with the buccal kinetosomes. In the peritrichs, *Campanella* (Rouiller and Fauré-Fremiet, 1957) and *Epistylis* (Fauré-Fremiet *et al.*, 1962), such a three-dimensional reticulum forms a spiral mass, believed to be an elastic, supporting structure, beneath the peristomal ciliature, and filaments from the reticulum clearly connect with kinetosomes.

Fauré-Fremiet (1961a), Grimstone (1961), and Pitelka (1963a) review other fibrillar and filamentous structures associated with protozoan kinetosomes, and some of these will be considered in Section III,B. The examples described above are representative of their variety of appearance and arrangement. This variety, and the possibility that some active kinetids (for example, those in the posterior flagellated zone of *Trichonympha*) bear no extrakinetosomal fibrils at all, argue against the essential participation of such fibrils in the mechanism of individual flagellar movement. Other hypotheses regarding their function will be mentioned later.

B. Chemistry and Physiology of Isolated Flagella and Cilia

1. the isolation of flagella and cilia from protozoa

A few species of ciliates and flagellates have been used successfully as material for isolating sufficient quantities of cilia or flagella for microchemical analysis. Among the flagellates, *Polytoma uvella* has been used by Tibbs (1957, 1958) for determination of protein, lipid, carbohydrate, and other properties, and by Brokaw (1961), in studies on the restoration of movement by adenosine

---

Fig. 4. Tangential section at cell surface, showing cilia cut in cross section at various levels through or near the axosome. Kineties run horizontally; anterior direction to the left. Kinetodesmal fibrils are longitudinally sectioned in the ectoplasmic ridges. The three sets of tubular fibrils are numbered as in Fig. 3. Because they diverge at different angles, fibrils 1 appear in this plane of section in cross-sectional or slightly oblique profile, while fibrils 2 and 3 appear as longer segments. KD, kinetodesmal fibrils; PS, parasomal sac. Magnification: ×33,000.

Fig. 5. Tangential section cutting into the deeper cortical ectoplasm and showing tracts of very fine filaments composing a rough lattice at the level of the kinetosome bases. Magnification: ×33,000.

triphosphate (ATP) and analysis of nucleotide phosphatase activity; and *Chlamydomonas moewusii*, by Jones and Lewin (1960), for amino acid and other microchemical tests, and also by Brokaw (1960), who compared ATPase activity of flagella of wild-type and paralyzed mutants, finding considerably less specific activity in the flagella of the paralyzed mutants.

Among the ciliates, only *Paramecium* and *Tetrahymena* have been used to date. Preer and Preer (1959) isolated cilia from quantities of *Paramecium aurelia*, and were able to identify and characterize a readily soluble immobilization antigen localized, at least partly, in the cilia. Siegel and Cohen (1962) isolated cilia from sexually reactive *P. bursaria* and were able to use these cilia as markers to study the topographic and diurnal variation in the localization of mating-type substance on cells of complementary mating type, since the isolated cilia would agglutinate with certain cilia of the tester cells. Child (1959, 1961) and Watson and colleagues (Watson *et al.*, 1961; Watson and Hopkins, 1962) have isolated cilia from strains of *Tetrahymena pyriformis* and the results of their chemical and microscopic analyses are summarized below.

It would be too involved to discuss here the different methods used to isolate cilia or flagella from gram quantities of cells, especially since the rationale for each method is either obscure or highly speculative. Three general techniques, however, seem to be effective: (1) careful breaking up of the cells by homogenization, slow cytolysis, etc., sometimes yields suspensions of cells and free cilia that can be separated by differential centrifugation (Siegel and Cohen, 1962); (2) a combination of anesthesia and mechanical agitation in a viscous medium sometimes detaches cilia or flagella from the cell bodies (compare, for instance, the use of cold solutions of glycerol by Child and by Brokaw); and (3) certain carefully controlled treatments seem to induce self-dehiscence of the cilia or flagella (Watson's use of Versene and calcium ions in dilute ethanol for *Tetrahymena*).

As material for isolating milligram quantities of cilia or flagella, the protozoa appear to be the organisms of choice, especially since many can be grown in gram quantities in the absence of bacteria and other organisms that are difficult to separate from isolated cilia or flagellar fragments. However, metazoan material is also useful, and we should mention the successful isolations from clam gills (Child, 1961) and from invertebrate and vertebrate spermatozoa (reviewed by Bishop, 1962).

2. THE COHERENCE OF THE FLAGELLAR STRUCTURE

Electron-microscope studies of whole mounts of flagella and cilia treated in ways that disrupt structure reveal that the parts of the organelle possess different degrees of coherence, some parts being more easily destroyed or dissociated than others. These differences undoubtedly reflect differences in chemical composition or in intermolecular bonding, but there is little information yet on these matters. A purely formal ranking of the coherence of the parts has been given by Child (1961).

The ciliary membrane is the weakest part of the shaft of the cilium. It becomes easily separated from the axoneme in isolated cilia or in dying cells; many workers have observed swollen cilia (Lewin and Meinhart, 1953; Preer and Preer, 1959; Child, 1961). In the simplest cases, the swelling is clearly osmotic and involves the expansion or stretching of the membrane, the axoneme becoming coiled within its confines. The membrane can be removed from the axoneme by several treatments, including glycerination; indeed, glycerinated models of frog ciliated epithelial cells (Alexandrov and Arronet, 1956) are devoid of plasma membrane (Satir and Child, 1963).

Many of the original electron-microscope studies of cilia and flagella (Jakus and Hall, 1946; Manton, 1952) were of whole mounts of splayed axonemes and clearly showed the fibrillar character of the axoneme. Manton first pointed out the greater fragility of the 2 central fibrils compared with the outer 9. The fact, however, that splayed preparations displaying 11 intact fibrils could be obtained indicates that the coherence of the inner matrix, which Fawcett and Porter (1954) characterized as paracrystalline, is responsible for the integrity of the axoneme.

There is no evidence, yet, that cilia or flagella possess any proximal-distal gradations or differentiation of structure. Near the tip the fibrils end one by one and at the base there usually are connections between the membrane and the axoneme (Section II,A,2). Theoretical considerations, especially of the apparent self-regulating properties of the formation and growth of cilia, suggest that proximal-distal differentiation might well exist. Child (1963a) has proposed that the apparent gradual dissolution of isolated cilia of *Tetrahymena* by increasing pH may be related to such an axial differentiation, and compared this with the centrally directed solubility gradient observed in mitotic asters by Mazia (1959). Recently, we have been able to demonstrate (Child, 1963b), with *Tetrahymena* under controlled conditions, that the membranes of cilia isolated in 25% glycerol can be caused to swell progressively and to limited extents, beginning first at the distal tip and culminating eventually at the base, by transferring the cilia to graded concentrations of sucrose. The results appear to be best explainable in terms of a proximal-distal graded reduction in the strength of connections between the axoneme and the membrane. Such connections remain postulated, as they have not generally been observed by electron microscopy. We have occasionally noted, however, that arms on some of the peripheral fibrils may appear in a good cross-sectional view to meet the adjacent membrane (Fig. 3, inset a).

3. CHEMICAL COMPOSITION OF FLAGELLA AND CILIA

Since Fauré-Fremiet (1961a) and Brokaw (1962) have reviewed this topic recently, we shall simply summarize the more important facts, relying mainly on information obtained from studies on the isolated cilia of *Tetrahymena*, with which one of us is most familiar, and for which there is more recent information (Watson and Hopkins, 1962; Alexander *et al.*, 1962). The chemical composition of the cilia of *Tetrahymena* is broadly the same as the composition of the flagella of *Chlamydomonas* (Jones and Lewin, 1960) and of *Polytoma* (Tibbs, 1958).

The cilia of *Tetrahymena* contain three major constituents: water (amount unknown), lipid (about 20% of the dry weight is soluble in chloroform-methanol), and protein (about 80% of the dry weight, by subtraction). The lipid fraction contains phosphorus and nitrogen, and may be largely phosphatidylethanolamine. The amino acid composition of hydrolyzed cilia includes at least 17 amino acids and is of a very generalized type: ionizable residues such as glutamic acid, aspartic acid, and arginine are relatively abundant, there is no high proportion of cysteine or nonpolar side chains to account for the relative insolubility, and hydroxyproline is absent (Watson and Hopkins, 1962).

Certain minor constituents of isolated cilia are present in variable amounts, generally <2% of the dry weight. Detectable amounts of hexose (up to 1.2% of the dry weight) are reported by Watson and Hopkins, total phosphorus amounts of 0.3% of the dry weight (Child, 1963b) and similarly small amounts of ribose, adenine, and uracil have been found (Child, 1959).

The possibility that nucleotides are present as a minor constituent is of heuristic interest. Some workers, searching for unifying physiological principles, wish to prove that cilia and flagella, being contractile systems like muscle, contain analogs of actin and myosin. Child (1959) has pointed out that the solubility properties of isolated cilia are not at all similar to the solubility properties of isolated myofibrils, or of actomyosin. The possible presence, however, of bound nucleotides (Child, 1959) and the rather general type of amino acid composition (Watson and Hopkins, 1962) are properties not unlike those of actin. We feel, however, that the continued searching for similarities between cilia and muscle may simply obscure the fundamental properties of ciliary contractile systems, outlined in the next section.

The identification of more than one macromolecular constituent, or species of protein, in cilia and flagella has long been a goal. It would seem necessary to have several components to arrive at the architectural complexity exposed by the electron microscope, and to explain the complexities that must exist in the mechanism of beating. The problem lies in the fact that the mildest conditions that will disperse or solubilize cilia in a manner amenable to standard physicochemical procedures are conditions of high alkalinity or acidity, or involving certain detergents (dodecyl sulfate, Cetrimide) at neutral pH, all of which conditions tend to denaturation of proteins. Child (1959), using cilia dissolved in dilute NaOH, pH 11, and brought to pH 7.4 in phosphate buffer, found but one boundary in the analytical ultracentrifuge. Recently, Alexander *et al.* (1962), using cilia extracted with 3.1N acetic acid, have found three boundaries in the acid extract, one of which fractions could be isolated after precipitation with trichloroacetic acid and extraction with ethanol. This ethanol-soluble fraction accounts for at least 15% of the ciliary protein, and has a characteristic amino acid composition differing from that of whole cilia by containing larger amounts of aspartic acid, glutamic acid, and alanine, and very small amounts of methionine and proline. These results are the first to give definite assurance that cilia are macromolecularly heterogeneous.

The antigenic analysis of isolated cilia may prove to be a powerful tool in identifying macromolecular components. Preer and Preer (1959) have identified a soluble protein antigen in isolated cilia of *Paramecium aurelia* which appears to be the immobilization antigen (Finger, 1956). It is not quite clear whether a corresponding antigen exists in the cilia of *Tetrahymena,* though Watson (1963) observes immobilization of *Tetrahymena* by antiserum against whole isolated cilia, and there is some evidence that cilia isolated from *Tetrahymena* contain sizable amounts of rapidly extracted protein (Child, 1963a). Alexander *et al.* (1962) obtain at least three precipitation bands in gel-diffusion plates when acetic acid extracts of isolated cilia are run against whole-cilia antisera. One of these bands corresponds to the ethanol-soluble fraction.

Enzymatic analysis of isolated cilia is complicated by the relative insolubility of the material. Quantitative conclusions and comparisons are difficult to justify (Child, 1961), but qualitative results show that cilia and flagella possess a wide range of enzymatic activities. Brokaw (1961) finds that isolated flagella of *Polytoma* will dephosphorylate adenosine triphosphate (ATP) and, at a much slower rate, cytidine, guanosine, uridine, and inosine triphosphates; the flagella dephosphorylate adenosine diphosphate (ADP) at the same rate as the triphosphate, but this reaction appears to involve the conversion of ADP to ATP by adenylate kinase, an enzyme analogous to myokinase of muscle; furthermore, the flagella can carry out a transphosphorylation between ADP and several nucleotide triphosphates, but adenosine monophosphate, guanosine diphosphate, and inosine diphosphate were not dephosphorylated. Child (1959, 1961) has described some of the dephosphorylating specificities of cilia from *Tetrahymena.*

4. THE REACTIVATION OF MODELS

The discovery by Hoffmann-Berling (1955) that the technique of preparing "glycerinated models" of muscle could be applied to flagellated and ciliated cells has been of major importance in subsequent studies of the mechanisms of flagellar movement and ciliary coordination. In brief, a "model" is a cell which has been killed in a solution (usually containing glycerol) that causes cell movement to cease, destroys the normal permeability and semi-permeability, and extracts whatever substances are soluble in it. A model is said to be reactivated if motility can be restored to it by immersing it in a solution of some different composition (usually containing ATP). Hoffmann-Berling showed that the technique could be applied to *Trypanosoma brucei, Paramecium,* and some sperms.

Brokaw (1961) has extended the technique to the isolated flagella of *Polytoma.* The flagella are detached and isolated in 70% glycerol containing 0.01M MgCl₂ and 0.02M Tris-thioglycolate buffer, pH 7.8, at −20°C. Reactivation occurred in a solution containing ATP, 0.05M KCl, 0.04M MgCl₂, and 0.2M Tris-thioglycolate buffer, pH 7.8, at 10–12°C. No movement is detected unless ATP is present. At low concentrations (5×10^{-6}M ATP) a few flagella beat very slowly (less than 1 beat per second) with amplitudes of 2–4 μ. As the concentration of ATP is increased, the frequency of beat increases but the amplitude decreases. "As the concentration approaches 10^{-3}M, the frequency becomes very high, probably at least as high as the natural rate of beat, but the amplitude decreases so that very little movement is apparent" (Brokaw, 1961, p. 155). In the slower flagella, contractile waves can be observed to pass from the basal end of the flagellum toward the tip. Raising the temperature increases the frequency without affecting the amplitude. In good preparations, the rhythmic, propagated undulations caused translational progression, that is, swimming, at speeds of 20–30 μ per second.

Alexandrov and Arronet (1956) prepared glycerinated models of the ciliated cells of the mucous membrane of the frog palate. The use of glycerol, however, hinders the preparation of intact models of ciliated protozoans because the high viscosity of the solution results in mechanical damage and removal of cilia when the cells are handled in it. Better results are obtained with ciliates when the glycerol is replaced with the detergent saponin, which also acts upon the cell membrane, though more rapidly. Alexandrov and Arronet have obtained models of *Paramecium caudatum* using the saponin method and have demonstrated the role of ATP in the ciliary movement of this organism (cited by Seravin, 1961).

Seravin (1961) independently adapted the saponin technique to producing models of *Spirostomum ambiguum* and *Euplotes patella.* His method involved washing the cells twice in double-distilled water and placing them in saponin solution (0.12M KCl, 0.01M phosphate buffer, 0.004M Na₂ EDTA, and 0.5% saponin) at 0°C. for 30–45 min. For *Spirostomum,* the pH was 6.5; for *Euplotes,* 7.0, with 0.15% saponin. Reactivation could be obtained by transferring the cells to a solution containing 0.12M KCl, 0.01M phosphate buffer, 0.001M ATP, and 0.001M MgCl₂, at 16–18°C. and at the pH of the saponin solution. Under these conditions, the models of *Spirostomum* continued beating for 40–60 min. and those of *Euplotes* continued for 60–90 min. The *Spirostomum* models were very sensitive to pH, the duration of the reactivation decreasing sharply outside the range 6.5–6.6. The models of *Euplotes* were less sensitive in this respect. The concentration of potassium in the reactivating solution was not critical and could go as low as 0.01M. Motility occurred even if sodium replaced potassium, but lithium salts prevented activity. Magnesium ion was essential and could not be replaced with calcium. ATP could not be replaced with ADP, AMP, or inorganic pyrophosphate. In the presence of ATP, however, pyrophosphate inhibited the activity whereas ADP and AMP did not. Seravin determined the effects of various agents on the motility of the models, and in general found that they were more sensitive (to $NiSO_4$, formalin, etc.) than the living cells. Cilia detached from the cell models were active in the presence of ATP and performed rhythmic, wave-like contractions. The cirri and membranelles of the models also were motile and showed considerable retention of coordinated activity (Section III,C,2,*c*).

5. THE COMPOSITION OF KINETOSOMES

Like centrioles, the basal bodies of cilia and flagella appear to be concerned with the elaboration of certain fibrous elements in the cell. It has been suggested by many workers that these kinetosomal organelles may be the site of synthesis of the proteins that go to make up the asters and achromatic spindle in the case of centrioles, and the fibers of the flagellum and rootlets in the case of basal bodies. Or, perhaps, they are merely the centers where the orderly polymerization of the proteins of the fibrous elements takes place. Furthermore, since these kinetosomes are "self-reproducing" and capable of "differentiation," one might expect to find in them a wide range of biochemical abilities, including genetic and differentiating mechanisms involving nucleic acid and protein metabolism.

Answers to these possibilities are eagerly awaited, from year to year. Very little published work deals directly with this enormously important problem, and, unfortunately, all work published to date on the composition of kinetosomes has been either unrepeatable in other laboratories or disputable for technical reasons. For what it is worth, we shall summarize the available information, already reviewed by Fauré-Fremiet (1961a).

Randall and Jackson (1958) and Randall (1959) reported the identification of deoxyribonucleic acid (DNA) and ribonucleic acid (RNA) in ciliary basal bodies of several species, including *Stentor* and *Tetrahymena,* by stringent cytochemical procedures. These results, published in preliminary form, remain unconfirmable in several other laboratories. Rampton (1962) has reported negative autoradiographic evidence on the incorporation of tritiated thymidine, uracil, and cytidine into the basal bodies of *Tetrahymena;* his evidence shows that there is less than 10^{-15} g. DNA per kinetosome in *Tetrahymena*. Seaman (1960) reports that isolated kinetosomes of the same strain of *Tetrahymena pyriformis* contain DNA at an amount equal to 3% of the dry weight of the kinetosomes. Seaman's paper does not include enough information to do a proper calculation, but by making several conservative assumptions we calculate that this represents an amount of DNA of the order of magnitude of 10^{-16} g. per kinetosome. This amount is probably enough for one or a few genes per kinetosome, but it might equally well represent a small amount of contaminating DNA.

Seaman (Seaman and Gottlieb, 1957; Seaman, 1960, 1961) has reported the successful isolation of milligram amounts of pure kinetosomes from *Tetrahymena pyriformis*. His procedure, which is an extension of the digitonin-solubilization technique of Child and Mazia (1956), involves the isolation first of "pellicles" and "pellicular fragments" containing kinetosomes but free of other cytoplasmic granules, and subsequent isolation of the kinetosomes from the pellicles by grinding with quartz powder and differential centrifugation. The published phase-contrast photomicrograph of the isolated preparation (Seaman, 1960, p. 300) shows a field of small granules at an unspecified magnification. It is clear that further critical microscopy and electron-microscope confirmation are necessary to demonstrate that these granules are indeed ciliary basal bodies and to assess the admixture of ribosomes and mitochondrial fragments. Seaman reports the following composition of the preparation in percentages of dry weight: protein 50%, carbohydrate 6%, lipid 5%, RNA 2%, and DNA 3%. In addition he finds the following enzymes: succinic dehydrogenase, fumarase, apyrase, and glycolytic and oxidative phosphorylating systems. A later paper describes protein synthesis in similar preparations (Seaman, 1961). The kinetosomal system differs in several respects from the two previously described protein-synthesizing systems in *Tetrahymena*: the microsomal and soluble system of Mager and Lipmann (1958), and the mitochrondrial system of Mager (1960). Unlike these systems, the kinetosomal system "requires nucleoside monophosphates (the di- or triphosphates do not stimulate activity), . . . is only slightly sensitive to high concentrations of chloramphenicol, and does not require an exogenously supplied ATP-generating system" (Seaman, 1961, p. 898).[*]

Until these results concerning the nucleic acid content and protein-synthesizing capacity of kinetosomes become generally confirmable, it seems best to adopt caution in characterizing the biochemical activities of kinetosomes. In a ciliate like *Tetrahymena* the ciliary basal bodies *in vivo* are surrounded by ribosomes and in close proximity to mitochondria; hence, there is no compelling logical necessity to assign them self-contained properties allowing for protein

[*] *Editor's note:* The results of Seaman *et al.* are also discussed by Kimball in this volume.

synthesis or oxidative phosphorylation, since these could easily be accomplished in a more traditional fashion by the neighboring organelles. On the other hand, what is most necessary in exploring kinetosomal function is material and techniques for approaching the problem of how the protein units become polymerized into the fibrous structures characteristic of the kinetid.

C. Movements of Flagella and Cilia

1. the form of beat

The individual flagellum or cilium of a protozoan is able actively to undergo virtually any contortion possible to a thread attached at one end, as an examination of *Peranema* or *Bodo* at high light-microscope magnification will readily demonstrate. Determination of the sequence of forms assumed during actual, *normal* swimming movements is something else again. The angular velocity of the normally beating organelle is too great for the human eye to follow at any microscopic resolution, hence one must resort to tricks of one sort or another. The slowing of activity by cold or a viscous medium is probably the most convenient artifice for direct observation but may substantially alter the form of beat. Use of high-speed cinematography combined with controlled intermittent illumination permits one in effect to slow down movement by observing momentary stages in successive beating cycles, but this is useful only if the organism under observation will stay in one field long enough to be photographed repeatedly, and cannot reveal flagella or cilia in a normally swimming cell. Improved modern techniques of ultra-high-speed cinematography have scarcely been exploited as yet but should yield so much more information that the best observations of the past may have to be revised (Jahn, 1963). In any event, the inescapable limitation of any photographic technique is that it can record only those movements occurring within the focal plane of the microscope, and any brief departure from that plane may escape notice.

The most satisfactory published observations on the form of beat of protozoan flagella are those by Lowndes (see 1941, 1943a,b, 1945). He placed flagellates in a trough roomy enough to accommodate their normal, spiral swimming paths and took high-speed motion pictures at a magnification low enough to have some depth of focus. The result was a recording of the changes in position of the cell at short intervals over a period of time. Since the anterior end of the cell vibrates in response to the main component of flagellar beat, he could determine the timing and the effect of each beat on the cell's position. These records were correlated with photographs taken at higher magnifications of moving flagella and with direct observations of the shapes and positions of flagella in living and fixed cells. His major conclusions are as follows:

(1) Waves of contraction pass along the flagellum in a continuous series

always from base to tip. (2) Direct photographic evidence (*Peranema*) demonstrates that the waves may increase both in velocity and in amplitude as they progress along the flagellum, hence the flagellum is adding energy to the wave and is not a passive structure. In a rapidly swimming flagellate, the resistance of the water therefore tends to push the distal side of a wave back on itself, so that each wave becomes loop-shaped and, as it passes off the tip of the flagellum, causes the latter to move around a circular path. (3) During rapid swimming, the flagellum of a flagellate is always held to the side, never in front, of the cell. These three phenomena result in two forces: one that pushes against the cell at the base of the flagellum, causing that end of the cell to vibrate away from the flagellum, and a rotatory force that tilts the body and the flagellum into a slightly different plane with each beat. Therefore the cell rotates and gyrates about its long axis and, acting on the principle of an inclined plane, screws itself through the water. Any spiral structure or flattening of the cell body will enhance the rotation or gyration. The flagellum itself need contribute no forward component at all; it only ensures inclination and rotation.

Most of Lowndes's observations were made on euglenoid flagellates, but he found the same sort of movement in others, including *Monas stigmatica*. He convincingly demonstrated that the classic diagrams of this species by Krijgsman (1925), which are still widely reproduced as representative of flagellate movement, depict only some of the variants that may be seen during slow or confined swimming.

If a flagellum is too short to accommodate a complete wavelength, Lowndes observed, it will rotate around a conical path, acting itself as an inclined plane or propeller and creating a current of water directed toward its base. Lowndes's observations of biflagellate cells are incomplete, and more study of these and of cells with flagella attached elsewhere than near the anterior pole is needed.

The movement of animal sperm tails, investigated in great detail recently, is well reviewed by Fawcett (1961) and does not need discussion here. We may mention that undulations pass along the tail from base to tip, and occur primarily in one plane. The tail commonly is attached to the minute head rather rigidly by the mid-piece, so that the normal swimming position, with the tail pushing the head in front, is mechanically credible.

Most observations of living cilia have necessarily been made on those that are large enough to see in action; for example, the long, compound cilia of mollusc gills or the membranelles of ciliate protozoa. The extensive records of the former by Gray (1930) and of the latter by Sleigh (1956, 1960) demonstrate that they move in one plane, the effective beat being erect and relatively rigid, brought about by an energetic bending of the base of the composite organelle, and the recovery being limp and flexural as the bend passes up the shaft and a weaker counter-bend brings it back to its initial angle relative to the body surface.

For the simpler and more fundamentally interesting case of individual cilia beating within a ciliated field, no comparable observations of normally active, living structures are possible. The best photographic records (for example, of *Opalina* by Sleigh, 1960) can present only profile views at the edge of a stationary cell and leave open the possibility that individual cilia within the field may constantly be bending out of the plane of the picture. The most reliable method yet devised for studying the configurations of such cilia is the instantaneous fixation of active ciliates, followed by gentle staining procedures, as introduced by Gelei and modified with great success by Párducz (1952, 1954, 1958b, 1962c). As shown in Figs. 6 to 8, this method can preserve with remarkable faithfulness the waves of ciliary activity representing successive beating cycles over the surface of the cell, and permits one to examine individual cilia fixed in successive stages of the cycle. Reliability of the method has been tested by various means (e.g., Doroszewski, 1958) and is indicated by the fact that characteristic wave patterns appear reproducibly in cells that are fixed in known states of locomotor activity (Section III,C,2,*b*).

Párducz (1954, 1958b, 1961) finds that the effective stroke of a *Paramecium* cilium during normal forward swimming begins when the cilium is directed anteriad and somewhat to the left (as seen by an observer looking down at the ciliated surface). The cilium executes a rapid, erect stroke toward the right posterior, the amplitude of the beat being about 90°. At the end of the effective stroke, the cilium becomes limp, bends over to the right, and rotates counterclockwise until the next effective stroke starts. The active stroke is about six times as fast as the recovery. Most interestingly, Párducz observed (and this observation has been confirmed in several other laboratories, including our own) that, following some kinds of trauma, cilia may eliminate the effective stroke, moving steadily counterclockwise in a continuation of their recovery phase. This conical, propeller-like rotation resembles that reported by Lowndes for short flagella and is assumed by Párducz to represent a primitive, apolar movement; it of course is ineffectual in locomotion of a ciliate. The effective stroke of an unspecialized ciliate cilium thus would appear to be superimposed on a primitive flagellar type of movement. Since protozoan cilia can readily change their beating direction, an effective stroke presumably may be initiated from any point in the apolar path.

Párducz has examined a number of ciliate species and finds the same primary apolar rotation, interrupted by an effective stroke, to be characteristic of all of their simple cilia. For the compound cirri of hypotrichs, and for the simple cilia of vertebrate ciliated epithelia, he confirms the observations of other workers that the effective and recovery strokes occur within a single plane. The metazoan epithelial cilium normally beats in a fixed direction, which only

Figs. 6–8. Photomicrographs of *Paramecium multimicronucleatum* fixed with osmium tetroxide-mercuric chloride and progressively stained with iron hematoxylin. (Contributed by B. Párducz.)

rarely is reversible within the same plane. Its activity thus is restricted and simplified, the possibility of a choice in angle of beating being reduced by the loss of the apolar recovery movement.

2. MECHANISMS OF BEAT

It is quite clear that the machinery responsible for the rhythmic beating of cilia and flagella exists within the shaft of the organelle itself. Direct evidence for this view comes most recently from experiments which have shown that isolated flagella and cilia obtained in the course of treatment designed to produce cell models (Section II,B,4) will beat rhythmically in the presence of ATP under the proper conditions. In all probability, these isolated, but beating, flagella and cilia do not possess an attached basal body, but confirmation of this probability is difficult to obtain. Indirect evidence is provided by micro-cinematographic observations of *Peranema* flagella (Lowndes, preceding section) and of beating sperm tails (Gray, 1955), which show that energy is expended throughout the length of the flagellar shaft.

Older (pre-electron-microscope) theories of ciliary and flagellar movement are of historical interest and have been summarized by Gray (1928) and Fawcett (1961). In addition, much work has been done on sperm motility, and recent views have been outlined by Fawcett and by Bishop (1962). We wish here to summarize two rather different modern points of view concerning the mechanism of beating. The first of these implicates the 9 peripheral fibrils as the seat of contractile processes; the second, instead, implicates the inner matrix that holds the 9 peripheral and 2 central fibrils together.

No hypothesis to date is adequate to explain all of the observed forms of flagellar and ciliary beat,* and the recent proposals are oriented toward assigning morphological correlates to the necessary functional elements designated by Gray (1951). These are (1) the contractile element, needed to produce changes in dimensions, (2) the compression element, needed to resist contraction so that the cilium does not simply collapse under stress but rather that the stress of contraction becomes expressed as a bending couple, and (3) a conducting element that effects the coordinated propagation of the wave of bending up the shaft.

* Ed's note: This subject is also discussed in this volume by Jahn and Bovee.

FIG. 6. Small portion of cell surface with parts of four metachronal waves. Most of the overlapping cilia shown are in the recovery phase; any cilia fixed in their much briefer effective stroke are erect and extend out of the plane of the photograph.

FIG. 7. Whole cell showing the metachronal wave pattern characteristic of normal forward swimming.

FIG. 8. Whole cell fixed after immersion in KCl. Metachronal wave pattern at posterior end of cell is that characteristic of backward swimming. Normal pattern has become reestablished at anterior end of cell.

The hypothesis proposed by Bradfield (1955) and variously discussed by many subsequent authors assigns these elementary functions in the following way: It is assumed (1) that the 9 peripheral fibrils are contractile, and that bending to one side is the result of localized shortening of one or more of these fibrils on the concave side of the cilium; (2) that the stiffness of the cilium, that is, the compression element, resides in the interfibrillar matrix, or in turgor pressure produced osmotically and contained by an elastic tension in the ciliary membrane (J. E. Harris, 1961); (3) that the propagation of contraction occurs in the outer fibrils in which a wave of contraction passes distally, the central pair of fibrils being specialized for a more rapid conduction of their own contraction; and (4) that the beat is initiated by a stimulus acting on the basal body beneath one of the outer fibrils, causing a wave of contraction to spread up that fibril, followed by a spread of the stimulus around and through the basal body initiating contractions successively in the other outer fibrils, and in the central pair, which, contracting rapidly, provides additional stiffness for the effective stroke.

This hypothesis offers the attractive and unifying idea that contraction in flagella and cilia, like contraction in muscle and in myonemes, is associated with visible fibrous structures. The model of muscle contraction proposed by Hanson and Huxley (1955), which involves the sliding of filaments of actin over interdigitating filaments of myosin, has even been extended to cilia by J. E. Harris (1961), though in a fashion that surpasses credulity; there is no evidence that any of the fibrils of the axoneme become arranged in a hexagonal array at any stage of beating. Furthermore, a weakness in the sliding-fibril hypothesis in ciliary movement is the fact that the fibrils appear not to be attached to each other or to anything else at their distal terminations (Gibbons and Grimstone, 1960).

The original proposal of Bradfield envisaged ciliary beating as occurring in Manton's plane with the effective stroke toward that side of the shaft occupied by fibril 1. It is clearly necessary, however, to have a mechanism that will allow an effective stroke in any direction, as well as a bending out of the plane of beat on the return stroke. Sleigh's modification of Bradfield's hypothesis meets at least the first of these requirements. Sleigh (1960) assumes that the effective and recovery phases are inseparable parts of one continuous contraction process. He suggests that only the 9 outer fibrils are contractile, that localized but self-propagating contractions occur in these, and that cross-bonding of the outer fibrils occurs, so that contraction of short lengths of outer fibrils produces localized bending. The contraction cycle is initiated in one or a neighboring pair of outer fibrils at their base, thus determining the plane of bending toward the initial point of contraction. A wave of contraction then spreads up the fibrils and around the fibril cylinder, effecting recovery as it spreads distally. Sleigh argues that the form of beat of various cilia and flagella is explainable by variations in (1) the interval between passage of the contraction stimulus to successive fibrils, (2) the time for which the fibrils remain contracted before relaxing, (3) the frequency of basal stimulation initiating successive beats, and (4) the rate of propagation of the contraction along the fibrils.

During the effective stroke the tip of the cilium often has a greater angular velocity than the base; hence, it appears likely that the cilium has at least an additional stiffness during the effective stroke. Sleigh's hypothesis does not include any factors that would make the cilium stiffer during its effective beat, but Bradfield (1955) has implicated a rapid over-all contraction of the central pair. Weber (1958) has suggested that the differing effects of inhibitors on the movement of "models" of flagella and cilia can be explained by assuming that (1) flagella are normally relaxed, ATP causing alternating contractions on both sides of the flagellum, whereas (2) cilia are symmetrically contracted at the beginning of the effective stroke, and ATP causes bending by relaxation. Hence, the stiffness might be a reflection of properties of the resting state. Direct measurements of stiffness during beating and recovery have not been undertaken for single cilia, though Carter (1924) and Yoneda (1960, 1962) have assessed the stiffness and torque produced during the beating of the large abfrontal cirri of the marine mussel *Mytilus*.

J. E. Harris's suggestion (1961) that an elastic membrane and internal turgor pressure are the factors responsible for the stiffness of the shaft (compression element) appears to be ruled out by the discovery of Satir and Child (1963) that the beating cilia in ATP-reactivated, glycerinated models of ciliated epithelium from frogs do not possess any membrane. Electron micrographs of these preparations clearly show that the ciliary membranes and much of the cell membrane have been destroyed; in essence, these beating cilia are naked axonemes. Hence, in the hypothesis assuming contracting peripheral fibrils, cross-bonding through the axonemal matrix must be the element resisting compression. A major obstacle to the confirmation of this hypothesis is the fact that the amount of shortening required of a fibril on the inside of a bending flagellum is only about 6% of the extended length, assuming the radius of maximum curvature is 4 μ. It is highly doubtful whether the electron microscope could reliably distinguish a variation in fibril length of this small a magnitude.

On the other hand, Satir (1963) has discovered dimensional changes of an entirely different sort associated with phases of ciliary beat. With the electron microscope, Satir has studied sections of cilia in known phases of beat, using for his material instantaneously fixed metachronal waves from the lateral epithelium of the gills of the fresh-water lamellibranch, *Elliptio*. In particular, he finds two changes, observable in cross sections, that appear to correlate with the phase of beat: (1) changes in the "inner area," that is, in the cross-sectional area of the axoneme or cylinder of 9 peripheral fibrils, and (2) changes in the angle of the axis of symmetry of the 9 + 2 pattern, especially during the recovery stroke. The first observation indicates that ciliary bending is accompanied by changes in the diameter and possibly the shape of the axoneme and suggests that, in the absence of an actual shortening of the peripheral fibrils, localized bending might occur by a "puckering" of the matrix, possibly by a shortening of radial elements seen in electron micrographs (Section II,A,2). The meaning of the second observation is not clear, but Satir's measurements led him to postulate that during the stroke the central pair of filaments rotates within the cross section and that the bridge (ordinarily assumed to be a constant connective between outer fibrils 5 and 6 in metazoan cilia) migrates from fibril to fibril following the central pair. In Satir's view, contraction *per se* is the property of the axonemal matrix, which expands and contracts during the course of the beat, and no change occurs in the lengths of the axial fibrils. We await with interest the publication and extension of these views; meanwhile it is quite clear that a closer observation of the morphology of sections of cilia in known phases of beat needs to be generally undertaken.

D. Genetic Aspects of Flagellar Motility

If flagellar movement involves a series of reactions or several macromolecular reactants, whose specificity is under genetic control, it should be possible to obtain genetic mutants showing impaired motility and to investigate the problem of flagellar movement by genetic analysis. Lewin (1952b, 1954) has obtained such mutants at several distinct loci for *Chlamydomonas moewusii*; the phenotypes range from mutants having no flagella to mutants having long or short flagella with varying degrees of impaired motility. Of the paralyzed mutants examined, no differences from wild-type flagella were found in fine structure (Gibbs *et al.*, 1958) or in serological specificity (Mintz and Lewin, 1954). Lewin (1954) suggests that certain of the genes are responsible for the production of "transmissible factors," since some mutants will recover their motility when paired in dikaryons with wild-type or with other "recoverable" mutants. The possible nature of these transmissible factors remains undetermined; they do not appear to be recoverable or transmissible in cell-free extracts. Recently, other physiological differences between wild type and certain paralyzed mutants have been found: Ronkin (1959) reports that the respiration of a paralyzed mutant was only 86% of that of the wild type; Ronkin and Buretz (1960) report that the same mutant has a much larger proportion of readily exchangeable intracellular potassium than the wild type; Brokaw (1960) reports that another paralyzed mutant contains only 30–40% of the flagellar ATPase activity of the wild type.

III. Locomotor Systems of Flagella and Cilia

A. Introduction to the Facts of Coordination

The observer of ciliated cells in action can scarcely doubt that cilia somehow cooperate. A one-way stream of fluid is caused to pass over a vertebrate ciliated epithelium. Considerably more complex currents and vortices are maintained by the ciliature of a feeding bivalve mollusc or a simultaneously feeding and swimming ciliate. In a sparsely ciliated organism such as a hypotrich or entodiniomorph ciliate, motor organelles widely separated on the body surface start, stop, or change their beating direction in harmony. Careful observation, under appropriate conditions, of an extensively ciliated surface usually reveals the passage over it of metachronal waves; each wave represents a sequence of rows of cilia that are in the same phase of beat within the row and just slightly out of phase with adjacent rows.

It is perhaps not very helpful to remind ourselves that the facts of ciliary coordination have usually been inferred from these sorts of behavior, or deduced from observation of metachronal waves, rather than having been the result of precise recording of the sequences of action of the individual cilia of one organism. In practically all cases we simply assume that these sequences are not random, and because of the difficulty of making ideal observations we are perforce almost entirely limited to studying the most obvious kind of coordination, namely *metachrony*. Less interesting, but nevertheless important, is coordination by *synchrony*, especially within cirri and membranelles. Lastly, we must acknowledge the virtual absence of useful information on the behavior of flagella in those flagellates that use two or more in locomotion; we do not know whether completely uncoordinated systems (*achrony*) ever occur.

Knight-Jones (1954) has categorized the varieties of metachronal coordination with great insight. The variety is a function of the relation between (1) the direction of passage of the metachronal wave crest and (2) the direction of the effective stroke of the cilia (Fig. 9). If these are both in the same direction the metachrony is called *symplectic;* if they are in opposite directions the metachrony is *antiplectic*. The intermediate condition, in which the direction of effective beat is perpendicular to the direction in which the wave travels is called *diaplectic;* if the beat is to your right, as you stand on the cell and look in the direction of the receding waves, it is *dexioplectic;* if to your left, it is *laeoplectic*.

Knight-Jones points out that symplectic metachrony is efficient in transporting particles, whereas anti- or diaplectic coordination is more efficient in producing water currents, and the diaplectic type most readily permits the fusion of cilia in compound organelles.

The functional significance of the kind of metachrony seems to make sense

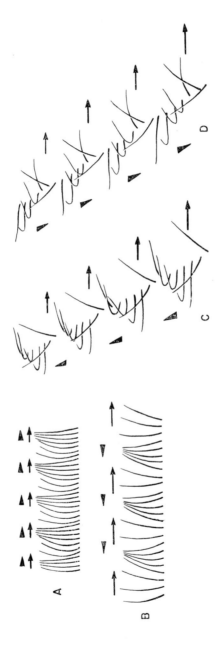

Fig. 9. Diagrams illustrating the four main types of metachronal coordination. In each diagram, the effective beat of the cilia is to the right (shafted arrows); the direction of passage of metachronal waves is shown by the wedge-shaped arrowheads. A, Symplectic metachrony. B, Antiplectic metachrony. C, Dexioplectic. D, Laeoplectic metachrony. In A and B, the cilia are seen from the side; in C and D, the rows are seen from above in perspective. (Redrawn from Knight-Jones, 1954.)

among the protozoa: symplectic metachrony is prominent in *Opalina* and *Isotricha,* both gut-dwellers living as it were in a particulate surrounding; antiplectic metachrony is the general condition in *Paramecium* and *Colpidium* when swimming free; diaplectic metachrony is evident in the coordination of the membranellar band of *Stentor,* functioning largely to circulate water.

The kind of metachrony displayed by a cell or tissue is a property that is fixed, relatively invariable, and characteristic of the species. Knight-Jones discusses the phylogenetic implications of the occurrence of dexio- versus laeo-plectic metachrony within the metazoa. Within the protozoa, comparable observations have not been recorded. However, it appears to be generally true that the kind of metachrony remains fixed. In *Opalina* the metachrony is always symplectic, even during backward swimming (Okajima, 1953). Hence, the direction of passage of the metachronal wave may bear a fixed relation to the direction of effective stroke. Some of the important implications of this are discussed in Section III,C. Exceptions probably occur; Párducz (1954) noted occasional antiplectic metachrony in *Isotricha.*

The inviting possibility that ciliary coordination is governed by differentiated proto-neural structures within the ciliated cells has been so often reiterated that, in spite of a spectacular scarcity of evidence, it is widely accepted as proven fact. In the following section (III,B) we shall first review briefly the historical bases for this assumption in the morphological studies of light microscopists, and then survey the known details of ultrastructure for the protozoan species that are most important in current experimental studies. The last decade has brought a surge of interest in mechanisms of protozoan ciliary coordination, largely as the result of: (1) the careful analyses of ciliary activity by Párducz, using his profitable technique of instantaneous fixation (Section II,C,1); (2) the studies of the Japanese school under Kinosita on metachrony and reversal in *Paramecium* and *Opalina;* (3) the demonstration by Seravin of coordination in ATP-reactivated models of *Euplotes;* and (4) the studies of Sleigh on membranellar metachrony in *Stentor.* These, with other relevant data and their theoretical interpretations, will be discussed in Section III,C.

B. PROTOZOAN FIBRILLAR SYSTEMS

1. LIGHT MICROSCOPY

The so-called fibrillar systems of protozoa comprise various fibrous and linear patterns occurring within and at the surfaces of protozoan cells and constituting a major feature of their morphological differentiation. The apparent direct association of many of these with the motor organelles of flagellates and ciliates suggests a morphogenetic or physiological relationship, recognized in the common terms "motor apparatus" or "flagellar apparatus." Inevitably, the light microscopists whose meticulous studies revealed the fibrillar systems were led to speculate on their significance, and several more or less distinct schools of thought emerged during the early decades of this century.

In flagellates, the fibrillar system commonly includes root fibrils and/or parabasal fibrils, plus an array of other structures peculiar to certain groups of zooflagellates. A characteristic tuft of flagella, its tight cluster of basal bodies (collectively called the blepharoplast or centroblepharoplast) and its complement of intracellular appendages, accompanied by a nucleus, form a unit in trichomonads that Janicki (1915) called the karyomastigont. The unit lacking the nucleus is the akaryomastigont, or, more simply, mastigont (Kirby, 1944). Either mastigonts or karyomastigonts may be multiplied in the complex organization of the higher zooflagellates.

Kofoid and Christiansen (1915) considered that the fibrillar system of *Giardia* might logically serve in the coordination of its four pairs of flagella, and applied to the complex the term "neuromotor apparatus" recently introduced for ciliates (see below). Swezy (1916) extended this hypothesis to include other zooflagellates. In general, however, the question of coordination in the flagellates has received little sustained attention.

Although he was not the first to suggest a neural function for ciliate fibrillar structures, Sharp (1914) initiated an era of free-wheeling speculation when he described for the complex ciliate, *Diplodinium*, a morphologically integrated system of fibers connecting a central "motorium" with the basal bodies of cilia and other parts of the cell. The whole array was called the neuromotor system or apparatus, and was assumed on the basis of its topography, considered in relation to the movements of the organelles, to be an intracellular nervous system. Subsequent students in Kofoid's laboratory reported analogous neuromotor systems in other ciliates (e.g., *Euplotes*, Yocom, 1918; *Paramecium*, Lund, 1933).

Beginning in 1926, Klein and Gelei independently described pellicular and subpellicular patterns revealed by silver-impregnation techniques (Klein, 1942; J. von Gelei, 1936); these were called the silverline, neuroneme, or neuroformative systems and were believed by both investigators to play leading roles in coordination and in morphogenesis. Some parts of the silverline systems coincide with some parts of the neuromotor systems of the Kofoid school.

Chatton's definition of the kinetid was first formulated in 1924 for flagellates and subsequently extended to apply to all ciliated and flagellated cells. His concept of basic cellular organization (1931) comprehended the energid, as the nucleocytoplasmic unit, and the kinetid as the kinetic unit. He stressed the genetic continuity and phylogenetic significance of the kinetosome, and proposed that centrioles in nonflagellated cells represent vestigial kinetids that have temporarily or permanently lost their flagella and retain only the ancillary function of participation in mitotic events. In ciliates, the secondary mitotic function has been lost, but kinetosomes play a dominant role in morphogenesis. They are always present as an infraciliature, even in species that discard some or all of their cilia at some stage in their life cycles (Chatton *et al.*, 1929). Chatton and his colleagues (Chatton and Lwoff, 1935a,b; Chatton and Brachon, 1935) identified the kinetodesmos and distinguished between this intracellular fiber (passing along the kinety always to the right of the kinetosomes: rule of desmodexy) and the superficial patterns that constitute the silverline system. Their silver technique impregnates the kinetosomes, as do those of Klein and Gelei, and at least some of the linear patterns described by the latter authors.

In its embattled career as everyman's research subject, *Paramecium* has been analyzed, interpreted, and argued over by leading proponents of all of these points of view, and others as well. Thoughtful reviews of the situation at the time have been published by Lund (1933), Taylor (1941), Wichterman (1953), Párducz (1958a, 1962a), and Ehret and Powers (1959). A brief summary of the light-microscope picture of it as a representative ciliate is in order.

The cell surface is sculptured in a highly characteristic mosaic of polygons, from the centers of which the cilia arise and at the anteroposterior boundaries of which trichocysts are located. The lattice defined by the polygon borders is visible in living cells. It appears in stained specimens and in some silver impregnations as a linear network. It has been considered variously as a fiber system (indirect connecting system of Klein) lying immediately beneath the pellicle in the ectoplasmic ridges, and as a representation of the ridges themselves. Kinetosomes and trichocysts in each longitudinal kinety are connected like beads on a string by a line that is not visible in life but shows up clearly following some staining and silver-impregnation techniques—not necessarily the same preparations as show the polygonal lattice. Cross-branches connect these meridional silverlines (neuronemes, interciliary fibers, direct connecting system) at occasional, apparently random intervals. According to Párducz (1958a, 1962a), the meridional silverlines do not appear to be continuous with the polygonal lattice; the two systems are contiguous only where the trichocysts perforate the cross-bars of the lattice.

In addition to these argentophilic patterns, kinetodesma are present, paralleling each kinety on its right side. Occasionally, following injury, the kinetodesma may be impregnated with silver (Párducz, 1958a), but ordinarily they are argentophobic. Yet another fiber system is the infraciliary lattice, seen only by G. von Gelei (1937) in a silver preparation. It lies deeper than any of the other systems, does not connect with them or with the basal bodies, and forms a very roughly polygonal network.

Fiber patterns in the oral region are complex, and include elaborations of at least the pellicular lattice and interciliary fiber systems. In addition, Lund (1933) identified as a motorium a small, bilobed mass on the left dorsal wall of the buccal cavity, from which fibers extended both out into the endoplasm and laterally to join the interciliary fiber system.

Thus the cortex of *Paramecium* is equipped with at least four sets of linear patterns that appear by light microscopy to be distinct, all of them topographically related to the fundamental infraciliature. Other ciliates are no less generously endowed. Superficial silverline networks are a property of most of them, interciliary fibers or primary silverline meridians (often much distorted from the meridional position) are common; kinetodesma are detected at least in a majority of holotrichs and heterotrichs (Villeneuve-Brachon, 1940); and other patterns not represented in *Paramecium* are frequent. The hypotrich ciliate, *Euplotes*, has a superficial, net-like silverline system, even on those parts of the body that lack cilia (Tuffrau, 1960), and in addition a system of deep intracellular fibers that are readily visible in life or after various staining procedures (including, spectacularly, protein silver; see Dragesco, 1962). These fibers diverge from each of the compound cirri on the ventral surface of the organism; most of them end shortly in the surrounding cytoplasm, but heavier ones from the large anal cirri pass anteriad and converge near the cytostome. Yocom (1918) and Taylor (1920) identified a motorium at this point of convergence, but later authors (Tuffrau, 1960) question its existence. A fiber lying beneath the membranellar band was also said to join the motorium.

2. ELECTRON MICROSCOPY

a. Paramecium. The polygonal sculpturing of the *Paramecium* cell surface is evident in all electron micrographs (Figs. 2–4). Pronounced ectoplasmic ridges separate dimples at the center of which the cilia are rooted. Trichocysts reach the surface in the ridges that provide cross-bars of the polygonal lattice. The silverline pattern, comprising both the external lattice and the interciliary meridians, consists not of fibers but of configurations of membranes that constitute the pellicle.

The outermost layer of the pellicle is a unit (three-ply) membrane that is continuous over the entire cell surface, including the surfaces of the cilia and all orifices. Immediately beneath this continuous membrane is a mosaic of membrane-limited alveoli. A symmetrical pair of inflated alveoli occupies each ectoplasmic dimple. The periphery of the pair coincides approximately with the crests of the ectoplasmic ridges. Medially, the membranes of the two members of the pair abut closely on each other along a line running from anterior trichocyst to cilium and from cilium to posterior trichocyst. Centrally, the alveoli are indented to permit the cilium (or pair of cilia) to emerge between them. To the right of each single cilium, or the posterior member of the pair, all three unit-membrane layers of the pellicle (the continuous surface membrane and the outer and inner boundaries of the alveolus) are invaginated to form a tiny, finger-like structure called the parasomal sac. The median line of contiguity of paired alveoli, repeated in each polygon along a kinety, is the primary silverline meridian or interciliary line. Silver is deposited along this line, at the points of trichocyst attachment between polygons, at the bases of the cilia where the alveolar membranes surround them tightly, and in the parasomal sacs (Dippell, 1962). When the external lattice is impregnated, the lines of contiguity between adjacent pairs of alveoli, coinciding generally with the ectoplasmic crests, presumably are the sites of silver deposition. There is no evidence in electron micrographs to explain the readily observed differences in staining properties of the external lattice and meridional systems (Párducz, 1962a).

The kinetodesmos is made up of overlapping kinetodesmal fibrils arising from successive kinetosomes along the kinety. The loose bundle passes anteriad in the ectoplasmic ridge separating laterally adjacent polygons (Figs. 2–4). Individual fibrils never make contact with each other or with any other element of the kinetome; they taper to an end four or five polygons anterior to their point of origin.

The infraciliary lattice is the network of very fine, slightly sinuous filaments found at the level of the kinetosome bases (Fig. 5). Details of its ramification are not clear at the electron-microscope level, but presumably G. von Gelei's photomicrograph (1937; Párducz, 1958a, 1962a) provides a good indication of its over-all pattern.

In addition to these four systems of the light microscopist, the tubular fibrils revealed by the electron microscope constitute yet another differentiation. As described above (Section II,A,4,b), two sets of these fibrils depart from each single kinetosome or the posterior member of each pair (the anterior partner being provided with only one set). These diverge, one set passing to the right and posterior and the other to the left and more or less anterior. They extend only as far as the near slope of the adjacent ectoplasmic ridge.

Each kinetosome or kinetosome pair on the *Paramecium* body surface thus is surrounded by its own territory, defined by an ectoplasmic dimple and a pair of pellicular alveoli. From the kinetosome(s) within this territory arise two (three) sets of tubular fibrils that never extend beyond it, and one kinetodesmal fibril that does extend anteriad between but not into other territories. Beneath it lies part of a network of filaments that may make only sporadic contact with the kinetosomes. With the possible exception of this filamentous system, no fibrous structure directly connects any body kinetosome with any other. Kinetodesmal and tubular fibrils diverge in an extremely precise pattern that has distinctive polarity and asymmetry.

Roth (1958a) observed a zone of interwoven fine filaments adjacent to the buccal cavity in *Paramecium aurelia* and suggested that this might correspond to the motorium of Lund (1933). In *P. multimicronucleatum*, however, which is the species studied by Lund, the filamentous reticulum surrounding much of the buccal wall is very much more extensive than his motorium.

b. Opalina. The cell surface of *Opalina*, studied by Noirot-Timothée (1959),

Blanckart (1957), and Pitelka (1956), is traversed longitudinally by very regular, high, narrow crests. In the cytoplasm within each crest runs a ribbon of tubular fibrils that, in this case, do not appear to arise from kinetosomes. Several such crests separate adjacent kineties. Kinetosomes are close-packed within each kinety, and from the base of each arise one or two bundles of fine fibrils, whose ultrastructure is not clear. Pitelka showed that these bundles pass anteriad, terminating at the next kinetosome in the row, but none of the authors was able to discover whether the fibrils, which run slightly to one side of the axis of the kinety, were on the right or the left. Noirot-Timothée, recognizing the suggestive similarity in position of these fibrils to ciliate kinetodesma, called them by that name. If, however, the direction of skewing of triplet fibrils in *Opalina* kinetosomes is the same (and this is not known) as that in organisms studied more recently, then Noirot-Timothée's Plate III, Fig. 2, is a view from the inside of the cell, and the interkinetosomal fibrils are at the organism's left of the kinety. No observations on soundly identified kinetodesmal fibrils in ciliates suggest that the rule of desmodexy is ever breached.

c. Euplotes. Taylor's (1920) experimental work on *Euplotes* makes this ciliate a particularly intriguing object and Roth (1956, 1957) chose the same species, *Euplotes patella,* for a critical, early, electron-microscope study. From his work it seems fairly clear that the neuromotor fibers of Yocom (1918) and Taylor are composed of orderly bundles of tubular fibrils. Smaller clusters or single fibrils diverge from many of the kinetosomes of cirri and membranelles and interconnect adjacent cilia and adjacent compound organelles. In addition, tubular fibrils are layered immediately beneath the cell membrane, and a mass of interwoven fibrils or filaments located near the cytostome is tentatively identified as the motorium. Fibrils from kinetosomes interconnect with both of these complexes. No kinetodesma are present. The ultrastructure of the silverline system has not been studied.

d. Stentor. *Stentor* is an organism of such extraordinary complexity that we can summarize only the most pertinent details (see review by Tartar, 1961; Randall and Jackson, 1958; Fauré-Fremiet and Rouiller, 1958a,b). Kinetodesma are conspicuously present and are composed of overlapping individual fibrils, but otherwise differ profoundly from kinetodesma of *Paramecium.* The fibrils depart from kinetosomes of the body kineties and pass to the right and *posteriad.* The kinetosomal attachment is broad and the substance of the fibril has a banded appearance. Randall and Jackson, however, believe that each fibril is bifurcated basally, the two branches being connected by cross-fibrils. In any event, as soon as the fibrils join the kinetodesmal bundle they are clearly tubular, with a constant diameter of about 20 mμ. The question might be raised, therefore, whether they are analogous to the posterior tubular-fibril ribbon of the *Paramecium* kinetid rather than to the anterior, striated, kinetodesmal fibril. The

Stentor kinetodesmal bundle is composed of a very large number of tubular fibrils, arranged in up to 24 slightly curving sheets with 20 to 30 fibrils per sheet. Lateral linkages are apparent between fibrils in a sheet, but adjacent sheets appear to be unconnected.

The oral membranelle system of *Stentor* is not associated with kinetodesma. A membranelle consists of two or three rows of 20 to 25 cilia each. From kinetosomes of each membranelle, tubular fibrils extend basally and converge, fan-like, to form a single compact bundle that reaches as much as 20 μ into the endoplasm. At their base the bundles bifurcate and meet those from neighboring membranelles in a continuous zigzag fiber. Cross sections of the fibril bundles at any level show a precise, hexagonal packing of constituent tubules. Tracts of fibrous material of uncertain structure connect adjacent membranelle roots at the cortical level.

In addition to the kinetodesma, *Stentor* possesses another longitudinal fiber system, which is not known to be directly connected to kinetosomes. Stout bundles of fine, slightly sinuous filaments lie beneath and slightly to one side of the kinetodesma. The filaments, of indeterminate length, are generally longitudinally oriented, but slender tracts pass laterally to connect adjacent bundles. Membrane-bounded vesicles and canals incompletely surround and partially penetrate the bundles. These filamentous structures are considered both by Randall and Jackson and by Fauré-Fremiet and Rouiller to be myonemes. Their identification as such is strongly supported by the fact that the stalk and body myonemes of the contractile vorticellid ciliates have a very similar structure. However, both sets of authors point out that the kinetodesma remain straight when the *Stentor* body is maximally contracted and hence are logically suspected of being contractile also.

Several other examples are known of tubular fibrils suspected of contractility. The contractile axostyle of the zooflagellate, *Pyrsonympha,* is quite similar in ultrastructure to the *Stentor* kinetodesmos (Grassé, 1956). Tubular fibrils surround contractile vacuoles and/or their exit canals in many ciliates (Rudzinska, 1958; Schneider, 1960; de Puytorac, 1960). The contractile haptonema of some chrysomonad flagellates is composed of tubular fibrils and membranes (Parke *et al.*, 1959). And tubular fibrils are present in the contractile tentacles of suctorian ciliates (Rouiller *et al.*, 1956; Rudzinska, 1962).

On the other hand, the rigid, skeletal trichites that compose the pharyngeal basket of gymnostome ciliates are also made up of regularly packed tubular fibrils (Rouiller *et al.*, 1957), as is the rigid pharyngeal rod organ of the euglenoid flagellate, *Peranema* (Roth, 1959). The arrangement of tubular fibrils in the cortex of *Paramecium* and in the very similar system of the tetrahymenid ciliates (Pitelka, 1961a) certainly does not seem consistent with a contractile function, and the same is true for *Euplotes.*

C. Mechanisms of Coordination

1. microsurgical experiments

A direct microsurgical attack on the problem of ciliary coordination has been attempted repeatedly. Almost always the results are equivocal because one cannot be certain what morphological entities within the cell are affected by the operation. A long series of investigators from Verworn (1889) and Jennings and Jamieson (1902) through Worley (1934), Hammond (1935), Balamuth (1942), and Doroszewski (1958) successfully demonstrated that ciliated fragments of cells can, provided enough cilia are present and even in the absence of endoplasm and nucleus, swim competently enough, showing coordination and some adaptive responses and generally behaving about as they would if they were parts of the intact cell. Within any continuous ciliary field, an ectoplasmic incision across the path of progression of metachronal waves usually (not always) results in some disturbance of metachrony, but not of ciliary reversal, which still occurs simultaneously all over the cell. Thus locomotor movements and responses are not dependent upon control by a single motor center, but continuity of metachrony requires continuity of the cell cortex, or of some undetermined part of it.

Sleigh (1957) has extended these results in experiments involving microdissection and careful measurements on the membranelle bands of *Stentor*. If cuts were made across the peristome, thereby separating the membranellar band into two or more proximal-distal segments (proximal being toward the cytostome), Sleigh usually observed a change (typically a decrease) in beating frequency distal to a cut, but there was no loss of metachrony within the isolated segments of the band. No transmission of metachronal waves across cuts was observed, but each segment set up its own set of waves conducted distally within it. The most proximal membranelle in a segment was regarded as a pacemaker in organizing the metachrony in its segment. In normal *Stentor*, Sleigh found that the wavelengths in the proximal region of the band were short, and that they increased with distance from the mouth; the mean intermembranellar distance also increased in this direction, however, so that in the normal animal there were always 6 membranelles in one wave. Hence, he concludes that the wave velocity depends on the number of membranelles involved in the transmission and not on the distance traveled by the wave. Sleigh's physiological experiments are discussed in the next section.

Choice of the hypotrich ciliate, *Euplotes patella,* permitted Taylor (1920) to perform a series of critical experiments. The cilia on the oral surface are aggregated into a row of adoral membranelles and 18 cirri precisely distributed in separated groups, accompanied by intracellular fibers described above (Section III,B,1). On the aboral surface are rows of single, nonmotile cilia. The membranelles and cirri together are responsible for all of the locomotor activities of the cell, and Taylor was able to classify these as nine distinct movements and to identify the manner of participation in each movement of each of the groups of ciliary organelles. Surgical transection of the anal cirri fibers or of the membranellar fiber, or destruction of the motorium, often resulted in disruption of those activities that depended upon integrated movement of membranelles and anal cirri. Movements of membranelles and cirri continued, but without concerted effect. Although these transections cut through the entire flattened body in the region of the fibers, similar cuts that did not involve the fibers had no disruptive effect on locomotion. Taylor, after considering and rejecting the possibilities of skeletal or contractile functions for the fibers, concluded that they serve to conduct excitations important in coordination of locomotor movements.

Although Taylor's observations are open to alternative interpretations (see Bělař, 1921; Jacobson, 1931), they constitute by far the most compelling argument—and in fact the only direct evidence—in favor of a coordinating function for *any* specific fibrillar structure in the protozoa. Because of its important implications, the work badly needs to be repeated.

2. PHYSIOLOGICAL EXPERIMENTS

a. Opalina. The beautiful work of Kinosita and Okajima, employing techniques of neurophysiology, has demonstrated a clear correlation in this organism between the direction of effective beat and the magnitude of the transmembrane potential of the cell. Figure 10, taken from Kinosita (1954), il-

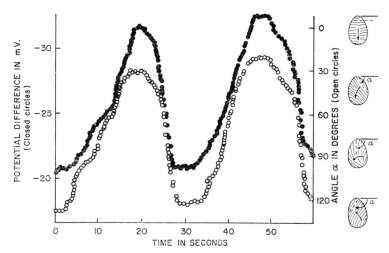

FIG. 10. A record of the simultaneous changes in transmembrane potential (dark circles) and beating direction of cilia (angle α; light circles) in *Opalina* during a period of spontaneously changing direction of ciliary beat. (Data from Kinosita, 1954.)

lustrates this correlation during two cycles of spontaneous ciliary reversal. Depolarization of the membrane can be produced experimentally by increasing the potassium concentration, and these depolarizations are accompanied by changes in the direction of beat. However, the change in beating direction follows the change in potential only if calcium is present; in calcium-depleted cells, potential changes occur without directional changes. Furthermore, Ueda (1956) has shown that the excitability of *Opalina* (measured as the threshold intensity of direct current stimulation needed to induce ciliary reversal) is dependent upon the presence of, and is proportional to the amount of, intracellular calcium. Microinjection of the common anions does not produce reversal, but a prolonged reversal is obtained by injecting citrate or oxalate.

Okajima (1953, 1954a,b) has described in great detail the transitions of patterns of metachronal activity in *Opalina*. The conduction velocity of the metachronal wave ranges from 80 to 240 μ per second; this is about 1/200 the speed of conduction of a very slow nerve impulse. As expected, the frequency of ciliary beat is proportional to the conduction velocity and equivalent to the number of waves passing over a fixed point in unit time. The frequency of beat is graded, however, over the surface, being higher at the anterior end; in addition, Okajima finds a gradient of excitability, determined by measuring the threshold of local direct-current stimulation of reversal. This gradient of excitability (1) is a property of the cell, not of the state of direction of beat, (2) corresponds to the gradient in frequency of beat and spread of metachronal waves, and (3) corresponds to variations in membrane resistance measured by Naitoh (1958). Okajima believes that the *pattern* of waves is determined by the membrane potential, but their *transmission* is by mechanisms of minimum interference, as proposed by Gray (1930; see Section III,C,3,*b*).

b. Paramecium. Worley (1934) showed that increasing levels of narcosis in *Paramecium* resulted first in loss of ability to change direction, second in loss of metachrony, and finally in cessation of ciliary beat. This suggests that different mechanisms operate in the three processes.

It is well known that ciliary reversal in *Paramecium* can be caused by chemical as well as electrical means. Kamada has long stressed the importance of intracellular calcium in ciliary reversal in *Paramecium caudatum* (1938, 1940; Kamada and Kinosita, 1940) and suggested that the chemical and electrical effects on ciliary beat were related through a mechanism involving intracellular calcium ions. In 1940, he proposed an hypothesis which we briefly adumbrate as follows: An anion (called X) exists within the cytoplasm which combines with and is stabilized by calcium ions, specifically. In the absence of calcium, this anion-X is unstable and breaks down. In so doing, anion-X acts on the cilia to cause a reversal in the direction of effective stroke.

Much of the recent work on ciliary coordination in *Paramecium* bears upon this hypothesis. In order to test directly some of Kamada's ideas, Yamaguchi

(1960b) studied the influx and efflux of calcium ions in *Paramecium caudatum* using the radioactive isotope Ca^{45}. Intracellular and extracellular calcium ions are readily exchangeable. Cells adapted to a medium of high calcium-ion concentration contain more calcium than cells adapted to a medium of low concentration. The rate of efflux of radioactive calcium is increased by increasing the proportion of potassium ions relative to calcium ions in the external medium. Furthermore, the rate of influx of radioactive calcium is more rapid into cells adapted to a medium of high K:Ca ion ratio than into cells adapted to a medium of low K:Ca ion ratio. This provides positive support to the assumption of Kamada and Kinosita (1940) and Kamada (1940) that in a medium rich in potassium ions, the latter enter in exchange with internal calcium ions.

The relationship between the transmembrane potential and the direction of ciliary beat (see preceding section) has been investigated in *Paramecium caudatum* by Yamaguchi (1960a). In this organism, there appears to be no *specific* depolarization of the membrane by potassium ions, sodium ions being equally effective, and calcium and magnesium ions being only less effective. The magnitude of the transmembrane potential increases with increasing dilu-

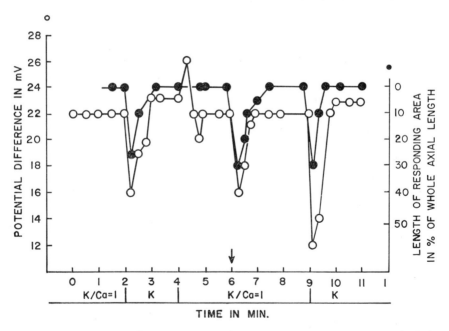

FIG. 11. A record of the simultaneous changes in transmembrane potential (light circles) and degree of ciliary reversal (dark circles) in *Paramecium caudatum* when the medium was altered from normal (K:Ca = 1) (2.5 mM KCl, 1.67 mM CaCl₂) to pure K ions (K; 5.0 mM KCl), and vice versa. A 1-sec. galvanic stimulus was also given, as indicated by the arrow. (From Yamaguchi, 1960a.)

tion of the medium. Using an intracellular microelectrode filled with 0.1M NH₄Cl, Yamaguchi found simultaneous changes in potential and degree of ciliary reversal when reversal was induced by an increase in K:Ca ratio or by galvanic stimulation (Fig. 11). Unlike the case in *Opalina,* potential changes in *Paramecium* could not be directly related to the direction of ciliary beat; rather, they correlated with the length of the anterior region which was in temporary reversal of beat. In instances in which the membrane became transiently hyperpolarized (Fig. 11, from 4.0 to 4.5 min.), the normal ciliary stroke was augmented, that is, presumably, the beating frequency increased temporarily.

Some of the older literature on ciliary reversal induced by electric currents has been reviewed by Jahn (1961) who has developed a consistent theory that makes it possible "by assuming *Paramecium* to be a core conductor immersed in a volume conductor and by applying the laws of polarizing currents . . . to explain all existing data on reversal of normal ciliary action, and also on activation of cilia in immobilized specimens by electrical current" (p. 369).

Precise data concerning the actual changes in direction of ciliary beat during potassium-induced reversal have been obtained by Párducz and Müller (1958) and Párducz (1959), using the techniques of dark-field time-exposure photomicrography and instantaneous fixation. During normal forward swimming, cilia beat posteriad and toward the right. Metachronal waves move from posterior to anterior (Párducz, 1954), their crests running diagonally across the body as shown in Fig. 7. In the high-potassium medium, after an initial, simultaneous, reverse stroke of all cilia, reversal becomes stabilized in a pattern of longitudinal metachronal waves that move almost transversely around the body (Fig. 12, stages 1–4). This changed pattern of "conduction of metachronal impulses" is gradually replaced by the normal forward-swimming pattern, which appears first at the anterior end and expands posteriorly (Fig. 8, and Fig. 12, stages 5–8). During this period of replacement, metachronal waves simultaneously move in different directions over different regions of the same cell, and at one stage (stage 7) this results in rotating movements around the posterior pole. Close analysis of the cilia themselves reveals that during reverse swimming the direction of ciliary beat is turned only about 30° away from normal, and the angle of the metachronal wave crest is turned by about an equal amount.

Potassium-induced reversal is an extreme and prolonged response, compared with responses exhibited under more normal conditions. The classic "avoiding reaction," analyzed in detail by Párducz (1956a) includes the same sequence of changes, but these are shorter and variable in duration. Still more interesting are limited responses to local stimuli (Párducz, 1956b, 1958b). Areas of varying size react with a change of varying degree in beating direction, as in *Opalina.* Following a stimulus of appropriate strength, metachronal waves radiate in all directions from the stimulated site, like ripples on water. Párducz vehemently concludes that no known fiber system can be held responsible for metachronal coordination, since excitation passes in broad waves, *in any direction* over the body surface. In further support of his conclusion, he points out that the metachronal waves of normal swimming pass over the body quite smoothly in a constant direction, and do not follow the pronounced curvature of the left pre-oral kineties.

Pigoń and Szarski (1955), using *Paramecium caudatum,* were able to obtain information relating to the net force exerted by the cilia during forward swimming. By using gum arabic to increase the viscosity of the medium, they showed that the velocity of forward movement is precisely inversely proportional to the

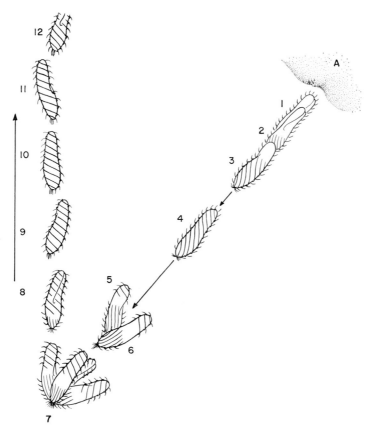

Fig. 12. The changes in ciliary metachrony of *Paramecium caudatum* during a typical avoiding reaction. The cilia, seen at the periphery of each stage, point roughly in the direction of their effective stroke; the solid lines, which run around the surface of each stage, represent metachronal wave crests. A, the stimulus causing ciliary reversal. 1–4, locomotion directly backward; 5–6, funneling backward; 7, skittling movement around the posterior pole; 8–12, forward swimming in the new direction. (After Párducz, 1959.)

viscosity of the medium. Hence, they conclude, following Stokes' law, that the net effective force of the ciliary beat is the same whether it is fast or slow. Furthermore, this supports the conclusions of Jensen (1893), Gray (1928), and others, that most of the work done by a cilium is in overcoming the viscous resistance of the medium.

c. *Membranellar Coordination in Spirotrichs.* Considerable attention recently has been focused on metachronal coordination in membranellar bands of spirotrichous ciliates. Two different lines of investigation will be discussed here, namely, Sleigh's work on *Stentor* using techniques of alteration of the medium, and Seravin's work on *Spirostomum* and *Euplotes* using ATP-activated models.

It is well known that in systems of metachronally coordinated cilia the frequency of beat is proportionally related to the velocity of passage of the metachronal waves, and that this velocity is equal to the product of the frequency and the wavelength. Sleigh (1956, 1957, 1961) has studied these relationships in the membranellar band of *Stentor polymorphus.* Like earlier workers, he has found that many physical and chemical agents can alter the frequency of beat or the wavelength, independently of each other. A decrease in temperature, for instance, decreased both the frequency and the wavelength; hence the wave velocity decreased also. With an increase in viscosity of the medium (up to 3 centipoises) the frequency of beat decreased but the wavelength increased, while the wave velocity remained constant. Magnesium chloride at 0.3 mM produced the reverse situation, namely, an increase in the frequency accompanied by a decrease in the wavelength such that, in this case also, the wave velocity remained constant. On the other hand, digitoxin (at 0.2 mg. per liter) caused only a slight increase in frequency but a large increase in wavelength, so that the wave velocity was greatly increased.

Using polyacrylamide, Sleigh (1961) studied metachronal changes in media with viscosities ranging from 3 to 9 centipoises. As the viscosity of the medium is increased through this range, the frequency of beat varies only about 10% from the average, but the wavelength is increased enormously as the viscosity increases, so that the wave velocity is actually doubled (Fig. 13). Sleigh points out, in this case, that this is exactly the behavior one would expect if the metachrony were governed largely by viscous-mechanical coupling, that is, by the interaction of neighboring membranelles through the external medium.

Seravin (1961) has made "models" of *Spirostomum ambiguum* and *Euplotes patella* by the saponin method (outlined in Section II,B,4). Essentially, these models are dead, extracted cells, much of whose morphology and organization, however, is preserved. When these models are placed in a medium of proper composition (pH, Mg ions, ATP, etc.), the cilia are reactivated and beat rhythmically. In the *Spirostomum* models, coordination among the cilia was completely lacking, and no locomotion of the models was observed. In the models of *Euplotes,* however, not only were the ciliary organelles reactivated, but the models began to crawl and swim. The swimming in *Euplotes* was largely the result of coordinated activity of the membranelles, which were said to contract "relatively harmoniously in the models"; Seravin does not specifically state that metachrony was observed. The cirri, responsible for crawling, were said to contract "very energetically but disorderly." These results are very important in their bearing on certain theories of conducted coordinating impulses, since they suggest that coordination of a sort can occur in "cells" that are deprived of their normal membrane permeabilities and mechanisms for regulating ion balance. Coordination was observed in models in a medium containing potassium ions (from 0.01 to 0.12M) or containing sodium ions (0.12M); hence it would seem unlikely that membrane phenomena, such as electrical potential or ion-regulating mechanisms, could be involved.

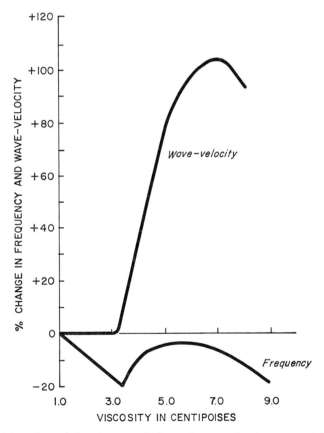

FIG. 13. The effect of the viscosity of the medium on the frequency of beat and on the velocity of passage of metachronal waves by the membranelles of *Stentor polymorphus*. (Simplified from Sleigh, 1961.)

3. THEORETICAL EXPLANATIONS OF METACHRONAL COORDINATION

The fact that all the cilia in a system may be beating with the same frequency but not beating in phase with each other provides the basis for metachrony. Metachrony does not always occur in such systems, especially in cases of very rapid beating such as the initial stage of ciliary reversal in *Paramecium* (Párducz, 1956a, 1959) and localized reversal induced in *Opalina* by deformation of the membrane (Naitoh, 1959). But the regular sequence of phasing observed in metachronal systems has long been a major problem for protozoologists and cell biologists.

Two general schools of thought have dominated discussion of this problem and continue to influence the design of experiments, the interpretation of results, and theoretical explanations. It seems easiest for us to couch our summary in terms of this dichotomy. The first, and older, school attempts to explain metachrony in terms of *phasing impulses conducted through the cell cortex;* the second school attempts explanations in terms of interactions of neighboring cilia by *mechanical and viscous coupling through the external medium.*

a. Impulses Conducted through the Cell Cortex. Most of the variations of theoretical explanations based on this idea assume that a ciliary beat (at least the effective stroke) requires an excitation-stimulus. In paramecia that exhibit depressed ciliary activity, the cilia undergo a simple rotating movement without any effective stroke (Section II,C,1); when an effective stroke is superimposed on this fundamental motion, metachrony can also be restored (Párducz, 1954, 1958b). Hence, a metachronal wave crest can be thought of as a locus of simultaneously excited cilia, each cilium being forced into the same phase of beat. The wave front of simultaneous excitation is thought to indicate the locus of simultaneously effective *metachronal impulses.* Hence the problem of workers in this school has been to localize the precise path of conduction of the metachronal impulse and to discover its physiological nature.

The discovery of complex systems of cortical fibrils led to the view that these fibrils may constitute the conducting paths of the metachronal impulse (Section III,B). Roth (1958b) has suggested that tubular fibrils might propagate impulses by processes similar to semiconduction. The possibility that impulses are mediated by acetylcholine, in a manner analogous to the way acetylcholine mediates the nervous control of muscle contraction, has prompted studies on the presence and localization of acetylcholine and acetylcholinesterase in protozoa. The evidence is confusing and contradictory: Beyer and Wense (1936) found acetylcholine and acetylcholinesterase in a species of *Paramecium;* Bülbring *et al.* (1949) found acetylcholine in *Trypanosoma rhodesiense;* Seaman and Houlihan (1951) found acetylcholinesterase in *Tetrahymena pyriformis* S, and showed that motility was reversibly inhibited by eserine and diisopropylfluorophosphate, which are specific inhibitors of acetylcholinesterase. Seaman (1951) reported that this esterase activity was localized in a "pellicular fraction" obtained by homogenization, extraction, and differential centrifugation. He suggests (1951, p. 170) "that conduction along the fibrillar structure which connects the base of individual cilium (sic) in the pellicle of the organism is similar to conduction along nerve fibers, and is dependent upon acetylcholinesterase activity for function."

On the other hand Mitropolitanskaya (1941) and Bullock and Nachmansohn (1942) could not demonstrate the presence of acetylcholinesterase in *Paramecium*; Tibbs (1960) could not find acetylcholinesterase activity in *Polytoma uvella, Polytomella caeca,* or *Tetrahymena pyriformis* W. Tibbs states (p. 121): "It is puzzling that Seaman and Houlihan were able to detect activity in this organism [*Tetrahymena*], albeit a different strain, to the extent of about 0.08 $\mu g/h/mg$ at room temperature, for such an activity would have easily been detected in our experiments. The smaller incubation times which these authors used must have given Beckmann reading differences which were approaching normal experimental variation." Similar criticism is deducible from the comments of Nachmansohn and Wilson (1955) concerning the requirements of the colorimetric assay used by Seaman and Houlihan. Nachmansohn and Wilson (p. 649) characterize the colorimetric method as being less accurate than the titration method "since it measures the remaining ester and the activity is obtained by difference. Generally about 30% of the ester must be hydrolyzed." The maximum hydrolysis achieved by Seaman and Houlihan could not have exceeded 17%, from their data. Tibbs (1960, p. 121) concludes, "The situation here is not clear, but the fact that we have (in unreported experiments) been able to confirm the result of Seaman and Houlihan that eserine depresses motility in *Tetrahymena* is in agreement with the presence of an acetylcholine-controlled system."

We conclude that the presence of acetylcholinesterase in protozoa has not been clearly demonstrated. As Bullock and Nachmansohn (1942, p. 239) state: "Any function of acetylcholine in nerve activity requires the presence of choline esterase. The presence of this specific enzyme can be considered as significant, whereas presence of acetylcholine, or its effect on the tissue, is of much less importance." Furthermore, a close analysis of the actual paths and distribution of cortical fibers in *Paramecium* (Párducz, 1958b) and in tetrahymenid ciliates (Pitelka, 1961a) does not reveal a sufficiently complete or adequate distribution to account for the variety of directions in which the metachronal impulse can be propagated.

The finding that in *Opalina* the direction of passage of the metachronal wave correlates with the magnitude of the transmembrane potential (Kinosita, 1954) suggests the possibility that the metachronal impulse might be a very slowly propagated change in the membrane potential. Satir and Miller (1963) have recorded oscillations of electric potential of an electrode inserted into the ciliated epithelium of the gill filaments of the fresh-water lamellibranch, *Elliptio*. These oscillations occur with a frequency that correlates with the frequency of ciliary beat, and hence with the frequency of passage of wave crests over one of the lateral ciliated cells. Kinosita (1963b) does not find similar oscillations in *Opalina*. Rhythmic oscillations of membrane potential were recorded by Yamaguchi (1960a) in *Paramecium caudatum*, but these were found only in the vicinity of the contractile vacuole and were phased with the cycles of that organelle. The possibility that good metachrony can occur in ATP-reactivated models of *Euplotes* suggests, in this case, that membranellar metachrony can occur in the absence of a cell membrane possessing its normal potential and ion-regulating capacities, since these models are relatively unaffected by changes in the concentration of potassium and sodium in the medium, and since they are readily permeable to all sorts of molecules (including ATP) to which the normal membrane is impermeable. It must be stressed, however, that most of the ciliates and flagellates that have been studied possess patterns of ionic content not dissimilar from those in metazoans (discussed in Dunham and Child, 1961), and their transmembrane potentials are related to ionic permeabilities and ion balances. Hence, the study of the possible relationships between membrane activities and ciliary activities is of considerable significance.

Both Sleigh and Párducz, whose theories are the most up to date, envisage the conduction of an excitation-impulse through the cortex, though both workers have left the particular morphological conducting entity unspecified, simply as ectoplasm. Sleigh's theory (1957) is summarized in Fig. 14. Since most cilia can beat rhythmically even when they are not members of a metachronally coordinated field, Sleigh postulates an intrinsic excitation build-up. The culmination of this intraciliary build-up in the pacemaker membranelle is the simultaneous contraction of all cilia in that membranelle (effective stroke) and the production of a short-range, ectoplasmically conducted impulse that adds to the excitation build-up of the next distal membranelle, causing it to culminate sooner. Hence, as Tartar (1961, p. 236) puts it, the membranelles of *Stentor* are pictured as "a series of triggers which fire each other in succession." In Sleigh's analyses of the effects of various agents on the pattern of metachrony, he suggests that the effects can be explained in terms of their influence on (1) the rapidity of the intraciliary excitation build-up and (2) the threshold at which the build-up will culminate. The conduction of the coordinating impulse, therefore, can be assumed to be a fixed property of the ectoplasm and need not be alterable in order to account for changes in the frequency of beat and the velocity of wave conduction.

Sleigh's theory avoids the difficulties inherent in having a coordinating metachronal impulse traveling long distances with the wave fronts, since his impulses need travel only a few microns, and no farther than to the next membranelle. Párducz (1962b), however, holds that in *Paramecium*, at least, the metachronal impulse must travel over fairly long distances since it appears to pass unhindered over large regions of ectoplasm that have been deciliated. Hence, Párducz adheres to the view that the coordinating impulse travels over longer distances and is separate from and not produced by the cilia themselves [but kinetosomes are still present in the deciliated areas (Pitelka and Párducz, 1962)]. It is not clear, from Párducz's preliminary report, to what extent short-range impulses of Sleigh's type could be carrying the coordination *around* the deciliated area, even though the metachronal wave crest appears to pass invisibly *through* the area.

b. Viscous-Mechanical Coupling through the Medium. Most of the theoretical explanations of metachronal coordination that derive their support from considerations of ciliary interactions through the external medium assume that ciliary beating is "automatic" but that because of their close proximity one beating cilium can have a phasing effect on its neighbors. These possibilities are clearly evident and have been summarized by Gray (1928).

Simple mechanical coordination, proposed by Verworn (1891), in which

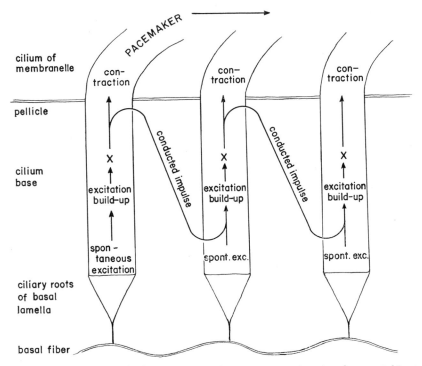

FIG. 14. A diagram of the sequence of events occurring in three neighboring membranelles of *Stentor,* as proposed by Sleigh to account for metachronal coordination. See text for explanation. (From Tartar, after Sleigh, 1957.)

the effective stroke of one cilium pushes a neighboring cilium, thereby inducing a slightly delayed effective stroke in it, is *clearly inadequate* to account for the fact that metachrony can be not only symplectic, but antiplectic and diaplectic as well.

That viscous coupling does occur (Gray, 1928) and can be experimentally manipulated (Sleigh, 1961) is definitely established. In this case, a beating cilium need not actually impinge on a neighbor, but rather need only exert a pressure on it through the drag produced by the viscosity of the medium at the small distances involved. Gray (1930) has suggested that a field of automatically beating cilia might become spontaneously coordinated by such means and produce a pattern of phasing that gives an average "minimum interference" of one cilium with another.

While the physiological and adaptive significance of minimum interference and metachronal coordination is clear (see Section III,A), the conditions in which such patterns might arise spontaneously in a field of automatically beating cilia are not at all clear. For instance, if the cilia were spaced very close together, and if the viscosity of the medium were high with respect to the dimensions of the cilia (as is the case in real ciliated systems), it seems obvious that the cilia would all have to beat together (synchronously) or be restrained not to beat at all. (Such an effect may indeed be operative in the synchronous activity of cilia within a membranelle or a cirrus, where individual cilia are long in addition to being closely packed.) Is this an extreme case of metachronal coordination in which the wavelength is long relative to the ciliated area? If the spacing between the cilia were increased so that absolute synchrony of neighbors need not obtain, would the system fall spontaneously into symplectic metachrony? As the distance between cilia in the field is increased further, would the symplectic metachrony convert to antiplectic metachrony? Questions such as these are not only difficult to answer, but reveal that our intuition may have failed, and show how desperately we need some models or analogs of ciliated systems in order to test the consequences of altering some of their intrinsic parameters.

For instance, the *frequency of beating* will undoubtedly affect the kind of coordination pattern in which the cilia may participate. Very slowly or very rapidly beating cilia do not usually show good metachrony. In ciliary "models," the beating frequency is determined by the concentration of ATP (among other factors), so that any agent acting through the cell's metabolism on its rate of ATP production could influence the beating frequency and, therefore, the coordination. Furthermore, the frequency is in some cases graded over the cell surface and is reflected in gradations of the metachronal wavelengths.

The *direction of beat* is also variable in *Opalina* and most ciliates, but its relation to the direction of progression of the metachronal wave appears to be largely fixed for any species. In *Paramecium,* if indeed the metachronal waves are produced by fronts of metachronal impulses conducted through the ecto-plasm, as Párducz postulates, then the direction of conduction of these im-pulses is different from the direction in which the cilia make their effective strokes. In *Stentor,* the membranelles beat at right angles to the direction of the metachronal impulse. In *Opalina,* on the other hand, the cilia beat in the direction of wave travel. In a system spontaneously coordinated through viscous coupling, the direction of beat might be determined by factors operating en-tirely in other contexts. For instance, the membrane potential alone might determine the direction of beat and have no direct influence on the metachrony. It is possible to imagine, in *Opalina,* that the membrane potential is topograph-ically graded over the surface of the cell, setting up weak, tangentially oriented, potential gradients, which effect a migration of charged particles such as ATP so that these accumulate preferentially on one side of the basal part of a cilium and induce an oriented effective beat in the direction of the potential gradient. A hypothesis similar to this was proposed and supported by Kinosita (1963a) to explain the migration of melanin granules in melanophores. So far, we do not know of any measurements in ciliated protozoa of transmembrane potential made with two intracellular microelectrodes simultaneously, which might support a potential-gradient hypothesis and an electrophoretic theory of the determination of direction of ciliary beat.

A viscous-coupled analog of a ciliary system would have to take into account, and be able to vary independently, not only (1) the frequency of beat, (2) the direction of beat, and (3) the viscosity of the medium, but also several less obviously meaningful parameters such as (4) the amplitude of beat, (5) the form of the beat, (6) the geometric arrangement of the cilia over the surface of the cell, (7) the length of the cilia, and (8) the distance between neighbors. It is obvious that a model of ciliary coordination based on truly mechanical and viscous-coupled interactions through the medium, which takes into account at least these eight variables, has not yet been devised. It seems to us, however, that the pattern of metachrony seen at any one time in organ-isms such as *Opalina* and *Paramecium* might well be explainable in the absence of any postulated, cortically conducted impulse if all these variables influencing ciliary interaction could be considered.

IV. Reproduction and Morphogenesis

No one who watches the process of reproduction in a ciliate or a moderately complex flagellate can fail to be impressed by the sensitive and sophisticated mechanisms that ensure duplication of an elaborate morphology. Precision in number and arrangement of kinetids is the dominant extranuclear feature of this morphogenesis: new kinetids develop, old ones disappear or are parceled out to the daughter cells, and new and old team up in oriented migrations that ultimately establish the specific architecture in the new adult. This architecture may be to a surprising degree independent of nuclear and endoplasmic control (Sonneborn and Dippell, 1960; Tartar, 1961). Certainly it reflects, in ciliates, anteroposterior and right-left gradients that exist in the cortex, and certainly kinetosomes are leading actors in the visible sequence of events. One of the bright hopes of ultrastructure research has been that a more intimate description of kinetosomes during morphogenesis will make the whole phenomenon more understandable.

Morphogeneis is a series of events, and electron microscopy provides, at best, a series of static scenes. It can see any event in any location only at one single moment in time; the next moment must be captured in a separate event and another site. The problem is exactly like trying to make a motion picture out of a large collection of stills, no two of them taken of the same individual subject.

A. Kinetosome Reproduction

In most instances, it is apparent that new kinetosomes or centrioles appear only in the immediate vicinity of preexisting ones. For various reasons, the timing of this appearance in any given cell can be predicted only within rather wide limits; hence one cannot be certain that a collection of still photographs includes its earliest stage. The clearest and most nearly complete sequences obtained to date depict metazoan centrioles. Gall's (1961) study of typical and atypical spermatogenesis in the snail, *Viviparus,* concerns centrioles that will ultimately form flagella. The earliest definite sign of centriole replication is the appearance of a short fibrous cylinder near one end of and at right angles to the mature centriole. It resembles the mature one in everything but length, and contains a cartwheel in its lumen. Maturation involves elongation of the triplet fibrils of the procentriole and, ultimately, increased spatial separation of new and old organelles. In atypical spermatocytes, clusters of as many as eleven procentrioles surround one end of the old centriole. It is possible, although not proven, that small, amorphous, dense masses sometimes seen as satellites radiating from mature centrioles may contribute substance to the formation of the new one. But there is nothing in the pictures that hints at a direct budding or splitting of parent centriole material to produce the daughters.

Protozoologists have been less successful in the search for evidence concerning kinetosome replication. Several authors have reported finding short or incomplete kinetosomes that are believed to be newly formed, but in no instance has sufficient evidence from serial sections been presented to prove that the presumed new kinetosome is not an oblique section of an already mature or a degenerating one. The most intensive and systematic search yet reported is that by Ehret and de Haller (1964) in predivision stages of *Paramecium bursaria*. Brand new kinetosomes are clearly identifiable by their location; they are morphologically identical with old ones. The authors consider the possibility that dissimilar structures in the neighborhood represent kinetosome precursors, but transitional stages have not been found.

The overwhelming impression gained from all of these considerable efforts, in metazoa as well as protozoa, is that the genesis of the kinetosome's fibrous structure is an abrupt orientation and polymerization within a preselected molecular milieu—an instant kinetosome mix. Condensation of satellite bodies around an old centriole might conceivably be a stage in preselection.

If a kinetosome–centriole is already present in a cell that is about to produce one, it always serves as an organizing locus. At the very least, its environment must be the most or only suitable one for the assembly of the kinetosome mix, or for the triggering of its crystallization. The elaborate morphogenetic contortions of flagellated and ciliated cells—wherein new kinetosomes with particular fates may arise exclusively near old ones in particular sites and thence have a long way to move to their final positions—are explainable only in terms of highly localized, essential determiners. Whether or not this constitutes self-reproduction becomes a matter of definition, since we have no way of knowing how much of the information required by the new organelle emanates from the old one. It simply must be granted that some of it does.

But what of those instances in which a kinetosome–centriole appears full-fledged in a cell that previously has lacked one? In an intensive electron-microscope study of *Naegleria gruberi*, Schuster (1963) found no evidence of the existence of a centriole in the ameboid cell, yet a complete set of two or four kinetids can develop within a half-hour. Dirksen (1961) showed that the cytasters of parthenogenetic sea-urchin eggs were organized around impeccable centrioles, although none have been found in the egg before activation. Discussing the question of apparent *de novo* origin of centrioles, Mazia (1961) points out that the hypothesis that escaped kinetochores can become centrioles will not account for all cases, since cytasters may appear in enucleate fragments. In an animal that has centrioles or flagella at some time in its ontogeny, Mazia suggests, there may be presumptive kinetosomes, microscopically unrecognizable, in the egg cytoplasm. The facts remain paradoxical. Since cells that have kinetosomes go to so very much trouble in order to duplicate them *in situ*, it is hard to imagine that other cells can completely lack them and yet can concoct identical new ones by fundamentally different means. We must admit the possibility that the information passed by an old kinetosome to a new one may pertain to the latter's orientation and specific fate, rather than to its fundamental construction.

B. Growth of Flagella and Cilia

Whatever its origin, a kinetosome must be present before other elements of the kinetid can make their appearance. High-resolution morphological studies of emerging cilia and flagella are not available, but the important work of Sotelo and Trujillo-Cenoz (1958a,b) showed that the centriole (in various animal sperms and in chick neural epithelium) establishes contact with a surface membrane, which bulges above it. Axonemal fibrils appear in the bulge, possibly organized from minute vesicles present there, and at first are unoriented, assuming the 9 + 2 arrangement after a time. Several reports of development of nonmotile cilia (sensory or of unknown function) in vertebrate tissues suggest a similar sequence of events (e.g., Sorokin, 1962; Tokuyasu and Yamada, 1959). Roth and Shigenaka (1962) report seeing disorganized single fibrils in certain young cilia of the ciliate *Diplodinium*.

For the most part, ciliates have not been used in physiological studies of the intimate mechanisms of formation and growth (elongation) of individual cilia, even though many ciliates, such as hypotrichs, undergo cyclic regrowth of their cilia during fissions. The possibility of studying ciliary regeneration in forms like *Paramecium* is clear from the work of Pitelka and Párducz (1962), and of Grebecki and Kuznicki (1961), who used nickel sulfate and chloral hydrate, respectively, to induce the detachment of body cilia. Regeneration of the body cilia occurred when the treated cells were transferred to water or culture medium.

The formation of flagella in algae has received much more attention, especially in the genus *Chlamydomonas*. *Chlamydomonas moewusii* loses its flagella during fission (Lewin, 1952a); cells grown on 1% agar medium have flagella, but if they are maintained in darkness the average flagellar length decreases over a week from 10–12 μ to 2 μ or less (Lewin, 1953). These cells with shortened flagella will elongate their flagella in the light on agar, or either in the light or in the dark if suspended in water. The rate of elongation is about 0.2 μ per minute (2 mm. per week!), and can be delayed by temporary plasmolysis and suppressed by hypertonic conditions. Hagen-Seyfferth (1959) reports that *C. moewusii* will resorb (not detach) its flagella if flagellated cells are plated on 5% agar. On the other hand, flagellar detachment can be induced by high temperature, a sufficiently high or low pH, or a high concentration of ethanol, and if then transferred to fresh medium, these cells will regenerate their flagella within 30 min. at 30°C. A succession of three repeated detachments and regenerations could be produced. The growth rate of the regenerating flagella was reduced by extremes of pH and temperature.

Dubnau (1961) has done the most extensive study on the kinetics and physiology of flagellar regeneration using the chrysomonad, *Ochromonas danica*. The kinetics of regeneration of the long flagellum were followed in a population after the flagella had been removed by mechanical agitation. After a definite lag period, elongation begins and continues at a decelerating rate. The lag period is temperature-sensitive, but not affected by inhibitors of respiration or protein synthesis; it represents the building up of an unstable state within the cell, "the presence of which is necessary for the onset of regeneration" (p. 40). The growth process, on the other hand, is depressed by inhibitors of energy metabolism, and amino acid, purine, and pyrimidine analogs. Although the analogs do decrease the initial rate of flagellar elongation, their maximum effect is after the flagellum is half grown; this suggests the presence of a quantity of precursor protein roughly equivalent to half a flagellum, and explains the result that the maximum inhibition of regeneration obtainable with inhibitors of protein synthesis was only 60% of the uninhibited controls. Hence, some protein synthesis probably occurs during regeneration; this gains support from an observed 15% decrease in the free amino acid pool during the initial phase of regeneration. Since the final length of a regenerating flagellum is constant, and not dependent upon the initial stump length, it would appear that the decelerating rate of elongation and the maximum length attained are determined by a feedback mechanism located in the flagellum, rather than by the gradual consumption of some critical substance needed for regeneration.

The feedback mechanism postulated by Dubnau to explain the maximum length of a flagellum has been demonstrated in *Chlamydomonas reinhardti* (Child, 1963c). Normally, this organism has two flagella of equal length. Observations have been made of flagellar regeneration in single cells that have had their flagella unequally amputated, producing two stumps of short and intermediate lengths. In all cases, the shorter stump undergoes a shorter lag period and begins elongating sooner than the longer stump. Both stumps elongate at a decelerating rate, but the longer stump decelerates more rapidly than the shorter. Hence, because of its head-start and less rapid deceleration, the flagellum regenerating from the shorter stump catches up with the longer, and both appear to culminate at the maximum length at the same time.

C. Growth of Intracellular Fibrils

A few scraps of pertinent information are at hand concerning the morphogenesis, at the ultrastructural level, of intracellular fibrils. The mature flagellate form of *Naegleria gruberi* (Schuster, 1963) has two or four flagella, associated with a striated rhizoplast and tubular fibrils. During the ameba-to-flagellate transformation, flagella emerge and become active at the posterior pole of the ameba, and seem to migrate up along its side before the polarity of the flagellate is established. Electron micrographs of new kinetids at the recognizable posterior end of the ameba show kinetosomes and flagella but no intracellular fibrils. Development of the latter clearly is not essential to flagellar motility and apparently occurs only when the cell is assuming its characteristic shape and polarity as a flagellate.

In *Paramecium*, both members of each pair of body cilia are active, although only one bears a kinetodesmal fibril and a set of posterior tubular fibrils. Kinetosome replication occurs in an equatorial zone around the body surface before nuclear division. Two new kinetosomes appear in each polygon (Ehret and de Haller, 1964), so that a longitudinal row, first of three and then of four, is present. The anterior two of these will migrate forward to become the center of a new polygonal territory. At this time—after the kinetosomes have appeared but before they have become ciliated or started to migrate— all four kinetosomes in each polygon bear kinetodesmal fibrils (Ehret and de Haller, 1964, Figs. 47, 48). The transitory fibrils on the anterior member of the pair thus are present when critical morphogenetic movements are about to take place, and when the new kinetosomes are going to stake out their territories.

Appearance of new intracellular fibrils is coincident in *Naegleria* with the assumption, and in *Paramecium* with the preservation and extension, of the pattern and polarity that dominate the organization of these cells. Polarity is undeniably important in every function that might be attributed to kinetids. Topographic distribution of cilia is important at least to the accomplishment of their specific locomotor functions. Lwoff (1950, p. 55) concluded that the kinetodesmos "appears as the framework of kinetosomal order, the visible agent by which the hitherto unknown 'morphogenetic forces' exert their mysterious orienting action." The morphogenetic forces are still unknown, but it may well be that by their presence, position, and extent, the intracellular fibrils assist the kinetosome to define and maintain its own, properly oriented sphere of influence.

V. Conclusions

It is evident that the goal indicated by our title—an integrated analysis of structure and function in the locomotor apparatus—is not yet attainable. The known structure of the apparatus has imposed some limitations upon and provided some inspiration for postulated explanations of function, but correlations, on the one hand, of electron microscopic with biochemical evidence of ultrastructure and, on the other hand, of either of these with observed patterns of movement remain imprecise and speculative. Nonetheless, the amount of information in all three areas is increasing rapidly, and we are at that exciting stage in the investigation when possibilities for testing many attractive hypotheses are beginning to appear.

The predominant fact about flagellar morphology is that it is remarkably complex and remarkably constant. Biochemical evidence suggests that this complexity is achieved with relatively few macromolecular constituents. It is reasonable to assume that the kinetosome contains the code for the assembly of these into the particular edifice of the axoneme. No other instance is known of a structure that is reproduced so faithfully, with such geometric precision, in so wide a variety of organisms.

The mechanism of beating remains obscure and controversial. The continued rhythmic activity of ATP-reactivated flagellar models is an incontrovertible, though curious, phenomenon. Clearly the axoneme is a beating machine, designed to undergo rhythmic bending in a medium of constant composition. Hoffmann-Berling (1958) showed that rhythmic alternations of contraction and relaxation can be induced in glycerinated *Vorticella* stalks in a medium of constant composition containing the appropriate levels of ATP and calcium ions. The great advances in the physiology and biochemistry of muscle contraction have left us unprepared to understand systems in which contraction and relaxation can alternate without changes simultaneously occurring in the bathing fluid. On the other hand, ATP-reactivated models ought to provide a means for gradually dissecting away the parts of the flagellum not necessary for beating, and give us a clearer picture of the ultrastructural elements that are essential.

The achievement of a conceptual model to account for all of the observed varieties of flagellar movement must wait until some of the less formidable and presently more important questions have been answered. The scheme cannot be based only on the two-dimensional movement that is predominant in metazoan material. However critical one may be of methods used to determine the configurations of a normal beating cycle, the fact remains that any repeatable observation of a living, moving flagellum or cilium provides evidence of what that organelle *can* do. There is no doubt that a protozoan cilium can move freely around a conical path.

Studies on *Opalina* and *Paramecium* show that the coordinated ciliary system has complexities and properties, heretofore unknown, that are experimentally approachable. It appears that certain properties of ciliated cells are separable from the complex of interactions that characterize the whole coordination pattern. For instance, the frequency of beat in *Paramecium* is not related to the force of the beat; in *Opalina,* the direction of beat can be a function of the transmembrane potential; areas on the cell surface can behave differently from neighboring areas; localized responses occur to localized applications of stimuli; the patterns of metachrony and direction of wave travel can differ simultaneously in different regions of one cell. It seems clear that future work will involve the approach of systems analysis in which the several parameters of ciliary activity (dimensions, frequency, direction, etc.) will be seen, by integration, to result in the more or less stable patterns characteristic of coordinated activity. Certainly, the trend is away from the idea of coordination governed by overriding forces emanating from a central motorium or mediated by specific fibers.

If cortical fibrillar structures are not to be accepted unquestioningly as conducting elements, then one is left to wonder what function these structures serve and why they are so routinely associated with the locomotor apparatus. Three possibilities are apparent: they may serve as anchors to the shallowly rooted but violently lashing motor organelles; they may provide skeletal support within the delicately modeled cortical ambit of each kinetid; they may be morphological indicators and second-grade determiners of the cortical gradients that do exist and do influence the morphogenesis and behavior of the organism.

The protozoa continue to provide highly favorable materials for the investigation of nearly every aspect of the problem of flagellar locomotion. One can obtain enormous numbers of docile organisms, either in a culture medium of known composition or, alternatively, under conditions that approximate the natural state much more closely than is possible for ciliated cells removed from the bodies of higher organisms. Furthermore, among the protozoa is to be found a spectrum of variations in topography of cilium distribution, in pattern of movement, and in degree and pattern of coordination. Within limits, one can utilize these variations as natural experiments to study varying parameters of flagellar and ciliary activity. The limits are imposed by the difficulty of making truly accurate observations of movement patterns, and by the necessity of bearing in mind that these variations may exist for reasons not related to our reasons for seeking them. Both limits are manageable, so long as they are clearly recognized.

ACKNOWLEDGMENTS

Both of us gratefully acknowledge the U.S. Public Health Service for grants supporting our research. We are deeply indebted to Béla Párducz for supplying the photomicrographs reproduced as Figs. 6–8; to Charles Ehret, Gerhard de Haller, Peter Satir and Frederick Schuster for making available to us unpublished manuscripts and other data; to William Balamuth for critical reading of the manuscript; and to Julia S. Child and Emily Reid for drawing the diagrams.

REFERENCES

Afzelius, B. A. (1959). *J. Biophys. Biochem. Cytol.* 5, 269–278.
Afzelius, B. A. (1961). *J. Biophys. Biochem. Cytol.* 9, 383–394.
Alexander, J. B., Silvester, N. R., and Watson, M. R. (1962). *Biochem. J.* 85, 27P.
Alexandrov, V. Y., and Arronet, N. I. (1956). *Dokl. Akad. Nauk SSSR* 110, 457–460.
Anderson, E., and Beams, H. W. (1959). *J. Morphol.* 104, 205–235.
Anderson, E., and Beams, H. W. (1961). *J. Protozool.* 8, 71–75.
André, J. (1961). *J. Ultrastruct. Res.* 5, 86–108.

André, J., and Vivier, E. (1962). *J. Ultrastruct. Res.* 6, 390–406.
Balamuth, W. (1942). *J. Exptl. Zool.* 91, 15–43.
Bělař, K. (1921). *Arch. Protistenk.* 43, 431–462.
Bernhard, W., and de Harven, E. (1960). *Proc. 4th Intern. Conf. on Electron Microscopy, Berlin, 1958* 2, 217–227.
Beyer, G., and Wense, T. (1936). *Arch. Ges. Physiol.* 237, 417–422.
Bishop, D. W. (1962). *Physiol. Rev.* 42, 1–59.
Blanckart, S. (1957). *Z. Wiss. Mikroskopie* 63, 276–287.
Bradfield, J. R. G. (1955). *Symp. Soc. Exptl. Biol.* 9, 306–334.
Brokaw, C. J. (1960). *Exptl. Cell Res.* 19, 430–431.
Brokaw, C. J. (1961). *Exptl. Cell Res.* 22, 151–162.
Brokaw, C. J. (1962). *In* "Physiology and Biochemistry of Algae" (R. A. Lewin, ed.), pp. 595–601. Academic Press, New York.
Bülbring, E., Lourie, E. M., and Pardoe, U. (1949). *Brit. J. Pharmacol.* 4, 290–294.
Bullock, T. H., and Nachmansohn, D. (1942). *J. Cellular Comp. Physiol.* 20, 239–242.
Carter, G. S. (1924). *Proc. Roy. Soc.* B96, 115–122.
Chatton, E. (1924). *Compt. Rend. Soc. Biol.* 91, 577–580.
Chatton, E. (1931). *Compt. Rend. 11th Congr. Intern. Zool., Padova, 1930* 6, 169–187.
Chatton, E., and Brachon, S. (1935). *Compt. Rend. Soc. Biol.* 118, 399–402.
Chatton, E., and Lwoff, A. (1935a). *Compt. Rend. Soc. Biol.* 118, 1068–1072.
Chatton, E., and Lwoff, A. (1935b). *Arch. Zool. Exptl. Gen.* 77, 1–453.
Chatton, E., Lwoff, A., and Lwoff, M. (1929). *Compt. Rend. Acad. Sci.* 188, 1190–1192.
Child, F. M. (1959). *Exptl. Cell Res.* 18, 258–267.
Child, F. M. (1961). *Exptl. Cell Res., Suppl.* 8, 47–53.
Child, F. M. (1963a). *Proc. 1st Intern. Conf. Protozool., Prague, 1961*, pp. 415–416.
Child, F. M. (1963b). Unpublished data.
Child, F. M. (1963c). *Biol. Bull.* 125, 361.
Child, F. M., and Mazia, D. (1956). *Experientia* 12, 161–162.
Christensen, A. K. (1961). *Biol. Bull.* 121, 416.
Cleveland, L. R. (1960). *J. Protozool.* 7, 326–341.
Dippell, R. V. (1962). *J. Protozool.* 9, Suppl., 24.
Dirksen, E. R. (1961). *J. Biophys. Biochem. Cytol.* 11, 244–247.
Doroszewski, M. (1958). *Acta Biol. Exptl., Polish Acad. Sci.* 18, 69–88.
Dragesco, J. (1962). *Bull. Microscop. Appl.* 11, 49–58.
Dubnau, D. A. (1961). Ph.D. Thesis. Columbia University.
Dunham, P. B., and Child, F. M. (1961). *Biol. Bull.* 121, 129–140.
Ehret, C. F., and de Haller, G. (1964). *J. Ultrastruct. Res. Suppl.* 6, 1–42.
Ehret, C. F., and Powers, E. L. (1959). *Intern. Rev. Cytol.* 8, 97–133.
Fauré-Fremiet, E. (1961a). *Biol. Rev. Cambridge Phil. Soc.* 36, 464–536.
Fauré-Fremiet, E. (1961b). *Pathol. Biol., Semaine Hop.* 9, 811–816.
Fauré-Fremiet, E., and Rouiller, C. (1958a). *Bull. Microscop. Appl.* 8, 117–119.
Fauré-Fremiet, E., and Rouiller, C. (1958b). *Compt. Rend. Acad. Sci.* 246, 2039–2042.
Fauré-Fremiet, E., Favard, P., and Carasso, N. (1962). *J. Microscopie* 1, 287–312.
Fawcett, D. W. (1961). *In* "The Cell" (J. Brachet and A. E. Mirsky, eds.), Vol. 2, pp. 217–298. Academic Press, New York.
Fawcett, D. W., and Porter, K. R. (1954). *J. Morphol.* 94, 221–282.
Finger, I. (1956). *Biol. Bull.* 111, 358–363.

Fredricsson, B., and Björkman, N. (1962). Z. Zellforsch. Mikroskop. Anat. 58, 387–402.

Gall, J. G. (1961). J. Biophys. Biochem. Cytol. 10, 163–194.

Gelei, G. von (1937). Arch. Protistenk. 89, 133–162.

Gelei, J. von (1936). Compt. Rend. 12e Congr. Intern. Zool., Lisbon, 1935, pp. 174–206.

Gibbons, I. R. (1961a). Proc. 2nd European Reg. Conf. on Electron Microscopy, Delft, 1960 2, 929–933.

Gibbons, I. R. (1961b). Nature 190, 1128–1129.

Gibbons, I. R. (1961c). J. Biophys. Biochem. Cytol. 11, 179–205.

Gibbons, I. R., and Grimstone, A. V. (1960). J. Biophys. Biochem. Cytol. 7, 697–716.

Gibbs, S. P. (1960). J. Ultrastruct. Res. 4, 127–148.

Gibbs, S. P., Lewin, R. A., and Philpott, D. E. (1958). Exptl. Cell Res. 15, 619–622.

Goreau, T. F., and Philpott, D. E. (1956). Exptl. Cell Res. 10, 552–556.

Grassé, P. P., ed. (1952). In "Traité de Zoologie," Vol. 1, Part 1, pp. 37–152. Masson, Paris.

Grassé, P. P. (1956). Arch. Biol. (Liège) 67, 595–611.

Gray, J. (1928). "Ciliary Movement." Cambridge Univ. Press, London and New York.

Gray, J. (1930). Proc. Roy. Soc. B107, 313–332.

Gray, J. (1951). Nature 168, 929.

Gray, J. (1955). J. Exptl. Biol. 32, 775–801.

Grebecki, A., and Kuznicki, L. (1961). Bull. Acad. Polon. Sci., Ser. Sci. Biol. 9, 459–462.

Grimstone, A. V. (1961). Biol. Rev. Cambridge Phil. Soc. 36, 97–150.

Hagen-Seyfferth, M. (1959). Planta 53, 376–401.

Hammond, J. C. (1935). Ohio J. Sci. 35, 304–306.

Hanson, J., and Huxley, H. E. (1955). Symp. Soc. Exptl. Biol. 9, 228–260.

Harris, J. E. (1961). In "The Cell and the Organism" (J. A. Ramsay and V. B. Wigglesworth, eds.), pp. 22–36. Cambridge Univ. Press, London and New York.

Harris, P. (1961). J. Biophys. Biochem. Cytol. 11, 419–431.

Harris, P. (1962). J. Cell Biol. 14, 475–488.

Hoffmann-Berling, H. (1955). Biochim. Biophys. Acta 16, 146–154.

Hoffmann-Berling, H. (1958). Biochim. Biophys. Acta 27, 247–255.

Hyman, L. H. (1940). "The Invertebrates. Protozoa through Ctenophora." McGraw-Hill, New York.

Jacobson, I. (1931). Arch. Protistenk. 75, 31–100.

Jahn, T. L. (1961). J. Protozool. 8, 369–380.

Jahn, T. L. (1963). Personal communication.

Jakus, M. A., and Hall, C. E. (1946). Biol. Bull. 91, 141–144.

Janicki, C. (1915). Z. Wiss. Zool., Abt. A 112, 573–689.

Jennings, H. S., and Jamieson, C. (1902). Biol. Bull. 3, 225–234.

Jensen, P. (1893). Arch. Ges. Physiol. 54, 537–551.

Jones, R. F., and Lewin, R. A. (1960). Exptl. Cell Res. 19, 408–410.

Kamada, T. (1938). Proc. Imp. Acad. (Tokyo) 14, 260–262.

Kamada, T. (1940). Proc. Imp. Acad. (Tokyo) 16, 241–247.

Kamada, T., and Kinosita, H. (1940). Proc. Imp. Acad. (Tokyo) 16, 125–130.

Kinosita, H. (1954). J. Fac. Sci., Univ. Tokyo, Sect. IV 7, 1–14.

Kinosita, H. (1963a). Ann. N.Y. Acad. Sci. 100, 922–1004.

Kinosita, H. (1963b). Personal communication.

Kirby, H. (1944). J. Morphol. 75, 361–421.

Klein, B. M. (1942). *Ann. Naturhist. Museums Wien* 53, 156–336.

Knight-Jones, E. W. (1954). *Quart. J. Microscop. Sci.* 95, 503–521.

Kofoid, C. A., and Christiansen, E. R. (1915). *Univ. Calif. Publ. Zool.* 16, 30–54.

Krijgsman, B. J. (1925). *Arch. Protistenk.* 52, 478–488.

Kümmel, G. (1958). *Z. Naturforsch.* 13b, 677–679.

Lansing, A. I., and Lamy, F. (1961). *J. Biophys. Biochem. Cytol.* 9, 799–812.

Lewin, R. A. (1952a). *Biol. Bull.* 103, 74–79.

Lewin, R. A. (1952b). *J. Gen. Microbiol.* 6, 233–248.

Lewin, R. A. (1953). *Ann. N.Y. Acad. Sci.* 56, 1091–1093.

Lewin, R. A. (1954). *J. Gen. Microbiol.* 11, 358–363.

Lewin, R. A., and Meinhart, J. O. (1953). *Can. J. Botany* 31, 711–717.

Lowndes, A. G. (1941). *Proc. Zool. Soc. London* A111, 111–134.

Lowndes, A. G. (1943a). *Nature* 152, 51.

Lowndes, A. G. (1943b). *Proc. Zool. Soc. London* A113, 99–107.

Lowndes, A. G. (1945). *Nature* 155, 579.

Lund, E. E. (1933). *Univ. Calif. Publ. Zool.* 39, 35–76.

Lwoff, A. (1950). "Problems of Morphogenesis in Ciliates." Wiley, New York.

Mager, J. (1960). *Biochim. Biophys. Acta* 38, 150–152.

Mager, J., and Lipmann, F. (1958). *Proc. Natl. Acad. Sci. U.S.* 44, 305–309.

Manton, I. (1952). *Symp. Soc. Exptl. Biol.* 6, 306–319.

Manton, I. (1955a). *Proc. Leeds Phil. Lit. Soc., Sci. Sect.* 6, 306–316.

Manton, I. (1955b). *Nature* 176, 123.

Manton, I. (1956). *In* "Cellular Mechanisms in Differention and Growth" (D. Rudnick, ed.), pp. 61–71. Princeton Univ. Press, Princeton, New Jersey.

Manton, I. (1959a). *J. Marine Biol. Assoc. U.K.* 38, 319–333.

Manton, I. (1959b). *J. Exptl. Botany* 10, 448–461.

Manton, I., and Clarke, B. (1952). *J. Exptl. Botany* 3, 265–275.

Manton, I., and Clarke, B. (1956). *J. Exptl. Botany* 7, 416–432.

Manton, I., and Parke, M. (1960). *J. Marine Biol. Assoc. U.K.* 39, 275–298.

Manton, I., Clarke, B., and Greenwood, A. D. (1953). *J. Exptl. Botany* 4, 319–329.

Mazia, D. (1959). *Harvey Lectures* 53, 130–170.

Mazia, D. (1961). *In* "The Cell" (J. Brachet and A. E. Mirsky, eds.), Vol. 3, pp. 77–412. Academic Press, New York.

Metz, C. B., Pitelka, D. R., and Westfall, J. A. (1953). *Biol. Bull.* 104, 408–425.

Mintz, R. H., and Lewin, R. A. (1954). *Can. J. Microbiol.* 1, 65–67.

Mitropolitanskaya, R. L. (1941). *Compt. Rend. Acad. Sci. URSS* 31, 717–718.

Nachmansohn, D., and Wilson, I. B. (1955). *In* "Methods in Enzymology" (S. P. Colowick and N. O. Kaplan, eds.), Vol. 1, pp. 642–651. Academic Press, New York.

Naitoh, Y. (1958), *Annotationes Zool. Japon.* 31, 59–73.

Naitoh, Y. (1959). *Fac. Sci., Univ. Tokyo, Sect. IV* 8, 357–369.

Nicander, L. (1962). *Proc. 5th Intern. Congr. for Electron Microscopy, Philadelphia, 1962* 2, M-4.

Noirot-Timothée, C. (1959). *Ann. Sci. Nat., Zool.* [12] 1, 265–281.

Okajima, A. (1953). *Japan. J. Zool.* 11, 87–100.

Okajima, A. (1954a). *Annotationes Zool. Japon.* 27, 40–45.

Okajima, A. (1954b). *Annotationes Zool. Japon.* 27, 46–51.

Párducz, B. (1952). *Ann. Hist.-Nat. Musei Natl. Hung.* (Zool.) 2, 5–12.

Párducz, B. (1954). *Acta Biol. Acad. Sci. Hung.* 5, 169–212.

Párducz, B. (1956a). *Acta Biol. Acad. Sci. Hung.* 7, 73–99.

Párducz, B. (1956b). *Acta Biol. Acad. Sci. Hung.* 6, 289–316.

Párducz, B. (1958a). *Acta Biol. Acad. Sci. Hung.* 8, 191–218.
Párducz, B. (1958b). *Acta Biol. Acad. Sci. Hung.* 8, 219–251.
Párducz, B. (1959). *Ann. Hist.-Nat. Musei Natl. Hung.* (*Zool.*) 51, 227–246.
Párducz, B. (1961). *In* "The Encyclopedia of the Biological Sciences" (P. Gray, ed.), pp. 232–233. Reinhold, New York.
Párducz, B. (1962a). *Acta Biol. Acad. Sci. Hung.* 13, 299–322.
Párducz, B. (1962b). *J. Protozool.* 9, Suppl., 27.
Párducz, B. (1962c). *Ann. Hist.-Nat. Musei Natl. Hung.* (*Zool.*) 54, 221–230.
Párducz, B., and Müller, M. (1958). *Acta Biol. Acad. Sci. Hung., Suppl.* 2, 30.
Parke, M., Manton, I., and Clarke, B. (1959). *J. Marine Biol. Assoc. U.K.* 38, 169–188.
Pigoń, A., and Szarski, H. (1955). *Bull. Acad. Polon. Sci., Classe II* 3, 99–102.
Pitelka, D. R. (1949). *Univ. Calif. Publ. Zool.* 53, 377–430.
Pitelka, D. R. (1956). *J. Biophys. Biochem. Cytol.* 2, 423–432.
Pitelka, D. R. (1961a). *J. Protozool.* 8, 75–89.
Pitelka, D. R. (1961b). *Exptl. Cell Res.* 25, 87–93.
Pitelka, D. R. (1962). *Proc. 5th Intern. Congr. for Electron Microscopy, Philadelphia, 1962* 2, M-7.
Pitelka, D. R. (1963a). "Electron-Microscopic Structure of Protozoa." Pergamon Press, New York.
Pitelka, D. R. (1963b). Unpublished data.
Pitelka, D. R., and Párducz, B. (1962). *J. Protozool.* 9, Suppl., 6–7.
Pitelka, D. R., and Schooley, C. N. (1955). *Univ. Calif. Publ. Zool.* 61, 79–128.
Pitelka, D. R., and Schooley, C. N. (1958). *J. Morphol.* 102, 199–246.
Preer, J. R., Jr., and Preer, L. B. (1959). *J. Protozool.* 6, 88–100.
Puytorac, P. de (1960). *Arch. Anat. Microscop. Morphol. Exptl.* 49, 241–256.
Rampton, V. W. (1962). *Nature* 195, 195.
Randall, J. T. (1959). *J. Protozool.* 6, Suppl., 30.
Randall, J. T., and Hopkins, J. M. (1962). *Phil. Trans. Roy. Soc. London* B245, 59–79.
Randall, J. T., and Jackson, S. F. (1958). *J. Biophys. Biochem. Cytol.* 4, 807–830.
Rivera, J. A. (1962). "Cilia, Ciliated Epithelium and Ciliary Activity." Pergamon Press, New York.
Ronkin, R. R. (1959). *Biol. Bull.* 116, 285–293.
Ronkin, R. R., and Buretz, K. M. (1960). *J. Protozool.* 7, 109–114.
Roth, L. E. (1956). *J. Biophys. Biochem. Cytol.* 2, Suppl., 235–242.
Roth, L. E. (1957). *J. Biophys. Biochem. Cytol.* 3, 985–1000.
Roth, L. E. (1958a). *J. Ultrastruct. Res.* 1, 223–234.
Roth, L. E. (1958b). *Exptl. Cell Res., Suppl.* 5, 573–585.
Roth, L. E. (1959). *J. Protozool.* 6, 107–116.
Roth, L. E., and Shigenaka, Y. (1962). *Am. Zoologist* 2, 442–443.
Rouiller, C., and Fauré-Fremiet, E. (1957). *J. Ultrastruct. Res.* 1, 1–13.
Rouiller, C., and Fauré-Fremiet, E. (1958). *Exptl. Cell. Res.* 14, 47–67.
Rouiller, C., Fauré-Fremiet, E., and Gauchery, M. (1956). *J. Protozool.* 3, 194–200.
Rouiller, C., Fauré-Fremiet, E., and Gauchery, M. (1957). *Proc. Stockholm Conf. on Electron Microscopy, 1956* pp. 216–218.
Rudzinska, M. A. (1958). *J. Biophys. Biochem. Cytol.* 4, 195–202.
Rudzinska, M. A. (1962). *Proc. 5th Intern. Congr. for Electron Microscopy, Philadelphia, 1962* 2, UU-12.

Satir, P. G. (1962). *J. Cell Biol.* 12, 181–184.

Satir, P. G. (1963). *J. Cell Biol.* 18, 345–365.

Satir, P. G., and Child, F. M. (1963). *Biol. Bull.* 125, 390.

Satir, P. G., and Miller, W. H. (1963). Personal communication.

Schneider, L. (1960). *J. Protozool.* 7, 75–90.

Schuster, F. L. (1963). *J. Protozool.* 10, 297–313.

Seaman, G. R. (1951). *Proc. Soc. Exptl. Biol. Med.* 76, 169–170.

Seaman, G. R. (1960). *Exptl. Cell Res.* 21, 292–302.

Seaman, G. R. (1961). *Biochim. Biophys. Acta* 55, 889–899.

Seaman, G. R., and Gottlieb, S. (1957). *J. Protozool.* 4, Suppl., 11.

Seaman, G. R., and Houlihan, R. K. (1951). *J. Cellular Comp. Physiol.* 37, 309–321.

Sedar, A. W., and Porter, K. R. (1955). *J. Biophys. Biochem. Cytol.* 1, 583–604.

Seravin, L. N. (1961). *Biokhimiya* 26, 160–164; *Biochemistry* (USSR) (*English Transl.*) 26, 138–142.

Shapiro, J. E., Hershenov, B. R., and Tulloch, G. S. (1961). *J. Biophys. Biochem. Cytol.* 9, 211–217.

Sharp, R. G. (1914). *Univ. Calif. Publ. Zool.* 13, 43–122.

Siegel, R. W., and Cohen, L. W. (1962). *Am. Zoologist* 2, 558.

Sleigh, M. A. (1956). *J. Exptl. Biol.* 33, 15–28.

Sleigh, M. A. (1957). *J. Exptl. Biol.* 34, 106–115.

Sleigh, M. A. (1960). *J. Exptl. Biol.* 37, 1–10.

Sleigh, M. A. (1961). *Nature* 191, 931–932.

Sonneborn, T. M., and Dippell, R. V. (1960). *J. Protozool.* 7, Suppl., 26.

Sorokin, S. (1962). *J. Cell Biol.* 15, 363–377.

Sotelo, J. R., and Trujillo-Cenoz, O. (1958a). *Z. Zellforsch. Mikroskop. Anat.* 49, 1–12.

Sotelo, J. R., and Trujillo-Cenoz, O. (1958b). *Z. Zellforsch. Mikroskop. Anat.* 48, 565–601.

Swezy, O. (1916). *Univ. Calif. Publ. Zool.* 16, 185–240.

Tartar, V. (1961). "The Biology of Stentor." Pergamon Press, New York.

Taylor, C. V. (1920). *Univ. Calif. Publ. Zool.* 19, 403–470.

Taylor, C. V. (1941). *In* "Protozoa in Biological Research" (G. N. Calkins and F. M. Summers, eds.), pp. 191–270. Columbia Univ. Press, New York.

Tibbs, J. (1957). *Biochim. Biophys. Acta* 23, 275–288.

Tibbs, J. (1958). *Biochim. Biophys. Acta* 28, 636–637.

Tibbs, J. (1960). *Biochim. Biophys. Acta* 41, 115–122.

Tokuyasu, K., and Yamada, E. (1959). *J. Biophys. Biochem. Cytol.* 6, 225–230.

Tuffrau, M. (1960). *Hydrobiologica* 15, 1–77.

Ueda, K. (1956). *Japan. J. Zool.* 12, 1–10.

Verworn, M. (1889). "Protisten-Studien." Fischer, Jena.

Verworn, M. (1891). *Arch. Ges. Physiol.* 48, 149–180.

Villeneuve-Brachon, S. (1940). *Arch. Zool. Exptl. Gen.* 82, 1–180.

Vivier, E., and André, J. (1961). *J. Protozool.* 8, 416–426.

Watson, M. R. (1963). Personal communication.

Watson, M. R., and Hopkins, J. M. (1962). *Exptl. Cell Res.* 28, 280–295.

Watson, M. R., Hopkins, J. M., and Randall, J. T. (1961). *Exptl. Cell Res.* 23, 629–631.

Weber, H. H. (1958). "The Motility of Muscle and Cells." Harvard Univ. Press, Cambridge, Massachusetts.

Westfall, J. A. (1963) *J. Appl. Physics* 34, 2529.

Wichterman, R. (1953). "The Biology of Paramecium." McGraw-Hill (Blakiston), New York.

Worley, L. G. (1934). *J. Cellular Comp. Physiol.* 5, 53–72.

Yamaguchi, T. (1960a). *J. Fac. Sci., Univ. Tokyo, Sect. IV* 8, 573–591.

Yamaguchi, T. (1960b). *J. Fac. Sci., Univ. Tokyo, Sect. IV* 8, 593–601.

Yocom, H. B. (1918). *Univ. Calif. Publ. Zool.* 18, 337–396.

Yoneda, M. (1960). *J. Exptl. Biol.* 37, 461–468.

Yoneda, M. (1962). *J. Exptl. Biol.* 39, 307–317.

Nutrition and Metabolism of Ciliates

G. G. HOLZ, JR.

*Department of Microbiology, State University of New York,
Upstate Medical Center, Syracuse, New York*

		Page
I.	Introduction	199
II.	Nutritional Requirements	201
	A. Amino Acids, Peptides, Proteins	201
	B. Purines and Pyrimidines	203
	C. Vitamins	204
	D. Organic Acids and Alcohols	207
	E. Lipids	208
	F. Carbohydrates	215
	G. Feeding	216
	H. Symbiosis and Parasitism	219
	I. Temperature	220
	J. Morphology	221
	K. Assays	222
III.	Metabolic Pathways	223
	A. Oxidative Metabolism	223
	B. Carbohydrates	226
	C. Nitrogen Metabolism	227
	D. Fatty Acid Synthesis	230
IV.	Comparative Biochemistry	232
	References	233

I. Introduction

Ciliates are marvels of macromolecular organization. Their complex in-fraciliature, intricate patterns of morphogenesis, enigmatic dual nuclear apparatus, atypical genetics, extensive nutritional needs, and infinitely various behavior lure the molecular biologist. They also attract microbiological assayists and those who seek "model systems" on which to test chemical agents for "biological activity." Regrettably, their full potential as research objects is not likely to be realized because of a mundane barrier: ciliates are difficult to culture.

Some 6,000 species have been described (Corliss, 1961). In the Catalogue of Laboratory Strains of Free-living and Parasitic Protozoa published in the *Journal of Protozoology* in 1958, 43 species were listed as available in culture. Of these, 15 were axenic, and only two were cultivable in a medium that was chemically defined (i.e., contained components that meet various contemporary purity standards of analytical chemistry). This list was only representative, but it is apparent that as of 1958 the material available for study under controlled conditions in the laboratory was an infinitesimal fraction of that available in nature. This situation has not changed significantly; to date, strains of only 6 species are cultivable axenically in completely defined media.

Greater efforts must be made. For incentive, recall the explosion of interest in *Tetrahymena* (described by Corliss, 1954) when directions for its cultivation were published. There is a challenge too—axenic cultivation of a ciliate in a "crude" medium (mixture of natural products) is an improbable event. The improbability of success is increased several orders of magnitude if attempts are made with mixtures of defined nutrients of precisely known composition.

Opposing incentive and challenge is a deterrent: the isolation, enrichment, and cleansing of ciliates, their exposure to a variety of culture media, crude then defined, and finally the precise definition of their requirements, qualitative and quantitative, for each component of a medium, is a tedious process; worse, it is unfashionable. The vogue for microbial nutrition dwindled when the supply of unidentified, water-soluble cofactors appeared to be exhausted, despite the fact that microbes unable to grow in mixtures of defined nutrients were available at every hand. In point of fact, microbial nutrition work became unfashionable when the information return on research time investment became low. Discovery of novel nutritional requirements is still the classic entering wedge into the trunk of an enzymatic tree. The wedges are harder to drive now.

Lipid nutrition is the one field of nutrition research that has achieved considerable recent popularity. Thanks to advances in gas-liquid, column, and thin-layer chromatography, lipid chemistry has become more precise and less laborious. Lipid analysis has become a feasible, routine laboratory procedure. Marriage of chromatographic techniques with liquid-scintillation counting and autoradiography has revolutionized study of the intermediary metabolism of complex lipids. Coincidence of these developments with contemporary interest in the association of dietary lipids (particularly cholesterol and long-chain fatty acids) with arteriosclerosis has attracted minds and money. Some of the resulting activity has spilled over into study of the complex lipids of microbes and excited interest in lipid-requiring microbes. The latter are scarce, but numbered among them are some trichomonads (Shorb and Lund, 1959; Lund and Shorb,

1962) and ciliates. The literature on ciliate nutrition has followed this tide of contemporary biochemical fashion and there has been a sharp increase in the number of papers dealing with aspects of lipid use and function.

There follows a summary of additions to our knowledge of ciliate nutrition, mostly since the last detailed reviews on the subject (Kidder, 1951, 1952, 1953a,b; Kidder and Dewey, 1951; van Wagtendonk, 1955; W. H. Johnson, 1956; Seaman, 1955). In the main, the discussion is restricted to work done with organisms in axenic culture in defined, or very nearly defined culture media. Since nutritional requirements are meaningful only as expressions of metabolic capacities, this summary is followed by comments on ciliate metabolism.

II. Nutritional Requirements

Essential nutrients include sources of energy, building blocks for biosynthesis, and molecules which compensate for defects in mechanisms of biosynthesis.

Among the animals some arthropods and vertebrates have been studied under conditions which permit clear definition of nutritional needs. Few animal cells (undifferentiated ones from vertebrates) and higher plant cells have been examined. Microbial nutrition has been exhaustively documented.

A. Amino Acids, Peptides, Proteins

Ciliates require the ten L-amino acids essential for growth of the rat, chick, some insects, vertebrate tissue cells, and some fastidious microbes (Table I). Serine is needed by most, and glycine, proline, and tyrosine by a few. Nonessential amino acids (alanine, aspartic acid, glutamic acid) are often stimulatory.

Dewey and Kidder (1960a,b) studied the serine requirement of many strains of *Tetrahymena pyriformis*. They found but one strain that was completely dependent upon an exogenous source of serine for growth. Most strains could substitute threonine or glycine for serine if the folic acid concentration was high. Many substances convertible to serine (glucose, pyruvate, lactate, fatty acids, ethanol, acetaldehyde), or dependent upon serine for their synthesis, spared the serine requirement or replaced serine if culture conditions were appropriate.

Complex interactions among serine, methionine, and folic acid in growth experiments with *T. pyriformis* H were revealed by simultaneous variation of their concentrations in a defined medium (Singer, 1961).

Although some ciliates can be cultured with mixtures of free amino acids, others grow very much better in the presence of intact complete proteins, and/or enzymatic hydrolyzates containing a variety of peptides; some appear to require peptides (*Colpidium campylum*; Kidder et al., 1954a). These pro-

Table I

CILIATE L-AMINO ACID REQUIREMENTS

Arginine	Phenylalanine
Histidine	Serine
Isoleucine	Threonine
Leucine	Tryptophan
Lysine	Valine
Methionine	

Above required by	Also required	Reference
Glaucoma chattoni A,[a] glycine can replace serine	Proline	Holz *et al.* (1961a); Kidder *et al.* (1954a).
Paramecium aurelia	Tyrosine	Miller and van Wagtendonk (1956).
P. caudatum	Tyrosine	Lilly and Klosek (1961).
P. multimicronucleatum	Tyrosine	W. H. Johnson and Miller (1957).
Tetrahymena corlissi Th-X		Holz *et al.* (1960).
T. paravorax RP	Glycine	Holz *et al.* (1961b).
T. patula L-FF		Holz *et al.* (1962c).
T. patula LI	Glycine	Kessler (1961).
T. pyriformis, all strains examined. Serine not required by "serine mutants" and some other strains	Glycine, proline, and tyrosine by a few strains	Kidder and Dewey (1951); Dewey and Kidder (1960a); Elliott *et al.* (1962); Elliott and Clark (1958b).
T. setifera HZ-1		Holz *et al.* (1962a).
T. vorax Tur		Kessler (1961); Shaw and Williams (1963).
T. vorax V₂S, V₂D, V₂M		Shaw and Williams (1963).

[a] *Glaucoma chattoni* A = *Glaucoma scintillans* A (Corliss, 1959).

teinaceous materials may: (1) correct multiple amino acid imbalances in the medium (Dewey and Kidder, 1958, 1960a; Kihara and Snell, 1960); (2) stimulate food vacuole formation and expedite nutrient translocation (Seaman, 1963b; Kidder *et al.*, 1954a); (3) supply, as contaminants, unrecognized stimulatory or essential metabolites (Holz *et al.*, 1961a,b); (4) bind toxic materials in the medium (Holz *et al.*, 1962a); or (5) provide peptides which are themselves essential metabolites, i.e., polypeptides with amino acid sequences of special significance to the cell that it cannot construct from free amino acids (K. M. Jones and Woolley, 1962). The dreary history of "protein requirements" in microbial nutrition favors every interpretation but the last.

The taste of *Tetrahymena* for polypeptides and its need for the 10 essential amino acids have been put to a practical use; the evaluation of the nutritional desirability of proteins (Anderson and Williams, 1951; Celliers, 1961; Dunn and Rockland, 1947; Rockland and Dunn, 1949; Fernell and Rosen, 1956; Rosen and Fernell, 1956; Rosen, 1959; Pilcher and Williams, 1954; Stott *et al.*, 1963). Ciliates can ingest and digest particulate protein and protein in solution

(Müller *et al.*, 1963a), and liberate proteinases that initiate digestion extracellularly (Abou Akkada and Howard, 1962; Viswanatha and Liener, 1955, 1956; Dickie and Liener, 1962a,b; P. P. Williams *et al.*, 1961).

The rumen ophryoscolecids, *Epidinium ecaudatum* and *Ophryoscolex caudatus*, use proteins and can take up free amino acids from the medium (P. P. Williams *et al.*, 1961; Gutierrez and Davis, 1962). They contribute to proteolysis in the rumen.

B. Purines and Pyrimidines

Absolute requirements for purines and pyrimidines are a constant feature of the nutrition of ciliates and many other microbes but not vertebrates or their cells. Insect growth may be stimulated by intact nucleic acids or some of their components. The various species of *Tetrahymena* that have been studied, and *Glaucoma chattoni* A, require a purine and a pyrimidine; guanine and uracil and their nucleosides and nucleotides are most effective. *Paramecium*

Table II

CILIATE PURINE AND PYRIMIDINE REQUIREMENTS

Requirements
Guanine or some derivative required. Requirement usually spared by adenine and some of its derivatives.
Uracil or some derivative, or cytidine or some derivative required.
Cytosine, and thymine and its derivatives show modest sparing activity or are inactive.

Species	Reference
Glaucoma chattoni A	Holz *et al.* (1961a); Kidder and Dewey (1955).
Tetrahymena corlissi, 3 strains	Erwin (1960); Kessler (1961).
T. limacis Mf. 1	Kessler (1961).
T. paravorax RP	Erwin (1960); Holz *et al.* (1961b).
T. patula LI	Kessler (1961).
T. pyriformis W	Kidder and Dewey (1951).
T. pyriformis MT II., var. 1	Holz *et al.* (1959).
T. setifera HZ-1	Holz *et al.* (1962a).
T. vorax Tur	Kessler (1961).

Requirements same as above but purine and pyrimidine bases inactive	
Species	Reference
Paramecium aurelia, ribosides active, deoxy compounds spare	Tarantola and van Wagtendonk (1959).
P. caudatum, mixture of ribotides best	Lilly and Klosek (1961).
P. multimicronucleatum, ribo- and deoxyribosides and ribo- and deoxyribotides active	Miller and Johnson (1957).

species are best served by a purine and a pyrimidine riboside or ribotide. Guanosine and cytidine, in a molar ratio of 0.4 (G:C), were best for *Paramecium aurelia,* stock 51 (Tarantola and van Wagtendonk, 1959), guanosine or deoxyguanosine and cytidine or uridine for *P. multimicronucleatum* (Miller and Johnson, 1957), and guanylic, adenylic, cytidylic, and uridylic acids for *P. caudatum* (Lilly and Klosek, 1961; Table II). The constraints of the patterns of sparing activity of purine and pyrimidine derivatives, and catalogs of inactive compounds, for particular species and strains of species are complex and the original literature should be referred to for details.

Concern about the impermeability of inactive compounds in experiments of this sort has been raised (Seaman, 1961b) and may be well founded, but germane to this point are the many observations that labeled nucleosides penetrate *Tetrahymena pyriformis, Paramecium,* and *Euplotes* (Prescott, 1962; Prescott and Kimball, 1961; Berech and van Wagtendonk, 1959, 1962; Butzel and van Wagtendonk, 1963; Kimball and Perdue, 1962; Gall, 1959), and the finding that 5-hydroxymethyluracil and 5-carboxyuracil, which fail to spare the folic acid requirement of *T. pyriformis,* permeate the ciliate, as judged by their ability to spare or replace uracil in satisfying the pyrimidine requirement (Erwin, 1960).

Strains of *T. pyriformis* and *T. rostrata,* and *G. chattoni* A liberate a heat-stable, acid ribonuclease into the culture medium. This extracellular enzyme comprises 60–70% of the total culture ribonuclease of *T. pyriformis* strain W (Eichel *et al.,* 1963).

C. Vitamins

Ciliates—like vertebrates, vertebrate tissue cells, and insects—need nicotinic acid, thiamine, riboflavin, pantothenic acid, and folic acid (Table III). Thiamine

Table III

CILIATE B-COMPLEX VITAMIN REQUIREMENTS

Nicotinic acid, thiamine, riboflavin, pantothenic acid, folic acid required	
Species	Reference
Colpidium campylum C	Dewey and Kidder (1954).
Colpoda steinii,[a] except folic?	Garnjobst *et al.* (1943).
Glaucoma chattoni A	Dewey and Kidder (1954), Holz *et al.* (1962a).
Paramecium aurelia	Miller and van Wagtendonk (1956).
P. caudatum	Lilly and Klosek (1961).
P. multimicronucleatum	W. H. Johnson and Miller (1956).
Tetrahymena corlissi, 4 strains	Holz *et al.* (1960), Kessler (1961).
T. paravorax RP	Holz *et al.* (1961b).
T. patula LI, L-FF	Kessler (1961); Holz *et al.* (1962c).
T. pyriformis, all strains examined except clones of variety 10 which do not require thiamine	Elliott *et al.* (1962); Kidder and Dewey (1951).
T. setifera HZ-1	Holz *et al.* (1962a).
T. vorax Tur	Kessler (1961).

[a] *Colpoda steinii* = *Colpoda duodenaria* (Burt, 1940).

is not required by clones of *Tetrahymena pyriformis*, variety 10. A few clones isolated in Europe require biotin and choline. Pyridoxine, which is active for vertebrates and their cells, insects, and some yeasts, is *relatively* less active for B_6-requiring ciliates; pyridoxal and pyridoxamine are highly active. Some *Tetrahymena* species have strains which do not require a B_6 vitamin (Table IV).

Table IV

CILIATE VITAMIN B_6-GROUP REQUIREMENTS

Species that require[a] vitamin B_6	Reference
Colpoda steinii	Garnjobst *et al.* (1943).
Glaucoma chattoni A	Holz *et al.* (1961a); Kidder *et al.* (1954a).
Paramecium aurelia	Miller and van Wagtendonk (1956).
P. caudatum	Lilly and Klosek (1961).
P. multimicronucleatum	W. H. Johnson and Miller (1957).
Tetrahymena patula LI, L-FF	Kessler (1961); Holz *et al.* (1962c).
T. pyriformis, most strains	Elliott *et al.* (1962); Kidder and Dewey (1951).
T. vorax Tur	Kessler (1961).

Species that do not require vitamin B_6	Reference
Tetrahymena corlissi, 4 strains	Holz *et al.* (1960); Kessler (1961).
T. paravorax RP	Holz *et al.* (1961b).
T. pyriformis, "pyridoxine mutants"	Elliott and Clark (1958a).
T. setifera HZ-1	Holz *et al.* (1962a).

[a] Pyridoxine *relatively* inactive; pyridoxal and pyridoxamine highly active and equivalent in activity. B_6 synthesized by *T. corlissi* 21 (*Saccharomyces carlsbergensis* assay; Kessler, 1961).

A comparative study of the pantothenic acid requirements of *Tetrahymena pyriformis* W, *Glaucoma chattoni* A, and *Colpidium campylum* C (Dewey and Kidder, 1954) showed that pantothenate was more active for *Tetrahymena* and *Colpidium* than were its conjugates (pantothenate > pantethine > pantetheine phosphate $\geqq$ coenzyme A). *Glaucoma* preferred pantethine (pantethine > pantetheine phosphate > pantothenate > coenzyme A). Remarkably larger amounts of pantothenate or its conjugates were needed for *Glaucoma* and *Colpidium* than for *Tetrahymena*. Coenzyme A use by all three ciliates (*Tetrahymena* needed at least 1 μg/ml) implies direct penetration by the coenzyme or a product of its extracellular digestion. Generally, ciliates are as capable of using conjugates of B-complex vitamins as the rat and chick.

Thioctic acid, which has never been found to be required in the diet of an animal, is needed by tetrahymenids (Table V).

Table V
CILIATE THIOCTIC ACID REQUIREMENTS

Species that require thioctic acid	Reference
Glaucoma chattoni A	Holz *et al.* (1961a); Kidder *et al.* (1954a).
Tetrahymena corlissi, 4 strains	Holz *et al.* (1960); Kessler (1961).
T. paravorax RP	Holz *et al.* (1961b).
T. patula LI, L-FF	Kessler (1961); Holz *et al.* (1962c).
T. pyriformis, all strains examined	Elliott *et al.* (1962); Seaman (1952).
T. setifera HZ-1	Holz *et al.* (1962a).
T. vorax Tur	Kessler (1961).

Species that do not require thioctic acid	Reference
Paramecium multimicronucleatum	W. H. Johnson and Miller (1956).
P. caudatum	Lilly and Klosek (1961).
P. aurelia	Miller and van Wagtendonk (1956).

No ciliate studied requires a member of the B_{12} group. *Tetrahymena pyriformis* synthesizes an unknown B_{12}, active for *Escherichia coli* and *Lactobacillus leichmannii* but not for *Euglena gracilis* or *Ochromonas malhamensis* (Erwin and Holz, 1962). The B_{12} requirements of other organisms are extraordinarily various. Cyanocobalamin is needed by vertebrates, some phytoflagellates, and some amebae.

The folic acid requirements of *Tetrahymena pyriformis*, MT II, var. 1, *Tetrahymena vorax* Tur, *Tetrahymena corlissi*, strains Th-X, C, and 21, and *Tetrahymena limacis* Mf. 1 were examined by Erwin (1960). In general, it was found that thymidine or deoxycytidine spared but did not replace folic acid. These separate sparing effects were not additive, and a wide variety of other compounds involved in the metabolism of folic acid and vitamin B_{12} were inactive, alone and in combinations.

Tetrahymena pyriformis was studied in particular detail. Thymine was less active than thymidine, and the following were inactive, alone and in combinations: 5-carboxyuracil and 5-hydroxyuracil, deoxypurines, and deoxyuridine, cytosine, uracil, guanine, adenine, xanthine, hypoxanthine and their ribosides, 5-methylcytosine, 5-hydroxymethylcytosine, 1-methyl purine, 2-methyladenine, 6-methyl aminopurine, 6-dimethyl aminopurine, S-methylmethionine, L-tyrosine, choline, betaine, p-aminobenzoic acid, p-aminobenzoylglutamic acid, B_{12}, cholesterol, stigmasterol, β-sitosterol, zymosterol, 7-dehydrocholesterol, and lanosterol. These compounds were also inactive in sparing folic acid in the presence of thymidine.

These results differ in some respects from those reported by Dewey and Kidder (1953) for *T. pyriformis* W. They also observed thymine (thymidine) sparing of the folic acid requirement but obtained some activity from glycine, p-aminobenzoic acid, creatine, and vitamin B_{12} as well.

Erwin (1960) also tested many isolated synthetic unconjugated pteridines. Of these, biopterin glucoside and 2,4-diamino-6,7-dimethyl pterin were the only ones that were chromatographically homogeneous and active in sparing but not replacing folic acid activity. Combinations of either of these pteridines with thymidine completely replaced folic acid in repeated subcultures of the ciliate.

The interpretation placed on these findings was that folic acid is required by the ciliate to synthesize a coenzyme involved in the methylation of deoxy-cytidine *and* as the source of a pteridine of unknown function.

Kidder and Dewey (1961) have also concluded that *Tetrahymena* requires an unconjugated pteridine, which it derives from folic acid when that is the only source. In their experiments, biopterin was inactive in sparing the folic requirement of strain W, but three triamino pyrimidines were active (2,6-di-amino-4-hydroxy-5-formylaminopyrimidine was the most active) and this activity was potentiated by thymine or thymidine, plus a mixture of compounds involved in folic acid-mediated functions. They also reported the synthesis of a *Crithidia-active* pteridine by *Tetrahymena* grown with a limited amount of folic acid. Unconjugated pteridines have been suggested as cofactors for: the hydroxylation of phenylalanine to tyrosine (Kaufman, 1962), the oxidation of dihydroorotic acid, the cyclization of squalene and the desaturation of long-chain fatty acids (Kidder and Dewey, 1963), and the degradative oxidation of glyceryl ethers (Tietz *et al.*, 1963).

The fat-soluble vitamins required by vertebrates are not known to be needed in the diets of ciliates.

D. ORGANIC ACIDS AND ALCOHOLS

Organic acids and alcohols have relatively little effect nutritionally on tetra-hymenids (Kidder and Dewey, 1951; Holz *et al.*, 1959, 1961a, 1962a). Acetate, however, can stimulate growth of some of them, particularly in the absence of thioctic acid and glucose (Kidder and Dewey, 1951). A mixture of acetate and pyruvate is used in media for *Paramecium* species (Lilly and Klosek, 1961; Miller and Johnson, 1960). Addition of glycogen, glucose-1-phosphate, glucose, fructose, galactose, or mannose to a medium for *P. multimicronucleatum* containing acetate encouraged no better population growth than the medium with acetate alone. Of these carbohydrates, glycogen, glucose, and fructose were used by the ciliate, the others were not (W. H. Johnson and Miller, 1956).

Ethanol or methanol, but not a wide variety of other alcohols, organic acids, or aldehydes was required for growth of *Tetrahymena setifera* HZ-1 in a chemically defined medium (Holz *et al.*, 1962a), and the carbon of methanol-C^{14} was incorporated during growth (Erwin, 1962). This requirement was not evident in peptone media. Ethanol may stimulate growth of some other microbes, *Lactobacillus heterohiochi* for example (Demain *et al.*, 1961), but the inflexibility of the ciliate requirement is surprising.

E. Lipids

Lipid requirements of microorganisms have been reviewed in a comparative treatment very recently (Hutner and Holz, 1962), so remarks to follow will be largely restricted to ciliates.

1. FATTY ACIDS

No absolute requirements for the polyunsaturated fatty acids essential for some vertebrates have been reported for ciliates. However, *G. chattoni* A was stimulated by the monounsaturated oleic acid and by the polyunsaturated linoleic, linolenic (in the presence of a synthetic phosphatide), and arachidonic acids (Holz *et al.*, 1961a). Saturated fatty acids (stearic, palmitic) were inactive, as were all methyl esters of fatty acids tested. Oleic acid promoted growth best (Table VI).

Paramecium species are responsive to long-chain acids even in the presence of large amounts of acetate and pyruvate, and different species and strains of species show different specificities of response. *Paramecium aurelia*, syngen 4, stock 47, mating type VIII, grew better with stearic than with oleic acid, and syngen 4, stock 51, mating type VII, KK, sensitive, preferred oleic to stearic acid, but consistent results were obtained if both saturated and monounsaturated acids were present (Miller and Johnson, 1960). *Paramecium multimicronucleatum* (*P. aurelia-multimicronucleatum* complex) syngen 2, mating type III *and* syngen 2, mating type IV, responded to a saturated (stearic) *or* monounsaturated (oleic) acid. Saturated acids of shorter chain lengths were inactive, as were palmitoleic and polyunsaturated acids. Polyunsaturated acids did not spare active acids. Combinations of stearic and oleic acids were no more active than individual acids (Miller and Johnson, 1960).

Growth of *Paramecium caudatum* was most favored by linoleic and oleic acids in a ratio of 3:1 (Lilly and Klosek, 1961; Table VI).

Table VI

CILIATE NUTRITIONAL RESPONSES TO C_{16}-C_{20} SATURATED AND UNSATURATED FATTY ACIDS

Species	Pal-mitic	Stearic	Palmi-toleic	Oleic	Lino-leic	α-Lino-lenic	Arachi-donic	Reference
Glaucoma chattoni A	—	—	——	+	+	—	+	Holz *et al.* (1961a).
Paramecium caudatum	——	——	——	+	+	——	——	Lilly and Klosek (1961).
P. multimicro-nucleatum	—	+	—	+	—	—	—	Miller and John-son (1960).
Tetrahymena corlissi Th-X	—	——	——	+	—	—	——	Holz *et al.* (1961c).
T. paravorax RP	—	——	——	+	——	——	——	Holz *et al.* (1960).
T. pyriformis W and MT II, var. 1 (35°C)	—	—	——	—	—	—	—	Kidder and Dewey (1951); Holz *et al.* (1960).

a Key to symbols:
—, Does not stimulate growth.
+, Stimulated growth.
——, No data.

As discussed in Section III, D, nutritionally inactive fatty acids may be readily incorporated and/or converted.

Synthetic lipids like Tween 80 (polyoxyethylene ester of sorbitan monooleate) and TEM-4T (diacetyl tartaric acid esters of tallow monoglycerides) have been useful in ciliate cultivation as soluble, relatively nontoxic, sources of fatty acids (Kidder and Dewey, 1951; Holz *et al.*, 1961a,c, 1962b; Miller and Johnson, 1960; Epstein *et al.*, 1963a). Unfortunately they are made to standards of chemical purity appropriate to commercial uses and their content of lipid contaminants (e.g., nonsaponifiables) disqualify them for use in chemically defined media; they may be ingested in such large amounts as to destroy the applicability of turbidimetric methods of estimation of population growth changes (Kidder *et al.*, 1954b); they cause fragility that is undesirable for many experimental applications to which the ciliates may be put; and they are dispersible rather than water soluble, which may disturb nutritional purists seeking to develop soluble culture media (Holz *et al.*, 1962a).

2. GLYCERIDES

Glycerides of growth-promoting fatty acids are themselves active; triolein and trilinolein-*Glaucoma chattoni* A (Holz *et al.*, 1962a); tristearin-*Paramecium aurelia*, stock 47; triolein-*P. aurelia*, stock 51; triolein > tristearin > tripalmitin-*P. multimicronucleatum* strains (Miller and Johnson, 1960). Extracellular lipases (Hill *et al.*, 1960) and phagocytosis of fat globules (Elsbach, 1962) are suspect as aids to utilization by rumen ciliates and tissue cells.

3. PHOSPHOLIPIDS

Phospholipid preparations have been useful in the axenic culture of some fastidious ciliates; *Tetrahymena corlissi* 24, *Tetrahymena limacis* Mf. 1, *Tetrahymena patula* LI and L-FF (Kessler, 1961); *Paramecium* (W. H. Johnson and Miller, 1963).

Synthetic phospholipids fabricated with high-purity fatty acids stimulated *Glaucoma chattoni* A growth (Holz *et al.*, 1962a). Glycerophosphoryl cholines were better than glycerophosphoryl ethanolamines, and dioleoyl compounds were better than dipalmitoyl ones.

Synthetic phosphatides also (1) supported growth of *Tetrahymena pyriformis*, mating type II, var. 1, in a defined medium at 40°C. (N. Rosenbaum, 1963); (2) spared (with oleic acid and glycerophosphate) the sterol requirements of *T. setifera* HZ-1 (Holz *et al.*, 1962a), *T. corlissi* Th-X (Holz *et al.*, 1961c), and *T. paravorax* RP (Wagner and Erwin, 1961); (3) protected *G. chattoni* A against the toxicity of polyunsaturated fatty acids (Holz *et al.*, 1962a); and (4) potentiated the action of sterols, fatty acids, or glycerides in annulling growth inhibition by triparanol (Holz *et al.*, 1962b).

Nutritional activity of phospholipids for microbes is generally attributed to (1) activity of some one (or a combination) of their constituent parts (fatty acids, choline, etc.), (2) ability (as charged molecules with lipophilic and hydrophilic poles) to complex with and detoxify or solubilize toxic or insoluble molecules, (3) susceptibility to contamination with other nutritionally significant molecules, (4) antioxidant properties, (5) dispersible (rather than soluble) particulate natures and potential as inciters of phagocytosis, and (6) essential metabolite characteristics. Phospholipids are involved directly or indirectly in metabolic activities at all membranous interfaces in cells (mitochondria, endoplasmic reticulum, plasma membrane). Thirty per cent of the weight of a mitochondrion is lipid, of which 90% is phospholipid. Supplied as nutrients they might be incorporated directly or, after alteration, into such sites, to meet needs arising from metabolic defects in the synthesis of phospholipids or their assembly into associations with proteins and sterols in membranes. Insufficient information exists to allow a choice to be made from among these alternatives.

4. STEROLS

Vertebrates and higher plants make sterols. Insects, crustacea (*Artemia*), annelids (*Lumbricus*), yeasts grown anaerobically, trichomonads, some *Labyrinthula* species, and some pleuropneumonia-like organisms require exogenous supplies. Some ciliates also need a sterol for best growth (Table VII). *Paramecium* species favor 3β-OH,Δ^5 plant sterols with ethylated side chains, such as stigmasterol and the sitosterols. Some *Tetrahymena* species use these sterols *and* cholesterol and structurally related sterols.

None of the ciliates tested responded to precursors of the cyclopentenophenanthrene ring system, e.g., mevalonic acid and squalene. Ring-methylated products of squalene cyclization and lanosterol demethylation were generally inactive, except lophenol, which was moderately active nutritionally for *T. corlissi* Th-X and was directly incorporated but not converted to cholesterol or sterols of comparable polarity (Holz *et al.*, 1961c). Zymosterol, a cholesterol precursor, satisfied *T. corlissi* Th-X and *T. paravorax* RP (Holz *et al.*, 1961b) but not *T. setifera* HZ-1 (Holz *et al.*, 1962a) or *P. aurelia*, stock 51.7 (S) (Conner and van Wagtendonk, 1955). More immediate cholesterol precursors, desmosterol, Δ^7-cholestenol and 7-dehydrocholesterol, were as active as cholesterol for the tetrahymenids. Steroid hormones of vertebrates were inactive or inhibitory.

The metabolic basis for ciliate sterol requirements is unknown, but differing specificities of responses to sterols shown by the species that require them, and the inactivity of lanosterol and its precursors, suggest impaired mechanisms for transforming sterol precursors of ciliate sterols. For example, zymosterol activity and lanosterol inactivity for *T. corlissi* suggest a block in lanosterol demethylation.

The nutritional activity of the ring-saturated cholestanol is unusual and may indicate ability to convert the sterol to a more biologically active form. Clayton and Edwards (1962) and Louloudes *et al.* (1962) have reported conversion of cholestanol to Δ^7-cholestenol by cockroaches.

Incorporation without conversion, as in insects (Clayton and Bloch, 1963), and doubts about permeability (discussed by Holz *et al.*, 1961c) preclude direct resolution of questions of sterol convertibility by nutritional experiments, but antimetabolite and isotopic tracer studies have begun to contribute relevant information.

Ciliates that do not require sterols are presumed to synthesize them. Steroids of unspecified nature were found in *T. pyriformis* (McKee *et al.*, 1947; Taketomi, 1961), and a recent preliminary communication reported dihydrolanosterol, methostenol, and zymosterol (Castrejon and Hamilton, 1962).

Population growth of *T. pyriformis* is impaired by inhibitors of vertebrate cholesterol synthesis (Aaronson *et al.*, 1962; Holz, 1963; Holz *et al.*, 1963;

Table VII

CILIATE STEROL REQUIREMENTS[a]

Sterol	Double bonds	Side-chain and ring-system substitutions	Paramecium aurelia var. 4, stock 51.7 (s)[b]	Tetrahymena corlissi Th-X[c]	Tetrahymena paravorax RP[d]	Tetrahymena setifera HZ-1[e]
Lanosterol	8, 24	4α, 4β, 14α—CH₃	——	−	−	−
Dihydrolanosterol	8	4α, 4β, 14α—CH₃	——	−	−	−
Dihydrolanosteryl acetate			−	——		
4′,4′-Dimethyl-Δ⁸-cholestenol	8	4α, 4β—CH₃	——	−	−	−
Citrostadienol	7, 24(28)	4α—CH₃, 24=CHCH₃	——	−	−	−
4α-Methyl-Δ⁷-cholestenol (lophenol)	7	4α—CH₃	——	++	−	−
4α-Methyl-Δ⁸-cholestenol	8	4α—CH₃	——	−	−	−
Zymosterol	8, 24		−	+	+	−
Desmosterol	5, 24		——	+++	+++	+++
Δ⁷-Cholestenol (lathosterol)	7		——	++	+++	+++
7-Dehydrocholesterol	5, 7		——	+++	+++	+++
Cholesterol	5		−	+++	+++	+++
24-Methylene cholesterol	5, 24(28)	24=CH₂	−	+++	+++	+++
Fucosterol	5, 24(28)	24=CHCH₃	++	+++	+++	+++
Campesterol	5	24α—CH₃		+++		+++
Campesteryl acetate			——	——	+++	+++
β-Sitosterol	5	24β—C₂H₅	++	+++	+++	+++
Clionasterol	5	24α—C₂H₅	++	+++		+++

Table VII—*Continued*

Sterol	Double bonds	Side-chain and ring-system substitutions	*Paramecium aurelia* var. 4, stock 51.7 (s) [b]	*Tetra-hymena corlissi* Th-X [c]	*Tetra-hymena paravorax* RP [d]	*Tetra-hymena setifera* HZ-1 [e]
Brassicasterol	5, 22	24β—CH$_3$	+++	+++		+++
Brassicasteryl acetate			—	+++	+++	—
Stigmasterol	5, 22	24β—C$_2$H$_5$	+++	+++	+++	+++
Poriferasterol	5, 22	24α—C$_2$H$_5$	+++	+++	+++	+++
Ergosterol	5, 7, 22	24β—CH$_3$	—	+++	+++	+++
Neospongesterol	22	24α—CH$_3$	——	+++	+++	——
Neospongesteryl acetate			—	——	——	——

[a] Key to symbols:
—, Does not satisfy sterol requirement for growth.
+, Fair source of sterol for growth.
++, Good source of sterol for growth.
+++, Excellent source of sterol for growth.
——, No data.

[b] van Wagtendonk, 1955.
[c] Holz *et al.*, 1961c.
[d] Holz *et al.*, 1961b.
[e] Holz *et al.*, 1962a.

W. J. Johnson and Jasmin, 1961). A study of sterol prevention of triparanol (MER-29) inhibition indicated that the drug impaired the reduction of the 24(25) double bond of sterols like zymosterol and desmosterol, and the 24(28) double bond of sterols like 24-methylene cholesterol and fucosterol, during their conversion to ciliate sterol(s) (Holz *et al.*, 1962b).

Many other chemical agents which inhibit population growth of *Tetrahymena* are reported to be antagonized by sterols: dinitrophenol, colchicine, progesterone and cortisone (Conner and Nakatani, 1958; Conner, 1959), purine analogs (Dewey *et al.*, 1959), 2,6-diamino-4-isoamyloxypyridine (Markees *et al.*, 1960), acetate antimetabolites (Dewey and Kidder, 1960c). A particularly instructive example is the action of 6-methyl purine on *T. pyriformis* (Dewey *et al.*, 1960). Sterols, phospholipids and branched-chain fatty acids partly protected against growth inhibition caused by the purine. Small amounts of adenine were active in the presence of these substances; high concentrations were completely effective alone. Glycolipids, inositol phosphatides, and phosphatidyl ethanolamine were active with sterols but not alone. It was found later that soybean lecithin (active alone) owed its activity to its contamination with a β-D-glycoside of β-sitosterol (Dewey and Kidder, 1962).

Probably many inhibitors of *Tetrahymena* growth, that are antagonized by sterols, fatty acids, phospholipids, and purines, have as their loci of action those steps in the intermediary metabolism of the protective agents which involve phosphorylations (ATP synthesis or utilization is impaired). The ubiquitous nature and high activity of sterols as protectors may indicate a sensitivity of the ciliate to impaired sterol synthesis, the canalized and irreversible nature of sterol synthesis, or the preferential commitment of acetate to sterol synthesis.

It is notable that a combination of oleic acid, glycerophosphate, and a synthetic phospholipid spared the sterol requirement of tetrahymenids (Holz *et al.*, 1961b, 1962a). When such a combination was used to grow *T. corlissi* Th-X in the absence of a sterol, triparanol still inhibited growth (Erwin, 1962). The inhibition was susceptible to sterol protection, with a sterol-specificity pattern comparable to that observed with *T. pyriformis,* and with *T. corlissi* Th-X grown with lophenol (methostenol), a sterol not converted to cholesterol by this ciliate. Triparanol inhibition of *T. pyriformis* was partly reversed by long-chain fatty acids, particularly oleic acid (Holz, 1963; Holz *et al.*, 1962b). The actions of fatty acids and sterol were additive, and a synthetic dipalmitoyl lecithin potentiated the combination's activity.

One explanation is that all the lipids which spared sterols for growth or protected ciliates against drugs were products of sterol-catalyzed reactions.

In a preliminary communication, Conner and Ungar (1962) reported the conversion of 4-C^{14}-cholesterol to a more polar sterol, and suggested that the protective effects of sterols against DNP-poisoning that he has observed (Conner, 1957; Conner *et al.*, 1961) may be attributed to their conversion to this sterol. Cholesterol was accumulated by *Tetrahymena* to an amount 500–1000 $\times$ the external concentration. The accumulation was temperature- and concentration-dependent and appeared to represent the actions of two processes: a rapid adsorption and a slower, metabolism-dependent transport. Cholesterol accumulated by *Tetrahymena* in a 4-hr. incubation in a non-nutrient medium was removable with acetone; 1% was esterified. Seventy-five % of the free sterol was cholesterol, and 25% was the polar sterol (Conner, 1963).

The extremely important recent finding by Mallory *et al.* (1963) of a pentacyclic triterpenoid alcohol in *Tetrahymena* may clarify *or* muddy our view of the metabolic basis for ciliate sterol requirements. This alcohol (tetrahymanol; 5β-glutinan-3α-ol) was reported to be the principal component of the nonsaponifiable fraction of *T. pypriformis*. If it should turn out that it subserves either the structural or the functional roles of sterols, the sterol nutritional requirements of tetrahymenids may represent a need for molecules readily convertible to tetrahymanol, and the growth inhibitory actions of drugs which impair sterol synthesis may be expressions of the impairment of synthesis of tetrahymanol.

Lund and Shorb (1962) have raised an issue of pressing concern to those studying microbial lipid nutrition. They observed loss of nutritional activity of β-sitosterol, in satisfying the sterol requirement of *Trichomonas gallinae* SLT, after it was "purified" by gas chromatography. Older criteria of sterol purity (crystallinity, melting point) will have to be abandoned; plainly, most of our information on microbial sterol requirements will have to be reexamined with experimental designs built around chromatographically homogeneous test substances. This applies as well with fatty acids, particularly unsaturated ones. Also, the autoclaving of complex lipids in culture media must be discouraged. The author has observed striking differences in responses of bacteria to linoleic acid supplied aseptically or autoclaved.

F. Carbohydrates

Studies of carbohydrate use by intact ciliates have been carried out (1) with nutrient-containing media to which carbohydrate was added before or after autoclaving, and population growth response over an incubation period of days used as the measure of carbohydrate use, *or* (2) with a nutrient or non-nutrient medium containing a carbohydrate, and acid and gas production by a large number of ciliates in a relatively short time was the response criterion.

Considerable effort has been made in growth experiments to find carbon substrates that are chemically pure and can be autoclaved with the usual defined media without decomposing or forming toxic, colored, or insoluble products.

In chemically defined media a source of carbohydrate seemed to be obligatory for best population growth of *Glaucoma chattoni* A (Holz *et al.*, 1961a) and some *Tetrahymena* species: *T. corlissi* (4 strains; Holz *et al.*, 1960; Kessler, 1961), *T. patula* (2 strains; Kessler, 1961), and one strain each of *T. limacis* (Kessler, 1961), *T. setifera* (Holz *et al.*, 1962a), and *T. paravorax* (Holz *et al.*, 1961b). Glucose (added after autoclaving of the medium) was best for all except *T. corlissi* strains, which preferred dextrin. The original papers should be consulted for lists of less active and inactive compounds.

Reynolds and Wragg (1962) obtained a shorter generation time, greater cell size and protein content, and greater final population of *T. pyriformis* W with dextrin than with glucose.

Growth of *T. pyriformis* in a carbohydrate-free medium, equivalent to that obtained in the presence of glucose, has been reported (Hutner, 1963).

Most amicronucleate (Kidder and Dewey, 1945; Loefer and McDaniel, 1950; Shaw and Williams, 1963) and mating strains (Elliott and Outka, 1956) of *T. pyriformis* fermented glucose, mannose, maltose, fructose, dextrin, and starch. A *Colpidium* and a *Glaucoma* fermented glucose, fructose, maltose, lactose, and starch, and the *Colpidium* fermented sucrose (Kidder, 1941). It is the only tetrahymenid which does so. Responses to lactose and galactose were variable.

Acetate and pyruvate supported growth of *Paramecium* species. Addition of carbohydrates did not improve growth over that obtained with acetate (W. H. Johnson and Miller, 1956).

G. Feeding

Relatively little attention has been given to problems of nutrient entry into ciliates. Questions of "permeability" are complicated by food vacuole formation.

Passage of materials in solution directly across the body surface may occur by diffusion or active transport. Cirillo (1962) described the movement of a nonmetabolizable sugar, L-arabinose, into and out of washed *T. pyriformis*, as facilitated diffusion (Cirillo, 1961; Wilbrandt and Rosenberg, 1961), with transport across the surface by a mobile carrier. Exposure of washed ciliates to a high concentration ($10^{-2} M$) of arabinose resulted in entry of the sugar but not accumulation. Intracellular concentration never reached more than 50% of extracellular. Rate of movement had a high Q_{10} (2.5 between 10° and 30°C.) and was competitively inhibited by glucose. If glucose was added to a suspension of ciliates equilibrated with arabinose, there was an arabinose efflux against the arabinose concentration gradient.

Characteristics of the uptake of L-phenylalanine-3-C^{14} by washed *T. pyriformis*—rapidity, sterospecificity, rate/concentration relationship, inhibition by dinitrophenol and temperature dependence—suggested an active transport of the amino acid (Stephens and Kerr, 1962).

Dunham and Child (1961) measured internal Na^+, K^+, and Cl^- in *Tetrahymena* and exchange rates of Na^+ and K^+ in media with different Na^+ and K^+ contents. They observed a capacity to maintain a high internal K^+ and lower internal Na^+ in a very dilute medium and the imbalance was not attributable to a Donnan equilibrium. A Na^+ extrusion mechanism was found which operated independent of internal binding sites for K^+ and Na^+. Andrus and Giese (1963) analyzed this Na^+ and K^+ regulation by observing the effects upon it of a series of agents which were capable of altering metabolism in general or properties of the cell surface. Sodium ion penetration accompanied low temperatures, but not anoxia or treatment with iodoacetate, DNP, or azide. Potassium ion loss was associated with all of these environmental changes. Restoration of the normal distribution of the ions was temperature-, oxygen-, and metabolism-dependent. The rates of the ion movements and the amounts of ions moved suggested a binding of 30% of the ciliate K^+ and a coupling of the movement of the free 70% with a Na^+ extrusion mechanism. *Paramecium* (Akita, 1941) and *Spirostomum* (Carter, 1957) may also have a Na^+ pump.

The high concentration of mitochondria in the cortex of many ciliates may be associated with metabolism-supported transport across the surface.

"Semipermeability" is evidenced also by changes in activities of some compounds with changes in pH. Succinate penetration (Seaman, 1955), and triparanol inhibition of *T. pyriformis* (Holz et al., 1962b), were pH dependent.

Micropinocytosis (membrane flow or membrane vesiculation; Bennett, 1956) at the body surface has not been described, but R. M. Rosenbaum and Wittner (1962) fed horseradish peroxidase to *P. caudatum* and found it in "droplets" gathered in the cytoplasm in the posterior end. Hydrolytic enzymes normally associated with food vacuoles were found with the "droplets," but food vacuoles induced to form with particulate matter were much larger than these "droplets." They postulated a preferential uptake of soluble protein at the ciliates' posterior end.

Entry of nutrients into food vacuoles at a locus on the body surface (a mouth) occurs by phagocytosis (engulfment of particles ranging in size from viruses (Groupè et al., 1955) to metazoans (Brown and Jenkins, 1962)) and pinocytosis (cell drinking). Some pinocytosis always accompanies phagocytosis.

Seaman (1961a) referred to food vacuoles containing substances in solution and to vacuoles containing particulate matter as phagotrophic vacuoles, and to the process of their formation at the mouth of *Tetrahymena* as phagotrophy. Holz et al. (1961a) commented on the similarities between ciliate drinking and pinocytosis, and ciliate particle-feeding and phagocytosis, and Grebecki (1963) considered the binding of dyes in the cytostome of *Paramecium* and their uptake and concentration in food vacuoles to be a special case of pinocytosis. Müller et al. (1963a) viewed ciliate food vacuoles as lysosomes of the phagosome type (Novikoff, 1960, 1961). They made penetrating studies of food vacuole formation, structure, and function (updating the beautiful review of Kitching, 1956) and noted that food vacuoles meet the criteria for lysosomes: (1) the encompassing of the vacuole in a unit membrane (in *Euplotes*, L. E. Roth, 1957; in *Paramecium*, Jurand, 1961), presumably originating from the surface membrane at the site of vacuole formation at the mouth, "isolating" the vacuolar contents from the cytoplasm; (2) the association with the vacuole (in *Paramecium*, Müller, 1962; R. M. Rosenbaum and Wittner, 1962) of acid phosphatase, acid deoxyribonuclease, acid ribonuclease, acid phosphoamidase, acid glucuronidase, neutral leucylaminopeptidase, neutral carboxylesterase, and lipase; and (3) the digestion of food in the vacuoles and passage of soluble products of digestion into the cytoplasm.

Small vacuoles (secondary vacuoles) have also been observed to form at food vacuole membranes of *Paramecium* (Jurand, 1961) and *Euplotes* (L. E. Roth, 1957).

Acid phosphatase and nonspecific esterases associated with cytoplasmic granules and with food vacuoles have been demonstrated in many ciliates: *T. corlissi* (Müller et al., 1960a), *T. pyriformis* (Seaman, 1961a; Müller et al., 1963; Allen et al., 1963; Bak and Elliott, 1963), *Ophryoglena* sp. (Müller et al., 1963a,b),

P. multimicronucleatum (Müller and Törő, 1962; Müller, 1962), *Stentor coeruleus* (Weisz, 1949), *Nassula* (Fauré-Frémiet, 1962); and R. M. Rosenbaum and Wittner (1962) associated acid phosphatase with the neutral red granules which earlier workers described clustering around food vacuoles. In studies of the enzymatic activity of the vacuoles, Müller *et al.* (1963a) observed a lack of correspondence between the time of maximum acid phosphatase activity and the time of lowest pH. Strangely, highest activity coincided with a period of slight alkalinity.

A clue to the rapidity of digestion and the transfer of materials from food vacuoles to sites of utilization, is offered by the startling observation of Kimball and Prescott (1962) that when *Tetrahymena* containing an intracellular pool of H^3-thymidine derivatives are offered as food to *Euplotes*, the deoxyribonucleic acid (DNA) in the reorganization band of the macronucleus becomes labeled within 2–4 min.

Particulate matter and substances in solution induce food vacuole formation. Ciliates can be highly selective when feeding on bacteria and some degree of selectivity may be anticipated when they are presented with inanimate materials. Non-nutritive particles were avidly ingested by *Paramecium* in a *non-nutrient* medium and the induced food vacuole formation was accompanied by intense acid phosphatase activity (Müller *et al.*, 1963a,b). Proteose-peptone-induced vacuole formation in *T. pyriformis*, in the absence of any particulate matter has been observed (Chapman-Andresen, 1963; Seaman, 1961b), and isolation of the vacuole-inducing factor has been reported (Seaman, 1963b). A variety of particulate matter may be ingested by tetrahymenids in media containing proteinaceous materials—charcoal (*Glaucoma;* Kidder, 1941) and colloidal gold (*Tetrahymena;* Cohen, 1959), for example.

On the basis of measurements of dye uptake, and ingestion of *Serratia marcescens* by *T. pyriformis* (indicators of rates of food vacuole formation), and comparison of values so obtained with figures for rates of acetate and glucose utilization, Seaman (1961b, 1962) arrived at the conclusion that . . . "uptake of material through the mouth region in *Tetrahymena pyriformis* is too slow to provide any real hope that the organism can be used at present for the assay of bound forms of required nutritional cofactors." This view seems unnecessarily pessimistic. Very little protein-bound *vitamin* would have to enter by this route to meet the nutritional needs of a single *Tetrahymena*. Generalizations about the extent of the contribution of the food vacuole route to the nutrition of *T. pyriformis* based on calculations of acetate and glucose consumption rates underplay the fact that *T. pyriformis* requires at least 20 organic nutrients, some of them in very small amounts.

Jurand *et al.* (1962) made the most provocative of all observations relevant to this subject when they found that ribonuclease penetrated living *Paramecium* and diminished the ribonucleic acid (RNA) content. The ciliates restored their normal amount of RNA after two fissions. We do not know whether the route of the enzyme was through the body surface or through the membranes of food vacuoles. In either case, movement of a protein into the organism (like the horseradish peroxidase in R. M. Rosenbaum and Wittner's experiments) occurred without loss of enzymatic activity, and we are challenged to explain the means by which this was accomplished.

Seaman (1961a,b) has stated that *T. pyriformis* forms no food vacuoles when it is cultured axenically in chemically defined media containing only small molecules. Some modification of this stand would seem necessary. The author and others (Allen *et al.*, 1963) have seen food vacuoles in *T. pyriformis* cultured in media of that description. Chapman-Andresen reports (1963) seeing 5–15 vacuoles per individual in strain GL cultured in Kidder's medium A (without Tween 80). Vacuoles have also been seen by the author in ciliates washed repeatedly and left to stand in distilled water during mating experiments. There is no question, however, that solutions of proteinaceous materials and suspensions of particulate matter greatly stimulate vacuole formation over rates seen in nonnutrient media and media composed of small molecules.

A contribution to illuminating these dark corners could be made by studying the operation of the sugar and amino acid transport systems described by Cirillo (1962) and Stephens and Kerr (1962) under conditions where food vacuole formation was being induced by inert materials [perhaps the latex particles used by Müller *et al.* (1963a) in their *Paramecium* experiments].

The intolerance of most ciliates for the rich media that grow tetrahymenids suggests that many may rely very little on nutrient translocation across their surfaces and depend, to varying degrees of exclusiveness, on forms of particle feeding.

The polemical nature of some of the foregoing discussion is based not so much on differences in matters of fact as on differences in emphasis. Dogmas are premature. Too little is known about food vacuole induction, formation, structure, and function under varying environmental conditions in ciliates of widely differing food habits *and* about movements of nutrients directly across membranous interfaces of ciliates.

Phagocytosis (Karnovsky, 1962) and pinocytosis (Chapman-Andresen, 1962) studies are guides for future work with ciliates.

H. SYMBIOSIS AND PARASITISM

Ciliates harbor a stunning variety of intracellular associates: bacteria, algae, flagellates, etc. (Kirby, 1941; Trager, 1961; Sonneborn, 1959). The nutrition of a ciliate acting as a host to one or more of these is, in fact, the nutrition of the community. Soldo (1960) has shown that successful cultivation of strains of *P. aurelia* containing kappa, lambda, mu, and pi particles—and maintenance of particle population—depend on the composition of the culture medium used. Particle maintenance was somewhat more dependent upon the presence of Proteose-peptone in a semidefined medium than was growth of the host.

Ciliates are excellent tools for studying symbiotic relationships but difficulties in cultivation have limited their use. The recent breakthrough in *Paramecium* culture, eliminating proteins (Reilly and Lilly, 1963) in otherwise defined media, makes feasible the analysis of the biochemistry of the association between *Paramecium bursaria* and its chlorellae—the classic example of the genre (Siegel, 1960; Karakashian, 1963). The application of continuous culture techniques to rumen ciliates (Quinn *et al.*, 1962; Quinn, 1962) should permit examination of the many curious associations between these protozoa and bacteria (Gutierrez and Davis, 1959).

Facultative parasitism is common in the genus *Tetrahymena* (Corliss, 1960; J. C. Thompson, 1958). The nutritional requirements of four strains of *T. corlissi* (Th-X, C, 21, 24) and one of *T. limacis* (Mf.1) have been studied in axenic culture in defined media (Holz *et al.*, 1961c; Kessler, 1961). No pervasive differences have been noted from those of free-living *Tetrahymena* species.

I. Temperature

During a survey of physiological characteristics of mating strains of *T. pyriformis* (Holz *et al.*, 1959), temperature tolerance was recognized as a varietal characteristics. Variety 1 mating types could be grown in a crude medium at 40°C., those of varieties 2, 3, and 5 at 35°C., and the remaining varieties at lower temperatures. All varieties grew at 25°C. Use of a defined medium lowered by several degrees the maximum temperature at which variety 1 mating types would show unimpaired population growth. Preer (1957) described a gene determining temperature sensitivity in *Paramecium*. When a resistant strain (TT) was crossed with a sensitive one (tt), there was no delay in expression of resistance (Tt). If the sensitive genotype was restored, 5–9 fissions were required before resistance disappeared.

The voluminous literature on temperature-induced nutritional requirements (see, for example, effervescent reviews by Hutner *et al.*, 1958c; Hutner, 1961) and the observations of heat-impairment of stomatogenesis, mitosis, and division of *Tetrahymena* (Holz *et al.*, 1957; N. E. Williams and Scherbaum, 1959; Thormar, 1962a,b; Frankel, 1962) led N. Rosenbaum (1963) to study the nutritional and morphological consequences of cultivation of *T. pyriformis*, MT II, var. 1, at temperatures from 35° to 40°C. in a defined medium which supported excellent population growth at 35° (Holz *et al.*, 1959). If this medium was supplemented with 1 mg/100 ml each of uridine, cytidine, and guanylate and 20 mg/100 ml each of synthetic L-α-(dipalmitoyl)-lecithin and L-α-(dipalmitoyl)-cephalin, equivalent and subculturable population growth was supported up to 38°–39° and about one-half that amount at 40°C. Growth in the unsupplemented medium was greatly diminished at 38°–39° and failed at 40° in serial transfer. No additional nutrients (sterols, fatty acids, protein hydrolyzates, vitamins, amino acids, nucleic acid hydrolyzates, carbon sources, phospholipid precursors, *Tetrahymena* extract, and combinations of these nutrients) stimulated growth in the nucleoside (-tide)- and phospholipid-supplemented medium at 40°C.

A 48- to 72-hr. exposure of the ciliates to 40°, in the unsupplemented medium, produced a population of pleomorphic ciliates. The abnormalities were: extreme variations in size and shape, cytoplasmic protrusions, crooked and broken kineties, reduced movement, various distortions of stomatogenesis, unequal cleavage, arrested or unequal macronuclear division, and abnormal nuclear complement. Cells were observed with two macronuclei, no micronucleus, and no nuclei. Though it permitted one-half the population growth attained by structurally normal cells at 35°, the supplemented medium did not offer remarkable protection against the abnormalities. Others have observed teratology associated with continuous growth of ciliates at supraoptimal temperatures; for recent examples see Prescott (1957), Holz *et al.* (1959), Quinn *et al.* (1962).

The exogenous supply of phospholipids may have supported normal mitochondrial function in the face of heat impairment of mitochondrial phospholipid integrity and/or synthesis, since mitochondrial oxidative enzymes are phospholipid dependent. *Tetrahymena* (H. Sato, 1960) suffers mitochondrial changes (swelling, surface irregularity, loss of cortical localization) at high temperatures.

Enhancement of the purine and pyrimidine requirement may have been a consequence of damaged phospholipid synthesis (itself cytidine-dependent), of heightened metabolic activities pacing more rapid proliferation, and/or of accelerated protein synthesis for repair of heat denaturation (Allen, 1953). Excesses of amino acids, vitamins, and trace metals in the 35°-medium may have masked increased organismic demands for these nutrients at 40°C., since N. Rosenbaum (1963) did not observe the sorts of temperature-associated needs reported for phytoflagellates (Baker *et al.*, 1955; Hutner *et al.*, 1957).

J. MORPHOLOGY

Tetrahymena vorax strains V_2 and Tur, *T. patula* strains LI and L-FF, and *T. paravorax* RP are polymorphic. Small microstomes can transform into large predacious macrostomes after an appropriate environmental ("nutritional") stimulus: presence of prey. Also, *T. vorax* V_2 microstomes may undergo spontaneous, relatively rare transformations into types with morphological and physiological characteristics which distinguish them from the parental type. A total of three are recognized (S-, D-, M-type; N. E. Williams, 1961; Shaw and Williams, 1963). They differ serologically and in their growth responses to serine and to soybean phospholipids.

The microstome-macrostome transformation can be induced in populations of *T. vorax* V₂ by the presence of *T. pyriformis*, even when the two ciliate species are mechanically separated by a barrier across which materials in solution can move (Claff, 1947; Buhse, 1962). Identification of the inducer should be feasible with such an assay system.

In axenic culture, the morphological state of a tetrahymenid competent to undergo the microstome-macrostome transformation depends upon the nature of the culture medium, the phase of the population growth cycle, and the species in question. *Tetrahymena vorax* V₂ macrostomes were seen only in the stationary phase (Shaw and Williams, 1963), while mixtures of micro- and macrostomes of *T. patula* L-FF appeared at all phases in a semidefined medium containing aqueous lettuce extract (N. E. Williams, 1960). In the author's experience the macrostome form of the L-FF strain of *T. patula* was much more evident at all stages of population growth in a defined medium containing phospholipids than was the macrostome form of strain LI (appears late in culture life). Stone (1963) reported that the number of macrostomes in a stationary phase culture of strain L-FF was pH- and temperature-dependent.

Trager (1963) has advertised the attractiveness of these cellular differentiation systems. Their utilizability is greatly enhanced by the ease with which they may be cultured under precisely defined conditions.

Other morphological features are influenced by what may, broadly speaking, be called the nutrient environment. The number of primary ciliary meridians with which *T. limacis* and *T. rostrata* are equipped is known to depend upon whether the ciliates are practicing their habit of facultative parasitism in an invertebrate host or are captive in culture (Kozloff 1956, 1957).

K. Assays

The usefulness of ciliates as assay agents may be judged by the following brief compilation of some of their applications:

1. *Vitamins.* Recently reviewed by Hutner *et al.* (1959) and Baker and Sobotka (1962). Practicalities were discussed by Hutner *et al.* (1958a).

2. *Carcinogens.* Exposure of *P. caudatum, P. aurelia,* and *T. pyriformis* to suspensions of hydrocarbons (particles are ingested into food vacuoles) followed by microscopic observation of the consequences of exposure to light, is the method of an exquisitely sensitive assay for carcinogens which are atmospheric pollutants. Reaction to benzpyrene is the standard (Epstein and Burroughs, 1962; Epstein *et al.*, 1963a,b). A similar assay measures carcinogens in tobacco smoke (Hull, 1961a,b, 1962; Wang, 1962).

3. *Antibiotics.* Particle-bearing *P. aurelia* (kappa, lambda, mu, pi) strains

have been used as model systems for testing the ability of antibiotics to discriminate between an intracellular parasite and its host (Soldo, 1961). Twelve of 102 substances tested were selective inhibitors of lambda. In appropriate amounts, 2,6-diaminopurine reduced the kappa content of *P. aurelia* (Stock *et al.*, 1951, 1954). *Tetrahymena pyriformis* rates high with those screening cancer antibiotics, as a microbe which responds like a tumor cell (Hutner *et al.*, 1958b; Foley *et al.*, 1958a,b; West *et al.*, 1962; K. E. Price *et al.*, 1962).

4. *Drug action.* Jírovec (1950), Sanders and Nathan (1959), and Aaronson (1963) recommended protozoa for studying drug actions, particularly metabolic effects. Examples of their use include the following: *T. pyriformis* screened hypocholesterolemic agents (W. J. Johnson and Jasmin, 1961; Aaronson *et al.*, 1962; Holz, 1963; Holz *et al.*, 1962b), and exposed a capacity of the tranquilizer chlorpromazine to increase permeability (Nathan and Friedman, 1962). Conjoint use of chlorpromazine in therapy with impermeable drugs was suggested, but the clinical effectiveness of phenothiazine tranquilizers tested alone was found to be independent of their ability to alter permeability of *Tetrahymena* (Guttman and Friedman, 1963). Nicotinic acid and nicotinamide adenine dinucleotide reversed inhibition of *Tetrahymena* growth by another tranquilizer, thalidomide, implying that human developmental abnormalities can be associated with impairment of terminal respiration (Frank *et al.*, 1963). Inhibition by the antithyroid propylthiouracil and the antidiabetic tolbutamide was prevented by pantothenic acid and pointed to interference with CoA-mediated functions (Shenoy and McLaughlan, 1959). Toxicity of radioopaque agents has been measured with *Tetrahymena* (Mark *et al.*, 1963).

III. Metabolic Pathways

A. Oxidative Metabolism

The carbohydrate metabolism of protozoa has been thoroughly reviewed very recently by von Brand (1963).

The Embden-Meyerhof mechanism for glycolysis (Geddes and Humphrey, 1951; Vloedman *et al.*, 1957; Ryley, 1952; Seaman, 1955; Warnock and van Eys, 1962) and the tricarboxylic acid cycle (Holland and Humphrey, 1953a,b; Vloedman *et al.*, 1957; Seaman, 1949, 1955) are used by *Paramecium* and *Tetrahymena* (and probably by *Balantidium coli*; Agosin and von Brand, 1953). The presence of pentose phosphate cycle enzymes in *Paramecium* and *Tetrahymena* has been reported (Vloedman *et al.*, 1957; Seaman, 1955), but labeling patterns in glucose polysaccharides synthesized from C^{14}-acetate by *Tetrahymena* did not encourage the belief that transaldolase and transketolase were very active (Hogg, 1962). The Pasteur effect (inhibition of glycolysis by respiration) and a pH- and CO_2-dependent Crabtree effect (inhibition of respiration by glycolysis) (Ibsen, 1961) have been demonstrated with *Tetrahymena* (Warnock and van Eys, 1962, 1963). Under anaerobic conditions in the presence of CO_2, glycogen was converted by *Tetrahymena* to succinate, acetate, and lactate, and CO_2 was fixed (van Niel *et al.*, 1942; Lynch and Calvin, 1952; Ryley, 1952) by a phosphoenolpyruvic acid carboxykinase-mediated reaction (Warnock and van Eys, 1962) in which phosphoenolpyruvate was carboxylated and the product subsequently reduced to succinate by reversal of the reactions of the tricarboxylic acid cycle. Succinate synthesis via acetyl CoA condensation is an oxidative process (Seaman and Naschke, 1955; Seaman, 1957). In the absence of CO_2, glycogen is converted to lactic acid.

The rumen holotrichs, *Isotricha* and *Dasytricha,* fermented soluble sugars, producing mainly lactic acid and lesser amounts of acetic and butyric acids (Heald and Oxford, 1953; Gutierrez, 1955; Howard, 1959). Though they could hydrolyze pectic substances, these ciliates seemed to have little ability to ferment the products of hydrolysis (Abou Akkada and Howard, 1961).

Fermentation of the products of intracellular starch digestion by rumen ophryoscolecids yielded acetic and butyric (and a little propionic and formic) acids, some lactic acid, and CO_2 and H_2. Exogenously supplied sugars, or soluble starch, were not metabolized (Abou Akkada and Howard, 1960; Gutierrez and Davis, 1962; P. P. Williams *et al.*, 1961).

The phosphagen of *Tetrahymena* is said to be unlike creatine phosphate, arginine phosphate, or annelid phosphagen (Seaman, 1952).

Hogg (1959) and Reeves *et al.* (1961) reported the presence of the glyoxylate cycle enzymes malate synthase and isocitrate lyase in strains of *T. pyriformis*. Hogg and Kornberg (1963) later showed that formation of these enzymes over constitutive levels was induced by acetate. Glucose repressed acetate-induced malate synthase synthesis but not isocitrate lyase synthesis (the two enzymes were not coordinately repressible). The concentration of both enzymes was very low in cells grown in the presence of glucose and in the absence of acetate. When cells capable of glycogen synthesis from fats were examined, both enzymes were present in high concentration and localized in a characteristic mitochondrial fraction. Cells incapable of glyconeogenesis contained less malate synthase and isocitrate lyase and the enzymes were no longer highly localized but were found in three different particulate cell fractions. Presumably, during glyconeogenesis from fat, acetate is converted to glycogen in an intracellular compartment isolated from sites of acetate oxidation. This important contribution is one of the very few which describes a metabolic regulatory mechanism in a ciliate and which associates it with a structural entity.

Warnock and van Eys (1962) also observed glyconeogenesis from lipids in *Tetrahymena.*

Present experience indicates that the glyoxylate cycle is a metabolic cycle ancillary to the tricarboxylic acid cycle and apparently restricted in distribution to protists and germinating seeds of higher plants (Kornberg and Krebs, 1957).

Glucose is relatively poorly oxidized by *Tetrahymena,* even though it stimulates growth. Lower fatty acids (acetic, propionic, butyric) are favored substrates for respiration (Chaix *et al.,* 1947; Ryley, 1952; Seaman, 1955), as they may be for mammalian liver and muscle (Krebs, 1961). Krebs-cycle acids were relatively inactive for intact *Tetrahymena* (Ryley, 1952; Seaman, 1955). Hunter (1958) and Hunter and Hunter (1957) reported oxidation of some of them by *Stylonychia pustulata* and *Colpoda cucullus.* An unusual lactic acid oxidase, not linked to terminal electron-transport chains of reduced diphosphopyridine nucleotide and succinoxidase systems (Eichel and Rem, 1959a,b, 1962), and a glutamic acid oxidase and β-hydroxybutyric acid oxidase (Eichel, 1959a; W. D. Thompson and Wingo, 1959), have been identified from *T. pyriformis.*

A few amino acids are very readily oxidized by *T. pyriformis.* Of 39 tested for ability to stimulate O_2 consumption of washed cells, L-phenylalanine was best. Many dipeptides containing phenylalanine were as effective as or more effective than the free amino acid (J. S. Roth *et al.,* 1954; J. S. Roth and Eichel, 1961). Since extracellular hydrolysis of two of the dipeptides was demonstrated, an explanation for the greater stimulation by the dipeptides could not be sought in permeability differences between the free amino acid and the peptides.

Enzymes of valine intermediary metabolism concerned with the oxidation of β-hydroxyisobutyric and β-hydroxypropionic acids and the deacylation of the sterol synthesis intermediate β-hydroxy-β-methyl glutaryl CoA have been studied in *T. pyriformis* extracts (Den *et al.,* 1959; Rendina and Coon, 1957; Robinson and Coon, 1957; Dekker *et al.,* 1958).

A coenzyme Q isolated from *T. pyriformis* (Taketomi, 1961) was identified as ubiquinone$_8$ (Crane, 1962; Vakirtzi-Lemonias *et al.,* 1963). Its synthesis did not proceed directly from phenylalanine (Braun *et al.,* 1962). A variety of tocopherol derivatives or Q coenzymes satisfy a nutritional requirement of *Trichomonas gallinae* in a chemically defined medium supplemented with solvent-extracted Trypticase (Shorb and Lund, 1962) and some bacteria are stimulated by K vitamins and Q coenzymes (Gibbons and MacDonald, 1960; Norman and Williams, 1960). Wagner and Folkers (1963) have called attention to the fact that members of the coenzyme Q and vitamins E and K groups share biological activities and that, "The final assignment of a veristic or quasi activity to a member of the E, K or Q groups in a given biological system can be exceptionally difficult because of the problem of establishing an intrinsic or extrinsic relationship between the compound and the given form of life." Experience to date is that these compounds play only intrinsic roles in ciliates.

Components of electron transport systems for terminal respiration of *Tetrahymena* have been studied (Eichel, 1956b,c, 1959a,b, 1961; Nishi and Scherbaum, 1962a): succinoxidase, reduced diphosphopyridine nucleotide oxidase, reduced diphosphopyridine nucleotide cytochrome C reductase, succinic dehydrogenase. Cytochrome oxidase was found by Seaman (1953) but not by Ryley (1952) or Eichel (1954). Studies of oxidative enzymes have been hampered by instability caused by an agent which inhibits electron transport, uncouples phosphorylation, and stimulates a latent adenosine triphosphatase. Eichel (1959b) believes it is a fatty acid (possibly a lysophosphatide), freed from particle-associated phospholipids by a phospholipase when cell integrity is destroyed. It is probably also responsible for the low P:O ratios observed for oxidative phosphorylation by particles from cell-free preparations (Nishi and Scherbaum, 1962b; Eichel, 1963).

When tetrahymenids are grown in media which are relatively colorless, it is possible to see that they often form a soluble reddish brown substance. Age of a culture, composition of the medium, and temperature of incubation influence this pigment production, but some strains are predisposed to it. Holz *et al.* (1959) cataloged the tendency in 45 mating types of *T. pyriformis*. The responsible material is protoporphyrin. Rudzinska and Granick (1953) first noted its accumulation by *T. pyriformis* grown on agar, and Granick (1954) found α-levulinic acid dehydrase (converts α-levulinic acid to porphobilinogen) in the ciliate. Lascelles (1957, 1961) studied the phenomenon in detail. She measured porphyrin synthesis from glycine or from α-levulinic acid, by washed suspensions of *T. vorax* V_2 harvested from a growth medium containing varying amounts of B-complex vitamins and iron, and incubated aerobically at 37°C. Synthesis was poor at 30°C. As the author has also observed, most of the porphyrin formed was passed into the medium. It consisted of a mixture of uroporphyrin III, protoporphyrin, and coproporphyrin III. Pyridoxal and pantothenate appeared to be involved in the reactions by which α-levulinic acid is formed from glycine and succinyl CoA. An ion-rich medium favored conversion of α-levulinic acid to protoporphyrin and impaired porphyrin synthesis from glycine. Iron-poor conditions favored uroporphyrin III accumulation.

Cytochromes and hemoglobin are found in *Tetrahymena* (Ryley, 1952; Keilin and Ryley, 1953) and *Paramecium* (T. Sato and Tamiyo, 1937; Keilin and Ryley, 1953; Smith *et al.*, 1962), and the accumulation of free porphyrins is probably symptomatic of derangement of their synthesis. The hemoglobin of *Paramecium* is thought to enhance the ability of the organism to keep the cytochrome system operating efficiently during periods of moderate oxygen deprivation, and does not act like myoglobin (Smith *et al.*, 1962).

B. CARBOHYDRATES

1. SYNTHESIS

Like animals, yeasts, many bacteria, and trichomonads, *T. pyriformis* synthesizes a glycogen-type polysaccharide (Manners and Ryley, 1952, 1963). For a contrary view, see Lindh and Christensson (1962) who studied the distribution of carbohydrate in *T. pyriformis* and concluded that much of it is associated with other macromolecules. They found that 10 to 12% of the polysaccharide could not be characterized as glycogen and the remainder was associated with RNA and proteins.

Cell-free extracts of *T. pyriformis* catalyzed the synthesis of the oligosaccharides panose and maltotriose from maltose, but not from glucose (Archibald and Manners, 1959).

A great proportion of the soluble sugar (glucose, fructose, sucrose, raffinose, inulin) taken up by the rumen ciliates *Cycloposthium, Dasytricha, Isotricha,* and *Entodinium* is incorporated into an amylopectin-type polysaccharide (Gutierrez, 1955; Heald and Oxford, 1953; Forsyth and Hirst, 1953; Forsyth *et al.,* 1953). Synthesis is by the common phosphorolytic mechanism (Mould and Thomas, 1958).

Phosphorylase activity was demonstrated in *Stylonychia* (Hunter, 1963).

2. HYDROLYSIS

Cell-free extracts of *T. pyriformis* hydrolyzed maltose, isomaltose, cellobiose, sucrose, methyl-α-D-glucoside, α-D-glucosyl phosphate, and starch (Archibald and Manners, 1959). *Stylonychia* extracts contained an amylase (Hunter, 1960).

The rumen ophryoscolecid genera *Ophryoscolex, Epidinium,* and *Entodinium* ingest and digest starch granules. Cell-free extracts of *Entodinium caudatum* contained maltase and amylase (Abou Akkada and Howard, 1960; Bailey and Howard, 1963). Extracts of *Epidinium ecaudatum* contained α-amylase (Bailey, 1958), and hydrolyzed various plant hemicellulases and starch to their constituent monosaccharides. Xylobiose, cellobiose, sucrose, isomaltose, and melibiose were also hydrolyzed, while cellulose (Bailey *et al.,* 1962; Bailey and Howard, 1963), pectin, and polygalacturonic acid (Abou Akkada and Howard, 1961) were not.

Suspensions of the rumen holotrich *D. ruminantium* hydrolyzed pectic substances to galacturonic acid (and some methanol), and extracts of the ciliate which converted pectin or polygalacturonic acid to oligo-uronides (little galacturonic acid; Abou Akkada and Howard, 1961) also contained cellobiase, β-glucosidase, and maltase (Bailey and Howard, 1963). Two species of isotrichs had only very small amounts of the latter three enzymes, and neither the dasytrichs nor isotrichs contained lactase, melibiase, trehalase, melezitase, or xylobiase. Their invertases were yeast-like (Howard, 1959).

C. NITROGEN METABOLISM

1. PROTEIN SYNTHESIS

Little is known about protein synthesis in ciliates, and ciliates have not been used by molecular geneticists probing relationships between structures of nucleic acids and proteins. Amino acid activation by enzymes in pH 5 precipitates from *Tetrahymena* (J. L. Rosenbaum and Holz, 1963), transfer RNA-mediated incorporation of amino acids into microsomal protein in cell-free preparations (Mager and Lipmann, 1958; Mager, 1960), and the characteristics of ribosomal structure and function (Plesner, 1961, 1963; Lyttleton, 1963) indicate that the mechanism of protein synthesis is the familiar one observed in other microbes and in vertebrate tissues.

Gross and Tarver (1955) observed the incorporation of ethionine into *T. pyriformis* proteins.

Free amino acid pools and protein amino acids of many ciliates have been analyzed qualitatively and quantitatively. Loefer and Scherbaum (1961, 1962, 1963) summarized their findings *and* the data in the literature, and concluded that interpretation of the significance of differences observed among species and strains of species, and differences associated with conditions of culture, would be premature.

Reynolds and Wragg (1963) reported qualitative and quantitative variations in extractable amino acid pools accompanying differences in the kind and amount of carbohydrate supplied in the growth medium for *Tetrahymena*.

2. NUCLEOTIDE SYNTHESIS

The fates of labeled compounds supplied to intact organisms and cell-free systems, and the demonstration of enzymes catalyzing transformations of intermediates, provide metabolic rationales for the specificities of the nutritional responses discussed earlier.

Purine and pyrimidine incorporation is basically the same in *Paramecium* and tetrahymenids. Guanine (guanosine for *Paramecium*) yields nucleic acid guanine and adenine, while adenine (adenosine for *Paramecium*) gives rise only to nucleic acid adenine. Cytosine or uracil (cytidine or uridine for *Paramecium*) yield nucleic acid cytosine, uracil, and thymine (Eichel, 1956a; Flavin and Graff, 1951a,b; Flavin and Engleman, 1953; Heinrich *et al.*, 1953, 1957; Kidder *et al.*, 1950; Soldo and van Wagtendonk, 1961).

Heinrikson and Goldwasser (1963) found that *T. pyriformis* W extracts synthesized uridine monophosphate from uracil by a conventional pyrophosphorylase mechanism, but 5-ribosyl-uridylic acid formation involved a reaction of uracil with ribose-5-pyrophosphate or some other ribose derivative, but not 5-phosphoribosyl pyrophosphate.

Tritiated pyrimidine nucleosides (thymidine, uridine, cytidine) are taken up readily by *Paramecium* and *Tetrahymena* and less well by *Euplotes*, and their intracellular localization is visualized by autoradiography (Berech and van Wagtendonk, 1959, 1962; Butzel and van Wagtendonk, 1963; Gall, 1959; Kimball and Perdue, 1962; Prescott, 1962; Prescott and Kimball, 1961; Prescott *et al.*, 1962).

Formate but not glycine was incorporated into nucleic acid adenine and guanine of *Paramecium*, indicating *de novo* purine synthesis coexisting with an absolute purine nutritional requirement (Soldo and van Wagtendonk, 1961). Glycine was not incorporated into Feulgen-positive material of the macronucleus or the acid-soluble fraction of *Paramecium* (Butzel and van Wagtendonk, 1963). Neither formate nor glycine were incorported into *Tetrahymena* nucleic acids (Heinrich *et al.*, 1953). Both ciliates appear to have a metabolic block in the synthesis of glycinamide ribotide.

In contrast to the above, the rat can incorporate adenine into nucleic acid guanine, and guanosine and inosine into nucleic acid purines (Brown *et al.*, 1948), but not uracil or cytosine into nucleic acid pyrimidines (Plentyl and Schoenheimer, 1944). Yeast incorporates, uridine and cytidine into nucleic acid pyrimidines (Hammarsten *et al.*, 1950).

The deoxyribonucleic acid composition of ciliates is under study as a guide to phylogenetic relationships. Sueoka (1961), Schildkraut *et al.* (1962) and Smith-Sonneborn *et al.* (1963) found the guanine and cytosine content of many species of the genera *Colpidium, Glaucoma, Paramecium,* and *Tetrahymena* to be among the lowest so far from any source (mole %, G + C = 22–35). Also, the range of compositional heterogeneity of the deoxyribonucleic acid molecules was narrow and more characteristic of bacteria than of higher organisms.

An adenine + thymine:guanine + cytosine ratio of 2.4 was reported for deoxyribonucleic acid of *T. pyriformis* (A. S. Jones and Thompson, 1963).

3. AMINO ACID DEGRADATION

Paramecium, Tetrahymena, and several rumen ciliates have been shown to be ammonotelic (Cunningham and Kirk, 1941; Wu and Hogg, 1952; Abou Akkada and Howard, 1962). Amino acid deamination is believed to be the source of the ammonia produced by *Paramecium* (Soldo and van Wagtendonk, 1961). It was the main nitrogenous excretory product and did not arise from deamination of purine bases, ribosides, or ribotides, or by hydrolysis of urea. *Paramecium* contained no urease, uric acid, or urea.

Seaman (1954) reported the presence of the Krebs-Henseleit cycle enzymes in *T. pyriformis* S extracts, urea in culture filtrates, and urease (cytochemical test) in intact ciliates (Seaman, 1959). Dewey *et al.* (1957) could not find the enzymes for urea synthesis in extracts of the same and other strains of *T. pyriformis,* nor evidence of urease activity (decomposition of labeled urea) by living cells.

During endogenous metabolism of *Entodinium caudatum* 50–70% of excreted nitrogen was ammonia. Some amino acid excretion may have occurred, but no urea was produced and no urease was found in cell-free extracts (Abou Akkada and Howard, 1962).

Hunter (1959a,b) observed a positive cytochemical test for urease in *Stylonychia pustulata* but not in *Paramecium putrinum*.

4. PURINE AND PYRIMIDINE CATABOLISM

The nitrogen of purine catabolism was excreted as hypoxanthine by *Paramecium* (Soldo and van Wagtendonk, 1961) and probably by *Tetrahymena* (Leboy and Conner, 1963). This is a new major nitrogenous excretory product of purine metabolism, to be compared with: guanine (spiders), uric acid (primates, Dalmatian dog, birds, reptiles, insects other than Diptera), allantoin (mammals, gastropods, Diptera), allantoic acid (some teleosts), urea (amphibia, most fishes), and ammonia (many aquatic invertebrates).

Soldo and van Wagtendonk (1961) observed hydrolytic cleavage of nucleosides by *Paramecium*, but were unable to demonstrate the following enzymes of purine degradation: adenosine deaminase, uricase, xanthine oxidase, adenase, guanase, or 5'-adenylic acid deaminase. Seaman (1963a) reported the presence of all of these enzymes in extracts of *Tetrahymena*. Like vertebrate cells (Kalckar, 1945; E. V. Price *et al.*, 1955), bacteria (Takagi and Horecker, 1957), and yeasts (Heppel and Hilmoe, 1952), *Tetrahymena* is said to cleave nucleosides phosphorolytically (Eichel, 1956a, 1957; Friedkin, 1953). Dewey and Kidder (1960d) reviewed purine metabolism in *Tetrahymena* recently in a discussion of modes of action of azapurines.

Soldo and van Wagtendonk (1961) suggested dihydrouracil as a possible end product of pyrimidine metabolism of *Paramecium*, and Leboy and Conner (1963) observed the loss of a pyrimidine from *Tetrahymena;* probably uracil.

D. FATTY ACID SYNTHESIS

Erwin and Bloch (1963a) examined the fatty acid composition of the lipids of *Tetrahymena pyriformis*, M.T. II, var. 1, *Tetrahymena corlissi* Th-X, *Tetrahymena paravorax* RP, *Tetrahymena setifera* HZ-1, and *Glaucoma chattoni* A grown in chemically defined media containing acetate. Myristic and palmitic were the major saturated acids. More than 50% of the total fatty acids of *Tetrahymena* species were unsaturated and 30% was γ-linolenic acid ($C_{18}\Delta^{6,9,12}$). Iso acids were present in considerable amounts in *T. paravorax* and *T. setifera*. Arachidonic or other C_{20} or C_{22} polyenoic acids were not detected. *Glaucoma chattoni* A contained relatively large amounts of oleic and palmitoleic acids and was poor in dienoic and trienoic C_{18} acids. In *T. pyriformis* the ratio of monounsaturated acids to their saturated counterparts decreased with increasing culture age or increasing incubation temperature, while the relative amounts of di- and trienoic acids remained the same.

Unsaturated fatty acids are associated with low environmental temperatures and saturated acids with high temperatures in many animals, plants, and microbes (Irving *et al.*, 1957; Howell and Collins, 1957; Marr and Ingraham,

1962). The bulk of the lipids of log-phase *T. pyriformis* were highly unsaturated phospholipids. The neutral lipids were principally triglycerides containing saturated and monounsaturated fatty acids.

The finding of γ-linolenic acid is of considerable interest since it was not known to be synthesized by microbes and is an intermediate in arachidonic acid synthesis in vertebrates. Arachidonic acid was found in the chrysomonad flagellate *Ochromonas danica* (Haines *et al.*, 1962) and α-linolenic acid in *Chlorella pyrenoidosa, Scenedesmus, Chlamydomonas reinhardi,* and the chloroplasts of light-grown *Euglena gracilis* (Erwin and Bloch, 1962, 1963b, 1964). Shorb (1963) also reported the synthesis of mostly straight-chain C_{14} to C_{20} fatty acids (68% unsaturated) by *T. pyriformis* in the presence of acetate. The nature of the precursor acid influenced the fatty acid end products. With propionate, over 30% of the acids were odd numbered, with isobutyric acid 30% were even numbered iso acids and 37% were unsaturated, and with α-methyl-*n*-butyric acid 35% were anteiso and 41% unsaturated acids.

Other analyses of *Tetrahymena* lipids, particularly phospholipids, have been made (Taketomi, 1961; Hack *et al.*, 1962). Meaningful comparisons are difficult because the ciliates were grown in different undefined media.

Tetrahymena contains insect juvenile hormone activity (Schneiderman *et al.*, 1960); polyisoprenoids are responsible (Schneiderman and Gilbert, 1964).

Synthesis of unsaturated fatty acids by the tetrahymenids was also studied by Erwin and Bloch (1963a). The ciliates were able to convert long-chain fatty acids to their unsaturated analogs and to chain-elongate C_{16} to C_{18} acids. For example, oleic acid was produced by desaturation of stearic acid and was converted to linoleic and then to γ-linolenic acid; degradation to C_2 units and resynthesis did not occur.

Iso acids were shown to be formed by chain elongation of isovaleryl units derived from leucine and not by methylation of straight-chain analogs.

The ciliate synthesis of polyunsaturated fatty acids combines reactions of aerobic plant and animal systems (Bloch *et al.*, 1961). In yeast, fungi, blue-green algae, green algae, phytoflagellates, and higher plants additional double bonds are inserted into oleic acid between the methyl end of the molecule and carbon 10, to form linoleic and α-linolenic ($C_{18}\Delta^{9,12,15}$) acids. Yeasts, fungi, blue-green algae, and vertebrates synthesize oleic from stearic acid. This conversion has not been demonstrated in green algae, phytoflagellates, and higher plants.

Vertebrates require a dietary source of polyunsaturated fatty acids. Linoleic acid cannot be formed from oleic, but can be converted to γ-linolenic, and finally arachidonic acid. The double-bond system is extended toward the carboxyl end of the molecule from the Δ^9 position, in contrast to the situation in plants where desaturation proceeds toward the methyl end of the molecule. The tetrahymenids can execute the stearic to oleic to linoleic conversions (like many plants), and the linoleic to γ-linolenic acid conversion (like vertebrates, and unlike plants which make α-linolenic acid), but stop at this point. Vertebrates convert γ-linolenic to arachidonic acid.

The growth-inhibitory and division-delaying actions of triparanol (MER-29) on *T. pyriformis* were partially annulled by some fatty acids and complex lipids, particularly oleic acid-containing ones (Holz *et al.*, 1962b; Holz, 1963), and it was suggested that the drug had at least a dual action; on loci in fatty acid *and* sterol intermediary metabolism. These findings have been confirmed and extended by Pollard *et al.* (1963) who reported that the total lipid synthesized by *T. pyriformis* W in a defined medium was reduced by exposure to triparanol, and that oleic acid antagonized triparanol growth inhibition. In the presence of triparanol the synthesis of saturated fatty acids was increased, and the synthesis of unsaturated fatty acids decreased when propionic or α-methyl-*n*-butyric acids were present in the medium, but no change in the pattern of fatty acid synthesis was observed when acetate was present or the medium was unsupplemented. Changes in the number and amounts of unidentified steroids also occurred in the presence of triparanol and additions of the short-chain fatty acids exaggerated these changes. Triparanol may impair desaturation of fatty acids in *T. pyriformis*.

Oleic acid was converted to stearic acid and an unknown acid by the rumen holotrich *Isotricha prostoma* (Gutierrez *et al.*, 1962; P. P. Williams *et al.*, 1963). Saturation of unsaturated fatty acids by protozoa in the rumen has been studied by others (Wright, 1959) but this is the first direct association of the process with a specific, individual biological agent from the rumen. If the reaction can be duplicated in a cell-free system and shown to be an enzyme-catalyzed biosaturation, it will be unique. The ciliate may be able to execute more conventional conversions. When it was incubated with stearic acid, it formed an acid tentatively identified as linoleic acid.

Isotricha prostoma and the ophryoscolecid *Entodinium simplex* incorporated oleic, palmitic and stearic acids, and endogenous gas production (CO_2 and H_2) by *I. prostoma* and *I. intestinalis* was stimulated by oleate, acetate and tributyrin. Isotrichs were rich in palmitic acid, and *Entodinium* in stearic acid.

IV. Comparative Biochemistry

Ciliates have often been described as "typical animal organisms," or even as "typical animal cells." Although most contemporary protozoologists would not indulge in such distortion, they share responsibility for this usage. Many protists have been rather arbitrarily labeled Protozoa (hence "animals"), often, it would seem, merely to spare them from being called "plants."

Also, physiologists and biochemists have used ciliates (particularly *Tetra-*

hymena pyriformis) as model animals in many experiments designed, hopefully, to provide information applicable to "higher animals." In the course of this work it has become apparent that the few ciliates that can be studied in controlled laboratory environments do not in fact perform consistently like "typical animal organisms" or "typical animal cells." Of course, since there is patently no such thing as a "typical animal organism" or a "typical animal cell," we can truthfully say only that these ciliates have some biochemical traits which are "plant-like"—an only slightly less ambiguous description.

Tetrahymenids: (1) require a purine, a pyrimidine, and thioctic acid; (2) synthesize a pentacyclic triterpenoid alcohol, γ-linolenic acid and a substance with B_{12}-activity; and (3) use the glyoxylate cycle. All this biochemical behavior is not normally associated with animals. It *is* consistent with the presumed flagellate ancestry of ciliates, and it reemphasizes the inapplicability to protists of the descriptive terms "plant" and "animal."

References

Aaronson, S. (1963). *In* "Progress in Protozoology" (J. Ludvík *et al.*, eds.), pp. 175–176, Academic Press, New York.

Aaronson, S., Bensky, B., Shifrine, M., and Baker, H. (1962). *Proc. Soc. Exptl. Biol. Med.* 109, 130–132.

Abou Akkada, A. R., and Howard, B. H. (1960). *Biochem. J.* 76, 445–451.

Abou Akkada, A. R., and Howard, B. H. (1961). *Biochem. J.* 78, 512–517.

Abou Akkada, A. R., and Howard, B. H. (1962). *Biochem. J.* 82, 313–320.

Agosin, M., and von Brand, T. (1953). *J. Infect. Diseases* 93, 101–106.

Akita, Y. K. (1941). *Mem. Fac. Sci. Agr., Taihoku Imp. Univ.* 23, 99–120.

Allen, M. B. (1953). *Bacteriol. Rev.* 17, 125–173.

Allen, S. L., Misch, M.S., and Morrison, B. M. (1963). *J. Histochem. Cytochem.* 11, 706–719.

Anderson, M. E., and Williams, H. H. (1951). *J. Nutr.* 44, 335–343.

Andrus, W. DeW., and Giese, A. C. (1963). *J. Cellular Comp. Physiol.* 61, 17–30.

Archibald, A. R., and Manners, D. J. (1959). *Biochem. J.* 73, 292–295.

Bailey, R. W. (1958). *New Zealand J. Agr. Res.* 1, 825–833.

Bailey, R. W., and Howard, B. H. (1963). *Biochem. J.* 86, 446–452.

Bailey, R. W., Clarke, R. T. J., and Wright, D. E. (1962). *Biochem. J.* 83, 517–523.

Bak, I. J. and Elliott, A. M. (1963). *J. Protozool.* 10, 21.

Baker, H. A., and Sobotka, H. (1962). *Advan. Clin. Chem.* 5, 173–235.

Baker, H. A., Hutner, S. H., and Sobotka, H. (1955). *Ann. N.Y. Acad. Sci.* 62, 349–376.

Bennett, H. S. (1956). *J. Biophys. Biochem. Cytol.* 2, Suppl., 99–103.

Berech, J., Jr., and van Wagtendonk, W. J. (1959). *Science* 130, 1413.

Berech, J., Jr., and van Wagtendonk, W. J. (1962). *Exptl. Cell Res.* 26, 360–372.

Bloch, K., Baronowsky, P., Goldfine, H., Lennarz, W. J., Light, R., Norris, A. T., and Scheuerbrandt, G. (1961). *Federation Proc.* 20, 921–927.

Braun R., Dewey, V. C., and Kidder, G. W. (1962). *Federation Proc.* 21, 240.

Brown, G. W., Roll, P. W., Plentyl, A. A., and Cavalieri, L. F. (1948). *J. Biol. Chem.* 172, 469–484.

Brown, H. and Jenkins, M. M. (1962). *Science* 135, 710.

Buhse, H. E. (1962). *J. Protozool.* 9, Suppl., 15.

Burt, R. L. (1940). *Trans. Am. Microscop. Soc.* 59, 414–432.

Butzel, H. M., Jr., and van Wagtendonk, W. J. (1963). *J. Gen. Microbiol.* 30, 503–507.

Carter, L. (1957). *J. Exptl. Biol.* 34, 71–84.

Castrejon, R. N., and Hamilton, J. G. (1962). *Federation Proc.* 21, 300.

Celliers, P. G. (1961). *So. Afr. J. Agr. Sci.* 4, 191–204.

Chaix, P., Chauvet, J., and Fromageot, C. (1947). *Antonie van Leeuwenhoek, J. Microbiol. Serol.* 12, 145–155.

Chapman-Andresen, C. (1963). Personal communication.

Chapman-Andresen, C. (1962). *Compt. Rend. Trav. Lab. Carlsberg* 33, 73–264.

Cirillo, V. P. (1961). *Ann. Rev. Microbiol.* 15, 197–218.

Cirillo, V. P. (1962). *J. Bacteriol.* 84, 754–758.

Claff, C. L. (1947). *Biol. Bull.* 93, 216.

Clayton, R. B., and Bloch, K. (1963). *J. Biol. Chem.* 238, 586–591.

Clayton, R. B., and Edwards, A. M. (1962). *Federation Proc.* 21, 297.

Cohen, A. I. (1959). *Ann. N.Y. Acad. Sci.* 78, 609–622.

Conner, R. L. (1957). *Science* 126, 698.

Conner, R. L. (1959). *J. Gen. Microbiol.* 21, 180–185.

Conner, R. L. (1963). Personal communication.

Conner, R. L., and Nakatani, M. (1958). *Arch. Biochem. Biophys.* 74, 175–181.

Conner, R. L., and Ungar, F. (1962). *J. Protozool.* 9, Suppl., 24.

Conner, R. L., and van Wagtendonk, W. J. (1955). *J. Gen. Microbiol.* 12, 31–36.

Conner, R. L., Kornacker, M. S., and Goldberg, R. (1961). *J. Gen. Microbiol.* 26, 437–442.

Corliss, J. O. (1954). *J. Protozool.* 1, 156–169.

Corliss, J. O. (1959). *J. Protozool.* 6, Suppl., 24.

Corliss, J. O. (1960). *Parasitology* 50, 111–153.

Corliss, J. O. (1961). "The Ciliated Protozoa: Characterization, Classification and Guide to the Literature." Pergamon Press, New York.

Crane, F. L. (1962). *Biochemistry* 1, 510–517.

Cunningham, B., and Kirk, P. L. (1941). *J. Cellular Comp. Physiol.* 18, 299–316.

Dekker, E. E., Schlesinger, M. J., and Coon, M. J. (1958). *J. Biol. Chem.* 233, 434–438.

Demain, A. L., Rickes, E. L., Hendlin, D., and Barnes, E. C. (1961). *J. Bacteriol.* 81, 147–153.

Den, H., Robinson, W. G., and Coon, M. J. (1959). *J. Biol. Chem.* 234, 1666–1671.

Dewey, V. C., and Kidder, G. W. (1953). *J. Gen. Microbiol.* 9, 445–453.

Dewey, V. C., and Kidder, G. W. (1954). *Proc. Soc. Exptl. Biol. Med.* 87, 198–199.

Dewey, V. C., and Kidder, G. W. (1958). *Arch. Biochem. Biophys.* 73, 29–37.

Dewey, V. C., and Kidder, G. W. (1960a). *J. Gen. Microbiol.* 22, 72–78.

Dewey, V. C., and Kidder, G. W. (1960b). *J. Gen. Microbiol.* 22, 79–92.

Dewey, V. C., and Kidder, G. W. (1960c). *Arch. Biochem. Biophys.* 88, 78–82.

Dewey, V. C., and Kidder, G. W. (1960d). *Z. Allgem. Mikrobiol.* 1, 1–12.

Dewey, V. C., and Kidder, G. W. (1962). *Biochem. Pharmacol.* 11, 53–56.

Dewey, V. C., Heinrich, M. R., and Kidder, G. W. (1957). *J. Protozool.* 4, 211–219.

Dewey, V. C., Kidder, G. W., and Markees, D. G. (1959). *Proc. Soc. Exptl. Biol. Med.* 102, 306–308.

Dewey, V. C., Heinrich, M. R., Markees, D. G., and Kidder, G. W. (1960). *Biochem. Pharmacol.* 3, 173–180.

Dickie, N., and Liener, I. E. (1962a). *Biochim. Biophys. Acta* **64**, 41–51.

Dickie, N., and Liener, I. E. (1962b). *Biochim. Biophys. Acta* **64**, 52–59.

Dunham, P. B., and Child, F. M. (1961). *Biol. Bull.* **121**, 129–140.

Dunn, M. S., and Rockland, L. B. (1947). *Proc. Soc. Exptl. Biol. Med.* **64**, 377–379.

Eichel, H. J. (1954). *J. Biol. Chem.* **206**, 159–169.

Eichel, H. J. (1956a). *J. Biol. Chem.* **220**, 209–220.

Eichel, H. J. (1956b). *J. Biol. Chem.* **222**, 121–136.

Eichel, H. J. (1956c). *J. Biol. Chem.* **222**, 137–144.

Eichel, H. J. (1957). *J. Protozool.* **4**, Suppl., 16.

Eichel, H. J. (1959a). *Biochem. J.* **71**, 106–118.

Eichel, H. J. (1959b). *Biochim. Biophys. Acta* **34**, 589–591.

Eichel, H. J. (1961). *Symp. Gen. Biol. Ital. (Pavia)* **8**, 381–417.

Eichel, H. J. (1963). *In* "Progress in Protozoology (J. Ludvík, *et al.*, eds.), Academic Press, New York.

Eichel, H. J., and Rem, L. T. (1959a). *Arch. Biochem. Biophys.* **82**, 484–485.

Eichel, H. J., and Rem, L. T. (1959b). *Biochim. Biophys. Acta* **35**, 571–573.

Eichel, H. J., and Rem, L. T. (1962). *J. Biol. Chem.* **237**, 940–945.

Eichel, H. J., Conger, N., and Figueroa, E. (1963). *J. Protozool.* **10**, Suppl., 6.

Elliott, A. M., and Clark, G. M. (1958a). *J. Protozool.* **5**, 235–240.

Elliott, A. M., and Clark, G. M. (1958b). *J. Protozool.* **5**, 240–246.

Elliott, A. M., and Outka, D. E. (1956). *Biol. Bull.* **111**, 301–302.

Elliott, A. M., Addison, M. A., and Carey, S. E. (1962). *J. Protozool.* **9**, 135–141.

Elsbach, P. (1962). *Nature* **195**, 383–384.

Epstein, S. S., and Burroughs, M. (1962). *Nature* **193**, 337–338.

Epstein, S. S., Burroughs, M., and Small, M. (1963a). *Cancer Res.* **23**, 35–44.

Epstein, S. S., Small, M., Koplan, J., Jones, H., Mantel, N., and Hutner, S. H. (1963b). *J. Natl. Cancer Inst.* **31**, 163–168.

Erwin, J. (1960). Ph.D. Thesis. Syracuse University.

Erwin, J. (1962). Personal communication.

Erwin, J., and Bloch, K. (1962). *Biochem. Biophys. Res. Commun.* **9**, 103–108.

Erwin, J., and Bloch, K. (1963a). *J. Biol. Chem.* **238**, 1618–1624.

Erwin, J., and Bloch, K. (1963b). *Biochem. Zeit.* **338**, 496–511.

Erwin, J., and Bloch, K. (1964). *Science* **143**, 1006–1012.

Erwin, J., and Holz, G. G., Jr. (1962). *J. Protozool.* **9**, 211–214.

Erwin, J. and Wagner, B. (1961). Personal communication.

Fauré-Frémiet, E. (1962). *Compt. Rend.* **254**, 2691–2693.

Fernell, W. R., and Rosen, G. D. (1956). *Brit. J. Nutr.* **10**, 143–156.

Flavin, M., and Engleman, M. (1953). *J. Biol. Chem.* **200**, 59–68.

Flavin, M., and Graff, S. (1951a). *J. Biol. Chem.* **191**, 55–61.

Flavin, M., and Graff, S. (1951b). *J. Biol. Chem.* **192**, 485–488.

Foley, G. E., McCarthy, R. E., Binns, V. M., Snell, E. E., Guirard, B. M., Kidder, G. W., Dewey, V. C., and Thayer, P. S. (1958a). *Ann. N.Y. Acad. Sci.* **76**, 413–438.

Foley, G. E., Eagle, H., Snell, E. E., Kidder, G. W., and Thayer, P. S. (1958b). *Ann. N.Y. Acad. Sci.* **76**, 952–960.

Forsyth, G., and Hirst, E. L. (1953). *J. Chem. Soc.* pp. 2132–2135.

Forsyth, G., Hirst, E. L., and Oxford, A. E. (1953). *J. Chem. Soc.* pp. 2030–2033.

Frank, O., Baker, H., Ziffer, H., Aaronson, S., Hutner, S. H., and Leevy, C. M. (1963). *Science* **139**, 110–111.

Frankel, J. (1962). *Compt. Rend. Trav. Lab. Carlsberg* **33**, 1–52.

Friedkin, M. (1953). *J. Cellular Comp. Physiol.* 41, Suppl. 1, 261–283.

Gall, J. G. (1959). *J. Biophys. Biochem. Cytol.* 5, 295–308.

Garnjobst, L., Tatum, E. L., and Taylor, C. V. (1943). *J. Cellular Comp. Physiol.* 21, 199–212.

Geddes, M., and Humphrey, G. F. (1951). *Australian J. Exptl. Biol. Med. Sci.* 29, 187–193.

Gibbons, R. J., and MacDonald, J. B. (1960). *J. Bacteriol.* 80, 164–170.

Granick, S. (1954). *Science* 120, 1105–1106.

Grebecki, A. (1963). *Protoplasma* 56, 89–98.

Gross, D., and Tarver, H. (1955). *J. Biol. Chem.* 217, 169–182.

Groupé, V., Herrman, E. C., Jr., and Rauscher, F. J. (1955). *Proc. Soc. Exptl. Biol. Med.* 88, 479–482.

Gutierrez, J. (1955). *Biochem. J.* 60, 516–522.

Gutierrez, J., and Davis, R. E. (1959). *J. Protozool.* 6, 222–226.

Gutierrez, J., and Davis, R. E. (1962). *Appl. Microbiol.* 10, 305–308.

Gutierrez, J., Williams, P. P., Davis, R. E., and Warwick, E. J. (1962). *Appl. Microbiol.* 10, 548–551.

Guttman, H. N., and Friedman, W. (1963). *Federation Proc.* 22, 569.

Hack, M. H., Yaeger, R. G., and McCaffery, T. D. (1962). *Comp. Biochem. Physiol.* 6, 247–252.

Haines, T. H., Aaronson, S., Gellerman, J. L., and Schlenk, H. (1962). *Nature* 194, 1282–1283.

Hammarsten, E., Reichard, P., and Saluste, E. (1950). *J. Biol. Chem.* 183, 105–109.

Heald, P. J., and Oxford, A. E. (1953). *Biochem. J.* 53, 506–512.

Heinrich, M. F., Dewey, V. C., and Kidder, G. W. (1953). *J. Am. Chem. Soc.* 75, 1741–1742.

Heinrich, M. F., Dewey, V. C., and Kidder, G. W. (1957). *Biochim. Biophys. Acta* 25, 199–200.

Heinrikson, R. L., and Goldwasser, E. (1963). *J. Biol. Chem.* 238, PC 485.

Heppel, L. A., and Hilmoe, B. L. (1952). *J. Biol. Chem.* 198, 683–694.

Hill, F. D., Saylor, J. H., Allen, R. S., and Jacobson, N. L. (1960). *J. Animal Sci.* 19, 1266.

Hogg, J. F. (1962). Personal communication.

Hogg, J. F. (1959). *Federation Proc.* 18, 247.

Hogg, J. F., and Kornberg, H. L. (1963). *Biochem. J.* 86, 462–468.

Holland, J., and Humphrey, G. F. (1953a). *Australian J. Exptl. Biol. Med. Sci.* 31, 291–298.

Holland, J., and Humphrey, G. F. (1953b). *Australian J. Exptl. Biol. Med. Sci.* 31, 299–310.

Holz, G. G., Jr. (1963). *In* "Progress in Protozoology" (J. Ludvík *et al.*, eds.) p. 222, Academic Press, New York.

Holz, G. G., Scherbaum, O. H., and Williams, N. E. (1957). *Exptl. Cell Res.* 13, 618–621.

Holz, G. G., Jr., Erwin, J., and Davis, R. J. (1959). *J. Protozool.* 6, 149–156.

Holz, G. G., Jr., Erwin, J., and Wagner, B. (1960). Unpublished observations.

Holz, G. G., Jr., Wagner, B., Erwin, J., and Kessler, D. (1961a). *J. Protozool.* 8, 192–199.

Holz, G. G., Erwin, J. A., and Wagner, B. (1961b). *J. Protozool.* 8, 297–300.

Holz, G. G., Jr., Wagner, B., Erwin, J., Britt, J. J., and Bloch, K. (1961c). *Comp. Biochem. Physiol.* 2, 202–217.

Holz, G. G., Jr., Erwin, J., Wagner, B., and Rosenbaum, N. (1962a). *J. Protozool.* **9**, 359–363.

Holz, G. G., Jr., Erwin, J., Rosenbaum, N., and Aaronson, S. (1962b). *Arch. Biochem. Biophys.* **98**, 312–322.

Holz, G. G., Jr., Patterson, K., and Watts, T. (1962c). Unpublished observations.

Holz, G. G., Jr., Rasmussen, L., and Zeuthen, E. (1963). *Compt. Rend. Trav. Lab. Carlsberg* **33**, 289–300.

Howard, B. H. (1959). *Biochem. J.* **71**, 675–680.

Howell, R., and Collins, F. I. (1957). *Agron. J.* **49**, 593–597.

Hull, R. W. (1961a). *J. Protozool.* **8**, Suppl., 13.

Hull, R. W. (1961b). *Am. Zoologist* **1**, 453.

Hull, R. W. (1962). *J. Protozool.* **9**, Suppl., 18.

Hunter, N. W. (1958). *Physiol. Zool.* **31**, 23–27.

Hunter, N. W. (1959a). *J. Protozool.* **6**, 100–104.

Hunter, N. W. (1959b). *Trans. Am. Microscop. Soc.* **78**, 363–370.

Hunter, N. W. (1960). *Physiol. Zool.* **33**, 64–67.

Hunter, N. W. (1963). *Canad. J. Microbiol.* **9**, 459–465.

Hunter, N. W., and Hunter, R., Jr. (1957). *J. Cellular Comp. Physiol.* **50**, 341–346.

Hutner, S. H. (1961). *Symp. Soc. Gen. Microbiol.* **11**, 1–18.

Hutner, S. H. (1963). *In* "Progress in Protozoology" (J. Ludvík *et al.*, eds.) pp. 135–136, Academic Press, New York.

Hutner, S. H., and Holz, G. G., Jr. (1962). *Ann. Rev. Microbiol.* **16**, 189–204.

Hutner, S. H., Baker, H., Aaronson, S., Nathan, H. A., Rodriguez, E., Lockwood, S., Sanders, M., and Petersen, R. A. (1957). *J. Protozool.* **4**, 259–269.

Hutner, S. H., Cury, A., and Baker, H. (1958a). *Anal. Chem.* **30**, 849–867.

Hutner, S., Nathan, H. A., Aaronson, S., Baker, H., and Scher, S. (1958b). *Ann. N.Y. Acad. Sci.* **76**, 457–468.

Hutner, S. H., Aaronson, S., Nathan, H. A., Baker, H., Scher, S., and Cury, A. (1958c). *In* "Trace Elements" (C. A. Lamb, O. G. Bentley, and J. M. Beattie, eds.), p. 47. Academic Press, New York.

Hutner, S. H., Nathan, H. A., Baker, H., Sobotka, H., and Aaronson, S. (1959). *Am. J. Clin. Nutr.* **7**, 407–410.

Ibsen, K. H. (1961). *Cancer Res.* **21**, 829–841.

Irving, L., Schmidt-Nielsen, K., and Abrahamsen, N. S. B. (1957). *Physiol. Zool.* **30**, 93–105.

Jírovec, O. (1950). *Pathol. Bakteriol.* **13**, 129–138.

Johnson, W. H. (1956). *Ann. Rev. Microbiol.* **10**, 193–212.

Johnson, W. H., and Miller, C. A. (1956). *J. Protozool.* **3**, 221–226.

Johnson, W. H., and Miller, C. A. (1957). *Physiol. Zool.* **30**, 106–113.

Johnson, W. H., and Miller, C. A. (1963). *In* "Progress in Protozoology" (J. Ludvík *et al.*, eds.) pp. 137–139, Academic Press, New York.

Johnson, W. J., and Jasmin, R. (1961). *Federation Proc.* **20**, 281.

Jones, A. S., and Thompson, T. W. (1963). *J. Protozool.* **10**, 91–93.

Jones, K. M., and Woolley, D. W. (1962). *J. Bacteriol.* **83**, 797–801.

Jurand, A. (1961). *J. Protozool.* **8**, 125–130.

Jurand, A., Gibson, I., and Beale, G. H. (1962). *Exptl. Cell Res.* **26**, 598–600.

Kalckar, A. M. (1945). *J. Biol. Chem.* **158**, 723–724.

Karakashian, S. J. (1963). *Physiol. Zool.* **36**, 52–68.

Karnovsky, M. L. (1962). *Physiol. Rev.* **42**, 143–168.

Kaufman, S. (1962). *J. Biol. Chem.* **237**, PC 2712.

Keilin, D., and Ryley, J. F. (1953). *Nature* 172, 451.

Kessler, D. (1961). M.S. Thesis. Syracuse University.

Kidder, G. W. (1941). *Biol. Bull.* 80, 50–68.

Kidder, G. W. (1951). *Ann. Rev. Microbiol.* 5, 139–156.

Kidder, G. W. (1952). *Intern. Rev. Cytol.* 1, 27–34.

Kidder, G. W. (1953a). *Proc. 6th Intern. Congr. Microbiol., Rome, 1953* 3, 44–61.

Kidder, G. W. (1953b). *In* "Biochemistry and Physiology of Nutrition" (G. H. Bourne and G. W. Kidder, eds.), Vol. 2, p. 162. Academic Press, New York.

Kidder, G. W., and Dewey, V. C. (1945). *Physiol. Zool.* 18, 136–157.

Kidder, G. W., and Dewey, V. C. (1951). *In* "Biochemistry and Physiology of Protozoa" (A. Lwoff, ed.), Vol. 1, p. 323. Academic Press, New York.

Kidder, G. W., and Dewey, V. C. (1955). *Arch. Biochem. Biophys.* 55, 126–129.

Kidder, G. W., and Dewey, V. C. (1961). *Biochem. Biophys. Res. Commun.* 5, 324–327.

Kidder, G. W., and Dewey, V. C. (1963). *Biochem. Biophys. Res. Commun.* 12, 280–283.

Kidder, G. W., Dewey, V. C., Parke, R. R., Jr., and Heinrich, M. R. (1950). *Proc. Natl. Acad. Sci. U.S.* 36, 431–439.

Kidder, G. W., Dewey, V. C., and Fuller, R. C. (1954a). *Proc. Soc. Exptl. Biol. Med.* 86, 685–689.

Kidder, G. W., Dewey, V. C., and Heinrich, M. R. (1954b). *Exptl. Cell Res.* 7, 256–264.

Kihara, H., and Snell, E. E. (1960). *J. Biol. Chem.* 235, 1409–1414.

Kimball, R. F., and Perdue, S. W. (1962). *Exptl. Cell Res.* 27, 405–415.

Kimball, R. F., and Prescott, D. M. (1962). *J. Protozool.* 9, 88–92.

Kirby, H., Jr. (1941). *In* "Protozoa in Biological Research" (G. N. Calkins and F. M. Summers, eds.), p. 1009. Columbia Univ. Press, New York.

Kitching, J. A. (1956). *Protoplasmatologia 3,* (D, 3, b), 1–54.

Kornberg, H. L., and Krebs, H. A. (1957). *Nature* 179, 988–991.

Kozloff, E. N. (1956). *J. Protozool.* 3, 20–27.

Kozloff, E. N. (1957). *J. Protozool.* 4, 75–79.

Krebs, H. A. (1961). *Biochem. J.* 80, 225–233.

Lascelles, J. (1957). *Biochem. J.* 66, 65–72.

Lascelles, J. (1961). *Physiol. Rev.* 41, 417–441.

Leboy, P. S., and Conner, R. L. (1963). *Bacteriol. Proc. (Soc. Am. Bacteriologists),* p. 122.

Lilly, D. M., and Klosek, R. C. (1961). *J. Gen. Microbiol.* 24, 327–334.

Lindh, N. O., and Christensson, E. (1962). *Arkiv. Zool.* 15, 163–180.

Loefer, J. B., and McDaniel, M. R. (1950). *Proc. Am. Soc. Protozool.* 1, 8.

Loefer, J. B., and Scherbaum, O. H. (1961). *J. Protozool.* 8, 184–192.

Loefer, J. B., and Scherbaum, O. H. (1962). *In* "Amino Acid Pools" (J. T. Holden, ed.), p. 109. Elsevier, Amsterdam.

Loefer, J. B., and Scherbaum, O. H. (1963). *J. Protozool.* 10, 275–279.

Louloudes, S. J., Thompson, M. J., Monroe, R. E., and Robbins, W. E. (1962). *Biochem. Biophys. Res. Commun.* 8, 104–106.

Lund, P. G., and Shorb, M. S. (1962). *J. Protozool.* 9, 151–154.

Lynch, V. H., and Calvin, M. (1952). *J. Bacteriol.* 63, 525–531.

Lyttleton, J. W. (1963). *Exptl. Cell Res.* 31, 385–389.

McKee, C. M., Dutcher, J. D., Groupé, V., and Moore, M. (1947). *Proc. Soc. Exptl. Biol. Med.* 65, 326–332.

Mager, J. (1960). *Biochem. Biophys. Acta* 38, 150–152.

Mager, J., and Lipmann, F. (1958). *Proc. Natl. Acad. Sci. U.S.* 44, 305–308.

Mallory, F. B., Gordon, J. T., and Conner, R. L. (1963). *J. Am. Chem. Soc.* 85, 1362–1363.

Manners, D. J., and Ryley, J. F. (1952). *Biochem. J.* 52, 480–482.

Manners, D. J., and Ryley, J. F. (1963). *J. Protozool.* 10, Suppl., 28.

Mark, M. F., Imparato, A. M., Hutner, S. H., and Baker, H. (1963). *Angiology* 14, 383–389.

Markees, D. G., Dewey, V. C., and Kidder, G. W. (1960). *Arch. Biochem. Biophys.* 86, 179–184.

Marr, A. G., and Ingraham, J. L. (1962). *J. Bacteriol.* 84, 1260–1267.

Miller, C. A., and Johnson, W. H. (1957). *J. Protozool.* 4, 200–203.

Miller, C. A., and Johnson, W. H. (1960). *J. Protozool.* 7, 297–301.

Miller, C. A., and van Wagtendonk, W. J. (1956). *J. Gen. Microbiol.* 15, 280–291.

Mould, D. L., and Thomas, G. J. (1958). *Biochem. J.* 69, 327–337.

Müller, M. (1962). *Acta Biol. Acad. Sci. Hung.* 13, 283–297.

Müller, M., and Törő, I. (1962). *J. Protozool.* 9, 98–102.

Müller, M., Tóth, J., and Törő, I. (1960). *Nature* 187, 65.

Müller, M., Röhlich, P., Tóth, J., and Törő, I. (1963a). *Ciba Found. Symp., Lysosomes,* pp. 201–216.

Müller, M., Törő, I., Polgár, M., and Druga, A. (1963b). *Acta Biol. Acad. Sci. Hung.* 14, 209–213.

Nathan, H. A., and Friedman, W. (1962). *Science* 135, 793–794.

Nishi, A., and Scherbaum, O. H. (1962a). *Biochim. Biophys. Acta* 65, 411–418.

Nishi, A., and Scherbaum, O. H. (1962b). *Biochim. Biophys. Acta* 65, 419–424.

Norman, J. O., and Williams, R. P. (1960). *Biochem. Biophys. Res. Commun.* 2, 372–374.

Novikoff, A. B. (1960). In "Developing Cell Systems and Their Control" (D. Rudnick, ed.), p. 167. Ronald Press, New York.

Novikoff, A. B. (1961). In "The Cell" (J. Brachet and A. E. Mirsky, eds.), Vol. 2, p. 423. Academic Press, New York.

Pilcher, H. L., and Williams, H. H. (1954). *J. Nutr.* 53, 589–599.

Plentyl, A. A., and Schoenheimer, R. (1944). *J. Biol. Chem.* 153, 203–217.

Plesner, P. (1961). *Cold Spring Harbor Symp. Quant. Biol.* 26, 159–162.

Plesner, P. (1963). *Symp. Internatl. Soc. Cell Biol.* 2, 77–91.

Pollard, W. O., Shorb, M. S., Lund, P. G., and Vasaitis, V. (1963). *J. Protozool.* 10, Suppl., 7.

Preer, J. R., Jr. (1957). *J. Genet.* 55, 375–378.

Prescott, D. M. (1957). *J. Protozool.* 4, 252–256.

Prescott, D. M. (1962). *J. Histochem. Cytochem.* 10, 145–153.

Prescott, D. M., and Kimball, R. F. (1961). *Proc. Natl. Acad. Sci. U.S.* 47, 686–693.

Prescott, D. M., Kimball, R. F., and Carrier, R. F. (1962). *J. Cell Biol.* 13, 175–176.

Price, E. V., Otey, M. C., and Pleaner, P. (1955). In "Methods in Enzymology" (S. P. Colowick and N. O. Kaplan, eds.), Vol. 2, p. 448. Academic Press, New York.

Price, K. E., Buck, R. E., Schlein, A., and Siminoff, P. (1962). *Cancer Res.* 22, 885–891.

Quinn, L. Y. (1962). *Appl. Microbiol.* 10, 580–582.

Quinn, L. Y., Burroughs, W., and Christiansen, W. C. (1962). *Appl. Microbiol.* 10, 583–592.

Reeves, H., Papa, M., Seaman, G., and Ajl, S. (1961). *J. Bacteriol.* 81, 154–155.

Reilly, S. M., and Lilly, D. M. (1963). *J. Protozool.* 10, Suppl., 12.

Rendina, G., and Coon, M. J. (1957). *J. Biol. Chem.* 225, 523–534.

Reynolds, H., and Wragg, J. B. (1962). *J. Protozool.* 9, 214–222.

Reynolds, H., and Wragg, J. B. (1963). *Bacteriol. Proc.* (*Soc. Am. Bacteriologists*), p. 49.

Robinson, W. G., and Coon, M. J. (1957). *J. Biol. Chem.* 225, 511–521.

Rockland, L. B., and Dunn, M. S. (1949). *Food Technol.* 3, 289–292.

Rosen, G. D. (1959). *Proc. Intern. Symp. Microchem., Birmingham Univ., 1958,* pp. 212–219.

Rosen, G. D., and Fernell, W. R. (1956). *Brit. J. Nutr.* 10, 156–169.

Rosenbaum, J. L., and Holz, G. G., Jr. (1963). *Federation Proc.* 22, 681.

Rosenbaum, N. (1963). Master's Thesis. Syracuse University.

Rosenbaum, R. M., and Wittner, M. (1962). *Arch. Protistenk.* 106, 223–240.

Roth, J. S., and Eichel, H. J. (1961). *J. Protozool.* 8, 69–71.

Roth, J. S., Eichel, H. J., and Cinter, E. (1954). *Arch. Biochem. Biophys.* 48, 112–119.

Roth, L. E. (1957). *J. Biophys. Biochem. Cytol.* 3, 985–999.

Rudzinska, M. A., and Granick, S. (1953). *Proc. Soc. Exptl. Biol. Med.* 83, 525–526.

Ryley, J. F. (1952). *Biochem. J.* 52, 483–492.

Sanders, M., and Nathan, H. A. (1959). *J. Gen. Microbiol.* 21, 264–270.

Sato, H. (1960). *Anat. Record* 138, 381.

Sato, T., and Tamiyo, H. (1937). *Cytologia* (*Tokyo*) Fujii Jubilee Vol. pp. 1133–1138.

Schildkraut, C. L., Mandel, M., Levisohn, S., and Smith-Sonneborn, J. E. (1962). *Nature* 196, 795–796.

Schneiderman, H. A., and Gilbert, L. I. (1964). *Science* 143, 325–333.

Schneiderman, H. A., Gilbert, L. I., and Weinstein, M. (1960). *Nature* 188, 1041–1042.

Seaman, G. R. (1949). *Biol. Bull.* 96, 257–262.

Seaman, G. R. (1952). *Biochim. Biophys. Acta* 9, 693–696.

Seaman, G. R. (1953). *Arch. Biochem. Biophys.* 48, 424–430.

Seaman, G. R. (1954). *J. Protozool.* 1, 207–210.

Seaman, G. R. (1955). *In* "Biochemistry and Physiology of Protozoa" (S. H. Hutner and A. Lwoff, eds.), Vol. 2, p. 91. Academic Press, New York.

Seaman, G. R. (1957). *J. Biol. Chem.* 228, 149–161.

Seaman, G. R. (1959). *J. Protozool.* 6, 331–333.

Seaman, G. R. (1961a). *J. Biophys. Biochem. Cytol.* 1, 243–245.

Seaman, G. R. (1961b). *J. Protozool.* 8, 204–212.

Seaman, G. R. (1962). *J. Protozool.* 9, 335.

Seaman, G. R. (1963a). *J. Protozool.* 10, 87–91.

Seaman, G. R. (1936b). *In* "Progress in Protozoology" (J. Ludvík *et al.*, eds.) 165, Academic Press, New York.

Seaman, G. R., and Naschke, M. D. (1955). *J. Biol. Chem.* 217, 1–12.

Shaw, R. F., and Williams, N. E. (1963). *J. Protozool.* 10, 486–491.

Shenoy, K. G., and McLaughlan, J. M. (1959). *Can. J. Biochem. Physiol.* 37, 1388–1389.

Shorb, M. S. (1963). *In* "Progress in Protozoology" (J. Ludvík *et al.*, eds.) pp. 153–158, Academic Press, New York.

Shorb, M. S., and Lund, P. G. (1959). *J. Protozool.* 6, 122–130.

Shorb, M. S. and Lund, P. G. (1962). *J. Protozool.* 9, suppl., 20.

Siegel, R. (1960). *Exptl. Cell Res.* **19**, 239–252.

Singer, S. (1961). *J. Protozool.* **8**, 265–271.

Smith, M. H., George, P., and Preer, J. R., Jr. (1962). *Arch. Biochem. Biophys.* **99**, 313–318.

Smith-Sonneborn, J., Green, L., and Marmur, J. (1963). *Nature* **197**, 385.

Soldo, A. T. (1960). *Proc. Soc. Exptl. Biol. Med.* **105**, 612–615.

Soldo, A. T. (1961). *Trans. N.Y. Acad. Sci.* **23**, 653–661.

Soldo, A. T., and van Wagtendonk, W. J. (1961). *J. Protozool.* **8**, 41–45.

Sonneborn, T. M. (1959). *Advan. Virus Res.* **6**, 229–356.

Stephens, G. C., and Kerr, N. S. (1962). *Nature* **194**, 1094–1095.

Stock, C. C., Jacobson, W. E., and Williamson, M. (1951). *Proc. Soc. Exptl. Biol. Med.* **78**, 874–876.

Stock, C. C., Williamson, M., and Jacobson, W. E. (1954). *Ann. N.Y. Acad. Sci.* **56**, 1081–1086.

Stone, G. E. (1963). *J. Protozool.* **10**, 74–80.

Stott, J. A., Smith, H., and Rosen, G. I. (1963). *Brit. J. Nutr.* **17**, 227–233.

Sueoka, N. (1961). *Cold Spring Harbor Symp. Quant. Biol.* **26**, 35–43.

Takagi, Y., and Horecker, B. L. (1957). *J. Biol. Chem.* **225**, 77–86.

Taketomi, T. (1961). *Z. Allgem. Mikrobiol.* **1**, 331–340.

Tarantola, V. A., and van Wagtendonk, W. J. (1959). *J. Protozool.* **6**, 189–195.

Tietz, A. M., Lindberg, M., and Kennedy, E. P. (1963). *Federation Proc.* **22**, 296.

Thompson, J. C., Jr. (1958). *J. Protozool.* **5**, 203–205.

Thompson, W. D., and Wingo, W. J. (1959). *J. Cellular Comp. Physiol.* **53**, 413–420.

Thormar, H. (1962a). *Exptl. Cell Res.* **27**, 585–586.

Thormar, H. (1962b). *Exptl. Cell Res.* **28**, 269–279.

Trager, W. (1961). *In* "The Cell" (J. Brachet and A. E. Mirsky, eds.), Vol. 4, p. 151, Academic Press, New York.

Trager, W. (1963). *J. Protozool.* **10**, 1–6.

Vakirtzi-Lemonias, C., Kidder, G. W., and Dewey, V. C. (1963). *Comp. Biochem. Physiol.* **8**, 331–334.

van Niel, C. B., Thomas, J. O., Rubens, S., and Kamen, M. D. (1942). *Proc. Natl. Acad. Sci. U.S.* **28**, 157–161.

van Wagtendonk, W. J. (1955). *In* "Biochemistry and Physiology of Protozoa" (S. H. Hutner and A. Lwoff, eds.), Vol. 2, p. 57. Academic Press, New York.

Viswanatha, T., and Liener, I. E. (1955). *Arch. Biochem. Biophys.* **56**, 222–229.

Viswanatha, T., and Liener, I. E. (1956). *Arch. Biochem. Biophys.* **61**, 410–421.

Vloedman, D. A., Jr., Berech, J., Jr., Jeffries, W. B., and van Wagtendonk, W. J. (1957). *J. Gen. Microbiol.* **16**, 628–641.

von Brand, T. (1963). *Ergeb. Mikrobiol. Immunitaetsforsch. Exptl. Therap.* **36**, 1–58.

Wagner, B., and Erwin, J. (1961). Personal communication.

Wagner, A. F., and Folkers, K. (1963). *Perspectives Biol. Med.* **6**, 347–356.

Wang, H. (1962). *Am. Zoologist* **2**, 457.

Warnock, L. G., and van Eys, J. (1962). *J. Cellular Comp. Physiol.* **60**, 53–60.

Warnock, L. G., and van Eys, J. (1963). *J. Cellular Comp. Physiol.* **61**, 309–316.

Weisz, P. (1949). *Biol. Bull.* **97**, 108–110.

West, R. A., Jr., Barbera, P. W., Kolar, J. H., and Murrell, C. B. (1962). *J. Protozool.* **9**, 65–73.

Wilbrandt, W., and Rosenberg, T. (1961). *Pharmacol. Rev.* **13**, 109–183.

Williams, N. E. (1960). *J. Protozool.* **7**, 10–17.

Williams, N. E. (1961). *J. Protozool.* **8**, 403–410.

Williams, N. E., and Scherbaum, O. H. (1959). *J. Embryol. Exptl. Morphol.* **7**, 241–256.

Williams, P. P., Davis, R. E., Doetsch, R. N., and Gutierrez, J. (1961). *Appl. Microbiol.* **9**, 405–409.

Williams, P. P., Gutierrez, J., and Davis, R. E. (1963). *Appl. Microbiol.* **11**, 260–264.

Wright, D. E. (1959). *Nature* **184**, 875–876.

Wu, C., and Hogg, J. F. (1952). *J. Biol. Chem.* **198**, 753–764.

Physiological Genetics of the Ciliates

R. F. KIMBALL

Biology Division, Oak Ridge National Laboratory,* Oak Ridge, Tennessee

	Page
I. Introduction	244
II. Cell Cycle	244
A. The DNA Synthesis Cycle	244
B. Macronuclear Duplication	245
C. Micronuclear Number and Function	247
D. RNA Synthesis	248
E. Conservation of Materials	248
F. Growth during the Cell Cycle	249
G. Control of Cell Size	249
H. Maintenance and Duplication of Structure	250
I. Replication of the Kinetosomes	252
III. Clonal Life History	253
A. Maturation	253
B. Senescence	254
IV. The Immobilization Antigens	256
V. Nuclear Differentiation	258
A. Nuclear Behavior at Conjugation	258
B. Mating Types	259
C. Other Cases of Caryonidal and Subunit Inheritance	261
D. Discussion	262
VI. Genetic Control of Intracellular Symbionts	263
VII. Other Loci	265
VIII. Physiological Aspects of Radiation Mutagenesis	265
IX. Conclusions	267
References	269

* Operated by Union Carbide Corporation for the United States Atomic Energy Commission.

I. Introduction

The genetics of the ciliate protozoa has developed along somewhat different lines from that of many other organisms. Although typical Mendelian inheritance has been found and studied, the main emphasis has been upon inheritance within the clone and upon the occurrence and persistence of variant phenotypes within a single genotype. This is not surprising. The ciliates are almost uniquely suited for studies of cell lineages and persistent variations within such lineages readily come to the investigator's attention.

As a result, the ciliate geneticist is faced immediately with questions that have been less obvious to his colleagues in other branches of genetics: How precise is reproduction by cell division? What mechanisms are available to restore minor variants to normal and how effective are they? How is gene action controlled so as to produce different phenotypes from the same genotype? What are the reasons for the persistence of some of these intraclonal differences?

Thus ciliate genetics must and does combine the approaches of genetics and cell physiology, and it is to this combination that the present chapter will be devoted. In some sections of the chapter cell physiology predominates, in others genetics; and no pretense is made that a true synthesis has been achieved. Nevertheless advances in both fields have been great enough to warrant the attempt at a combined treatment.

The earlier work on ciliate genetics has been reviewed by Sonneborn (1947) and Beale (1954) and is largely omitted here. It has been assumed that the reader is familiar with the elementary features of ciliate life history and genetics that are covered in these reviews. Recent reviews are more specialized and will be mentioned in the appropriate sections. A brief but thoughtful survey of much of this material (Sonneborn, 1964) came to the reviewer's attention after this chapter was written.

II. Cell Cycle

The basic unit of clonal history is the cell cycle, the period from one division to the next. In the last few years, advances in cytochemistry have allowed a more precise description of the events in this cycle than was possible previously, and it is with these studies that this chapter will begin.

A. The DNA Synthesis Cycle

The advent of autoradiography and Feulgen microspectrophotometry has made it possible to establish the time course of deoxyribonucleic acid (DNA) synthesis for a wide variety of cells. This has led to the division of the cell cycle into four periods: presynthesis interphase (G1), the synthesis period (S), the postsynthesis interphase (G2), and mitosis (M). The nuclear dimorphism of the ciliates necessitates designating which nucleus is meant by these terms and substituting amitosis for mitosis in referring to the macronucleus.

The DNA synthesis cycle has been worked out for several ciliates by autoradiography or microspectrophotometry, and good agreement has been found when both methods have been used. Different species vary considerably in the duration of S and its position within the cell cycle (Hanson and Twichell, 1962; Kimball and Barka, 1959; McDonald, 1958, 1962; Prescott, 1960; Prescott et al., 1962; Walker and Mitchison, 1957; Woodard et al., 1961). Furthermore, the relations between micro- and macronuclear S vary with the species, though macronuclear S is usually longer. In *Tetrahymena pyriformis* (McDonald, 1962) and *Euplotes eurystomus* (Prescott et al., 1962), micronuclear S occurs between the end of anaphase and early interphase whereas macronuclear S does not begin until some time after the completion of cytokinesis. In *Paramecium caudatum* (Walker and Mitchison, 1957) and *P. aurelia* (Woodard et al., 1961) micro- and macronuclear S begin together. In *P. aurelia*, the onset of micronuclear S can be delayed without delaying that of macronuclear S (Kimball, 1961). Thus the onset of DNA synthesis appears to be independently controlled in the two kinds of nuclei. Nevertheless some control is exerted by the state of the cell since two macronuclei in a common cytoplasm start synthesis together (Kimball and Prescott, 1962).

B. Macronuclear Duplication

Of greater concern from the point of view of the present chapter is the degree of precision in the division and replication of the polygenomic macronucleus. Feulgen measurements have shown that amitosis does not always divide the macronucleus into precisely equal halves in either *T. pyriformis* (McDonald, 1958) or *P. aurelia* (Kimball and Barka, 1959). Even greater inequalities can occur in *P. aurelia* homozygous for the gene, *am*, whose main phenotypic effect is to cause unequal macronuclear division (Nobili, 1959, 1961a,b; Sonneborn, 1954a). It is certain, however, that the macronucleus divides more precisely than it would if it were a simple "bag of chromosomes" (for review, see Nanney and Rudzinska, 1960). The genetic evidence for both *Tetrahymena* and *Paramecium* suggests that the macronucleus consists of a number of diploid subunits, which maintain their individual integrity. Thus the inequalities in division are probably the result of unequal distribution of subunits to the two daughter cells; consequently no change in genetic constitution should result. No basis for the precise duplication of the subunits has been discovered, however; indeed no clear identification of the subunits with any cytologically observable structure has been made. Consequently, the possibility of imprecise division of the subunits cannot be totally ignored although the constancy of the characteristics of the amicronucleate strains of *Tetrahymena* that have been in the laboratory for many years certainly suggests that the replication is precise.

Certainly the number of subunits is not constant, and the problem is whether there is a way to keep this variation within bounds. That a way exists is suggested by Nobili's report (1961a,b) that normal macronuclear size eventually is restored after unequal division in *P. aurelia* homozygous for the *am* gene. The most obvious mechanism would be a compensating variation in the amount of DNA synthesized per cell generation, and Nobili (1961b) shows that the next cell generation is prolonged when paramecia with very small macronuclei are produced. No restoration to normal size occurs, however, when paramecia with very large macronuclei are produced, suggesting to Nobili (1961b) that restoration can occur in one direction but not the other. That the amount of DNA synthesized within a cell generation can vary is shown by the observation that individuals of *Stentor coeruleus* cut so as to contain only one macronuclear node can regenerate and restore the normal multinode condition (for review, see Tartar, 1961). There is also evidence that more than double the amount of DNA can be synthesized in a single cell generation during temperature cycling in *T. pyriformis* (Scherbaum *et al.*, 1959), and that two complete replications occasionally occur in *E. eurystomus* (Kimball and Prescott, 1962). Apparently temperature-cycled *T. pyriformis* returns to normal by division without replication; no information about restoration of the normal amount of DNA is available in *E. eurystomus*. In the absence of clear evidence for anything except an integral number of duplications of DNA, it remains uncertain whether variations in synthesis could allow precise control of the amount of DNA.

A phenomenon that might allow finer control is the chromatin elimination at division in *T. pyriformis* (Scherbaum *et al.*, 1958; Dysart, 1963). At most divisions in this species, a small piece of the macronucleus is cut off and degenerates. Variations in the size of this piece might provide some control of the size of the nucleus, but the phenomenon requires that more than double the amount of DNA be formed in each cycle, thus returning us to the problem of variation in the amount of synthesis.

Whatever the controlling mechanisms may be, it is clear that they do not always restore the macronucleus to normal size within a single cell generation. If all inequalities were removed within one cell cycle, the only variation would be between the macronuclei of sister cells; whereas, in fact, there is even greater variation between different sister pairs, measured at the same stage in the cycle (Kimball and Barka, 1959; McDonald, 1958). Thus some breaking up into subclones with macronuclei of different sizes certainly occurs, and the only question is how persistent these subclonal differences are.

A point that may be of some importance for studies of intraclonal inheritance is the finding for both *T. pyriformis* (McDonald, 1958) and *P. aurelia* (Kimball and Vogt-Köhne, 1961) that there is no detectable decrease in macronuclear DNA during starvation, although marked decreases in dry weight and RNA occur. Some decrease in DNA has been found in starved *Urostyla* (Pigon and Edström, 1959) but only when the starvation was sufficient to decrease appreciably the survival. On the other hand, some genetic data for *T. pyriformis* can be explained most easily by a decrease in the number of macronuclear subunits during starvation (Allen and Nanney, 1958). This apparent discrepancy between the cytochemical and genetic data remains to be explained.

It is of some interest from the point of view of the distribution of the subunits at division that complete mixing of DNA occurs in preparation for division (Kimball and Prescott, 1962) in *Euplotes*. A short pulse of H^3-thymidine labels two fairly short lengths of the elongate macronucleus, and the label remains localized until shortly before division. Then it becomes spread throughout the nucleus. Thus it seems probable that the subunits are completely mixed and distributed at random to the daughter nuclei. There is no opportunity for the subunits in different regions to remain segregated from one another for longer than one cell generation.

C. Micronuclear Number and Function

The micronuclear number is usually characteristic for a species, but appreciable variation sometimes occurs. Thus variation around the standard number of two has been found in *P. aurelia* (Geckler and Kimball, 1953; Kimball and Gaither, 1955; Kimball *et al.*, 1957), presumably as a consequence of misdistribution at division, and even more extreme variations occur in homozygotes for the gene *am* (Nobili, 1962a). The data suggest that the micronuclear number, once changed, remains as constant at the new number as at the old; i.e., there seems to be no mechanism in this species for restoring the normal number except by redevelopment of the whole nuclear complement at conjugation or autogamy. In *P. caudatum*, however, some bimicronucleates have been reported to return to the unmicronucleate state whereas others do not (Miyake, 1956, 1957).

Sonneborn (1954b) has reported that the micronucleus of *P. aurelia* is genetically inactive, at least in respect to the action of the *k* locus. In accord with this inactivity is the finding in this species of little or no incorporation of RNA precursors in the micronucleus under conditions in which massive incorporation occurs in the macronucleus (Kimball and Perdue, 1964). Moreover, paramecia with small pieces of macronucleus can survive and multiply, but paramecia with no macronucleus but with enough extra micronuclei to make about the same total nuclear mass cannot (Nobili, 1962a).

In contrast to this evidence for inertness, most newly formed amicronucleate lines in various species, including in our experience *P. aurelia,* grow poorly (for review, see Wells, 1961), suggesting an important role for the micronucleus in growth and multiplication. Amicronucleates with good growth have arisen, especially in *Tetrahymena;* but even in this organism there are reasons to suspect that a second step is required, in which the functions of the micronucleus are taken over by some other part of the cell (Wells, 1961). It seems likely that most of the genes in the micronucleus are inactive, but that some important nuclear functions are still retained.

D. RNA Synthesis

Ribonucleic acid (RNA) is synthesized in the macronucleus more or less continuously during the cell cycle in *T. pyriformis* (Prescott, 1960, 1961a,b, 1962), *P. aurelia* (Kimball and Perdue, 1962a; Kimball et al., 1960), and *E. eurystomus* (Prescott and Kimball, 1961). In *T. pyriformis,* the rate of synthesis is low early in the cycle and increases. In *P. aurelia,* it appears to be more or less constant during macronuclear G1 and increases more or less in proportion to macronuclear size during macronuclear S. The RNA passes from the macronucleus into the cytoplasm continuously in *T. pyriformis* (Prescott, 1961a,b, 1962) and *P. aurelia* (Kimball and Perdue, 1962a), and there is no evidence for cytoplasmic synthesis of RNA (Prescott, 1961a,b, 1962). Insofar as the RNA in question carries genetic information, this information must be passing to the cytoplasm continuously during the cell cycle.

In *Euplotes,* DNA synthesis is confined to narrow replication bands (Gall, 1959), and RNA synthesis does not occur in these bands (Prescott and Kimball, 1961). This mutual exclusion of RNA and DNA synthesis is expected if DNA serves as a template for both. The *Euplotes* case is one of the most direct pieces of evidence for this mutual exclusion.

E. Conservation of Materials

Cells are often considered as being in a constant state of flux. For many substances this is undoubtedly true, but for others it is not. It is well established, of course, that DNA is conserved without exchange with the environment, but under limited circumstances this is true for other molecules as well. Thus ribosomal RNA is conserved in bacteria (Davern and Meselson, 1960) and ascites tumor cells (Scott et al., 1962), and labeled amino acids are conserved, possibly as protein, in bacteria (van Tubergen and Setlow, 1961).

Conservation of materials was first clearly shown for ciliates by the P[32] studies of Kaudewitz (1958). He showed, for several species that P[32], once incorporated into the cell's own materials, was retained for a number of cell generations with little or no loss. Studies with tritium-labeled pyrimidine ribosides and amino acids have shown (Kimball, 1962b, Kimball and Perdue,

1964) that these substances are completely conserved in *P. aurelia* during log-phase growth but partially lost under conditions of starvation. Although neither the P^{32} nor the H^3 studies prove conservation in macromolecular form, they make this sufficiently probable to be taken into consideration in any studies of short term variation within clones.

F. Growth during the Cell Cycle

A number of studies of the growth in linear dimensions and volume were carried out on ciliates during the earlier part of this century (for review, see Richards, 1941). More recently, it has been possible to return to the problem of cell growth with the methods of cytochemistry. Two different patterns of growth have been reported in the species most carefully studied. *Tetrahymena pyriformis* appears to increase in mass at essentially a linear rate throughout the cycle as measured by "respiratory mass" (Zeuthen, 1953) and incorporation of C^{14}-methionine (Prescott, 1960). *Paramecium aurelia*, on the other hand, shows an approximately exponential increase in dry mass (Kimball *et al.*, 1959c; Kimball and Vogt-Köhne, 1962) and possibly a still greater departure from linear increase in protein (Woodard *et al.*, 1961). A number of different growth curves have been reported for other cells (see Prescott, 1961a).

The approximately exponential increase in dry weight in *P. aurelia* is what would be expected (Kimball and Perdue, 1962a) if the rate of protein synthesis were dependent on the amount of ribosomal RNA, if this RNA were formed continuously during the cell cycle at a rate proportional to the amount of DNA, and if ribosomal RNA were conserved. As previous sections show, evidence for all these propositions except the first has been obtained. The precise form of the growth curve, since it depends on all these factors, might be expected to vary in species with different patterns of RNA and DNA synthesis.

G. Control of Cell Size

It is obvious that the size of a cell at division will depend upon the integrated growth rate during the intervening interval and upon the generation time. The relation between these two quantities is such that the size at division under standard conditions is usually nearly constant for a given species and strain. When conditions change, however, the relation may change in such a way that the size at division is altered. In *P. aurelia* (Kimball *et al.*, 1959c), limiting the food supply decreases the growth rate relative to the generation time so that the size at division is reduced. Size is restored after starvation by a reverse relation between these quantities. In *T. pyriformis*, temperature cycling delays division while allowing growth to proceed (Scherbaum *et al.*, 1959), and size is restored by decreased generation time after the cycling is stopped. In *Spathidium spathula* (D. B. Williams, 1962) cells of unequal size are produced at each division, the proter being larger than the opisthe. Size is restored by a longer generation time for the latter. Thus there is no question that homeostatic mechanisms exist for the control of cell size, and there is some evidence that size itself plays some sort of role in this control. It is also certain, however, that the control is complex and no one factor, size or any other, is entirely determining (for more extensive discussion, including work with other kinds of cells, see Prescott, 1961a). Whether the homeostatic mechanisms are sufficiently precise to avoid breaking a clone up into subclones of different cell size is a question that has not yet been attacked with modern methods.

H. Maintenance and Duplication of Structure

The complex cortical pattern of the ciliates is duplicated at division by a series of morphogenetic events which have been described in some detail for a number of species (see reviews and discussions by Ehret and Powers, 1959; Fauré-Fremiet, 1954; Lwoff, 1950; Sonneborn, 1963; and Tartar, 1961). These events resemble in many respects the morphogenetic events accompanying regeneration from micrurgical operations, and indeed the processes at division can be considered as a special case of "regeneration," resulting in two complete morphological entities (Fauré-Fremiet, 1954). The most complete study of morphogenesis has been made in *Stentor coeruleus* (Tartar, 1961; Uhlig, 1960). The results show that particular organelles, such as the adoral membranelles and the buccal cavity, normally form at specific places in the preexisting structure, but often can form in other places when the preferred place is not present. There are definite dominance rules in this respect and also definite rules for the relation of the preexisting structure to the symmetry and other details of form of the new ones. Such semiphysical concepts as "gradient" may be useful for systematizing these rules, but this should not obscure the fact that we know essentially nothing (cf. Grimstone, 1961) about the molecular and physical events by which particular combinations of proteins, lipids, etc., are organized as structures at specific places within the preexisting pattern.

In some cases, a particular organelle may appear essential for the formation of the same organelle in the new pattern. Microbeam studies (Hanson, 1955, 1962) of *P. aurelia* have shown that destruction of the buccal cavity (gullet) can prevent the formation of a new one. More detailed analysis (Hanson, 1962) shows, however, that only a small part of the organelle or perhaps a nearby region is essential. Whatever the situation in *P. aurelia*, the buccal cavity can clearly originate *de novo* in other species since regeneration regularly follows in several other genera (for review, see Hanson, 1962). As far as the reviewer is aware, there is no better ground for speaking of self-duplication of any other ciliate organelle (cf. Grimstone, 1961) probably not even the kinetosomes (see next section), although such negative evidence cannot exclude the possibility that self-duplicating organelles will eventually be found.

On the other hand, the term self-duplication can be usefully applied to the whole cortical pattern. Certain variations of the pattern are such that they are duplicated with considerable regularity at division by the normal morphogenetic processes that produce two patterns from one. The classic example of this is the homopolar double (an individual with two sets of cortical organelles with the same anterior-posterior orientation), which was first described by Dawson (1920) and has been reported repeatedly since (see Fauré-Fremiet, 1954; and Tartar, 1961). Reasonably stable homopolar triples and quadruples have also been found (Sonneborn, 1963; Sonneborn and Dippell, 1961a; Tartar, 1961; Uhlig, 1960). In *P. aurelia* at least, certain smaller variants of the normal pattern also are duplicated (Sonneborn, 1963; Sonneborn and Dippell, 1961b,c, 1962).

In all these cases, there are multiple sets of some of the major cortical organelles and regions (sometimes of nuclei as well) arranged in such a way that the normal division processes lead to the same multiple condition in both daughters (cf. Sonneborn, 1963). The variant pattern is less stable than the normal one but may be sufficiently stable to allow production of large clones of the variant and to persist through the cortical reorganization attending conjugation and autogamy.

The origin of doubles and other stable variants of the cortical pattern by fusion of conjugants, incomplete division, or regeneration following various micrurgical procedures suggested that genic differences were not responsible for the differences between the patterns. This was also suggested by the observation that the double condition was preserved in conjugation between doubles and singles even though exchange of genes occurred (Powers, 1943). More recently this conclusion has been established beyond any doubt by breeding experiments that have excluded genic differences between doubles and singles (Sonneborn, 1963; Sonneborn and Dippell, 1960a). Thus there can be no question that homopolar doubles and similar stable variants are perpetuated by the effect of the old pattern on the morphogenesis of new ones at division.

Of course the pattern can also be influenced by gene-controlled reactions. This is shown by the fact that several loci are known that affect shape (mostly unpublished) or the ability to divide properly (Maly, 1958). In one of the cases of chain and monster formation reported by Maly (1958), there were departures from simple Mendelian expectations, which suggested to him some nongenic inheritance as well. Maly (1960a,b) also studied the effects of metal ions and metabolic inhibitors on the expression of these gene-determined variants.

A penetrating discussion of the problem of pattern inheritance in ciliates has recently been published by Sonneborn (1963) but came to the reviewer's attention too late for detailed inclusion.

I. Replication of the Kinetosomes

It has been suggested many times in the past that the kinetosomes and their apparent structural homologs, the centrioles, are self-duplicating. This idea was developed with considerable thoroughness in a book by Lwoff (1950). Light microscope studies seemed to show new kinetosomes arising in close proximity to old ones, and the term "division" has often been applied to this observation. As Sonneborn (1950) pointed out in reviewing Lwoff's book, no evidence was presented for persistent, inherited differences among kinetosomes. Thus the evidence for self-duplication was not very compelling. Others have also questioned the idea of self-duplication (e.g., Ehret, 1958, 1960; Ehret and Powers, 1959; Grimstone, 1961; Tartar, 1961) and have pointed out that the observations were compatible with new kinetosomes normally arising in close proximity with old ones, perhaps by some kind of "induction." The recent electron microscope observations on the origin of the centrioles in the egg of a snail (Gall, 1961) are certainly more compatible with this latter view than with true division, although Gall leaves open the possibility of true division of a centriole precursor.

On the other hand, Seaman (1960, 1962) has reported that the kinetosomes of *T. pyriformis* contain DNA and speaks of them as self-duplicating. The evidence consists in showing that the amount of DNA per unit weight increases as the kinetosomes are purified by centrifugation and that protein synthesis, sensitive to DNase as well as RNase, can be obtained in such non-cellular preparations. This evidence is subject to the objection that nuclear DNA might be released from the macronucleus and adsorbed on the kinetosomes during the preparative procedure. Randall and Fitton-Jackson (1958) reported Feulgen staining of the kinetosome of *Stentor*. On the other hand, Rampton (1963) could not find any incorporation of H^3-thymidine into *Tetrahymena* cytoplasm but points out that the method was not very sensitive. It is true that label from H^3-thymidine is incorporated into cytoplasmic materials in *P. aurelia* (Berech and van Wagtendonk, 1959, 1962; Kimball and Perdue, 1962a), but most and quite possibly all this label is in compounds other than DNA. It can be concluded that some but not conclusive evidence exists for kinetosomal DNA. Even if some of the proteins of the kinetosomes are specified by kinetosomal DNA, at least some of the proteins of such alleged kinetosomal products as cilia and trichocysts are specified by nuclear genes (Preer, 1959a). Thus, although the question cannot be considered finally settled, the evidence does not give strong support to the concept of self-replicating kinetosomes and even less to the concept that the proteins in such structures as cilia and trichocysts are specified by kinetosomal genetic information.*

* This subject is also discussed in the chapter in this volume by Pitelka and Child (Ed.'s note).

Even if the kinetosome, or at least some part of it, is self-duplicating, it is clear that inherited differences between kinetosomes cannot explain the self-duplication of pattern discussed in the previous section. The kinetosomes of a new organelle do not always arise from the kinetosomes of the corresponding old organelle. The duplication of pattern remains a problem in morphogenesis whether or not one of the elements of the pattern is self-duplicating.

III. Clonal Life History

In many ciliates, a clone beginning with an exconjugant or exautogamous individual passes through a series of gradual changes that give the clone a characteristic life history (for reviews of earlier work, see Preer, 1957a, 1959a; Sonneborn, 1954c, 1957). Two main phenomena can be distinguished. One, which may be called "maturation," is a gradual change in the ability to initiate conjugation and autogamy. The other, which may be called "senescence," is a gradual decline in fission rate and viability during vegetative reproduction and in viability after the sexual processes of autogamy and conjugation. What, if any, causal relations exist between these two phenomena is uncertain. Some ciliates, e.g., *T. pyriformis* syngen 1, undergo maturation (Nanney and Caughey, 1953) but rarely if ever senescence (Nanney, 1959a). Others, e.g., *P. aurelia,* regularly undergo both.

A. Maturation

Maturation in *P. aurelia* involves a series of stages in which the clone is: (1) unable to undergo either conjugation or autogamy; (2) able to undergo conjugation but not autogamy; (3) able to undergo both; (4) gradually declining in ability to undergo either with the ability to undergo conjugation declining before the ability to undergo autogamy. Stage (1) occurs only after conjugation, not autogamy, and only in some stocks. Siegel (1961) has shown that macronuclear differentiation is involved in maturation since individuals that develop their macronuclei by regeneration of fragments of the old macronucleus rather than from anlagen are fully mature. Stocks differ in the period of immaturity (Sonneborn, 1957), and some form of genic control is suggested by the results of crosses (Siegel, 1957).

In *P. bursaria,* a species in which conjugation but not autogamy is known, Siegel and Cohen (1963) have evidence for stepwise production of two pairs of mating type substances. Each pair is controlled by a genetic locus with two alleles (Cohen and Siegel, 1963; Siegel and Larison, 1960). Siegel and Cohen (1963) present evidence for successive "switching on" of first one locus and then the other with the consequence that during an intermediate "adolescent" period only one of the two substances, in some cases one, in some the other, are found. Thus in this instance there is a temporal sequence of gene expression.

In *P. caudatum*, Hiwatshi (1960a,b) has published evidence of an inherited difference between rapidly and slowly maturing stocks. He has also found (1958) a remarkable kind of phenomic lag for sexual immaturity. Under certain culture conditions, some clones remain sexually reactive for a time (10 or more days with between 2 and 2.5 fissions per day) after conjugation and, during this time, retain their preconjugation mating type. They then become sexually unreactive for a time and finally become sexually reactive again, now with the definitive, postconjugation mating type. It would appear that the onset of sexual immaturity is delayed and that this delay is associated with a retention of the preconjugation mating type, but whether this is a true phenotypic lag or some other phenomenon is not clear.

B. Senescence

The second kind of progressive alteration during the clonal life history has been most completely investigated in *P. aurelia* where two, possibly interrelated, phenomena can be distinguished. One is a gradual decline in division rate with eventual death of the clone; the other is an increasing amount of inviability and low division rate among the clones arising by conjugation or autogamy from the aging one. The latter phenomenon has now been explained by the accumulation of micronuclear mutations, presumably chromosomal aberrations, that result in the segregation of lethal genomes during the sexual processes (Dippell, 1955; Sonneborn and Dippell, 1960b; Sonneborn and Schneller, 1955a, 1960b). These mutations occur at a higher rate late in clonal history than early, possibly as a secondary consequence of the changes in cellular physiology that are responsible for the progressive decline in division rate. Except when otherwise stated, only the latter will be considered in this discussion.

Sonneborn (1954c; Sonneborn *et al.*, 1960) has summarized in some detail the evidence for progressive decline in division rate within a clone of *P. aurelia*. Eventually, after many divisions, most sublines die, and the clone can no longer be maintained. Recovery from these effects can be brought about by autogamy (Sonneborn, 1954c; Sonneborn and Schneller, 1955b, 1960a) and to some, but apparently to a much less extent, by macronuclear regeneration (Sonneborn and Schneller, 1960a; Nobili 1961c). There has been some variation in the reports of the effectiveness of macronuclear regeneration (Mitchison, 1955; Nobili, 1960; Sonneborn, 1954c; Sonneborn and Schneller, 1955c). Some of this variation may result from the increase with age in the proportion of macronuclear regenerates that are inviable or slowly growing. Practically, it is apparently impossible to continue a line of descent indefinitely by successive macronuclear regenerations (Nobili, 1961c) under conditions in which it can be done by autogamy. Sonneborn and Schneller (1960a) suggest that the macronuclei or their fragments are damaged by "old" cytoplasm, much as is the micronucleus, with the risk of damage increasing with age. It is not clear whether an appropriate version of this nuclear damage hypothesis could account for the difference between macronuclear regeneration and autogamy or whether some other factors are involved.

Gradual decline and eventual death seems to be the fate of all clones of *P. aurelia* (but see clone 0-44-9, Sonneborn, 1954c). On the other hand many amicronucleate and micronucleate strains of *T. pyriformis* have been kept in the laboratory for many years without conjugation and without evident deterioration. Nanney (1959a) has shown that a number of micronucleate clones of this species produce a few abnormal sublines that eventually die, but only a few of these abnormal sublines show gradual decline in division rate. Thus either gradual decline during vegetative reproduction is not the universal fate of all ciliate clones or it is delayed so long in some cases as to be essentially unobservable, thus putting it outside the range of phenomena in which we are ever likely to be able to take an effective interest.

A number of hypotheses have been discussed to explain the decline in division rate and viability during the life of the clone (Sonneborn 1954c; Sonneborn *et al.*, 1960). Genic imbalance resulting from irregular distribution of chromosomes at amitosis (Fauré-Fremiet, 1953) appeared plausible when subclones showing the homozygous recessive phenotype were found in heterozygotes of *P. aurelia* (Sonneborn and Schneller, 1955c), but this phenomenon was later shown to result from reversible "turning off" of the phenotypic effect of one allele (Sonneborn *et al.*, 1956). Variation of gene expression with age has also been reported in *P. bursaria* (Siegel and Cohen, 1963; see Section III,A, this chapter). Thus possibilities for which some evidence exists are "switching off" of genes with age and progressive damage to the macronucleus. There is some evidence, however, against macronuclear mutations, at least of the kind induced by X-rays, being an important factor in senescence (Kimball and Gaither, 1954). It seems possible to the reviewer that an explanation for senescence might also be found in the imprecision of the mechanisms that restore the cell to normal after such events as unequal division, variation in cell size, and so on have caused departures from normality. Although the restoring mechanisms must be quite effective, we know that they may be slow to act (Section II,B); and it is difficult to believe that they are completely efficient. Cumulative minor failures of these homeostatic mechanisms could lead to gradual deterioration of the cell lineage. Autogamy, conjugation, and macronuclear regeneration all greatly change the growth pattern and cause regrowth of the macronucleus from anlagen or fragments. Thus special mechanisms must be acting at this time to restore the cell to normal, and the effects of previous departures might tend to be obliterated. Perhaps the problem should be turned around to ask how it is that in view of the many ways in which departures from normal can occur some ciliate clones can persist so long without obvious change.

IV. The Immobilization Antigens

In *P. aurelia,* a number of serologically distinct antigens can be recognized by the immobilization of the paramecia by isologous antisera. The system has been reviewed and discussed frequently (Beale, 1954, 1957a, 1958, 1959; Beale and Wilkinson, 1961; Nanney, 1958a,b; Nanney and Rudzinska, 1960; Preer, 1957a, 1959a; Sonneborn, 1960). Consequently only a few particular features will be emphasized here, especially the most recent developments.

The immobilization antigens are located at or near the surface of the cortex and cilia (Beale and Kacser, 1957; Beale and Mott, 1962; Mott, 1963; Preer and Preer, 1959; van Wagtendonk *et al., 1956*). The antigens have been partially purified, some of their properties have been studied, and they have been shown to comprise a relatively homogeneous group among the various antigens that can be detected by precipitin reactions (Bishop, 1961, 1963; Bishop and Beale, 1960; Finger and Heller, 1962; Finger *et al.,* 1960, 1963; Preer, 1959b,c,d,e; Preer and Preer, 1959; Steers, 1961).

The immobilization antigens, despite their similarity in major properties, are controlled by a large series of unlinked loci. The alleles at a given locus determine antigens that are distinguishable, but often, though not always, closely related serologically. Marked differences in the fingerprints of tryptic digests of antigens determined by nonallelic genes have been found (Steers, 1962), and some difference, though generally less, between antigens determined by different alleles at the same locus (Jones and Beale, 1963). Thus there is no doubt that the loci control the amino acid sequences in the antigens. Finger and Heller (1963) give some evidence for hybrid antigens in heterozygotes and also find phenotypic variation between genotypically identical heterozygotes, a phenomenon which in one form or another occurs for other characters as well (see Sections III,B and V,C).

The remarkable feature of the system is that, with rare exceptions (Finger *et al.,* 1962; Margolin, 1956), only the one or two antigens controlled by a single locus are detectable in any one paramecium. All the other loci appear to be inactive as far as serological tests go. Once a locus is active in producing detectable antigen it remains so except for sudden shifts, which can be induced more or less at will, at any time during the clonal history.

Each locus has a limited number of temperature and other conditions under which it will remain expressed. These conditions are determined by the particular allele at the locus itself and by the residual genome. If conditions change, some other locus comes to expression, though sometimes only after many cell generations. Other treatments (e.g., Austin *et al.*, 1956; Balbinder and Preer, 1959; Dryl, 1959) can cause sudden shifts even within the time required for one cell generation (Austin *et al.*, 1956; Koizumi, 1958).

Once a locus is expressed, it tends to remain so (e.g., Skaar, 1955) provided the conditions are appropriate and no treatment is given to change the situation. Several loci may have the potentiality for expression under a given set of conditions; and, if so, the one that is actually expressed depends on the past history of the clone. Studies at conjugation (for review, see Beale, 1954) have shown that there is a cytoplasmic component in the controlling system since the expressed locus is usually that of the cytoplasmic parent.

Somewhat similar though less complete findings have been reported for *T. pyriformis* (Inoki and Matsushiro, 1958; Loefer and Owen, 1961; Loefer *et al.*, 1958; Margolin *et al.*, 1959). Certain antigens (L) are expressed at low temperature; others at high. Several alleles at one locus controlling the H antigens, and the special behavior of the heterozygotes for these alleles, will be discussed in the next section. No allelic differences in the L antigen have been found. Inoki and Matsushiro (1958) report that the antigenic state of the cytoplasmic parent determines that of the exconjugant progeny just as in *P. aurelia.* Nanney (1963) could not confirm this, however, in carefully controlled experiments, leaving the role, if any, of the cytoplasm in doubt. Possibly similar semistable states exist in respect to the occurrence of polymorphism in *Tetrahymena vorax* (N. E. Williams, 1961), but genetic data are lacking.

A wide variety of explanations has been suggested for this system of mutually exclusive, semistable antigenic states. Most of the recent explanations have involved in some way the inhibition of the action of all loci except one, and it is often suggested that the products of the active locus inhibit all the rest. It has long been realized that there are parallels between enzyme induction and the sudden change in serotype, and Sonneborn (1960) has discussed this similarity in some detail. The idea that the immobilization antigens may adapt the surface to the external conditions has been shown to be quite plausible by Austin *et al.* (1956). Thus the parallel to enzyme induction seems to extend to the adaptive features as well.

The recent formulation of the regulator-operon concept of gene action (Jacob and Monod, 1961) suggests a shift in emphasis from the inactivation to the activation of the loci. According to this formulation, loci with variable expression are normally repressed by internal repressors and must be derepressed by inducers that block the repressor action. At the risk of adding another to the long list of speculations about the immobilization antigens, the reviewer suggests that the loci for the immobilization antigens may be self-induced (an idea presented in general form by Monod and Jacob, 1962) by their own products. Once a locus is induced, it should stay induced unless the repressor-inducer system is disturbed in some way. No special explanation would be required for the continued repression of the other loci. The mutual exclusion feature could be explained by some aspect of the "molecular ecology" of the brief, unstable change-over period. This is only one of many schemes for semi-stable states that can be based on the regulator-operon model (for a discussion of other possibilities, see Monod and Jacob, 1962), but it has the advantage of simplicity in requiring only one continuously acting feedback loop, with the other features of the system attributed to the normal repression of loci and purely transitory events of a change-over period brought about by a temporary disturbance of the inducing system.

V. Nuclear Differentiation

A series of phenomena have been reported that are best put in the descriptive category of nuclear differentiation but without any implications about the similarity of the mechanisms involved. These phenomena have been given special prominence in discussions by Nanney (1954, 1956, 1958a) and Sonneborn (1954d, 1960).

A. NUCLEAR BEHAVIOR AT CONJUGATION

In many organisms, there are stages in the life history at which nuclei in a common cytoplasm become differentiated from one another and go on to different fates. Some instructive examples of this are found at conjugation and autogamy in ciliates, one of the most obvious being the differentiation of the products of the postgamic mitoses into macronuclei and micronuclei. Nanney (1953) has given evidence for *T. pyriformis* that what the postgamic nuclei become depends on the cytoplasmic region in which they are located and suggests that disturbances of these locations by centrifugation can alter the fate of the nuclei.

Another example is the diverse fate of the meiotic products in *P. aurelia*. Normally one meiotic product gives rise by mitosis to the two pronuclei; the other products degenerate. The successful product is regularly found in or near the paroral cone region. Sonneborn (1954d) has found a mutant in which no product reaches the cone region and all degenerate. He hypothesizes that the cone region protects the successful product from some substance that destroys the others. He notes that the expansion of the old macronucleus into a skein is delayed in the mutant and suggests that this expansion is required to push the successful product into the cone.

An additional, more active role of the meiotic product is suggested by evidence that the product's own genome is of importance for its success in reaching the cone and that competition between products with different genomes occurs. The evidence consists in showing that meiotic products with less than a haploid set of chromosomes (Kimball and Gaither, 1955, 1956) or with radiation-induced mutations (Kimball et al., 1957) are less likely to form the synkaryon than are normal products when abnormal and normal products are present together. An autonomous role of the nucleus in its own movement is made more plausible by electron microscope evidence for ameboid-like movement of the migratory pronucleus of P. caudatum (André and Vivier, 1962).

B. Mating Types

Another kind of nuclear differentiation was first discovered in the early work on mating types. Before considering this matter some general remarks about mating types will be made.

In many ciliates, conjugation is most readily induced by mixing cultures of different origin. From the results of these mixtures, the cultures can be classified into two or more mating types, cultures being classified as different mating types if conjugation is induced by mixture (for review, see Sonneborn, 1957). In some species (e.g., P. aurelia), conjugation in such mixture is usually between individuals of different mating type, but in other species (e.g., Euplotes patella) mixture may induce a high frequency of conjugation between individuals of the same as well as different mating types. Selfing conjugation can also be induced in unmixed cultures by certain procedures (Hiwatashi, 1959; Katashima, 1959; Larison and Siegel, 1961; Metz, 1954; Miyake, 1958, 1959, 1960, 1961).

The basis for the induction of conjugation by mixture is not the same in all species. Thus the interaction between the mating types in the genus Paramecium can be explained, at least formally, by Metz's hypothesis (1954) of complementary pairs of substances on the surface. Direct evidence for such substance has been obtained for P. bursaria by studying interactions between isolated cilia and living animals, both of known mating type (Cohen and Siegel, 1963). On the other hand, individuals of any one mating type of E. patella secrete substances into the fluid that induce conjugation including selfing involving individuals of other mating types. Thus the physiological and biochemical basis for mating type diversity may be quite different even in the same genus. In other species of Euplotes, quite different systems have been found (Katashima, 1959; Heckmann, 1963).

In some ciliates, each mating type seems to be determined by a distinct genotype (Siegel, 1963; Siegel and Larison, 1960; Heckmann, 1963). Even in these, the situation may be complicated by selfing within some clones and by changes of mating type resulting from only partial expression of the genome at certain stages of the clonal history (Siegel and Larison, 1960).

In P. aurelia, P. multimicronucleatum syngen 2, and T. pyriformis syngen 1, the relation between genotype and mating type is even less direct and two or more mating types are regularly produced by a single genotype. This brings us back to the main theme of this section.

The inheritance of mating types in *P. aurelia* has been reviewed a number of times (Beale, 1954; Nanney, 1954, 1956, 1957; Sonneborn, 1954d, 1957, 1960). There are two main patterns of inheritance. The group A syngens show caryonidal inheritance in its standard form. The members of a caryonide (the group of individuals whose macronuclei come from one macronuclear anlage) are all alike in mating type; but different caryonides, even from the same exconjugant or exautogamous specimen, may be and often are different. When he first discovered the phenomenon, Sonneborn recognized that some sort of permanent or nearly permanent differentiation of the newly developing anlagen must be involved, and this view has been retained in most of the later discussions. The differentiation of the anlagen in the group A syngens can be influenced by environmental factors such as temperature, but only during the very early development of the anlagen, not later. A form of genic control exists. Caryonidal inheritance is found only when a dominant allele of the *mt* locus is present. Homozygotes for the recessive allele are always of one mating type, e.g., type I in syngen 1. Several independent mutants at this locus all show the same restriction (Butzel, 1955).

A modified form of caryonidal inheritance occurs in the B group of syngens (Nanney, 1954; Sonneborn, 1954d). The mating type of the conjugant normally determines the mating type for which the new macronuclei will be differentiated. This can be shown to be an effect, by way of the cytoplasm, of the old macronucleus on the new ones. Thus this is a special form of hereditary transmission in which the old nucleus affects the new by means of a cytoplasmic intermediary. Occasionally the system breaks down and typical caryonidal inheritance is found.

A complication of the group B system was found in syngen 7 (Taub, 1963) and shows that it is not the mating type *per se* that determines the differentiation of the developing anlage. Individuals of this syngen homozygous for mt^{XIII} are always type XIII, but their cytoplasm determines the exconjugants to be type XIV when the dominant $mt^{XIII,XIV}$ allele, which allows the development of type XIV as well as type XIII, is introduced from the other conjugant. A second unlinked locus, which also restricts the mating type to type XIII, has recently been described (Taub, 1963).

In some instances, mating type expression seems to be much more directly under the control of the environment. Thus in *P. multimicronucleatum* syngen 2, there is a circadian rhythm of mating type change. Some stocks of this syngen act as type III at certain times of day, type IV at others (Barnett, 1959a,b; Sonneborn, 1957; Sonneborn and Barnett, 1958; Sonneborn and Sonneborn, 1958). Evidence has been given for a locus controlling the ability to cycle, with the ability to cycle dominant to the inability (Barnett, 1961). The phase relations of the cycle and the mating type of the noncyclers appear to be caryonidally inherited. A circadian rhythm in the ability to conjugate at all has been known for a long time in certain stocks of *P. aurelia* and *P. bursaria* (Sonneborn, 1957).

In *P. caudatum* syngen 12, there is also evidence of more or less immediate environmental control of the mating type in certain selfing clones (Hiwatashi, 1960b). High fission rate favors one type, low another.

A somewhat more complicated form of caryonidal or better subunit inheritance has been found in *T. pyriformis* syngen 1 by Nanney and his associates. There are seven mating types instead of the two in *P. aurelia*. A gene, *mt*, limiting the mating-type potentials has been found (Nanney *et al.*, 1955) with two main allelic types—one allowing all types except IV and VII, the other, all except I. Subsidiary loci and perhaps allelic differences at the *mt* locus itself influence the relative frequencies of the allowed types (Nanney, 1959b).

The peculiar feature of this system is that two different mating types, rarely more, often are found within one caryonide (Nanney and Caughey, 1955). Each caryonide has its own pair of types, which can differ even for caryonides from the same exconjugant. A detailed analysis of the distribution of the two mating types among the lines of descent in a caryonide has led to the following hypothesis (Allen and Nanney, 1958; Nanney, 1958a; Schensted, 1958). The subunits of the newly developing macronuclear anlage are differentiated in respect to mating type at a time when a number of subunits are present. Just as in *P. aurelia,* the differentiation is temperature sensitive (Nanney, 1960a). The subunits are not necessarily differentiated in the same way though there is some sort of interrelation such that only rarely are more than two kinds produced (Nanney and Allen, 1959). The different subunits are segregated at succeeding divisions until finally sublines arise with all subunits identical. The pattern of segregation of mating types to sublines follows quantitatively the pattern predicted by the theory.

C. Other Cases of Caryonidal and Subunit Inheritance

Similar patterns of segregation of phenotypically diverse sublines within a caryonide have been found for other characters in *T. pyriformis* syngen 1. These instances differ from the mating type case in that the segregation occurs only in the heterozygote and appears to result from an early and permanent inhibition of the action of one of the two alleles, the macronuclear subunits differing among themselves in which allele is inhibited.

Such a case is the H immobilization serotype (Nanney and Dubert, 1960). As mentioned earlier, the immobilization antigens of *T. pyriformis* syngen 1 show the same pattern of mutually exclusive, semistable expression as in *P. aurelia.* The H antigens are expressed at high temperature and are controlled by a locus with several alleles. Heterozygotes for this locus, when in the H state, show both allelic antigenic specificities early in the caryonidal history, but eventually sublines appear that show only one or the other of the specificities. The pattern of this intracaryonidal segregation is nearly identical with that for mating type, although quite independent of the latter (Nanney, 1960b). Nanney and Dubert (1960) conclude that one or the other of the two alleles is irreversibly inhibited in each macronuclear subunit at an early stage in macronuclear development and that the subunits eventually segregate out to give pure types.

Inhibition of the H alleles apparently occurs late in the development of the macronuclear anlage but before the first postconjugation division (Nanney and Nagel, 1964). The data show that little if any coordination occurs between subunits, unlike the situation for the mating types. The authors point out that all degrees of coordination of macronuclear subunits have been found from complete coordination in some cases in syngen B of *P. aurelia* to the complete absence of coordination in the present case.

The ratio in which the two alleles at the H locus segregate out to give pure types is a function of the pair of alleles, certain alleles tending to predominate over others (Nanney *et al.*, 1963). Several environmental factors, including temperature, have no effect on the ratio. From time to time anomalous serotypes have appeared that cannot be fully accounted for as yet (Nanney, 1962).

A very similar system has been found for a set of esterases in the same organism (Allen, 1960, 1961a). An isozymic series of esterases (E1) were found to be controlled by a single locus (linked to the mating-type locus; Allen, 1961b) with two known alleles. Heterozygotes express both alleles early in clonal history, but eventually sublines expressing only one are produced. The details of this segregation have not been worked out, but Allen (1961a) suggests that allelic inhibition and subunit segregation are involved. Allen (1961a) also discusses the interesting questions raised by the fact that each allele controls not one but a series of similar though not identical enzymes (isozymes).

Allen *et al.* (1963a,b) have studied the acid phosphatases of *T. pyriformis*. Stocks were found that differed in respect to one group of these phosphatases and were shown to differ at one locus or perhaps at two linked loci. Hybrids between these stocks were at first all alike in respect to the five electrophoretic positions involved. Later phenotypic drift set in just as it does for the serotypes and esterases. Unlike the esterase case not only the two parental and the hybrid pattern but other patterns as well appeared. Allen *et al.* (1963b) discuss various models for this somewhat complicated case of phenotypic drift.

D. Discussion

Genetically the most interesting but also the most obscure step in caryonidal and subunit inheritance is the initial differentiation of the anlage or its subunits to determine a specific mating type, antigen, or enzyme. This event occurs quite early in development and can be influenced by a variety of factors, internal and external. Once it has occurred, however, it appears to be irreversible.

A wide variety of hypotheses have been proposed to account for this differentiation ranging from physical loss of chromosomes to some kind of dynamic stable state. There is some resemblance to the semistable antigen states in that only one of two or more genotypically permissible potentialities (i.e., permissible by the genotype of the synkaryon from which the macronucleus arose) is expressed. This similarity has been stressed by Nanney (1958a,b, 1960c) in his discussions of the concept of epigenetic control systems and led him to suggest control systems in the nucleus, a concept that has since been formulated at the molecular level by Jacob and Monod (1961).

There are major dissimilarities between the antigen states and the mating types, however. Nanney and Rudzinska (1960) emphasized the continuing importance of the cytoplasm for the stability of the former, the lack of such a continuing dependence in the latter. Sonneborn (1960) emphasized the stability of the mating type as compared to the antigen system.

In terms of the regulator-operon concept of Jacob and Monod (1961), the antigen phases could be thought to be controlled by the repressor-inducer part of the system and stabilized through some form of dynamic feedback involving this system. The mating type and other similar systems must involve some part of the operon itself, the operator, the structural gene, or both. Whether differentiation involves a true loss of all or part of this system or a very stable blocking of it is not clear. What is clear is that the initial differentiating event, whatever it may be, can be confined to single subnuclear units or even to single alleles and that once it occurs the system is either irreversible or reversible with great difficulty, despite long continued replication. In these respects, it would appear that the nearest analogy is to nuclear differentiation in amphibian development (Briggs and King, 1959).

VI. Genetic Control of Intracellular Symbionts

Certain stocks of P. aurelia kill other stocks when mixed with them (killers) or when conjugating with them (mate killers). The killer property depends on cytoplasmic entities, which were first thought to be normal constituents but are now known to be symbiotic, bacteria-like organisms (Beale and Jurand, 1960; Dippell, 1958, 1959a,b; Sonneborn, 1959, 1961). When these symbionts were still thought to be normal cytoplasmic constituents, they were given Greek letter names, kappa, mu, etc., and this practice has continued.

A very complete review of the work with these symbionts has been given by Sonneborn (1959). Since then, several new or mutant symbionts have been described (Beale, 1957b; Holzman, 1959; Nobili, 1962b; Sonneborn et al.,

1959; Widmayer, 1961). The nature of the infective agent in breis of killer paramecia and the conditions for infection have been the subject of several communications (Mueller, 1961; Smith, 1961; Sonneborn, 1961; Sonneborn and Mueller, 1959; Tallan, 1959, 1961). The nature of the killing agent and the conditions required for its production and action have been further defined (Butzel et al., 1960; Butzel and Pagliara, 1962; Butzel and van Wagtendonk, 1963; Mueller, 1962; Mueller and Sonneborn, 1959; Nobili, 1960; and Schneller, 1959). The macronucleus has been shown to be essential for kappa multiplication and for some aspects of the killing action (Nobili, 1961d,e).

It was established early that certain genetic loci were required in the paramecia for successful maintenance of the symbionts, and several new findings of this sort have been published (Balbinder, 1959; Gibson and Beale, 1961; Schneller, 1961; Schneller et al., 1959). Siegel (1960) has discussed the relations between host cell strain and symbiont in the somewhat different case of the green algae in P. bursaria.

The most extensive new findings are those of Gibson and Beale (1961, 1962, 1963) on the mate-killer symbiont of P. aurelia syngen 1. In crosses in which the genes necessary for the maintenance of this symbiont were lost, the number of symbionts per paramecium remained essentially unchanged for a number of cell generations after conjugation. Then individual paramecia lost all the symbionts within less than one cell generation. Different lines of descent lost the symbionts after different numbers of cell generations, and one daughter of a given division might lose them while the other retained them.

The distribution of this loss among sublines has led to the hypothesis (Gibson and Beale, 1962; Reeve, 1962) that the cytoplasm contains a thousand or so nonreplicating or very slowly replicating gene-controlled particulates ("metagons" in Gibson and Beale's terminology). Once the genes are lost, these particulates are gradually diluted out by growth and division until paramecia are eventually produced without any of them. In such paramecia, the symbionts are rapidly destroyed. For the most part, the kinetics of loss are in good agreement with the theoretical expectation; but there are some discrepancies leading to the suggestions that there may be some clumping (Gibson and Beale, 1962), a limited amount of multiplication (Reeve and Ross, 1962, 1963), or unequal distribution to the daughter cells of the particulates. Autoradiographic studies (Kimball and Perdue, 1964) show that the old macronuclear fragments continue to synthesize RNA for several cell generations. The discrepancies just noted might be accounted for by synthesis of the particulates by the macronuclear fragments for a few cell generations after conjugation.

Gibson and Beale (1962) point out that the particulates cannot be fragments of the old macronucleus since the number of the latter is much too small, and they consider it unlikely that they are nonreplicating "genes" liberated into the cytoplasm at the time of macronuclear fragmentation. They suggest that the particulates are persistent gene products and have obtained support for this view from the finding (Gibson and Beale, 1963) that the particulates can be completely destroyed by exposure of the living paramecia to ribonuclease. The particulates are completely restored within about two cell generations after ribonuclease treatment. The particulates are not destroyed by 8-azaguanine, which completely destroys the symbionts; the latter are not destroyed by ribonuclease. The difference between the action of ribonuclease and 8-azaguanine demonstrates that the gene-controlled particulates and the symbionts are different entities. The evidence that an RNA-containing gene product is conserved is in good agreement with the autoradiographic evidence that RNA and protein are conserved in this species (see earlier section).

VII. Other Loci

A number of loci in addition to those already mentioned are known. Most of these have been described very briefly, if at all. In *P. aurelia* loci have been found that control the presence of cytoplasmic crystals (Butzel, 1953; Kimball, 1953), affect form (mostly unpublished), rate of growth (Butzel and Vinciguerra, 1957), and temperature sensitivity (Preer, 1957b).

In *T. pyriformis*, loci concerned with requirements for pyridoxine and serine (Elliott and Clark, 1958) have been reported, surprisingly enough with the requiring type dominant to the nonrequiring. The possibility of dominant suppressors is considered by the authors. Orias (1960) has found two independently assorting recessive lethal loci in this species.

VIII. Physiological Aspects of Radiation Mutagenesis

So far we have been concerned with the stability of the phenotype in clones of cells and the influence of factors acting at what Nanney calls the epigenetic level. We turn now to the problem of the stability of the genome itself, especially when it is subjected to radiation. Not too long ago, it was common to look upon this as a problem in radiation physics and chemistry. In recent years, however, it has become obvious that it is also a problem in cell physiology.

The evidence shows that the great stability of the gene involves something more than the physical stability of the DNA double helix. The cell itself appears to have enzymes by which a large fraction of at least some kinds of lesions in the DNA can be repaired. This evidence comes from a variety of organisms and is of different degrees of certainty. The best established case, and the only case in which repair can be carried out *in vitro* is that of the photoreactivating enzyme, which recent evidence suggests breaks ultraviolet-induced thymine dimers

(Rupert *et al.*, 1958; Setlow and Setlow, 1963; Wulff and Rupert, 1962). The reader can find fairly complete coverage of the general field of repair in one book (Hollaender, 1960) and two symposia (Hollaender, 1961; Sobels, 1963). Part of the evidence for repair of premutational damage has been obtained with *P. aurelia,* and it is this evidence that will be reviewed here.

Before doing so, however, the earlier work on mutation induction in this organism will be summarized. The method for detecting mutation is based on the complete homozygosis produced by autogamy. The established procedure is to irradiate, allow the irradiated paramecia to multiply, induce autogamy, isolate autogamous specimens, and check 4 days later for survival and growth of the exautogamous clones. The method detects lethal and slow growth micronuclear mutations, whether recessive or dominant. The early work establishing the method has been reviewed by Kimball (1955a).

The following features of the mutational process have been established for this organism: (1) The induction of mutation by ultraviolet but not by X-rays is subject to photoreactivation (Kimball and Gaither, 1951), suggesting that thymine dimer formation may be an important first step in ultraviolet but not X-ray mutagenesis. (2) Oxygen increases the yield of X-ray induced mutations (Kimball, 1955b; Kimball and Gaither, 1953). (3) This oxygen effect is probably mediated by short-lived, diffusible radicals or by a reaction between oxygen and radicals produced in the macromolecules of the chromosomes. It is not mediated by long-lived mutagens such as H_2O_2 (Hearon and Kimball, 1955; Kimball, 1955b; Kimball *et al.*, 1955). (4) Phosphorus-32 in the medium is more effective than H^3 or $Sr^{89,90}$, Y^{90} in inducing mutations, suggesting that transmutation of incorporated P^{32} to S^{32} may be able to produce mutations in this system (for review, see Powers, 1956).

It has also been shown that certain complicating circumstances make it difficult to determine mutation rates in absolute units, i.e., mutations per genome, although relative rates can be measured with high precision. These complications include interaction between nonallelic mutations (Kimball, 1949), abnormal nuclear behavior at conjugation and autogamy (Kimball and Gaither, 1956; Sonneborn *et al.*, 1953), and selection of less mutant meiotic products (Kimball and Gaither, 1956; Kimball *et al.*, 1957). It is probable that these complications are responsible for the departures from simple expectation in breeding experiments reported by Geckler (1950) for nitrogen mustard and Mitchison (1955) for ultraviolet.

To return to the major theme of this section, the principal results concerning repair of premutational damage after X-irradiation are the following: (1) The amount of mutation increases the later in the G1 period the radiation is given, with a maximum just before micronuclear S (Kimball, 1961, 1962a; Kimball *et al.*, 1957). (2) When stationary phase (prolonged G1) paramecia are irradiated, the amount of mutation decreases the longer the time between irradia-

tion and refeeding (Kimball *et al.*, 1959a). (3) The rate of decrease of mutation as the time between irradiation and micronuclear S increases is greater the
more rapid the cellular metabolism (Kimball *et al.*, 1959a, 1961). (4) Various
postirradiation treatments, which have in common only that they delay division
and, as far as tested, micronuclear S, decrease the amount of mutation (Kimball,
1957, 1961, 1962a; Kimball *et al.*, 1961). (5) Similar decreases in mutation can
be caused by the same treatments when used after α-particles and 2537-A ultraviolet (Kimball *et al.*, 1959b).

These results have been interpreted to mean that many of the initial lesions,
whatever the radiation that causes them, produce mutation only through misreplication of the chromosomes and are subject to repair before replication. The
rate of this repair is dependent on cellular metabolism, suggesting some sort of
enzymatic process.

It has also been possible to identify by dose-rate experiments a two-hit component of mutation. The lesions, presumably chromosomal breaks, leading to
such two-hit mutations are repaired much more rapidly than those leading only
to one-hit mutations, strongly suggesting that the latter lesions are not breaks
but something, possibly an alteration of DNA bases, that remains reversible
and produces mutation only by misreplication (Kimball, 1963a,b).

Finally, it would appear that almost all the initial lesions produced by X-rays,
α-particles, or 2537-A ultraviolet can be repaired under favorable circumstances. Irradiation of *P. aurelia* during micronuclear G2 produces no more than
one-tenth the amount of mutation produced by irradiation in G1 (Kimball and
Perdue, 1962b). Yet there is no reason to think that fewer initial lesions are
produced.

Thus the studies with *P. aurelia* have shown how important the metabolic
conditions of the cell are for the fate of initial lesions in the chromosomes. This
is in excellent accord with the many studies that have demonstrated the great
dependence of mutation rate on cell type and cell stage. Cellular enzymes are
almost certainly an important factor in stabilizing the genome against the ac-
cidental alterations to which it is subject.

IX. Conclusions

The main purpose of this chapter has been to discuss the clonal genetics of
the ciliates with emphasis on the physiological aspects. The elementary unit of
clonal history is the cell life cycle. Ideally all cell life cycles should terminate in
the production of identical daughter cells if the clone is to remain constant.
Actually considerable departures from this ideal occur. The variants arising in
this way are restored more or less to normal by processes about which we still
know too little. The restoration is not always complete, at least within a single

cell generation, with possible, though unproven, long-range consequences for the clone. Recent advances in cytochemistry are making quantitative studies of these problems feasible.

Division of the ciliates requires a complex series of morphogenetic events to produce two cortical patterns from one. These events are such that many variant patterns are automatically restored to normal. Some variants are not restored, however, and a few of these have the proper structure to be duplicated fairly regularly at division by the normal morphogenetic processes by which two patterns are produced from one.

Many ciliates exhibit a clonal life history, which is most easily treated as two separate phenomena, sexual maturation and senescence. Very little is known about the genetic and physiological processes responsible for maturation but there are some indications that a regular temporal sequence of "turning on and off" certain genes could be involved. Senescence is of general occurrence in some species but seems to be sporadic or missing in others. It is tempting to think that it is a consequence of the imprecision of the mechanisms that restore a cell to normal after the various accidents of cell existence. If so, the real problem is the apparent lack of senescence in some species, for this implies restoring mechanisms of remarkable efficiency and precision.

A number of phenomena of clonal history can be brought under the general head of the expression of one genetic locus or one allele to the exclusion of others. In some instances, e.g., the immobilization antigens, the shift from the expression of one locus to another can come about repeatedly and reversibly throughout clonal history. Nevertheless, a locus once expressed tends to remain so; consequently, the past history of the clone, and specifically of its cytoplasm, influences locus expression. This set of observations has its closest analogy in the adaptive enzymes of bacteria and may well concern the repressor-inducer part of the gene-action sequence. Some sort of feedback mechanism must exist, however, that tends to stabilize the system against rapid changes.

Two main sets of phenomena can be put in the descriptive category of nuclear differentiation. One is the different fate of nuclei in a common cytoplasm; e.g., the differentiation of the products of the postgamic mitoses into macro- and micronuclei. This form of differentiation seems to be controlled both by local differences between regions of the cytoplasm and by the genotype of the nucleus itself. The other set of phenomena is the differentiation of macronuclei to express only part of their genetic potentials. The expression of these potentials is set once for all early in development of the macronuclei and remains unchanged thereafter. The phenomenon has its closest analogy to nuclear differentiation during early amphibian development and appears to involve some sort of permanent or nearly permanent change that is localized to single macronuclear subunits or even to single alleles within the subunits.

Recent studies on the role of the ciliate genotype in maintaining certain intracellular symbionts have given new insights into the phenomenon of phenomic lag. It has been shown that particulates which were originally formed under the influence of the ciliate genes, may persist, though with little if any increase in total number, after the genes responsible for their formation are lost. The number of particulates per cell is reduced by successive divisions, but as long as at least one remains the symbionts survive; once all are gone the symbionts disappear rapidly. The nature of these persistent, gene-controlled particulates is still a matter of speculation though it appears that RNA is an essential ingredient.

Finally, the problem of the stability of the genome has been discussed on the basis of studies of radiation-induced mutation in *P. aurelia*. These studies have shown that the genome is stabilized not only by the molecular structure of the chromosome but also by metabolically controlled mechanisms that tend to repair lesions in the chromosomes before they can give rise to mutations.

REFERENCES

Allen, S. L. (1960). *Genetics* 45, 1051–1070.
Allen, S. L. (1961a). *Ann. N.Y. Acad. Sci.* 94, 753–773.
Allen, S. L. (1961b). *Genetics* 46, 847–848.
Allen, S. L., and Nanney, D. L. (1958). *Am. Naturalist* 92, 139–160.
Allen, S. L., Misch, M. S., and Morrison, B. M. (1963a). *J. Histochem. Cytochem.* 11, 706–719.
Allen, S. L., Misch, M. S., and Morrison, B. M. (1963b) *Genetics* 48, 1637–1658.
André, J., and Vivier, E. (1962). *J. Ultrastruct. Res.* 6, 390–406.
Austin, M. L., Widmayer, D., and Walker, L. M. (1956). *Physiol. Zool.* 29, 261–287.
Balbinder, E. (1959). *Genetics* 44, 1227–1241.
Balbinder, E., and Preer, J. R., (1959). *J. Gen. Microbiol.* 21, 156–167.
Barnett, A. (1959a). *J. Protozool.* 6, Suppl., 22.
Barnett, A. (1959b). *Science* 130, 1412.
Barnett, A. (1961). *Am. Zoologist* 1, 341–342.
Beale, G. H. (1954). "The Genetics of *Paramecium aurelia*." Cambridge Univ. Press, London and New York.
Beale, G. H. (1957a). *Intern. Rev. Cytol.* 6, 1–23.
Beale, G. H. (1957b). *Proc. Roy. Phys. Soc. Edinburgh* 26, 11–14.
Beale, G. H. (1958). *Proc. Roy. Soc.* B148, 308–314.
Beale, G. H. (1959). *Proc. Roy. Phys. Soc. Edinburgh* 28, 71–78.
Beale, G. H., and Jurand, A. (1960). *J. Gen. Microbiol.* 23, 243–252.
Beale, G. H., and Kacser, H. (1957). *J. Gen. Microbiol.* 17, 68–74.
Beale, G. H., and Mott, M. R. (1962). *J. Gen. Microbiol.* 28, 617–623.
Beale, G. H., and Wilkinson, J. F. (1961). *Ann. Rev. Microbiol.* 15, 263–293.
Berech, J., Jr., and van Wagtendonk, W. J. (1959). *Science* 130, 1413.
Berech, J., Jr., and van Wagtendonk, W. J. (1962). *Exptl. Cell Res.* 26, 360–372.
Bishop, J. (1961). *Biochim. Biophys. Acta* 50, 471–477.
Bishop, J. O. (1963). *J. Gen. Microbiol.* 30, 271–280.
Bishop, J. O., and Beale, G. H. (1960). *Nature* 186, 734.

Briggs, R., and King, T. J. (1959). *In* "The Cell" (J. Brachet and A. E. Mirsky, eds.), Vol. 1, pp. 537–617. Academic Press, New York.

Butzel, H. M., Jr. (1953). *Microbial Genet. Bull.* 8, 56.

Butzel, H. M., Jr. (1955). *Genetics* 40, 321–330.

Butzel, H. M., Jr., and Pagliara, A. (1962). *Exptl. Cell Res.* 27, 382–395.

Butzel, H. M., Jr., and van Wagtendonk, W. J. (1963). *J. Protozool.* 10, 250–252.

Butzel, H. M., Jr., and Vinciguerra, B. (1957). *Microbial Genet. Bull.* 15, 7–8.

Butzel, H. M., Jr., Brown, L. H., and Martin, W. B., Jr. (1960). *Physiol. Zool.* 33, 213–224.

Cohen, L. W., and Siegel, R. W. (1963). *Genet. Res.* 4, 143–150.

Davern, C. I., and Meselson, M. (1960). *J. Mol. Biol.* 2, 153–160.

Dawson, J. A. (1920). *J. Exptl. Zool.* 30, 129–157.

Dippell, R. V. (1955). *J. Protozool.* 2, Suppl., 7.

Dippell, R. V. (1958). *J. Biophys. Biochem. Cytol.* 4, 125–128.

Dippell, R. V. (1959a). *Anat. Record* 134, 554.

Dippell, R. V. (1959b). *Science* 130, 1415.

Dryl, S. (1959). *J. Protozool.* 6, Suppl., 25.

Dysart, M. P. (1963). *J. Protozool.* 10, Suppl., 8–9.

Ehret, C. F. (1958). *In* "Symposium on Information Theory in Biology" (H. P. Yockey, ed.), pp. 218–229. Pergamon Press, New York.

Ehret, C. F. (1960). *Science* 132, 115–123.

Ehret, C. F., and Powers, E. L. (1959). *Intern. Rev. Cytol.* 8, 97–133.

Elliott, A. M., and Clark, G. M. (1958). *J. Protozool.* 5, 235–246.

Fauré-Fremiet, E. (1953). *Rev. Suisse Zool.* 60, 426–438.

Fauré-Fremiet, E. (1954). *Bull. Soc. Zool. France* 79, 311–329.

Finger, I., and Heller, C. (1962). *Genetics* 47, 223–239.

Finger, I., and Heller, C. (1963). *J. Mol. Biol.* 6, 190–202.

Finger, I., Kaback, M., Kittner, P., and Heller, C. (1960). *J. Biophys. Biochem. Cytol.* 8, 591–601.

Finger, I., Heller, C., and Green, A. (1962). *Genetics* 47, 241–253.

Finger, I., Heller, C., and Smith, J. P. (1963). *J. Mol. Biol.* 6, 182–189.

Gall, J. G. (1959). *J. Biophys. Biochem. Cytol.* 5, 295–308.

Gall, J. G. (1961). *J. Biophys. Biochem. Cytol.* 10, 163–193.

Geckler, R. P. (1950). *Genetics* 35, 253–277.

Geckler, R. P., and Kimball, R. F. (1953). *Science* 117, 80–81.

Gibson, I., and Beale, G. H. (1961). *Genet. Res.* 2, 82–91.

Gibson, I., and Beale, G. H. (1962). *Genet. Res.* 3, 24–46.

Gibson, I., and Beale, G. H. (1963). *Genet. Res.* 4, 42–54.

Grimstone, A. V. (1961). *Biol. Rev. Cambridge Phil. Soc.* 36, 97–150.

Hanson, E. D. (1955). *Proc. Natl. Acad. Sci. U.S.* 41, 783–786.

Hanson, E. D. (1962). *J. Exptl. Zool.* 150, 45–68.

Hanson, E. D., and Twichell, J. B. (1962). *J. Protozool.* 9, Suppl., 11.

Hearon, J. Z., and Kimball, R. F. (1955). *Radiation Res.* 3, 283–294.

Heckmann, K. (1963). *Arch. Protistenk.* 106, 393–421.

Hiwatashi, K. (1958). *Sci. Rept. Tohoku Univ., Fourth Ser.* 24, 119–129.

Hiwatashi, K. (1959). *Sci. Rept. Tohoku Univ., Fourth Ser.* 25, 81–90.

Hiwatashi, K. (1960a). *Bull. Marine Biol. Sta. Asamushi, Tohoku Univ.* 10, 157–159.

Hiwatashi, K. (1960b). *Japan. J. Genet.* 35, 213–221.

Hollaender, A., ed. (1960). "Radiation Protection and Recovery." Pergamon Press, New York.

Hollaender, A., ed. (1961). *J. Cellular Comp. Physiol.* 58, Suppl. 1, 1–248.
Holzman, H. E. (1959). *J. Protozool.* 6, Suppl., 26.
Inoki, S., and Matsushiro, A. (1958). *Med. J. Osaka Univ.* 8, 763–770.
Jacob, F., and Monod, J. (1961). *J. Mol. Biol.* 3, 318–356.
Jones, I. G., and Beale, G. H. (1963). *Nature* 197, 205–206.
Katashima, R. (1959). *J. Protozool.* 6, 75–83.
Kaudewitz, F. (1958). *Arch. Protistenk.* 102, 321–448.
Kimball, R. F. (1949). *Genetics* 34, 412–424.
Kimball, R. F. (1953). *Microbial Genet. Bull.* 8, 10–11.
Kimball, R. F. (1955a). *In* "Radiation Biology" (A. Hollaender, ed.), Vol. II, pp. 285–331. McGraw-Hill, New York.
Kimball, R. F. (1955b). *Ann. N.Y. Acad. Sci.* 59, 638–648.
Kimball, R. F. (1957). *Proc. Intern. Genet. Symp., Tokyo & Kyoto, 1956 (Cytologia)* pp. 252–255.
Kimball, R. F. (1961). *J. Cellular Comp. Physiol.* 58, Suppl. 1, 163–170.
Kimball, R. F. (1962a). *In* "Strahlenwirkung und Milieu" (H. Fritz-Niggli, ed.), pp. 116–125. Urban & Schwarzenberg, Munich.
Kimball, R. F. (1962b). *Proc. Second Ann. Meeting Am. Soc. Cell Biol.* p. 92.
Kimball, R. F. (1963a). *In* "Symposium on Repair from Genetic Radiation Damage and Differential Radiosensitivity in Germ Cells" (F. H. Sobels, ed.), pp. 167–178. Pergamon Press, New York.
Kimball, R. F. (1963b). *Genetics* 48, 581–595.
Kimball, R. F., and Barka, T. (1959). *Exptl. Cell Res.* 17, 173–182.
Kimball, R. F., and Gaither, N. (1951). *J. Cellular Comp. Physiol.* 37, 211–233.
Kimball, R. F., and Gaither, N. (1953). *Proc. Soc. Exptl. Biol. Med.* 82, 471–477.
Kimball, R. F., and Gaither, N. (1954). *Genetics* 39, 977.
Kimball, R. F., and Gaither, N. (1955). *Genetics* 40, 878–889.
Kimball, R. F., and Gaither, N. (1956). *Genetics* 41, 715–728.
Kimball, R. F., and Perdue, S. W. (1962a). *Exptl. Cell Res.* 27, 405–415.
Kimball, R. F., and Perdue, S. W. (1962b). *Genetics* 47, 1595–1607.
Kimball, R. F., and Perdue, S. W. (1964). Unpublished data.
Kimball, R. F., and Prescott, D. M. (1962). *J. Protozool.* 9, 88–92.
Kimball, R. F., and Vogt-Köhne, L. (1961). *Exptl. Cell Res.* 23, 479–487.
Kimball, R. F., and Vogt-Köhne, L. (1962). *Exptl. Cell Res.* 28, 228–238.
Kimball, R. F., Hearon, J. Z., and Gaither, N. (1955). *Radiation Res.* 3, 435–443.
Kimball, R. F., Gaither, N., and Wilson, S. M. (1957). *Genetics* 42, 661–669.
Kimball, R. F., Gaither, N., and Wilson, S. M. (1959a). *Proc. Natl. Acad. Sci. U.S.* 45, 833–839.
Kimball, R. F., Gaither, N., and Wilson, S. M. (1959b). *Radiation Res.* 10, 490–497.
Kimball, R. F., Caspersson, T. O., Svensson, G., and Carlson, L. (1959c). *Exptl. Cell Res.* 17, 160–172.
Kimball, R. F., Vogt-Köhne, L., and Caspersson, T. O. (1960). *Exptl. Cell Res.* 20, 368–377.
Kimball, R. F., Gaither, N., and Perdue, S. W. (1961). *Intern. J. Radiation Biol.* 3, 133–147.
Koizumi, S. (1958). *Sci. Rept. Tohoku Univ., Fourth Ser.* 24, 23–31.
Larison, L. L., and Siegel, R. W. (1961). *J. Gen. Microbiol.* 26, 499–508.
Loefer, J. B., and Owen, R. D. (1961). *J. Protozool.* 8, 387–391.
Loefer, J. B., Owen, R. D., and Christensen, E. (1958). *J. Protozool.* 5, 209–217.
Lwoff, A. (1950). "Problems of Morphogenesis in Ciliates." Wiley, New York.

McDonald, B. B. (1958). *Biol. Bull.* 114, 71–94.
McDonald, B. B. (1962). *J. Cell Biol.* 13, 193–203.
Maly, R. (1958). *Z. Vererbungslehre* 89, 397–421.
Maly, R. (1960a). *Z. Vererbungslehre* 91, 226–236.
Maly, R. (1960b). *Z. Vererbungslehre* 91, 333–337.
Margolin, P. (1956). *Genetics* 41, 685–699.
Margolin, P., Loefer, J. B., and Owen, R. D. (1959). *J. Protozool.* 6, 207–215.
Metz, C. B. (1954). *In* "Sex in Microorganisms," (D. H. Wenrich, ed.), p. 284. Am. Assoc. Advance. Sci., Washington, D.C.
Mitchison, N. A. (1955). *Genetics* 40, 61–75.
Miyake, A. (1956). *J. Inst. Polytech., Osaka City Univ.* D7, 147–161.
Miyake, A. (1957). *J. Inst. Polytech., Osaka City Univ.* D8, 11–19.
Miyake, A. (1958). *J. Inst. Polytech., Osaka City Univ.* D9, 251–296.
Miyake, A. (1959). *Science* 130, 1423.
Miyake, A. (1960). *J. Protozool.* 7, Suppl., 15.
Miyake, A. (1961). *Am. Zoologist* 1, 373–374.
Monod, J., and Jacob, F. (1962). *Cold Spring Harbor Symp. Quant. Biol.* 26, 389–401.
Mott, M. R. (1963). *J. Roy. Microscop. Soc.* 81, 159–162.
Mueller, J. A. (1961). *Am. Zoologist* 1, 375.
Mueller, J. A. (1962). *J. Protozool.* 9, Suppl. 26.
Mueller, J. A., and Sonneborn, T. M. (1959). *Anat. Record* 134, 613.
Nanney, D. L. (1953). *Biol. Bull.* 105, 133–148.
Nanney, D. L. (1954). *In* "Sex in Microorganisms." (D. H. Wenrich, ed.), p. 266. Am. Assoc. Advance. Sci., Washington, D.C.
Nanney, D. L. (1956). *Am. Naturalist* 90, 291–307.
Nanney, D. L. (1957). *J. Protozool.* 4, 89–95.
Nanney, D. L. (1958a). *Cold Spring Harbor Symp. Quant. Biol.* 23, 327–335.
Nanney, D. L. (1958b). *Proc. Natl. Acad. Sci. U.S.* 44, 712–717.
Nanney, D. L. (1959a). *J. Protozool.* 6, 171–177.
Nanney, D. L. (1959b). *Genetics* 44, 1173–1184.
Nanney, D. L. (1960a). *Physiol. Zool.* 33, 146–151.
Nanney, D. L. (1960b). *Genetics* 45, 1351–1358.
Nanney, D. L. (1960c). *Am. Naturalist* 94, 167–180.
Nanney, D. L. (1962). *J. Protozool.* 9, 485–487.
Nanney, D. L. (1963) *J. Protozool.* 10, 152–155.
Nanney, D. L., and Allen, S. L. (1959). *Physiol. Zool.* 32, 221–229.
Nanney, D. L., and Caughey, P. A. (1953). *Proc. Natl. Acad. Sci. U.S.* 39, 1057–1063.
Nanney, D. L., and Caughey, P. A. (1955). *Genetics* 40, 388–398.
Nanney, D. L., and Dubert, J. M. (1960). *Genetics* 45, 1335–1349.
Nanney, D. L., and Nagel, J. (1964). *Develop. Biol.* in press.
Nanney, D. L., and Rudzinska, M. A., (1960). *In* "The Cell" (J. Brachet and A. E. Mirsky, eds.), Vol. 4, p. 109. Academic Press, New York.
Nanney, D. L., Caughey, P. A., and Tefankjian, A. (1955). *Genetics* 40, 668–680.
Nanney, D. L., Reeve, S. J., Nagel, J., and DePinto, S. (1963). *Genetics* 48, 803–813.
Nobili, R. (1959). *J. Protozool.* 6, Suppl., 29.
Nobili, R. (1960). *J. Protozool.* 7, Suppl., 15.
Nobili, R. (1961a). *Caryologia* 14, 43–58.
Nobili, R. (1961b). *Atti Soc. Toscana Sci. Nat. Pisa,* B67, 217–232.
Nobili, R. (1961c). *Atti Assoc. Genetica Italiana* 6, 75–86.

Nobili, R. (1961d). *Atti Soc. Toscana Sci. Nat. Pisa*, **B67**, 158–172.

Nobili, R. (1961e). *Boll. di Zool.* **28**, 579–596.

Nobili, R. (1962a). *Atti Accad. Naz. Lincei, Rend. Classe Sci. Fis., Mat. Natl., Serie VIII* **32**, 392–396.

Nobili, R. (1962b). *Boll. di Zool.* **29**, 555–565.

Orias, E. (1960). *J. Protozool.* **7**, 64–69.

Pigon, A., and Edström, J.-E. (1959). *Exptl. Cell Res.* **16**, 648–656.

Powers, E. L. (1943). *Am. Midland Naturalist* **30**, 175–195.

Powers, E. L. (1956). *In* "A Conference on Radioactive Isotopes in Agriculture," Atomic Energy Comm. Rept. No. TID-7512, pp. 17–29. U.S. Govt. Printing Office, Washington, D.C.

Preer, J. R. (1957a). *Ann. Rev. Microbiol.* **11**, 419–438.

Preer, J. R. (1957b). *J. Genet.* **55**, 375–378.

Preer, J. R. (1959a). *In* "Developmental Cytology." D. Rudnick, ed.), p. 3. Ronald Press, New York.

Preer, J. R. (1959b). *J. Immunol.* **83**, 276–283.

Preer, J. R. (1959c). *J. Immunol.* **83**, 378–384.

Preer, J. R. (1959d). *J. Immunol.* **83**, 385–391.

Preer, J. R. (1959e). *Genetics* **44**, 803–814.

Preer, J. R., and Preer, L. B. (1959). *J. Protozool.* **6**, 88–100.

Prescott, D. M. (1960). *Exptl. Cell Res.* **19**, 228–238.

Prescott, D. M. (1961a). *Intern. Rev. Cytol.* **11**, 255–282.

Prescott, D. M. (1961b). *In* "Biological Structure and Function," IUB/IUBS Intern. Symp., Stockholm, 1960 (T. W. Goodwin and O. Lindberg, eds.), Vol. 2, p. 527. Academic Press, New York.

Prescott, D. M. (1962). *J. Histochem. Cytochem.* **10**, 145–153.

Prescott, D. M., and Kimball, R. F. (1961). *Proc. Natl. Acad. Sci. U.S.* **47**, 686–693.

Prescott, D. M., Kimball, R. F., and Carrier, R. F. (1962). *J. Cell Biol.* **13**, 175–176.

Rampton, V. W. (1963). *Nature* **195**, 195.

Randall, J. T., and Fitton-Jackson, S. F. (1958). *J. Biophys. Biochem. Cytol.* **4**, 807–830.

Reeve, E. C. R. (1962). *Genet. Res.* **3**, 47–50.

Reeve, E. C. R., and Ross. G. J. S. (1962). *Genet. Res.* **3**, 328–330.

Reeve, E. C. R., and Ross, G. J. S. (1963). *Genet. Res.* **4**, 158–161.

Richards, O. W. (1941). *In* "Protozoa in Biological Research" (G. N. Calkins and F. M. Summers, eds.), pp. 517–564. Columbia Univ. Press, New York.

Rupert, C. S., Goodgal, S. H., and Herriot, R. M. (1958). *J. Gen. Physiol.* **41**, 451–471.

Schensted, I. V. (1958). *Am. Naturalist* **92**, 161–170.

Scherbaum, O. H., Louderback, A. L., and Jahn, T. L. (1958). *Biol. Bull.* **115**, 269–275.

Scherbaum, O. H., Louderback, A. L., and Jahn, T. L. (1959). *Exptl. Cell Res.* **18**, 150–166.

Schneller, M. V. (1959). *J. Protozool.* **6**, Suppl., 31.

Schneller, M. V. (1961). *Am. Zoologist* **1**, 386–387.

Schneller, M. V. (1962). *Am. Zoologist* **2**, 446.

Schneller, M. V., Sonneborn, T. M., and Mueller, J. A. (1959). *Genetics* **44**, 533–534.

Scott, J. F., Taft, E. B., and LeTourneau, N. W. (1962). *Biochim. Biophys. Acta* **61**, 62–71.

Seaman, G. R. (1960). *Exptl. Cell Res.* **21**, 292–302.

Seaman, G. R. (1962). *Biochim. Biophys. Acta* 55, 889–899.

Setlow, J. K., and Setlow, R. B. (1963). *Nature* 197, 560–562.

Siegel, R. W. (1957). *Genetics* 42, 394–395.

Siegel, R. W. (1960). *Exptl. Cell Res.* 19, 239–252.

Siegel, R. W. (1961). *Exptl. Cell Res.* 24, 6–20.

Siegel, R. W. (1963). *Genet. Res.* 4, 132–142.

Siegel, R. W., and Cohen, L. W. (1963). *Am. Zoologist* 3, 127–134.

Siegel, R. W., and Larison, L. L. (1960). *Proc. Natl. Acad. Sci. U.S.* 46, 344–349.

Skaar, P. D. (1955). *Exptl. Cell Res.* 10, 646–656.

Smith, J. E. (1961). *Am. Zoologist* 1, 390.

Sobels, F. H., ed. (1963). "Symposium on Repair from Genetic Radiation Damage and Differential Radiosensitivity in Germ Cells." Pergamon Press, New York.

Sonneborn, T. M. (1947). *Advan. Genet.* 1, 263–358.

Sonneborn, T. M. (1950). *J. Heredity* 41, 222–224.

Sonneborn, T. M. (1954a). *Microbial Genet. Bull.* 11, 24–25.

Sonneborn, T. M. (1954b). *Microbial Genet. Bull.* 11, 25–26.

Sonneborn, T. M. (1954c). *J. Protozool.* 1, 38–53.

Sonneborn, T. M. (1954d). *Caryologia* 6, Suppl., 307–325.

Sonneborn, T. M. (1957). In "The Species Problem" (E. Mayr, ed.), p. 155. Am. Assoc. Advance. Sci., Washington, D.C.

Sonneborn, T. M. (1959). *Advan. Virus Res.* 6, 229–356.

Sonneborn, T. M. (1960). *Proc. Natl. Acad. Sci. U.S.* 46, 149–165.

Sonneborn, T. M. (1961). In "Perspectives in Virology" (M. Pollard, ed.), Vol. II, p. 5. Burgess, Minneapolis, Minnesota.

Sonneborn, T. M. (1963). In "The Nature of Biological Diversity" (J. M. Allen, ed.), p. 165. McGraw-Hill, New York.

Sonneborn, T. M. (1964). *Proc. 16th Intern. Congr. Zool., Washington, D.C., 1963* in press.

Sonneborn, T. M., and Barnett, A. (1958). *J. Protozool.* 5, 18.

Sonneborn, T. M., and Dippell, R. V. (1960a). *J. Protozool.* 7, Suppl., 26.

Sonneborn, T. M., and Dippell, R. V. (1960b). In "The Biology of Aging," Am. Inst. Biol. Sci. Symp. No. 6 (B. L. Strehler, ed.), p. 285. Am. Assoc. Advance. Sci., Washington, D.C.

Sonneborn, T. M., and Dippell, R. V. (1961a). *Am. Zoologist* 1, 390.

Sonneborn, T. M., and Dippell, R. V. (1961b). *Genetics* 46, 899–900.

Sonneborn, T. M., and Dippell, R. V. (1961c). *Genetics* 46, 900.

Sonneborn, T. M., and Dippell, R. V. (1962). *J. Protozool.* 9, Suppl., 28.

Sonneborn, T. M., and Mueller, J. A. (1959). *Science* 130, 1423.

Sonneborn, T. M., and Schneller, M. V. (1955a). *Genetics* 40, 596.

Sonneborn, T. M., and Schneller, M. V. (1955b). *J. Protozool.* 2, Suppl., 6–7.

Sonneborn, T. M., and Schneller, M. V. (1955c). *J. Protozool.* 2, Suppl., 6.

Sonneborn, T. M., and Schneller, M. V. (1960a). In "The Biology of Aging," Am. Inst. Biol. Sci. Symp. No. 6 (B. L. Strehler, ed.), pp. 283–284. Am. Assoc. Advance. Sci., Washington, D.C.

Sonneborn, T. M., and Schneller, M. V. (1960b). In "The Biology of Aging," Am. Inst. Biol. Sci. Symp. No. 6 (B. L. Strehler, ed.), pp. 286–287. Am. Assoc. Advance. Sci., Washington, D.C.

Sonneborn, T. M., and Sonneborn, D. R. (1958). *Anat. Record* 131, 601.

Sonneborn, T. M., Dippell, R. V., Schneller, M. V., and Tallan, I. (1953). *Microbial Genet. Bull.* 7, 25–26.

Sonneborn, T. M., Schneller, M. V., and Craig, M. F. (1956). *J. Protozool.* 3, Suppl., 8.

Sonneborn, T. M., Mueller, J. A., and Schneller, M. V. (1959). *Anat. Record* 134, 642.

Sonneborn, T. M., Dippell, R. V., and Schneller, M. V. (1960). *In* "The Biology of Aging," Am. Inst. Biol. Sci. Symp. No. 6 (B. L. Strehler, ed.), pp. 279–291. Am. Assoc. Advance. Sci., Washington, D.C.

Steers, E. (1961). *Science* 133, 2010–2011.

Steers, E. (1962). *Proc. Natl. Acid. Sci. U.S.* 48, 867–874.

Tallan, I. (1959). *Physiol. Zool.* 32, 78–89.

Tallan, I. (1961). *Physiol. Zool.* 34, 1–13.

Tartar, V. (1961). "The Biology of Stentor." Pergamon Press, New York.

Taub, S. R. (1963). *Genetics* 48, 815–834.

Uhlig, G. (1960). *Arch. Protistenk.* 105, 1–109.

van Tubergen, R. P., and Setlow, R. B. (1961). *Biophys. J.* 1, 589–625.

van Wagtendonk, W. J., van Tijn, B., Litman, R., Reisner, A., and Young, M. L. (1956). *J. Gen. Microbiol.* 15, 617–619.

Walker, P. M. B., and Mitchison, J. M. (1957). *Exptl. Cell Res.* 13, 167–170.

Wells, C. (1961). *J. Protozool.* 8, 284–290.

Widmayer, D. (1961). *Am. Zoologist* 1, 398.

Williams, D. B. (1962). *J. Protozool.* 9, 119–122.

Williams, N. E. (1961). *J. Protozool.* 8, 403–410.

Woodard, J., Gelber, B., and Swift, H. (1961). *Exptl. Cell Res.* 23, 258–264.

Wulff, D. L., and Rupert, C. S. (1962). *Biochem. Biophys. Res. Commun.* 7, 237–240.

Zeuthen, E. (1953). *J. Embryol. Exptl. Morphol.* 1, 239–249.

Phototaxis in Protozoa

PER HALLDAL

Department of Plant Physiology, University of Gothenburg, Gothenburg, Sweden

		Page
I.	Introduction	277
II.	Phototaxis in Flagellates	279
	A. The Photoreceptor	279
	B. Phototactic Activity and Alternation between Positive and Negative Response	281
	C. Action Spectra of Phototaxis	285
III.	Phototaxis in *Amoeba*	291
IV.	Phototaxis in Ciliates	292
V.	Phototaxis in Ecology	293
	References	295

I. Introduction

Free-living motile organisms may in their movement be directed by external stimuli such as light, chemical substances, temperature, etc. As a result an organism may actively seek out environments favorable for growth and reproduction. Phototaxis is such movements induced by light stimulus.

Since the early part of the 19th century a great many observations have been gathered on phototaxis in protozoa, in the beginning naturally mostly along descriptive lines both from laboratory experiment and population analyses in natural habits. As far back as 1865 Cohn was able to conclude that blue and green light was effective in phototaxis of some zoospores, and even with refined measurements not too much besides this knowledge has been gained in later years concerning the pigments involved in phototaxis. The question of the light absorbers has for many years been a matter of uncertainty and dispute, and still is, though recent measurements of action spectra of phototaxis in a green alga performed in near and far ultraviolet region strongly indicate that a carotenoprotein is involved (Halldal, 1961a).

Much attention has been paid to the alternation between positive and negative phototaxis and how the movement is directed. The changes from positive to negative response and vice versa have proved to be controlled by a series of factors, both internal and external, such as the age of the culture, intensity and quality of light, and the cation concentration and balance. Interactions with all these variables naturally give a very complicated picture, which becomes even more complicated when attempts are made to include in the explanation the many data from earlier observations.

When we include the photic reaction in the purple bacteria two distinct reaction types occur in phototaxis. The purple bacteria react phototactically by a reversal in the movement when passing a light-dark boundary or when exposed to sudden drops in radiant intensity. This type of reaction is called phobo-phototaxis, and the action spectrum determination gives the same curve as the action spectrum of photosynthesis (Manten, 1948; Thomas and Nijenhuis, 1950). This shows that general metabolism is involved. The purple bacteria, however, cannot respond to ray direction in the manner protozoa can. In the flagellates and ciliates an active orientation and movement toward or away from the light source can be observed. This is called topo-phototaxis and is denoted as positive when the organism is attracted by the light and negative when it is repelled. In the flagellates this orientation occurs independent of light intensity (Buder, 1919; Halldal, 1959; Sachs and Mayer, 1961), as illustrated in Fig. 1. How this direction mechanism works is not

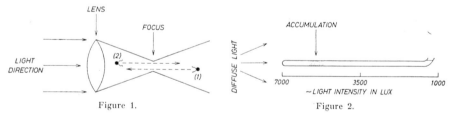

Figure 1.   Figure 2.

FIG. 1. The behavior of a positively phototactic organism (1), and a negatively phototactic organism (2) in a focused beam. Light intensity in focus ∼ 200,000 lux. (After Halldal, 1959.)

FIG. 2. The accumulation of phototactic organisms in long-time experiments in properly balanced medium, e.g., sea water. (After Halldal, 1959.)

known. Several possibilities have been proposed, one of them being that the topo-phototactic reaction is composed of a series of single-shock reactions, which step by step adjust the organism according to the light path through intermittent shading of a photoreceptor. A clear topo-phototactic response is easily demonstrated in most of the light-sensitive protozoans, and a distinct shock reaction has been observed in the extensively investigated *Euglena* (Engelmann, 1882; Bünning and Tazawa, 1957) when these are exposed to sudden changes in intensity. This shock reaction could, however, quite possibly be the part reaction which results in topic orientation, and it has never been demonstrated convincingly that these two responses are distinct. The considerations above apply to short-time experiments where thus both topic orientation and shock response are observed. Over longer periods, from minutes up to some hours, it can be shown that the flagellates may gather at a certain light intensity (Fig. 2), which evidently is preferred to higher or lower ones. This clustering seems to be determined through general metabolism and could in this respect be consistent with the phobic reaction in the purple bacteria. The action spectrum determination of the reaction (induced phototactic response changes) indicate that photosynthesis is involved. A separate study of the topic and phobic response in phototaxis is not easy, and the author's statement in this respect will admittedly be somewhat speculative. Nevertheless the data available seem to point to the following conclusion:

Topo-phototaxis consists of a series of isolated shock reactions which step by step orient the flagellates in the light path. As observed under sudden changes of light intensity it resembles the phobic response in purple bacteria, although it is basically of another nature. Phobo-phototaxis is directed through general metabolism and is the reaction which directs the organisms according to light intensity. In this manner it is basically analogous to the phobic response of the purple bacteria. This phobic gathering is achieved through an induced positive or negative topo-phototaxis.

The phototactic behavior of ameba and ciliates has been scarcely analyzed. Photic orientation, particularly within the ciliates, is difficult to analyze. A statement as to which type of reactions are involved in their responses for light cannot be given. The response may be of quite another nature than among the flagellates with a distinct photoreceptor or in the purple bacteria, where general metabolism is decisive.

II. Phototaxis in Flagellates

A. The Photoreceptor

Most of the flagellates that respond phototactically to light possess a brightly colored, usually red or yellow, stigma or eyespot situated at diverse places within the cell. It is obvious that this spectacular item has attracted attention when explanations of the mechanism of phototaxis are attempted. This was especially the case when it was shown that blue light was effective in phototaxis, which indicated a yellow-red light absorber. The variability in the morphological structure of stigmas has been analyzed by a number of investigators, in recent years by the use of electron microscopy. The literature about this has been carefully reviewed by Haupt (1959) and Bendix (1960). It is evident that the simple optical laws for deflection, scattering, and reflection, cannot be applied to objects with the same order of magnitude as that of the wavelength of light. Some of the theories for the function of different types of stigmas do not hold true for this reason (Luntz, 1931; Halldal, 1958), and phototaxis can readily be demonstrated in forms lacking this organ: in colorless forms (Strasburger, 1878; Luntz, 1931; Gössel, 1957); in dinoflagellates (Metzner, 1929; Nordli, 1957; Halldal, 1958); and in coccolithophorids (Mjaaland, 1956). The stigma has most certainly in some cases a function in phototaxis, but it is definitely less elaborate than formerly assumed. In searching for an explanation of photic orientation, one is inclined to look for a basic principle which will interpret phototaxis in all forms and also those without a stigma.

When Engelmann in 1882 studied the behavior in *Euglena* when a shadow was allowed to pass over the cell, he discovered that a distinct response occurred when the light-dark border reached the apical colorless fraction of the cell, before the stigma was darkened. The possibility of doing such detailed analyses with the equipment available at that time has been questioned by Luntz (1931). However, from this observation and from later analyses it is now generally assumed that the photoreceptor in *Euglena* is the thickening of the flagellar base, and Gössel (1957) showed that *Euglena gracilis,* lacking this organelle, did not respond to light. From the experiments on *Euglena* (Engelmann, 1882; Gössel, 1957; Vávra 1956) and further from the observations of Metzner (1929) on the behavior of *Ceratium cornutum* exposed to light from different directions, it is assumed that the photoreceptor is situated close to the flagellar base. This tiny photosensitive spot is then assumed to contain pigment involved in topo-phototaxis. In *Euglena,* where this item can be observed, it is "colorless" i.e., the pigment must be present in an exceedingly small amount. Light absorbed by this pigment triggers a biochemical system which will give the necessary signal for an altered flagellar beating. As this tiny body does not possess any structure which reasonably has the ability to focus the light, as for instance in an eye, and in this way detect light direction, another principle must be applied. The experimental data available indicate that this principle is based upon sudden increases or drops in radiant intensity. In a spherical organism the source of light can be located as the body itself casts a shadow that can be identified by dermal sensitivity (Milne and Milne, 1956). Under continuous irradiation it would therefore be required that the flagellate has an item within the cell which can act as a light switch. A pigmented mass within the cell would in some positions cast a shadow upon the photoreceptor. This would change the light intensity falling upon it and give the necessary signal for a change in flagellar beating.

In *Euglena,* where this mechanism has been studied in some detail, Mast

(1911) showed that in crawling *Euglena* no response occurred as long as the ventral surface faced the light. As the cell turned and the pigmented stigma cast a shadow upon the flagellar enlargement, a response to the decreased light occurred, resulting in a bending more toward the ventral surface, and strangely enough, away from the light in positively reacting cells. Also in positively reacting swimming *Euglena,* Jennings (1906) reported that a response occurred when a shadow from the stigma shielded the thickening of the flagellar base, resulting in a turn toward the dorsal side. Further details about this mechanism are unknown. This principle has been extended somewhat, and accordingly any object which effectively screens the light in the spectral region, where the photoreceptive pigment involved in topo-phototaxis absorbs, will do the job. Its efficiency would be determined by its absorption characteristics, its size, and position in relation to the photoreceptor (Halldal, 1958, 1961b). The stigma in normal *Euglena* is most suited in this respect, both by its content of carotenoids, which will effectively screen the presumed other carotenoid involved in topo-phototaxis (Halldal, 1961b), and by its position near the photoreceptor in the anterior colorless portion of the cell. However, the stigma is evidently not sufficient for an effective phototactic response in the visible region due to its small size. The experiments of Bünning and Schneiderhöhn (1956) and Gössel (1957) strongly indicate that the chloroplasts also function as light switches, as the normal form with chloroplasts responded much more efficiently in the visible region than the bleached form with stigma. This subject is discussed further in Section II,C (Action Spectra of Phototaxis).

B. Phototactic Activity and Alternation between Positive and Negative Response

When a population of flagellates is studied over a longer period of time, great changes in light sensitivity may be observed. Sometimes gathering can be observed near the light source, sometimes farthest away from it, and a population of the same species may also be divided into different sections, one with a positive response, another with a negative, and others again clustered at distinct spots. In a mixed population different species may be phototactically separated as was noted as early as in 1863 by Cohn. Several factors are for certain decisive in this respect, and many have been reported to influence the reaction.

1. Necessary Ions and Ion Balance

The source of the driving power in flagellar movement, in flagellates, sperm, and ciliates, is adenosinetriphosphate (ATP) as has been demonstrated by Hoffmann-Berling (1954), Links (1955), and others. In muscle work the actomyosin system contracts in the presence of Mg^{++} with actomyosin as the ATPase. This reaction is dependent upon K^+, and the Mg^{++} activation may be antagonized by Ca^{++} (see Weber, 1958). Something similar to this would be expected to occur in the flagella, where positive ATPase has been demonstrated in flagella from *Polytoma* and sperms (Jibbs, 1958; Brokaw, 1960). The flagella consist of about 60 to 65% of proteins (Jones and Lewin, 1960). It has, however, been shown that the structural proteins responsible for movements of cilia and flagella are distinctly different from myosin or actomyosin-like proteins (Finch and Holtzer, 1961).

For the salt-water alga *Platymonas subcordiformis* it was shown that the motility was entirely dependent upon the presence of K^+ plus one of the divalent cations Mg^{++} and Ca^{++}, and further that within the physiological range all combinations of K^+ and Mg^{++} caused positive phototaxis, while a negative response resulted from a K^+-Ca^{++} combination when the relative content of K^+ was low. This negative response distinctly changed to positive at relatively higher K^+ concentration (Halldal, 1959). An effect similar to this was also observed by Heilbrunn and Daugherty (1932) in their analyses on the shifting of crystals within the cortex (plasmagel) in *Amoeba proteus* after centrifugation. Calcium ions retarded the movement of crystals, while both Mg and K ions caused an increase in the speed of centrifugation. Sodium ions had little effect. Antagonism is thus caused by the same combination of cations as for phototaxis in *Platymonas*. Thus, in *Platymonas* motility and the same mode of response along with other variables (see below) are determined by these three cations. These experiments with K^+, Ca^{++}, and Mg^{++} are indirect evidences of a participation of ATPase in phototaxis, and further it implies that the ATP of the motor apparatus in some way is tied up with a photochemical reaction where a carotenoprotein is the light absorber. No attempt has been made to evolve theories about the way these factors interact.

2. GASES IN THE ENVIRONMENT

The experiments that have been performed on the effect of the partial and total O_2 and CO_2 pressures in the medium have given divergent results. It is doubtful whether the variations that occur in natural habits influence the response or activity directly to any noticeable extent. Blum and Fox (1932) did not record any changes in the phototactic activity in the absence of air for *Dunaliella salina*, and Halldal (1959) confirmed this for *Platymonas subcordiformis*, where it was also shown that the mode of response in a balanced medium did not change during variations in O_2 and CO_2 pressures. An effect of CO_2 on the phototactic activity of zoospores has quite recently been reported by Brucker (1954), but this may be indirect, through changes in pH as pointed out by Haupt (1959). Sachs and Mayer (1961) showed that the motility in *Chlamydomonas snowiae* was reversibly stopped when a stream of CO_2 was bubbled through a culture of *Chlamydomonas*. Nothing is stated about the pH changes that occurred during the experiment, and as pH around

5 is critical for *Chlamydomonas* (Tsubo, 1960), this might be of importance in this connection.

3. pH

Before any conclusion can be drawn from the effect of pH on motility and phototactic activity or from the mode of response, it is necessary to make a complete pH-curve determination for all these variables. Scattered analyses of pH effects and CO_2 experiments, where the pH has not been controlled, give information of little value. Lately the pH activity curve for both positive and negative phototaxis in *Platymonas* have been measured (Halldal, 1959). The flagellate moved between pH 5.2 and 9.5, with not motion outside these limits. The optimum was between pH 6 and 8.5 where the activity was nearly constant. These results are in agreement with motility analyses in *Chlamydomonas* (Tsubo, 1960). At no pH was a change from positive to negative phototaxis observed (Halldal, 1959) in populations which were fairly well balanced. It remains to do pH analyses exactly at the random motion stage for phototaxis.

4. LIGHT

The most obvious factor to investigate in phototaxis is naturally light, and both light intensity and quality have for a number of years been subject to analyses. It has been stated that light is not needed for motion. The cells will move in the dark, photosynthetic organisms utilizing energy stored during photosynthesis. No clear picture is given as to the influence of light on the mode of reaction and on its sensitivity to light. Reviews of the older literature (Haupt, 1959; Bendix, 1960) give a rather confused picture. Buder (1919) demonstrated that topo-phototaxis was independent of light intensity. His experiments have in somewhat modified forms been repeated and confirmed by Halldal (1959) and Sachs and Mayer (1961) with several green flagellates and dinoflagellates. Halldal (1959) needed to distinguish between short-time and long-time experiments. In short-time experiments, i.e., from seconds up to a few minutes, the light intensity would not influence the mode of response (see Fig. 1). This demonstrates that the intensity of the light primarily is not acting on a process which is decisive for positive or negative response. Were this the case, the flagellates would at a certain intensity abruptly change from positive to negative response or vice versa. The mode of response is evidently determined by other factors such as cation balance and general metabolism. Therefore, in photosynthetic flagellates both light intensity and quality would be expected to influence phototaxis indirectly through the photosynthetic apparatus. Such indirect effect is illustrated in Fig. 2, where a distinct gathering occurred at a certain intensity after some time in a balanced medium.

Also the quality of light has proved to influence the mode of response in phototaxis. In colonial forms of Volvocales, Mast (1917) reported that the effective wavelengths were restricted to the blue region of the spectrum, while Terry (1909) for *Volvox* induced galvanotactic reponse changes with red light. As galvanotaxis and phototaxis correlate (Mast, 1927), some inconsistencies seem to occur in the observations of Mast and Terry. The many other factors which are involved in phototaxis, in this case especially the intensity and dose, may be the reason for this, and a combination of these results were observed for *Platymonas* where blue and red light induces positive phototaxis in a negatively reacting population, and yellow light caused negative phototaxis; 2,100 μW./cm.^{2} for 5 min. completely changed a negative population into positive and vice versa (Halldal, 1960).

Some experiments performed on photokinesis indicate that the light has some effect increasing both the amplitude and the frequency of flagellar motion, while other experiments denied this (see Haupt, 1959, p. 348). As flagellar beating is driven by an ATP motor, any factor reducing the ATP content under a certain level must be reflected by a reduction in motility. Thus, after starving photosynthetic flagellates by darkness, a subsequent illumination resumes general metabolism and ATP formation, resulting in increasing flagellar beating. Since all the experiments on photokinesis have been performed on photosynthetic forms, this indirect effect must not be overlooked. The action spectrum determination on photokinesis in *Euglena* performed by Wolken and Shin (1958), which resolved distinct peaks in blue and red, is undoubtedly reflecting the photosynthetic apparatus.

5. ANALYSES WITH METABOLIC INHIBITORS

On the assumption that ATP is the driving power in flagellar movement, the effect of metabolic inhibitors on phototaxis has been studied (Mayer and Poljakoff-Mayber, 1959; Halldal, 1959; Sachs and Mayer, 1961). Sachs and Mayer could not show a direct relation between taxis and respiration, as the addition of ATP or a CO_2 stream stopped motility immediately. Table I gives some of their results with inhibitors on phototaxis.

The table shows that the selective inhibitor on photosynthesis chlorophenyldimethylurea (CMU) did not affect phototaxis, and it was concluded that photosynthesis was not directly affecting phototactic activity in *Chlamydomonas*. A distinct effect was observed when 2,4-dinitrophenol (DNP) was added to a population of negatively reacting *Platymonas* (Halldal, 1959). The mode of response immediately changed from negative to positive at 10^{-3}M and after 3 hr., positive phototaxis was observed above 5×10^{-4}M, negative at lower. This distinct effect with DNP initiated a series of tests with different metabolic inhibitors. It was hoped that some clue about the mechanism which directs the mode of response would be obtained by studying cells which by cation ratio were carefully balanced at the random stage. When such cells were exposed to the commonly employed metabolic inhibitors in studies on respiration, oxi-

Table I

THE EFFECT OF METABOLIC INHIBITORS ON *Chlamydomonas* PHOTOTAXIS[a]

Inhibitor	M concentration effective after		
	60 min.	24 hrs.	1 week
NaF	5×10^{-2}	5×10^{-2}	10^{-2}
DNP (2,4-dinitrophenol)	7×10^{-4}	5×10^{-4}	3×10^{-4}
NaCN	10^{-2}	5×10^{-3}	5×10^{-3}
NaAsO₂	10^{-2}	5×10^{-3}	5×10^{-3}
CH₂ICOOH	5×10^{-3}	10^{-3}	10^{-3}
o-Phenanthroline	3×10^{-4}	10^{-4}	5×10^{-4}
Coumarin	10^{-3}	5×10^{-4}	—
Chlorophenyldimethylurea (CMU)	—	—	2.5×10^{-5}

[a] After Sachs and Mayer, 1961.

dative- and photophosphorylation, and ATPases, the mode of phototactic response was retained with all inhibitors, at all concentrations, except DNP. Phototaxis decreased and ceased at higher concentration of the inhibitors only through a decrease in motility (Halldal, 1960 unpublished results). So far the effect of DNP in changing phototaxis is unique. No attempt has been made to determine where in the metabolic pathway DNP acts in this way or whether DNP, which may cause leaky membranes (Robertson *et al.*, 1951), alters available K, Mg, and Ca ions in the motor system.

6. CYCLES IN PHOTOTAXIS

Endogenous rhythm in the phototactic behavior has been recorded for *Euglena*. Pohl (1948) demonstrated a persistent diurnal rhythm with maximum phototactic activity in the middle of the day and minimum at night. This continued, with approximately a 24-hr. period in the absence of light-dark cycles or temperature changes. A single light shock definitely altered the phase of the rhythm (Bruce and Pittendrigh, 1956, 1958).

C. ACTION SPECTRA OF PHOTOTAXIS

Action-spectra measurements of photobiological reactions may give information about the absorption characteristics of the chromophore involved in the process. When doing action-spectra determinations with topo-phototactic flagellates, one must keep in mind that the analyses imply more than the recording of a simple photochemical reaction, using light orientation as index. The radiant energy absorbed by the chromophore certainly acts on a photochemical system, and the effectiveness of different wavelengths would at least partly reflect some of the absorption characteristics of the light absorber. Besides, phototactic flagellates can detect the direction of rays. This implies that the principle for this orientation, and the morphology of the organism, must be taken into consideration. In action spectra analyses of photobiological processes, it is often necessary to adjust the data obtained for the effect of screening noneffective pigments. However, considering phototaxis in flagellates screening bodies is a required part of the light orientation apparatus. Serious distortions may therefore occur in the action spectra derived from analyses on colorless of faintly colored forms. The colored organelles, as stated (Section II,A), act like built-in light switches and are needed in order to produce the necessary signal for light orientation.

Action-spectra determinations of phototaxis have been performed on several different types of flagellates—colorless heterotrophic forms and photosynthetic algae. In these measurements also different methods have been applied. The following two types of photoreactions are dealt with in phototaxis: (1) The *topic* response where the flagellates are oriented in the light path. The *shock* reaction which has been reported for some organisms when exposed to sudden changes in light intensity is assumed to contribute to this orientation (Section II,A). The action-spectra measurements of this topo-phototactic response have given divergent results. The different curves published may, however, still represent the same pigment (Halldal, 1961b). (2) Phobo-phototaxis which directs the flagellates to a distinct light intensity, involves general metabolism, and induces positive or negative topo-phototaxis.

1. TOPO-PHOTOTAXIS

Mast (1917) measured the spectral sensitivity of several colored forms when exposed to two beams of light at an angle to each other, one "white" reference beam and the other with rather broad spectral bands isolated by filters. His measurements meet all the requirements for such analyses, concerning both the organisms and the experimental set-up. The spectral purity was, however, insufficient and the readings rather scattered. All the curves from these experiments have peaks in the blue and green part of the spectrum, implying a yellow pigment as the light absorber. Similar action spectra were also reported by Luntz (1931) for some green flagellates. The action spectra of negative and positive *Euglena viridis* are essentially identical. Bünning and Schneiderhöhn (1956) performed analyses on *Euglena gracilis* with chloroplasts and stigma (Fig. 3). In their experiments only the measurements performed on the positively reacting flagellates meet the requirements of topo-phototaxis according to Halldal's view (Halldal, 1958, 1961b). In the readings taken on the negatively responding population, induced phototaxis may be involved too. This will shift the action spectrum peak in the blue region toward the blue chlorophyll absorption peak around 435 mμ. The curve is, however, rather similar to those reported by Gössel (1957) for bleached and colorless *Euglena*. Bünning and

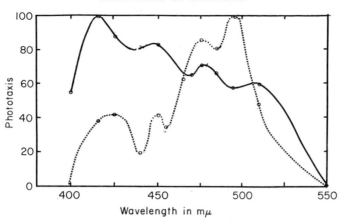

FIG. 3. Action spectrum of positive phototaxis (------), and negative phototaxis (———) in *Euglena gracilis*. (After Bünning and Schneiderhöhn 1956.)

Tazawa (1957) and Haupt (1959) conclude that the negative response in *Euglena* represents the phobic response. An experiment which clearly shows a distinction between topo-phototaxis and the sudden shock reaction ("phobophototaxis") has not been performed, however.

The positively reacting form shows a maximum at 495 mμ, which corresponds closely to that observed by Mast (1917) for both positive and negative *Euglena viridis*.

The action spectra determinations by Gössel (1957) for colorless and chlorophyll-free *Euglena gracilis* give valuable information about the mechanism of

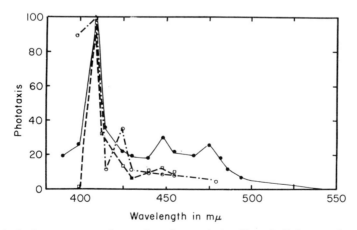

FIG. 4. Action spectrum of negative phototaxis in chlorophyll-free *Euglena gracilis* (———); in a colorless form with positive response (–•–•–•–); and in a colorless form with negative response (------). (After Gössel, 1957.)

photic orientation in flagellates. It is, however, questionable whether the results reflect absorption characteristics of any pigment involved in the reaction (Fig. 4). These results do support the assumption that light orientation in flagellates is based upon a principle including shading bodies within the cells acting as built-in light switches (see Section II,A). In colorless forms only ultraviolet radiation is absorbed, but selective scattering results in a screening of short-wave visible light. A peak was observed around 400 mμ, and as expected no noticeable effect at longer wavelengths. The same argument explains the peak at 405 mμ for the chlorophyll-free form with stigma. In this curve, however, the absorption characteristics of the stigma are also reflected (see Strother and Wolken, 1961), with the two maxima at 445 and 475 mμ.

Halldal (1958) measured the action spectra of topo-phototaxis in a number of flagellates (Volvocales, *Ulva* gametes, Dinophyceae). In one of the employed methods, where a projected spectrum with an intensity gradient was used, several complications could theoretically arise. The results obtained by this method were therefore checked by a point-by-point method using a monochromator, where these complications could be controlled. Measurements were performed on both positively and negatively reacting forms. No difference in peak position or shape could be observed in negative or positive forms of flagellates within the same species. Some differences occurred from species to species. Most peaks were observed between 475 and 500 mμ. A distinct difference was recorded for the dinoflagellate *Prorocentrum micans* which had action spectrum maximum at 570 mμ.

The action-spectra determinations performed in the visible region do not provide the necessary details to allow a definite conclusion about the chromophore involved in topo-phototaxis. A reasonable guess is that a carotenoid is involved, but the absorption characteristics of carotenoids within the narrow spectral region between 400 and 500 mμ have too much in common with other blue-absorbing pigments (flavins, pterins) to make a distinction based upon action-spectra measurements possible. Therefore action-spectra measurements were extended to the ultraviolet region for *Platymonas subcordiformis*. Measurements were performed on both positively and negatively reacting cells (Halldal, 1961a; Fig. 5). Between 300 and 570 mμ the absorption characteristics of a carotenoid are reflected with peaks at 335, 405, an inflection at 450, and a maximum at 495 mμ. Between 220 and 300 mμ the typical absorption characteristics of a protein are shown, where the peak around 275 mμ stands for aromatic amino acids.

In their analyses of the carotenoids of *Euglena gracilis*, Krinsky and Goldsmith (1960) reported that 3 keto-carotenoids, echinenone, euglenanone, and hydroxy-echinenone were present in trace amounts. Hydroxy-echinenone should be capable of binding to protein, with accompanying shifts of absorption spectrum to longer wavelengths. It is therefore theoretically possible that the photoreceptive chromophore of topo-phototaxis in *Euglena* (also the colorless forms), Volvocales, *Ulva* gametes, and the dinoflagellates is the same carotenoid and, possibly, hydroxy-echinenone. Goodwin (1959) also assumed that the difference in absorption maxima of nearly 100 mμ observed for the dinoflagellates *Goniaulax* and *Prorocentrum* is not significant, as the pigment *in vivo* could exist as different carotenoproteins.

Goodwin and Gross (1958) analyzed the carotenoid content of some natural and artificial mutants of *Euglena gracilis* and recorded qualitative differences in the composition. These variations are probably restricted to the chloroplasts. The possibility does exist that similar qualitative differences occur in the pigments involved in phototaxis. It is unlikely, however, that the maximum observed at around 400 to 420 mμ in action spectra measurements of colorless and negatively reacting *Euglena gracilis* could be explained in this way.

A sensitivity difference was observed between positive and negative phototaxis in the measurements on *Platymonas* in visible and ultraviolet region, where the positively reacting cells had a threshold value of about one-third of the negatively reacting cells (Fig. 5). This may not necessarily reflect a sensitivity

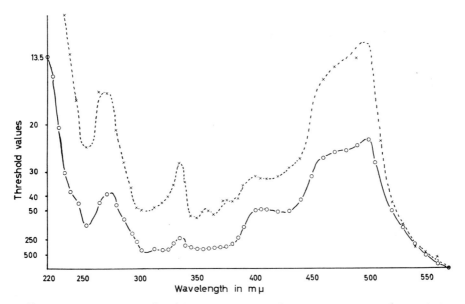

FIG. 5. Action spectra of positive (------), and negative (————) phototaxis in *Platymonas subcordiformis*. Ordinate: quanta/cm.^{2} sec. $\times$ 10^8. (After Halldal, 1961a.)

difference in the photochemical system, but is more likely to be due to the morphology of the flagellate. If the assumption that the photoreceptor is located near the flagellar base is correct, the shift between shadow and light, caused by the chloroplast, occurs within a much narrower angle when the organism is swimming toward the light than when swimming away from it (Fig. 6), i.e.,

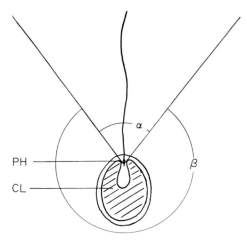

FIG. 6. A model to attempt an explanation of the sensitivity difference observed between positive and negative phototaxis (see Fig. 5). *Key:* PH, photoreceptor; CL, chloroplast; α, angle of adjustment in positive and β, angle of adjustment in negative response.

the flagellate can much more frequently make adjustments according to the ray direction in positive phototaxis than in negative and consequently can approach the light source faster than it can get away from it (Bennet-Clarke, 1961). No measurements have been performed to check this.

2. PHOBO-PHOTOTAXIS

Accumulation at certain intensities and alternations between positive and negative response have been observed since the very beginning of research on phototaxis. This gathering according to light intensity (phobo-phototaxis) is evidently a distinct reaction from topo-phototaxis. Several analyses have been performed on the effect of light intensity and other environmental factors (pH, age of culture, CO_2-content), but only a few on the effect of light quality. Mast (1919) studied phototactic response changes in populations of colonial *Volvocales* induced by colored light and reported that blue light caused positive phototaxis, while yellow and red light induced negative response in his experiments, acting in the same way as darkness. The results were not consistent, however; the colors to which the colonies were exposed were not spectroscopically tested, and no energy measurements performed.

Lately, action spectra of induced phototactic response changes have been measured in *Platymonas* (Halldal, 1960). These analyses revealed distinctly the red and blue chlorophyll absorption peaks after irradiation for 5 min. or more at 2,100 μW./sec., and it was concluded that photosynthesis was involved. The negative → positive transformation was antagonized by a reaction involving a pigment that absorbed maximally around 590 mμ. Irradiation at this wavelength induced a negative response. No precise measurements have been performed on induced phototaxis in the ultraviolet, but so far only the change from negative to positive response has been observed between 400 and 220 mμ. The opposite reaction (positive to negative) has been attempted but so far without results (Halldal, 1960 unpublished results).

The experimental set-up used in Wolken and Shin's (1958) experiments makes a distinction between topo-phototaxis and phobo-phototaxis impossible. The results are therefore difficult to interpret. The curve in the blue corresponds fairly well to the action spectrum measured for positive *Euglena* by Bünning and Schneiderhöhn (1956). The effect in the red with maximum around 600 mμ is more difficult to explain. It does have some similarities to the action spectrum of induced negative phototaxis in *Platymonas* (Halldal, 1960).

III. Phototaxis in *Amoeba*

The basic principle for the mechanism of ameboid movement is still not known, though numerous investigations have been performed to elucidate this. Various theories have been proposed: local differences in surface tension, rhythmic contraction of the cell membrane, contraction of the cytoplasm due to a plasmagel-plasmasol transformation, pH or water content differences between the front and the rear of the cell (see Goldacre and Lorch 1950; Käppner, 1961a,b). (See chapter by Jahn and Bovee, this volume.)

Goldacre and Lorch (1950) gave evidence that in ameba, protein molecules fold up at one end of the surface and unfold at the other resulting in osmotic activity and cytoplasmic streaming, and that ATP injected into the cell caused rigidity around the point of injection. Hoffmann-Berling (1954) also gave evidence that the energy supply for cell movement was delivered through ATP. The motor system of the ameba has thus much in common with the driving mechanism of flagellated and ciliated forms (see Section II,B,1).

If *Amoeba proteus* is exposed to strong illumination, movement usually stops and a directed horizontal beam usually orients the cells (Mast, 1931). The apparent two distinct types of reaction (shock response and cell orientation) are assumed to be the same (Mast, 1931), and the reaction induced by mechanical shocks was by Folger (1927) shown to be identical with the response that occurred after sudden illumination. Mast (1931) analyzed the effect of directed light rays on *Amoeba proteus* in some detail and concluded that a negative phototaxis occurred in strong light and ". . . probably positive in very weak light." The negative phototaxis was due to inhibition in the formation of pseudopods in the portion of the cell facing the light.

In analyses of the photokinesis of ameba, Mast and Stahler (1937) showed a definite correlation between light intensity and rate of locomotion. In all intensities but very low ones movement ceased shortly after the specimens were exposed. Optimum motility was obtained at 15,000 lux where the ameba moved at a maximum speed of about 200 μ per minute. The increase in the rate of locomotion up to 15,000 lux was assumed to be due to some unknown action of the red light, while the decrease that followed with still more intense radiation was attributed to the action of shorter wavelength light. These assumptions were based upon results from analyses on the color sensitivity of protoplasmic streaming in *Amoeba proteus* performed by Harrington and Leaming (1900). They showed that protoplasmic streaming was stimulated by red light but stopped or reversed by violet. These results also held true for enucleated forms. No measurements were performed to check filter purity or radiant energy. The effect of white and colored light on ameba has also been investigated by Schaeffer (1914) with results somewhat contradictory to those of Harrington and Leaming (1900) and Mast (1931). Schaeffer obtained positive, negative, and indifferent responses in white light and at all the other spectral bands tested (violet, blue, green, orange, and red). A positive response was usually obtained in very weak (scattered) light. Sudden changes between positive and negative response and vice versa were frequently observed, and environmental conditions, including light intensity, were assumed to be of importance. Schaeffer's experiments did not allow any conclusions to be drawn about the relative spectral sensitivity of ameba.

Recently spectral sensitivity analyses of ameboid movements using narrow spectral bands and controlled energy levels have been performed by Hitchcock (1961), and plasmasol movement suppression was measured. The maximum sensitivity occurred in the green at 515 $m\mu$. This is at a somewhat, probably insignificantly, longer wavelength than the maximum of about 450–490 $m\mu$ previously recorded by Harrington and Leaming (1900).

IV. Phototaxis in Ciliates

Phototaxis in ciliates is less defined than in flagellates and ameba. This is especially the case for *Paramecium* where neither photoreceptor nor any particular photosensitive area has been localized; and phototaxis in *Paramecium bursaris* is so far the only report for a directed photic response (see Gelber, 1956). A photoreceptive system in *Paramecium* is indicated in the "training" experiments of Gelber, who showed a significantly higher response for *Paramecium aurelia* in approaching a platinum wire in light than in darkness. On the other hand Dabrowska (1956) did not succeed in obtaining similar results with *Paramecium caudatum*, which evidently was insensitive to moderate light intensities.

The literature on the light response in *Stentor* has been included in the recent monograph on this genus (Tartar, 1961). Mast (1906) showed that free-swimming *Stentor* oriented and swam away from the light by turning toward a structural defined side (aboral) when exposed to sudden increases in light intensity. Great variations in threshold values were reported, and the ciliates were easily acclimated. No particular photosensitive spot has been localized in *Stentor*, but Mast (1906) claimed that the anterior part is more light sensitive than any other portion of the body. Several other investigators have observed both positive and negative phototactic response, evidently determined by en-vironmental conditions and strains (see Tartar, 1961).

The yellow *Stentor niger* reacted distinctly positively to light according to analyses by Tuffrau (1957), who also claimed that no part of the body had a preferably higher sensitivity than any other. Spectral sensitivity analyses re-vealed that the shorter wavelengths of visible light were more effective than longer ones, indicating a yellow pigment to be involved in the photosensory mechanism. However, no action-spectrum plot could be made from these data.

For *Paramecium*, Fox (1925) demonstrated a correlation between gravity and light. Darkness caused the ciliate to respond negatively geotactically, while light induced downward swimming.

V. Phototaxis and Ecology

Light responses are frequently observed in protozoa. In flagellates, in ameba, and in *Stentor* among the ciliates, light usually directs definite orientation or accumulation. *Paramecium* is an exception. In this genus the light effects are doubtful or very rare. Thus light, even in nonphotosynthetic forms, is one of the factors responsible for distribution of protozoa in natural habits. In the preceding chapters examples were given that both light intensity and ray direc-tion are decisive in this respect, and that these factors must be separated in con-sideration of their actions.

In ecology there is still much room for speculation as the ecologists are faced with considerably greater difficulties than the laboratory worker in evaluating the effect of all the different, frequently changing, factors acting at one time on populations. The really reliable data available from experiments performed under carefully controlled laboratory conditions are few, and these data may hold true for only one particular species or strain. Nevertheless, it seems at this time possible to restrict speculations to a limited number of factors and to draw some general conclusions.

For the most extensively analyzed group, the photosynthetic flagellates, the often recorded accumulation is explained as a result of changes between positive and negative responses, finally resulting in a balanced population at a distinct light intensity. The factors which have been shown to be of importance for *Platymonas subcordiformis* and some other forms are: cation balance and concentration, and light intensity and quality acting through the photosynthetic apparatus. Alternations in total and partial gas pressures or pH have been demonstrated not to be directly involved. In natural habits in uniform water masses, it is reasonable to assume that the changes that occur in the concentration of available ions are of little importance. Exceptions to this could be that extreme pH changes may alter the relative amount of available Ca, Mg, and K cations significantly, and that the mode of response, or the rate of motion, also may be influenced by the great salt variations which are found in highly stratified waters set up by salinity gradients. In other cases photosynthesis seems to be the decisive factor for accumulation and distribution in flagellates, and a possible interaction with geotaxis could be essential.

The photoreceptive pigment involved in the mechanism of light orientation in flagellates absorbs in the blue, and is most probably a carotenoprotein. An ecologist may wish to discuss the absorption characteristics of this chromophore in connection with the selective penetration of light into natural waters. The spectral transmission of light varies greatly with the water types. In clear far off-shore oceanic water the maximum penetration lies around 400–500 mμ with a peak near 475 mμ. Owing to certain dissolved blue-absorbing substances ("yellow substance") and increased numbers of particles, a distinct shift of maximum transmission toward longer wavelengths is observed in coastal waters. The maximum transmission occurs around 575 mμ (see Jerlov, 1951). It is therefore evident that the pigment involved in the photosensory mechanism in phototaxis does not meet any particular requirement in regard to preferential absorption of the wavelength region penetrating most deeply into the sea. The often distinct deviations that are observed in action spectra peaks from one species to another do not show any correspondence to the selective transmission of waters which they inhabit. The high phototactic effect which was observed in the far ultraviolet between 220 and 300 mμ for *Platymonas*, at a spectral region where no solar radiation penetrates the atmosphere, certainly does not have any ecological implication. In conclusion: the photoreceptor in phototaxis poorly covers the spectral region of visible light, and it is not particularly adapted to the light conditions in natural waters. We thus arrive at a conclusion similar to that of Rabinowitch (1951) in his considerations about chlorophyll and its optical characteristics; he states that chlorophyll actually is a poor light absorber with its two relatively narrow absorption bands in blue and red. However, it probably became adapted for photosynthesis because of its peculiar photosensitizing properties.

REFERENCES

Bendix, S. W. (1960). *Botan. Rev.* **26**, 145–208.
Bennet-Clarke, T. A. (1961). Verbal communication.
Blum, H. F., and Fox, D. L. (1932). *Univ. Calif. (Berkeley) Publ. Physiol.* **8**, 21–30.
Brokaw, C. J. (1960). *Exptl. Cell Res.* **19**, 430–431.
Bruce, V. G., and Pittendrigh, C. S. (1956). *Proc. Natl. Acad. Sci. U.S.* **42**, 676–682.
Bruce, V. G., and Pittendrigh, C. S .(1958). *Am. Naturalist* **92**, No. 866, 295–306.
Brucker, W. (1954). *Arch. Protistenk.* **99**, 294–327.
Buder, J. (1919). *Jahrb. wiss. Botan.* **58**, 105–220.
Bünning, E., and Schneiderhöhn, G. (1956). *Arch. Mikrobiol.* **24**, 80–90.
Bünning, E., and Tazawa, M. (1957). *Arch. Mikrobiol.* **27**, 306–310.
Cohn, F. (1863). *Jahresber. Schlesischen Ges. Vaterlandische Kultur* **41**, 102–105.
Cohn, F. (1865). *Jahresber. Schlesischen Ges. Vaterlandische Kultur* **42**, 35.
Dabrowska, J. (1956). *Folia Biol. (Warsaw)* **4**, 77–91.
Engelmann, T. W. (1882). *Arch. Ges. Physiol.* **29**, 387–400.
Finch, H., and Holtzer, M. (1961). *Exptl. Cell Res.* **23**, 251–257.
Folger, H. T. (1927). *Biol. Bull.* **53**, 405–412.
Fox, H. M. (1925). *Biol. Rev. Cambridge Phil. Soc.* **1**, 219–224.
Gelber, B. (1956). *J. Genet. Psychol.* **88**, 31–36.
Goldacre, R. J., and Lorch, I. J. (1950). *Nature* **166**, 497–500.
Goodwin, T. W. (1959). *Advan. Enzymol.* **21**, 295–368.
Goodwin, T. W., and Gross, J. A. (1958). *J. Protozool.* **5**, 292–295.
Gössel, I. (1957). *Arch. Mikrobiol.* **27**, 288–305.
Halldal, P. (1960). Unpublished results.
Halldal, P. (1958). *Physiol. Plantarum* **11**, 118–153.
Halldal, P. (1959). *Physiol. Plantarum* **12**, 742–752.
Halldal, P. (1960). *Physiol. Plantarum* **13**, 726–735.
Halldal, P. (1961a). *Physiol. Plantarum* **14**, 133–139.
Halldal, P. (1961b). *Proc. 3rd Intern. Congr. Photobiol., Copenhagen, 1960* pp. 121–126.
Harrington, N. R., and Leaming, E. (1900). *Am. J. Physiol.* **3**, 9–18.
Haupt, W. (1959). *In* "Encyclopedia of Plant Physiology" (W. Ruhland, ed.), Vol. 17, Part 1, pp. 318–370. Springer, Berlin.
Heilbrunn, L. V., and Daugherty, K. (1932). *Physiol. Zool.* **5**, 254–274.
Hitchcock, L., Jr. (1961). *J. Protozool.* **8**, 322–324.
Hoffmann-Berling, H. (1954). *Biochim. Biophys. Acta* **14**, 182–194.
Jennings, H. S. (1906). "Behavior of the Lower Organisms." Norwood, Massachusetts.
Jerlov, N. G. (1951). Rep. Swedish Deep Sea Exped. Vol. 3, Fac. 1. Elander, Gothenburg.
Jibbs, J. (1958). *Biochim. Biophys. Acta* **28**, 636–640.
Jones, R. F., and Lewin, R. A. (1960). *Exptl. Cell Res.* **19**, 408–410.
Käppner, W. (1961a). *Protoplasma* **53**, 81–105.
Käppner, W. (1961b). *Protoplasma* **53**, 504–529.
Krinsky, N. I., and Goldsmith, T. H. (1960). *Arch. Biochem. Biophys.* **91**, 271–274.
Links, J. (1955). Ph.D. Thesis. University of Leyden, Netherlands.
Luntz, A. (1931). *Z. Vergleich. Physiol.* **14**, 68–92.
Manten, A. (1948). Ph.D. Thesis. University of Utrecht, Netherlands.
Mast, S. O. (1906). *J. Exptl. Zool.* **3**, 359–399.

Mast, S. O. (1911). "Light and the Behavior of Organisms." Wiley, New York.

Mast, S. O. (1917). *J. Exptl. Zool.* 22, 471–528.

Mast, S. O. (1919). *J. Exptl. Zool.* 27, 367–390.

Mast, S. O. (1927). *Z. vergleich. Physiol.* 5, 739–761.

Mast, S. O. (1931). *Z. vergleich. Physiol.* 15, 139–147.

Mast, S. O., and Stahler, N. (1937). *Biol. Bull.* 73, 126–133.

Mayer, A. M., and Poljakoff-Mayber, A. (1959). *Physiol. Plantarum* 12, 8–14.

Metzner, P. (1929). *Z. Botan.* 22, 225–265.

Milne, L. J., and Milne, M. L. (1956). *In* "Radiation Biology" (A. Hollaender, ed.), Vol. 3, p. 621. McGraw Hill, New York.

Mjaaland, G. (1956). *Oikos* 7, 2–12.

Nordli, E. (1957). *Oikos* 8, 2–20.

Pohl, R. Z. (1948). *Z. Naturforsch.* 3b, 367–374.

Rabinowitch, E. I. (1951). "Photosynthesis and Related Processes." Vol. 2, Part 1. Interscience Publ., New York.

Robertson, R. N., Wilkins, M. J., and Weeks, D. C. (1951). *Australian J. Sci. Res.* B4, 248–264.

Sachs, T., and Mayer, A. M. (1961). *Phycologia* 1, 149–159.

Schaeffer, A. A. (1914). *Biol. Bull.* 32, 45–74.

Strasburger, E. (1878). *Jena. Z. Naturwiss.* 12, 551.

Strother, G. K., and Wolken, J. J. (1961). *J. Protozool.* 8, 261–265.

Tartar, V. (1961). *Intern. Ser. Monographs Pure Appl. Biol. Zool. Div.* 5, Pergamon Press, New York, London.

Terry, O. P. (1909). *Am. J. Physiol.* 15, 235–243.

Thomas, J. B., and Nijenhuis, L. E. (1950). *Biochim. Biophys. Acta* 6, 317–324.

Tsubo, Y. (1960). *J. Protozool.* 8, 114–121.

Tuffrau, M. (1957). *Bull. Soc. Zool. France* 82, 354–356.

Vávra, J. (1956). *Arch. Mikrobiol.* 25, 223–225.

Weber, H. H. (1958). "The Motility of Muscle and Cells." Harvard Univ. Press, Cambridge, Massachusetts.

Wolken, J. J., and Shin, E. (1958). *J. Protozool.* 5, 39–46.

Studies of Cell Heredity with Chlamydomonas

Ruth Sager

Department of Zoology, Columbia University, New York, New York

	Page
I. Introduction	297
II. Genetic Analysis	298
A. Life Cycle	298
B. Chromosomes	299
C. Chromosomal Genetics	300
D. *In Vitro* Protein Synthesis and the Genetic Code	300
E. Nonchromosomal Genes in *Chlamydomonas*	302
III. The Chloroplast as a Model Organelle	305
A. Chloroplast Structure	307
B. Chlorophyll and Carotenoid Mutants	307
C. Photosynthetic Mutants	311
D. Nucleic Acid Content of Chloroplasts	312
IV. Toward an Organelle Genetics	315
References	316

I. Introduction

Because of the universality of its ground rules, the science of genetics has been amenable to study in organisms as diverse as *Drosophila*, maize, the silkworm, the mouse, *Paramecium*, *Neurospora*, and *Escherichia coli*. Each organism has contributed evidence in support of the great generalizations of genetic theory, but some organisms have been far better suited than others for illuminating particular aspects of the story.

For example, the use of microorganisms was essential in developing workable systems for the molecular analysis of gene action in terms of the control of protein structure and the regulation of enzyme formation, although both of these gene functions were clearly foreshadowed by studies with higher organisms. In this volume, Kimball discusses some of the unique properties of *Paramecium* which have made possible the dissection of aspects of nucleocytoplasmic interactions which are inaccessible to comparable analysis in other organisms.

This chapter summarizes the existing information about the control of cell heredity in the green phytoflagellate *Chlamydomonas* and indicates frontier areas of genetic research for which this organism appears particularly well suited. Recent reviews have summarized the present knowledge of formal genetics—linkage and recombination—and of mutants inducing biochemical lesions (Levine and Ebersold, 1960; Ebersold, 1962). Results in these areas will be briefly mentioned in this chapter, but emphasis will be given to other aspects of cell heredity which can be systematically investigated with this organism: the identification of nonchromosomal genetic systems, and the genetic control of subcellular structure and organelle formation.

II. Genetic Analysis

A. Life Cycle

Chlamydomonas reinhardi is an isogamous, heterothallic species. There are two mating types, morphologically indistinguishable, and the mating type difference is controlled by a single gene pair. Any fertile clone can be classified as mating-type-plus (mt^+) or mating-type-minus (mt^-) by its response to a reference pair of strains. The life cycle is shown in Fig. 1.

Mating occurs only between cells of opposite mating type which have differentiated to become gametes (Sager and Granick, 1953). The differentiation process, which is molecular but not morphogenetic, requires a regime of nitrogen starvation. The biochemical changes which occur have not been studied in detail, but would provide interesting material for analysis (Ishida and Sager, 1963 unpubl.). For instance, nitrogen starvation induces, among other events, a block to deoxyribonucleic acid (DNA) replication.

Substances which are sexual in the sense of being produced only by gametes and eliciting responses only from gametes, have been described. Tsubo (1961) reported the presence of volatile compounds produced by gametes of mt^-, which attract mt^+ gametes of the same species and both mt^+ and mt^- gametes of other species of *Chlamydomonas*. The natural compounds were not identified but similar chemotactic responses were observed to coal gas, CO, C_2H_2, and C_2H_4. Forster *et al.* (1956) have reported that high molecular weight glycoproteins are sexual substances formed by gametes of some species of *Chlamydomonas*. These substances are involved only in the clumping process; whether they or any other sexual substances are required for cell fusion and zygote formation is unknown (Wiese and Jones, 1963).

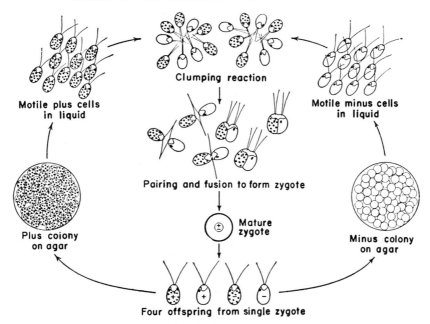

Motile plus cells in liquid

Clumping reaction

Motile minus cells in liquid

Pairing and fusion to form zygote

Plus colony on agar

Mature zygote

Minus colony on agar

Four offspring from single zygote

FIG. 1. The life cycle of *Chlamydomonas reinhardi,* showing the segregation of mating type, denoted by plus and minus signs, and of the marker y_1 (the dotted cells are $y_1{}^+$, the undotted are $y_1{}^-$).

The fusion process requires enzymatic digestion of cell membranes to permit interpenetration of the mt^+ and mt^- gametes leading to zygote formation. The mating pairs fuse completely with no evident extrusion of any cellular material. Usually, mitosis is blocked and the newly formed diploid cells differentiate as zygotes. Recently persistent diploids have been observed (Ebersold, 1964 unpubl.; Gillham, 1963b), opening a new avenue in the study of gene action in *Chlamydomonas* and also providing material for studying the regulatory control of meiosis.

Zygotes may be induced to undergo meiosis after a maturation period of several days in the dark, by transferring them to the light. Under these conditions, meiosis and germination are well synchronized, in the large majority of zygotes (Sager, 1963 unpubl.). No electron microscope studies of zygote formation, maturation, or germination have yet been reported but would be extremely useful.

B. Chromosomes

The chromosomes of several species of *Chlamydomonas* have been studied in the light microscope after staining of squash preparations with carmine or Feulgen. In *Chlamydomonas reinhardi,* the haploid number is probably 8 (Buffaloe, 1958, 1959; Levine and Folsom, 1959; Sager, 1963 unpubl.). As yet, no fully satisfactory studies of meiosis have been reported. However, the high fertility of crosses and the regularity of genetic segregation ratios indicate that meiosis is conventional and that very little chromosome aberration exists in the stocks now in use.

A study of deoxyribonucleic acid (DNA) replication in *Chlamydomonas* (Sueoka, 1960) indicates a similar pattern to that observed in *Escherichia coli* (Meselson and Stahl, 1958), and in higher plants (Taylor *et al.*, 1957), interpreted as semiconservative replication. In Sueoka's study, cells divided not only into 2 but also into 4 and 8, complicating the analysis; however, this species can be grown so that cell division occurs after each round of chromosome duplication (Sager, 1963 unpubl.).

C. CHROMOSOMAL GENETICS

After germination, the zygote releases 4 zoospores, representing the 4 genetic products of meiosis. These cells can be separated manually on agar, each giving rise to a distinct colony. Thus tetrad analysis of crosses is readily feasible with this organism. In addition to tetrad analysis, genetic analysis is sometimes performed by allowing undissected zygotes to form zygote colonies which subsequently can be cloned and classified for progeny types.

The linkage maps shown in Fig. 2 indicate the current status of genetic mapping of this species. Most of the data are based upon tetrad analysis of markers from two-point and three-point crosses (Ebersold *et al.*, 1962).

The paucity of auxotrophic mutants is noteworthy. Despite concerted efforts by several investigators, only auxotrophs blocked in the biosynthesis of arginine, thiamine, *p*-aminobenzoic acid, and nicotinamide have been recovered, apart from mutants affecting the photosynthetic apparatus and those resulting from nonchromosomal gene mutations to be discussed below. If mutants are lost because of poor permeability of this strain to most metabolites, a screening program to find a more permeable sexual strain would be a valuable contribution to research with this organism.

D. *In Vitro* PROTEIN SYNTHESIS AND THE GENETIC CODE

In the future, genetic analysis may be carried out entirely *in vitro*, employing the purified enzymes of nucleic acid and protein synthesis to study the replication and metabolic role of individual genes. The use of synthetic polynucleotides to unravel the genetic code is an important step in this direction.

A cell-free system, prepared from extracts of exponentially growing cultures of *Chlamydomonas*, can incorporate amino acids into polypeptides (Sager *et al.*, 1963). The system is similar to that described from *E. coli* (Nirenberg and Matthaei, 1961) in many properties and in its activity: approximately 10 mμmoles of amino acid incorporated per milligram of ribosomal protein. The endogenous activity, resulting from the presence of preformed messenger RNA,

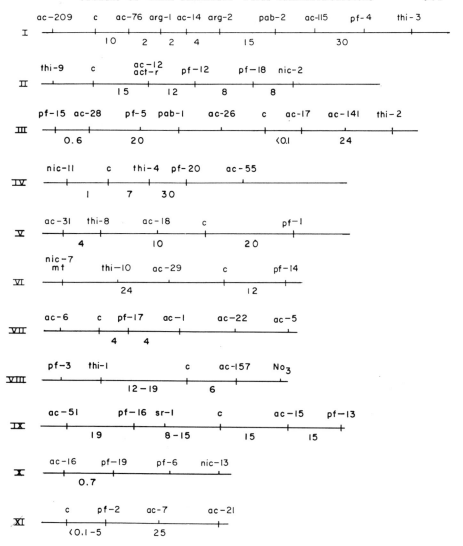

Fig. 2. Linkage groups of *Chlamydomonas reinhardi.* Numbers between vertical bars below the line represent map distances between genes; where numbers are not given between vertical bars above the line the map distances are not known.

KEY TO SYMBOLS:

c, centromere   thi, thiamine-requiring
ac, acetate-requiring   act-r, resistant to actidione
pf, paralyzed flagella   nic, nicotinamide-requiring
arg, arginine-requiring   sr-1, resistant to streptomycin
pab, *p*-aminobenzoic acid-requiring   No₃, cannot use nitrate as N source

is fairly low and similar for each of the amino acids. Addition of polyuridylic acid (polyU) results in up to 100-fold stimulation of phenylalanine incorporation.

The specificity of the response to polyuridylic acid is shown by comparing the incorporation of individual amino acids into polypeptide in the presence and absence of *synthetic* polyU. Phenylalanine incorporation is greatly stimulated by polyU, and leucine is also stimulated significantly, but none of the other amino acids respond. A typical time course of incorporation is shown in Fig. 3.

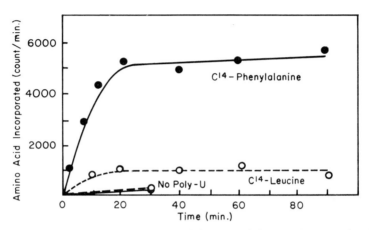

Fig. 3. Rate of polyU-stimulated phenylalanine and leucine incorporation in the *Chlamydomonas system*. (From Sager et al. 1963.)

That leucine and phenylalanine both respond to polyU indicates that coding ambiguity, that is, the response of two amino acids to the same nucleotide sequence, does occur in the *Chlamydomonas in vitro* system. It has also been reported to occur to a smaller extent in *E. coli* (Bretscher and Grunberg-Manago, 1962).

The response of amino acids to other synthetic polynucleotides has also been studied with extracts of *Chlamydomonas*, and no qualitative differences have been noted from the published data on *E. coli* for the amino acids phenylalanine, leucine, serine, isoleucine, tyrosine, valine, proline, and lysine (Weinstein *et al.*, 1963). In view of the central phylogenetic position of *Chlamydomonas*, as a representative of the flagellates, from which both the higher plants and animals have evolved, these data provide strong supporting evidence of the universality of the genetic code.

E. Nonchromosomal Genes in *Chlamydomonas*

The existence of stable nonchromosomal genetic factors has been recognized ever since the first well documented report of non-Mendelian inheritance by

Correns in 1908 and subsequent systematic studies with higher plants in a number of laboratories in the 1920's and 1930's (summarized in Rhoades, 1955). Neither identification of the factors, nor any direct evidence about their mode of action could be elicited from these studies because of the complexities of the system. Indeed, it could not be established with certainty that primary genetic information was involved, although the data were most simply interpreted in such a context. Mutations of nonchromosomal factors in *Neurospora* (Mitchell and Mitchell, 1952), in *Aspergillus* (Subak-Sharpe, 1956) and in yeast (Ephrussi, 1953) further indicated the widespread existence of these factors but proved recalcitrant to biochemical analysis.

With *Chlamydomonas*, a mutagenic method has been devised which is providing a diversity of phenotypes resulting from mutation of nonchromosomal genes. Although our studies with these mutants are still very new, the evidence already demonstrates that the mutations occur in primary genetic material (Sager and Ramanis, 1963). It is our working hypothesis that these nonchromosomal (NC) genes represent a significant component of the hereditary apparatus of all cells, and consequently that the understanding of their role must be included in any evaluation of the mechanisms of cellular heredity.

The first nonchromosomal gene (NC gene) detected in *Chlamydomonas* arose by mutation from streptomycin sensitivity to resistance (Sager, 1954). The inference that this genetic factor was nonchromosomal was based initially upon the following lines of evidence: transmission of the factor from the mating-type-plus parent to all progeny (Fig. 4) but from the mating-type-minus parent to none of the progeny; a similar pattern of inheritance in four

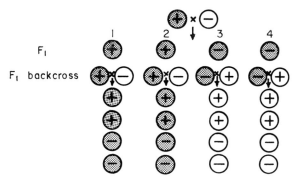

FIG. 4. Inheritance of streptomycin resistance of strain *sr-500*. Plus and minus signs refer to mating type. The initial cross, *sr mt*$^+$ × *ss mt*$^-$, gave rise exclusively to *sr* offspring which segregated 2:2 for the markers *mt* and *y*$_1$. F$_1$ clones of plus mating type backcrossed to *ss mt*$^-$ produced all *sr* offspring (4:0), but F$_1$'s of minus mating type backcrossed to *ss mt*$^+$ produced mainly sensitive progeny (0:4). Stippled, streptomycin-resistant; unstippled, streptomycin-sensitive.

successive backcross generations, ruling out multifactorial chromosomal heredity; stability of the phenotype through hundreds of generations of clonal growth at many different growth rates, entirely in the absence of streptomycin; and stability of the phenotype under drastic conditions of heat shock, cold treatment, and growth at extreme temperatures. Further evidence based upon segregation and recombination of NC genes will be discussed below.

Studies of the origin of this mutation demonstrated that it was not spontaneous and preexisting in the cell population before treatment with streptomycin, but rather that it arose in the presence of the drug (Sager, 1960, 1962a; Gillham and Levine, 1962). Thus, streptomycin acted as a mutagenic agent for this nonchromosomal mutation (Sager, 1962a). The information gained in these studies on the origin of the nonchromosomal mutation to streptomycin resistance was applied to the induction of other nonchromosomal mutations. If one starts with the wild-type streptomycin-sensitive strain, the yield of NC mutants is very low, but starting with a strain which is already streptomycin resistant, it has proven possible to obtain nonchromosomal mutants from the clonal progeny of almost every treated cell.

The biochemical nature of the mutagenic process is not known. Successful conditions have been worked out empirically and include the use of toxic but sublethal concentrations of the drug, allowing very slow growth on agar, such that each cell plated will finally produce a colony after a long lag. The mutations are established slowly, in just a fraction of the cells of the colony, but once established they are stable. The method was worked out with a visible mutation from y_1^+ to y_1^- (green, chlorophyll-containing to yellow, chlorophyll-free; Sager and Tsubo, 1961) and then applied to other mutations.

The nonchromosomal mutant types obtained thus far include several classes: streptomycin-resistant and streptomycin-dependent mutants; acetate-requiring mutants which cannot grow photosynthetically; auxotrophic mutants which require some growth factor as yet unidentified; slow growing mutants and tiny colony types which do not grow better on a supplemented medium than on minimal medium. Fifteen of these strains have now been crossed and found to show the same pattern of uniparental transmission of the NC gene from the mating-type-plus parent (Sager and Ramanis, 1963) as that originally described for sr-500.

A further and more powerful genetic analysis of NC genes has become possible with the finding that a fraction of zygotes transmit their NC genes from both parents to the progeny. These exceptional zygotes represent about 0.1% of the population when matured at 25°C. but about 1% at 37°C. With the use of suitable combinations of NC genes, the exceptional zygotes can be selected for, under conditions where they alone can germinate and produce progeny.

Using two-NC-factor crosses, progeny have been obtained which are segregating for two pairs of NC genes, in addition to three pairs of unlinked chromosomal genes. The segregation of chromosomal gene pairs serves to identify the four products of meiosis, the zoospores, which are haploid for the chromosome complement. The zoospores and their clonal descendants can be classified at each mitotic division for the traits controlled by the NC gene pairs, in order to determine at which division segregation of the NC genes occurs.

With this system, it was shown that (1) the NC genes segregate in postmeiotic divisions; (2) they do not segregate uniquely at a particular division; (3) each NC gene pair segregates independently; (4) on the average, the ac^-/ac^+ gene pair segregates earlier than does the sd/ss gene pair observed in the same cross. Gillham (1963a) has studied the NC gene pair sr/ss and similarly found postmeiotic segregation.

This analysis has provided strong evidence that the nonchromosomal genes under observation are particulate carriers of primary genetic information. They share with chromosomal genes a number of essential properties, including stability, mutability, maintenance of identity in heterozygotes, segregation of alleles, and the classic dichotomy between genotype and phenotype.

A different kind of genetic factor, which may also be nonchromosomal has been described in *Chlamydomonas*. This factor, y_1, exhibits 2:2 (i.e., Mendelian) segregation in crosses (Sager, 1955). However, it segregates only at the first division in meiosis, requiring very close linkage to a centromere, if chromosomal in location. Two lines of evidence suggest it may not be chromosomal, despite its behavior as a unit factor. (1) In contrast to chromosomal genes, which are not responsive to streptomycin as a mutagen, the y_1 factor can be mutated by streptomycin under the same conditions which induce other NC gene mutations (Sager and Tsubo, 1961). (2) In a linkage test in which y_1 was crossed to a series of stocks carrying centromere-linked markers for each of the known linkage groups, y_1 showed no linkage with any of them (Sager, 1962b). Thus the y_1 factor presents the paradox of Mendelian segregation but nonmapability. Further studies will be required to establish the relationship between y_1 and the other NC genes.

Some speculative remarks concerning the molecular identity and functional role of NC genes will be presented in the last section of this chapter, but first it will be useful to consider aspects of the subcellular organization of *Chlamydomonas*, particularly with reference to organelle formation and nucleic acid distribution.

III. The Chloroplast as a Model Organelle

Knowledge of the subcellular organization of *Chlamydomonas* comes primarily from electron microscope studies of osmium-fixed material (Sager and

Palade, 1954, 1957; Gibbs, 1962a; Lang, 1963). A diagrammatic sketch of the normal green cell, based upon electron microscope studies, is shown in Fig. 5, and may be compared with the micrograph of a longitudinal section

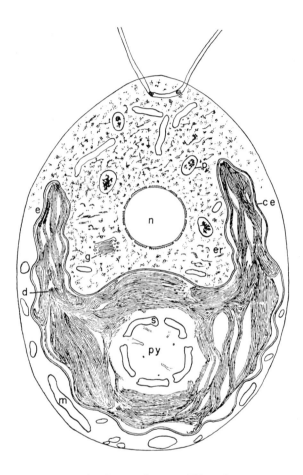

FIG. 5. Diagrammatic sketch of normal green *Chlamydomonas* as seen at low magnification in the electron microscope. The chloroplast is shown surrounded by the double chloroplast envelope (ce) within which the eyespot (e), pyrenoid (py), and starch plates (s) are located, as well as the paired lamellar membranes arranged as discs. At low magnification the disc arrangement is clearly seen only in occasional well oriented regions. The cytoplasm also contains other systems of organelles, including mitochondria (m), Golgi material (g), endoplasmic reticulum (er) consisting of membranes and ribonucleic acid-containing granules, and vacuoles containing metaphosphate (p). The nucleus (n) is surrounded by a double membrane with pores and a dense coating of ribonucleic acid-containing granules on its outer surface.

shown in Plate I. Only the chloroplast will be discussed in this chapter; for further information the reader is referred to the literature.

A. Chloroplast Structure

The single cup-shaped chloroplast constitutes about 50% of the volume of the cell, and is enclosed within a double chloroplast envelope. In the normal green cell, the chloroplast is full of lamellar membranes, containing chlorophyll, and representing the sites of photosynthesis. The membranes are arranged in pairs which are closed at their ends, forming flat sacs which appear in section as discs. Each membrane is probably asymmetrical in molecular cross section, with the discs providing a physical basis for charge separation and for the compartmentalization of primary photosynthetic products (Sager, 1958).

The chloroplast also contains an orange eyespot (stigma), which lies just under the chloroplast envelope near the anterior end of the plastid and usually consists of two parallel plates. Each plate is composed of carotenoid-containing dense spheres arranged in hexagonal packing and lined up along a lamellar membrane. This structure is photosensitive, and is the receptor site responsible for the phototactic responses of the organism. An eyeless mutant with greatly decreased photosensitivity has been reported (Hartshorne, 1953).

The pyrenoid, a large proteinaceous body in the chloroplast, is surrounded by starch plates and is thought to be a region specialized for starch synthesis. Tubules which are continuous with lamellar discs penetrate into the pyrenoid, forming a dense network. The position of the pyrenoid within the chloroplast differs from one species to another, suggesting that pyrenoid location is under genetic control. However, no mutations affecting pyrenoid structure, function, or position have been described. The ultrastructure of algal pyrenoids has been described by Gibbs (1962b).

B. Chlorophyll and Carotenoid Mutants

Mutant strains differing from wild-type in their pigment composition can be readily obtained after ultraviolet irradiation of *Chlamydomonas*. Those which have been crossed with wild-type all exhibit 2:2 segregation (Tsubo, 1961) and are probably the result of chromosomal gene mutations. However, the studies with y_1 (Section II,E) indicate that unit factor segregation does not establish chromosomal location unambiguously. Only two pigment mutants have been mapped (Sager, 1955).

A detailed study of the structure and pigment content of the yellow mutant, y_1, has indicated a probable regulatory role of chlorophyll in the development of chloroplast lamellae. When strains carrying y_1^- are grown in the dark, protochlorophyll is formed (Sager, 1961) but only traces of chlorophyll, if any. However, the chloroplast is present, still constituting about 50% of the

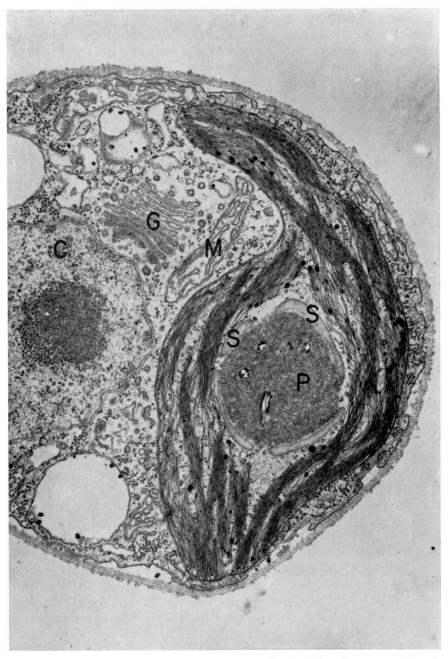

PLATE I. Lower two-thirds of a normal green cell. The chloroplast is cut obliquely showing only one arm of the cup-shaped organelle. Lamellar membranes arranged in closed discs contain the chlorophyll and other components of the photosynthetic apparatus. The dense pyrenoid (P) embedded in the basal region of the plastid is sur-

cell volume, but containing only a few disorganized bits of lamellae, in addition to the eyespot and pyrenoid (Plate II). The carotenoid content is the same as in the normal green strain. When such yellow cells are placed in the light, chlorophyll synthesis begins and so does lamella formation. After about 24 hr. of light, the yellow cells have become indistinguishable from normal green ones. Thus, in the absence of chlorophyll, lamella formation is blocked, despite the genetic potentialities of the cell and despite the presence of carotenoid pigments.

The role of carotenoids in lamella formation and in photosynthesis has also been investigated with a pale green mutant. This strain contains only about 5% of the wild-type chlorophyll content and is almost devoid of carotenoids, containing less than 0.5% of the wild-type amount (Sager and Zalokar, 1958). As in the yellow mutant, the chloroplast is present but in the pale green mutant, some lamellar membranes are also present, approximately proportional in amount to the chlorophyll present (Sager, 1958). Thus the presence of lamellae in both mutants seems to be a function of the chlorophyll concentration and to be independent of carotenoid content.

The photosynthetic capacity of the pale green mutant was measured in terms of CO_2 uptake, O_2 release, and cytochrome oxidation in response to light (Chance and Sager, 1957). This strain can carry on photosynthesis with an efficiency greater than the wild-type strain on the basis of CO_2 assimilation per chlorophyll present. Carotenoid pigments are evidently not required for any of the measured activities. On the other hand, there is a pigment in normal green cells that changes its absorbancy at 510 to 520 mμ in response to light, which is absent in the pale green mutant. Thus, this compound, which may be a carotenoid, is not essential for photosynthesis.

The pale green mutant, because of its low chlorophyll and carotenoid content, has been very useful in studies of changes in absorbancy of pigmented enzymes in photosynthesis and respiration. Photosynthetic cytochromes of the c and b types have been identified, as have respiratory cytochromes of the c and b groups. As in many plants, little if any terminal cytochrome oxidase activity has been detected. Absorbancy changes as seen with the double-beam spectrophotometer are a sensitive measure of cytochrome activity, and under controlled

---

rounded by starch plates (S) and contains a network, seen here in section, of fine tubules which connect with the lamellae. Dense granules, probably ribosomes, can be seen between the lamellae. A pair of smooth membranes surround the plastid. The nucleus with its envelope, dense nucleolus, and chromosomes (C) seen in section lies above the chloroplast. Mitochondria (M) are found throughout the cytoplasm, which also contains Golgi bodies (G) and ribosomes both free and attached to the endoplasmic reticulum. Vacuoles are commonly present. Magnification: 24,000×. [Photomicrograph by Dr. G. E. Palade. Fixed in 1% OsO_4 in 0.1 M phosphate buffer pH 7.4; embedded in epon; section stained with uranyl and $Pb(OH)_2$.]

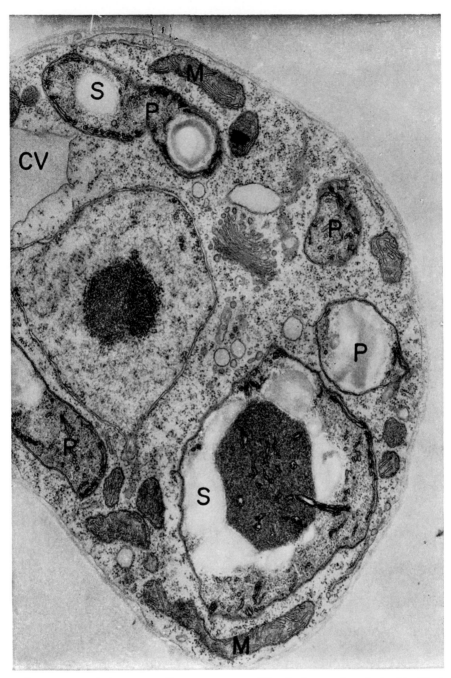

PLATE II. A dark-grown yellow mutant, y_1. The single cup-shaped plastid (P) is here seen in five profiles as a result of the plane of the section and undulating plastid surface. The plastid differs greatly from the normal green in the absence of lamellae.

conditions may provide a method to detect mutational alterations in cytochrome enzymes.

C. Photosynthetic Mutants

Mutant strains of *Chlamydomonas* have been described which are normal green but cannot grow photosynthetically. These strains are known as "acetate-requiring," since acetate is the best carbon source for heterotrophic growth of this organism. Presuming that each mutant block is located at a particular enzymatic step in photosynthesis, these acetate-requiring strains may be expected to provide valuable material for the analysis of photosynthetic pathways. However, in no instance has the enzymatic position of a mutant block to photosynthesis been firmly established as yet.

Two classes of acetate-requiring mutants have been described. One class consists of chromosomal gene mutants of which about 200 have been identified; many of them have been mapped. They are scattered throughout the linkage groups, showing no pattern of organization at the chromosome level (Ebersold, 1962). The second class consists of nonchromosomal (NC) gene mutants recovered after streptomycin treatment (Section II,E). These strains show uniparental transmission of the NC genes and cannot be mapped (Section II,E).

In preliminary biochemical studies, some of the chromosomal gene mutants have been analyzed for their ability to do the Hill reaction, for PPNR (photosynthetic pyridine nucleotide reductase) activity (Levine and Volkmann, 1961) and for their ability to photoreduce TPN (Levine and Smillie, 1962). The results led Levine and Smillie to postulate that two of the mutants (*ac-115* and *ac-141*) are blocked before the Hill reaction, at the level of the photooxidation of water, and that a third mutant *ac-21* is blocked between cytochrome b_6 and cytochrome f.

The application of electron-spin resonance (ESR) measurements to the study of photosynthesis has met with continuous difficulty in the identification of the compounds emitting the light-induced signals. Recently, with the aid of nonphotosynthetic mutants of the alga *Scenedesmus,* the two signals characteristic of photosynthesis have been correlated with particular steps in the over-all process with some success. The rapid signal R is absent in a mutant unable to photoreduce CO_2 but able to evolve O_2 in the Hill reaction with added quinone as

---

Bits of disorganized lamellar material and dense granules, probably ribosomes, are present. The pyrenoid is surrounded by starch plate (S) and contains tubules as in Plate I. Starch is also stored in other parts of the plastid. The mitochondria (M) differ from those of the light grown cells in being much denser and containing more cristae per unit length. The rest of the cytoplasm and nucleus do not appear to differ from their organization in the light-grown cell. The nuclear envelope shows one connection with the endoplasmic reticulum, and a part of a contractile vacuole (CV), present in all cells, occurs in this section. Magnification: 24,000×. [Photomicrograph by Dr. G. E. Palade. Fixed in 2% OsO_4 in 0.1M phosphate buffer pH 7.4; embedded in epon; section stained with uranyl and $Pb(OH)_2$.]

electron acceptor. The slow signal S is absent in mutants which are blocked in
O_2 release, but can photoreduce CO_2 (Weaver and Bishop, 1963).

Weaver and Bishop postulate that the R signal may be due to the photo-
oxidized form of a special chlorophyll (P700) acting as energy collector from
other chlorophyll molecules in the excited state. No comparable mutants lacking the R signal have yet been found in *Chlamydomonas* or any other algae.

There is considerable evidence suggesting that the semiquinone of plastoquinone is the source of the free radical seen as the S signal. Photosynthetic
bacteria have no S signal, nor have manganese-deficient cultures which are unable to evolve O_2. In addition to the *Scenedesmus* mutants, similar mutants of
Chlamydomonas with a reduced S signal and impaired Hill reactivity have also
been reported (Levine and Piette, 1962).

D. Nucleic Acid Content of Chloroplasts

The presence of extranuclear Feulgen-positive particles in *Chlamydomonas*
was first described by Ris and Plaut (1962). They considered the particles to
be located in the chloroplast, but their evidence was inconclusive because of the
irregular contours of the chloroplast in whole-cell preparations for light microscopy. The problem was taken up by Sager and Ishida (1963) who isolated
intact chloroplasts from *Chlamydomonas* by breaking the organism with a
French pressure cell and banding the particulate fractions in a sucrose gradient.
The major fractions band as shown in Fig. 6. By isolating B_3 and rebanding

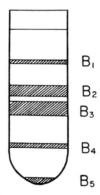

Fig. 6. Banding of chloroplasts in sucrose gradient. Five milliliters of broken cell
suspension was layered on a discontinuous gradient, 5 ml. each of 1.0, 1.5, 2.0, 2.5
sucrose, top to bottom, all in W medium, and centrifuged at 25,000 r.p.m. in SW 25
rotor, Spinco Model L, at 2–3°.

under the same conditions, a clean and relatively intact chloroplast preparation
was recovered. Electron micrographs of the fractionated material have indicated
a very low contamination with other cell particulates.

Critical evidence that the chloroplasts contain DNA is based upon finding a minor DNA component in the chloroplast differing in base composition from the major DNA constituent (Fig. 7). Total DNA extracted from *Chlamydomonas* consists of two fractions with different buoyant densities, which can be separated by density gradient equilibrium centrifugation in cesium chloride. The major component, about 95% of the cellular DNA, has a buoyant density of 1.726 and a guanine-cytosine (GC) content of 62%; the minor, or satellite DNA has a buoyant density (by calculation) of 1.705 and a GC content of 39%. The DNA extracted from isolated chloroplasts, amounting to some 3% of cell DNA, in different preparations contained 25–40% of the satellite DNA, representing a 7-fold enrichment over that present in the total DNA. Thus it is likely that the satellite DNA is a chloroplast constituent, and may correspond to the Feulgen-positive particles. Whether the small amount of major DNA is also native to the chloroplast or is a contaminant cannot be resolved by these methods.

Ribonucleoprotein particles sedimenting at about 70 S have also been isolated from *Chlamydomonas* chloroplasts (Ishida and Sager, unpublished). It seems likely that these bodies are chloroplast ribosomes and correspond to the electron-dense granules seen in electron micrographs, lying within the chloroplast matrix in normal green (Plate I) and in yellow cell plastids (Plate II).

The chemical composition of isolated chloroplasts during the isolation procedure is shown in Table I. The chlorophyll content remains constant, providing

Table I

CHEMICAL COMPOSITION OF ISOLATED CHLOROPLASTS DURING ISOLATION PROCEDURES

Steps in isolation	% of intact chloroplasts	Amounts (per cell or intact chloroplast)			
		Chlorophyll ($\times 10^9$ molecules)	Protein ($\times 10^{-8}$ mg.)	DNA ($\times 10^{-10}$ mg.)	RNA ($\times 10^{-9}$ mg.)
Intact cell	100.0	1.22	5.0	3.5	6.0
After 1st S.G.C.[a]	43.7	1.57	2.90	2.30	1.61
After 2nd S.G.C.[a]	28.3	1.54	2.29	0.62	0.42
After 1st wash	20.4	1.30	0.96	0.21	0.44
After 2nd wash	12.4	1.19	0.76	0.11	0.31
After 3rd wash	10.6	1.28	0.77	0.12	0.29

[a] Sucrose gradient centrifugation.

further evidence that the chlorophyll is membrane bound. After the second sucrose gradient banding, the protein content is about 40% that of the intact

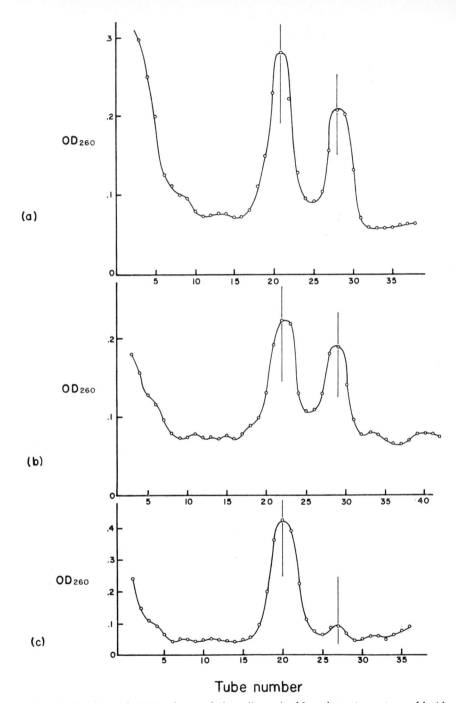

FIG. 7. Banding of DNA from whole cells and chloroplasts in cesium chloride gradient, SW 39 rotor, Spinco Model L, 33,000 r.p.m., 70 hr., 18–20°. (a) and (b)

cell, a reasonable value since the chloroplast volume is about 50% that of the cell. During the washing procedure, two-thirds of the protein is lost. However, it is not established whether the remaining one-third includes some soluble proteins in addition to those that are membrane bound.

IV. Toward an Organelle Genetics

This chapter has briefly summarized the available information concerning the genetic systems of *Chlamydomonas,* both chromosomal an nonchromosomal, and concerning the chloroplast: its structure, its chemical composition, and its alteration by mutations both chromosomal and nonchromosomal. Our purpose in restricting the discussion in this way has been to focus principally upon a particular problem: the genetic control of organelle formation.

It is evident that our information is as yet too scant for a serious analysis of this question, but perhaps it is adequate to provide some clarity in the planning of further research. Let us examine the current status of the problem from this point of view.

The existence of two genetic systems, one chromosomal and the other non-chromosomal, poses the obvious question of their respective roles in cell heredity. In terms of gene action, we may consider three possibilities: (1) coding for amino acid sequence in proteins, (2) regulating the rate of synthesis of particular proteins, and (3) all other as yet undocumented modes of action, including template-generated replication of structures composed of macro-molecules (e.g., chloroplast lamellae). The nonchromosomal genes may act just like chromosomal genes, coding for and regulating special sets of proteins, or they may have some unique and different function.

Evidence of interaction between the chromosomal and nonchromosomal genes affecting particular phenotypes comes from a variety of organisms. In maize, cytoplasmic determinants of pollen sterility interact with chromosomal genes which are fertility restorers (Rhoades, 1955). In *Chlamydomonas* a chromosomal gene A amplifies the resistance to streptomycin of either chromosomal streptomycin-resistant strains (from 100 μg./ml. to over 2 mg./ml.) or of nonchromosomal streptomycin-resistant and streptomycin-dependent strains (from 500 μg./ml. to over 2 mg./ml.) (Sager and Tsubo, 1961). Reports of less localized interactions of particular cytoplasmic factors with particular genomes abound in the literature of cytoplasmic inheritance in higher plants (Rhoades, 1955).

It would seem that the existence of nonphotosynthetic mutants, both chromosomal and nonchromosomal, should provide an ample supply of experimental

Chloroplast DNA from two experiments; the satellite band is 39% of the total DNA in each. (c) Whole cell DNA with major band (94%) and satellite band (6%).

material with which to study interactions of the two genetic systems in the photosynthetic apparatus. The results of such studies would clearly be of value in the analysis of both photosynthesis and cell heredity.

The existence of nucleic acids in the chloroplast provides another point of attack upon the problem of chloroplast development. It now becomes possible to study macromolecule synthesis in an organelle, which is complex but much simpler than an entire cell. The function of the plastid DNA represents perhaps the leading question. Does it code for plastid proteins? Has it a regulatory role or some other role as yet unknown? Washed chloroplasts contain about 10^{-14} g. of DNA, corresponding to about 10^7 nucleotide pairs. Assuming a triplet code and average molecular weight per protein subunit of 30,000, this DNA could code for about 100 proteins.

The presence of chloroplast ribosomes and the ability of isolated plastids to incorporate amino acids into an acid-insoluble form (Sager, 1963) provides preliminary evidence that protein synthesis occurs within the chloroplast *in vivo*. Whether both soluble and membrane-bound proteins are synthesized in the chloroplast should now be readily answerable. With the isolation of immature chloroplasts, it should become possible to study membrane formation in the isolated system, thus opening the way to a critical analysis of the factors controlling organelle formation.

As may be evident to the reader, recent developments in both the genetic and the biochemical analysis of *Chlamydomonas* have provided the material for a direct attack upon the genetic control of organelle formation, using the chloroplast as a model. It is probable that the same principles of organization and control will apply as well to other organelles, especially to mitochondria and to the flagellar-ciliary apparatus. Nonchromosomal genes may be of particular importance in subcellular organization, in which the synthesis of membrane-bound proteins and the correct spatial arrangement of macromolecules are involved (Sonneborn, 1964).

It is our view that the NC genes represent an essential fraction of the genetic material of all cells (excluding perhaps the bacteria) and that their role has been virtually ignored hitherto because of the dearth of mutants. The development of a method for the induction of NC gene mutations has made it possible to begin a systematic study of the role of this genetic system in *Chlamydomonas*. It should be possible to induce NC gene mutations in other organisms as well.

References

Bretscher, M. S., and Grunberg-Manago, M. (1962). *Nature* 195, 283–284.
Buffaloe, N. D. (1958). *Bull. Torrey Botan. Club* 85, 157–178.
Buffaloe, N. D. (1959). *Exp. Cell Res.* 16, 221–231.
Chance, B., and Sager, R. (1957). *Plant Physiol.* 32, 548–561.

Ebersold, W. T. (1964). Unpublished observations.

Ebersold, W. T. (1962). *In* "Physiology and Biochemistry of Algae" (R. A. Lewin, ed.), pp. 731–737. Academic Press, New York.

Ebersold, W. T., Levine, R. P., Levine, E. E., and Olmstead, M. A. (1962). *Genetics* 47, 531–543.

Ephrussi, B. (1953). "Nucleo-cytoplasmic Relations in Micro-organisms." Oxford Univ. Press (Clarendon), London and New York.

Forster, H., Wiese, L., and Braunitzer, G. (1956). Z. *Naturforsch.* 11b, 315–317.

Gibbs, S. P. (1962a). *J. Ultrastruct. Res.* 7, 418–435.

Gibbs, S. P. (1962b). *J. Ultrastruct. Res.* 7, 262–272.

Gillham, N. W. (1963a). *Genetics* 48, 431–440.

Gillham, N. W. (1963b). *Nature* 200, 294.

Gillham, N. W., and Levine, R. P. (1962). *Genetics* 47, 1463–1474.

Hartshorne, J. N. (1953). *New Phytologist* 52, 292–297.

Ishida, M. R., and Sager, R. (1963). Unpublished data.

Lang, N. J. (1963). *Am. J. Botany* 50, 280–300.

Levine, R. P., and Ebersold, W. T. (1960). *Ann. Rev. Microbiol.* 14, 197–216.

Levine, R. P., and Folsom, C. E. (1959). Z. *Vererbungslehre* 90, 215–222.

Levine, R. P., and Piette, L. H. (1962). *Biophys. J.* 2, 369–379.

Levine, R. P., and Smillie, R. (1962). *Proc. Natl. Acad. Sci. U.S.* 48, 417–421.

Levine, R. P., and Volkmann, D. (1961). *Biochem. Biophys. Res. Commun.* 6, 264–269.

Meselson, M., and Stahl, F. W. (1958). *Proc. Natl. Acad. Sci. U.S.* 44, 671–682.

Mitchell, M. B., and Mitchell, H. K. (1952). *Proc. Natl. Acad. Sci. U.S.* 38, 442–449.

Nirenberg, M. W., and Matthaei, J. H. (1961). *Proc. Natl. Acad. Sci. U.S.* 47, 1588–1602.

Rhoades, M. M. (1955). *In* "Handbuch der Pflanzen Physiologie" (W. Ruhland, ed.), Vol. 1, pp. 19–58. Springer, Berlin.

Ris, H., and Plaut, W. (1962). *J. Cell Biol.* 13, 383–392.

Sager, R. (1954). *Proc. Natl. Acad. Sci. U.S.* 40, 356–363.

Sager, R. (1955). *Genetics* 40, 476–489.

Sager, R. (1958). *Brookhaven Symp. Biol.* 11, 101–117.

Sager, R. (1960). *Science* 132, 1459–1465.

Sager, R. (1961). *Carnegie Inst. Wash. Yearbook* 60, 374–376.

Sager, R. (1962a). *Proc. Natl. Acad. Sci. U.S.* 48, 2018–2026.

Sager, R. (1962b). *Genetics* 47, 982.

Sager, R. (1963). Unpublished observations.

Sager, R., and Granick, S. (1953). *Proc. 6th Congr. Intern. Microbiol., Rome, 1953* 1, 684.

Sager, R., and Ishida, M. R. (1963). *Proc. Natl. Acad. Sci. U.S.* 49, 725–730.

Sager, R., and Palade, G. E. (1954). *Exptl. Cell Res.* 7, 584–588.

Sager, R., and Palade, G. E. (1957). *J. Biophys. Biochem. Cytol.* 3, 463–488.

Sager, R., and Ramanis, Z. (1963). *Proc. Natl. Acad. Sci. U.S.* 49, 260–268.

Sager, R., and Tsubo, Y. (1961). Z. *Vererbungslehre* 92, 430–438.

Sager, R., and Zalokar, M. (1958). *Nature* 182, 98–100.

Sager, R., Weinstein, I. B., and Ashkenazi, Y. (1963). *Science* 140, 304–306.

Sonneborn, T. M. (1964). *Proc. 16th Intern. Congr. Zool., Washington, D.C., 1963* in press.

Subak-Sharpe, H. (1956). Ph.D. Dissertation, Part II. Univ. of Birmingham.

Sueoka, N. (1960). *Proc. Natl. Acad. Sci. U.S.* 46, 83–90.

Taylor, J. H., Woods, P. S., and Hughes, W. L. (1957). *Proc. Natl. Acad. Sci. U.S.* 43, 121–128.

Tsubo, Y. (1961). *J. Protozool.* 8, 114–121.

Weaver, E. C., and Bishop, N. I. (1963). *Science* 140, 1095–1097.

Weinstein, I. B., Sager, R., and Fresco, J. R. (1963). *Federation Proc.* 22, 644.

Wiese, L., and Jones, R. (1963). *J. Cellular Comp. Physiol.* 61, 265–274.

The Plastid Pigments of Flagellates

T. W. GOODWIN

Department of Biochemistry and Agricultural Biochemistry,
The University College of Wales, Aberystwyth, Wales

		Page
I.	Introduction	319
II.	Chlorophylls	320
	A. Distribution of Chlorophylls	320
	B. Native Forms of Chlorophylls	322
	C. Formation of Chlorophylls	325
III.	Carotenoids	327
	A. Distribution of Carotenoids	327
	B. Formation of Carotenoids	332
IV.	Biliproteins	334
	A. Distribution of Biliproteins	334
	B. Formation of Biliproteins	334
V.	Pigmentation and Phylogeny of Phytoflagellates	335
VI.	Nonphotosynthetic Flagellates	336
	References	337

I. Introduction

The chloroplasts of all photosynthetic organisms contain chlorophylls and carotenoids; this appears to be a biological generalization without any qualifying clauses. To a biochemist interested in pigments as such the higher plants exhibit a dull uniformity; the main chlorophylls and carotenoids appear to be the same in all species of higher plants examined; the best one can hope for is to detect small variations in the minor carotenoid components. The algae, on the other hand, synthesize a rich variety of chloroplast pigments including a novel group, the biliproteins. This chapter will describe the intriguing variation in chloroplast pigments within the various classes of phytoflagellates, with

319

special reference to recent work which has been made possible by the isolation in axenic culture of many of these organisms. The biosynthesis of the pigments will only be discussed briefly because many of the biochemical investigations in this area have been carried out on organisms other than the phytoflagellates. The chapter will end with a consideration of the relevance of these pigment studies to the development of biochemical views on the evolution of phyto-flagellates.

II. Chlorophylls

A. DISTRIBUTION OF CHLOROPHYLLS

1. CHLOROPHYTA

All the green flagellates so far examined contain both chlorophyll *a* (I) and chlorophyll *b* (II). The species investigated include *Chlamydomonas* spp.

Chlorophyll *a*

(I)

Chlorophyll *b*

(II)

(Strain, 1958; Sager and Zalokar, 1958), *Dunaliella tertiolecta, Nannochloris atomus, Chlorella stigmatophora,* and *Tetraselmis suecica* (Jeffrey, 1961). The total concentrations of chlorophylls in *D. tertiolecta* and *N. atomus* are 8.19 and 1.84 mg./g. dry weight, respectively (Jeffrey, 1961). These should be compared with 0.35 mg./g. protein found in *Chlamydomonas reinhardi* (Sager and Zalokar, 1958). More quantitative data are urgently required but it is clear that wide variations in concentration can occur. The ratio *a:b* is essentially the same (2:1) in both *D. tertiolecta* and *N. atomus* (Jeffrey, 1961), but is somewhat lower (1.5:1) in *C. reinhardi*. The concentration of chlorophyll *b* is reduced to a very low level in a number of mutants of *Chlamydomonas* (Chance and Sager, 1957) and is absent from *Nannochloris oculata*, which however may belong to the Xanthophyceae (Allen *et al.*, 1960a). Pale green mutant strains of *C. reinhardi* for example contain from about one-tenth to one-twentieth the total chlorophylls (of which about 90% is chlorophyll *a*) found in the native strains, depending on whether the latter are cultured in the dark or in the light; the mutants die when grown in the light (Sager and Zalokar, 1958).

2. EUGLENOPHYTA

Chlorophylls *a* and *b* are also present in the euglenoids, but according to Allen *et al.* (1960a) the relative amount of chlorophyll *b* is less than in other green forms. This conclusion is supported by a graph published by Kirk (1962) which records the synthesis of chlorophylls when etiolated cells of *Euglena gracilis* are illuminated; an *a:b* ratio of about 4:1 is indicated.

3. CHRYSOPHYTA; CHRYSOPHYCEAE

The situation with regard to chlorophyll distribution in the golden brown flagellates is less clear cut than is the case with the green flagellates and the Euglenoids. Allen *et al.* (1960) reported that in the Ochromonadales, *Ochromonas danica* and *O. malhamensis* only chlorophyll *a* is present; on the other hand, they indicate that preliminary investivations suggest that chlorophyll *c* is present in *Prymnesium parvum*. Furthermore, Jeffrey (1961) has clearly demonstrated the presence of both chlorophylls *a* and *c* in *Isochrysis galbana* and *Sphaleromantis* sp. She considers that an earlier report that chlorophyll *c* was absent from *I. galbana* (Dales, 1960) was a result of using light petroleum instead of diethyl ether as extracting solvent: chlorophyll *c* is insoluble in light petroleum. This criticism may also apply to Dale's claim that chlorophyll *c* is absent from *Pseudopedinella* sp., *Phaester* type, *Hymenomonas* sp., *Pavlova gyrans*, *Phaeocystis pouchetti*, *Chrysochromulina ericina*, and *Dicrateria inornata*.

The *a:c* ratios in *Isochrysis galbana* and *Sphaleromantis* sp. are 2.6:1 and 3.6:1, respectively. The exact nature of chlorophyll *c* is unknown but it apparently does not contain phytol as a lipophilic side chain. The species of *Sphaleromantis* examined by Jeffrey contained another chlorophyll in trace amounts which is rather similar to chlorophyll *a* but which is not phaeophytin *a*.

4. CRYPTOPHYTA

All the cryptomonads so far examined contain both chlorophyll *a* and chlorophyll *c*. Species investigated include *Rhodomonas lens* (Haxo and Fork, 1959), *Cryptomonas ovata* var. *palustris* (French and Elliott, 1958; Haxo and Fork, 1959), and *Hemiselmis virescens* (Allen *et al.*, 1960b). Haxo and Fork (1959) found in traces an additional pigment, similar to chlorophyll *a*, and which did not appear to be an artifact, in *R. lens* and *C. ovata*; it does not appear to be the same pigment that Jeffrey (1961) reported in traces in a *Sphaleromantis* sp.

5. PYRROPHYTA; DINOPHYCEAE

The occurrence of chlorophylls *a* and *c* has been reported in *Peridinium cinctum* (Strain *et al.*, 1943), and in a *Gymnodinum* sp. (Jeffrey, 1961); the *a:c* ratio in the latter is 1.7:1.

6. CHLOROMONADOPHYCEAE

These organisms are rare and difficult to culture (Allen *et al.*, 1960a), so the biochemist must wait for the microbiologist to solve the nutritional problems involved in growing these flagellates before he can fill this gap in our knowledge of protistan pigments. Such impressive progress has been made in recent years in this field that his agony of suspense will surely not be excessively extended.

B. NATIVE FORMS OF CHLOROPHYLLS

The important technique of derivative spectrophotometry introduced by French (1957) has clearly revealed that a single molecular species of chlorophyll can exist *in vivo* in higher plants and algae in a number of forms, characterized by different absorption maxima in the red region of the spectrum. Instead of measuring the conventional absorption spectrum of a leaf or an alga, French measures the derivative spectrum, that is, the rate of change of absorption with wavelength, or in other words, the slope of the absorption curve. In this way any deviation from a simple curve is accentuated and the existence of additional peaks revealed. If the measurements are made at low temperatures $(-180°)$ then the derivative spectra can be made even sharper. In this way it has been shown that there are at least three forms of chlorophyll *a* in leaves: *Ca* 673, *Ca* 683, and *Ca* 695 (Brown and French, 1959; Brown, 1963a). The reality and functional importance of these different pigment forms have clearly been demonstrated by Duysens, among others, who has shown that for complete photosynthesis light must be absorbed by both *Ca* 673 and *Ca* 683. Detailed discussion of these important developments is not appropriate here, but the reader is referred to papers by Duysens *et al.* (1961), Witt *et al.* (1961), and Smith and French (1963).

Figure 1 illustrates the basis of the technique of derivative spectrophotometry. The derivative absorption spectrum of chlorophyll *a* crosses the base line at 662 mμ, that is at its point of maximum absorption, which is the change-over-point at which the slope $(dE/d\lambda)$ changes from a negative value to a positive value; the curve is also essentially symmetrical. The derivative spectrum of the red band of *Ochromonas danica* on the other hand crosses the base line at 678 mμ and this represents the maximum of the integral absorption band. However, the obvious asymmetry of the derivative spectrum indicates the presence of other components. By studying changes in the derivative spectrum of *O. danica*

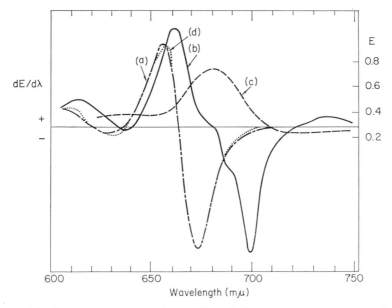

Fɪɢ. 1. The derivative spectrum of pure chlorophyll *a* in acetone (a) compared with the derivative absorption spectrum of an acetone extract of *Ochromonas danica* (d) and the integral (c) and derivative (b) absorption spectra of the red band of chlorophyll *a* in *Ochromonas danica*. (Adapted from Allen *et al.*, 1960a.)

under various conditions, e.g., in cultures of different ages (Fig. 2), it has been possible to show that there are three chlorophyll *a* components in O. *danica* and that their absorption maxima are at 670, 682, and 693 mμ, respectively (Allen *et al.*, 1960a). It will be recalled that *Ochromonas* spp. do not contain a chlorophyll other than chlorophyll *a,* so that the existence of more than one form of chlorophyll *a in vivo* is important from the point of view of photosynthesis. Allen *et al.* (1960a) point out that the *in vivo* absorption spectrum of O. *malhamensis* is much less complex than that of O. *danica,* and that this correlates with the fact that photosynthesis in O. *malhamensis* is feeble compared with that in O. *danica* (Myers and Graham, 1956). Similar experiments with *Euglena* have demonstrated native chlorophyll *a* components with maxima at 672–673, 683–684 and 694–695 mμ (Brown and French, 1959). Occasionally an absorption band also appears at 701 mμ (Brown, 1960). This is an *in vivo* complex of phaeophytin *a* which occurs in the cytoplasm (Brown, 1962).

It must be emphasized that these native forms of chlorophyll are so far identifiable only spectroscopically and functionally. It remains to be shown whether they have a separate existence and can be extracted as, for example, some form of chromoprotein, or whether the spectral properties result from different degrees of orientation of chlorophyll *a* itself in the chloroplast. In this con-

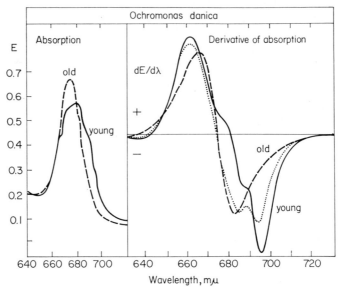

Fig. 2. Effect of age of culture on the absorption spectrum of *Ochromonas danica*. Integral spectra on left; derivative spectra on right. (After Allen *et al.*, 1960a.)

nection Wolken (1958) has reported the isolation and purification of "chloroplastin" from *Euglena*. This pigment-protein complex, which was extracted with digitonin is homogeneous in the ultracentrifuge, has an apparent molecular weight of 40,000, and probably contains one chlorophyll molecule associated with each protein macromolecule, although "the possibility that there may be two pigment molecules cannot be excluded." Brown (1959) was not able to separate the various *in vivo* forms of chlorophyll in *Euglena* by chromatography on, for example, DEAE columns, but she did achieve a demonstration of differential stability under different conditions (Brown, 1960, Table I) (see also Brown, 1963b).

Table I

RELATIVE STABILITY OF THE *in vivo* FORMS OF CHLOROPHYLL *a* IN EUGLENA[a]

Treatment	Chlorophyll *a* 673	Chlorophyll *a* 683	Chlorophyll *a* 695
Bright light	Slightly bleached	Partly bleached	Bleached
Heat (45°, 15 min.)	Stable	Stable	Bleached
Acid (isolated chloroplasts at pH 2 overnight)	Slightly bleached	Bleached	Stable

[a] Brown, 1960.

C. Formation of Chlorophylls

It is not intended here to discuss the considerable information on the biosynthetic pathway by which chlorophylls are synthesized from their building units acetate and glycine. This aspect has been authoritatively discussed by Bogorad (1960) and Smith (1960), and, in any case, the flagellated algae have not been employed in these investigations to any considerable extent. Here only experiments carried out with *Euglena* will be discussed.

Smith and his colleagues (see Smith, 1960) have clearly shown that the final specific step in the pathway of chlorophyll synthesis is the photoreduction of ring D of protochlorophyll (III) either in its chlorophyllide form or with phytol

Protochlorophyll

(III)

already attached. Wolken (1958) found that the action spectrum for chlorophyll synthesis in *Euglena gracilis* was very similar to the absorption spectrum of protochlorophyll and to the action spectrum for the protochlorophyll → chlorophyll conversion in illuminated etiolated oat seedlings (Frank, 1946). This has been confirmed by Nishimura and Huzisige (1959) who also demonstrated the presence of protochlorophyll in low concentration in dark-grown cells, and its conversion into chlorophyll on illumination. The absorption traces of acetone extracts of *E. gracilis* var. *bacillaris* grown in the dark and illuminated for varying times as reported by Schiff *et al.* (1961) indicated that under their experimental conditions protochlorophyll had reached a steady state which appeared to be unaffected by the onset of rapid chlorophyll synthesis.

The marked influence of light intensity on chlorophyll synthesis in *Euglena* is illustrated in Table II (Brown, 1960). Although a reduction in light intensity reduces growth considerably, the concentration of chlorophyll is markedly increased, as is the *a:b* ratio. When light-grown *E. gracilis* cells are transferred

Table II

INFLUENCE OF LIGHT INTENSITY ON CHLOROPHYLL *a* AND *b* CONTENT
OF 2-DAY CULTURES OF *Euglena*[a]

	Light intensity (foot candles)	
Chlorophyll content	1200	50
Total chlorophyll (mg./ml. culture)	1.0×10^{-2}	0.2×10^{-2}
Cell number/ml. culture	980×10^{3}	86×10^{3}
Chlorophyll *a* (mg./cell)	0.86×10^{-8}	2.4×10^{-8}
Ratio *a:b*	4.1:1	7.2:1

[a] Brown, 1960.

to darkness, a phaeophytin-like pigment is produced; the nature of this pigment is still unknown (Greenblatt and Schiff, 1959).

A number of investigators have examined the greening of colorless *Euglena* when illuminated. Kirk (1962) used 3-day cells of *E. gracilis* strain 1224/5 g and found that when these cells were washed, resuspended in 0.04M phosphate buffer at pH 7.0 (which also contained 0.001M $MgCl_2$), and intensely illuminated, chlorophyll synthesis began immediately and proceeded at a rate of 5.0–7.8 µg. per mg. dry weight per 6 hr. (Fig. 3); during this period there was

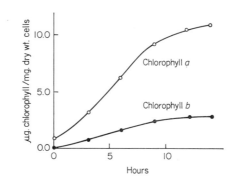

FIG. 3. Chlorophyll *a* and chlorophyll *b* synthesis in illuminated etiolated *Euglena* (for experimental conditions see text). (Adapted from Kirk, 1962.)

an insignificant increase in protein, nucleic acid, and cell count of the cultures. This was some 7 times as fast as that previously reported by Huzisige *et al.* (1957). Brawerman *et al.* (1962) on the other hand found a lag period of 24 hr. before chlorophyll synthesis began in illuminated etiolated *E. gracilis,* strain Z; for 48 hr. thereafter there was a rapid formation of pigment. In Kirk's experiments on the other hand, chlorophyll began to disappear from the cells after 9–10 hr. The etiolated cultures used by Kirk contained about 5% of the chlorophyll content of normal green cells and he reported that if cells containing no detectable chlorophyll were used chlorophyll synthesis began only after a long lag period. This is possibly one of the main differences between Kirk's experimental conditions and those of Brawerman *et al.*

Brawerman *et al.* (1962) also found that during the early greening period most of the chlorophyll synthesized appeared in small particles (mitochondria and microsomes) but later progressively larger amounts appeared in the plastids; the authors believe that this is probably due to the fact that in their early stages of development chloroplasts are very fragile and easily disrupted. The increase in protein synthesis during this period exactly parallels the synthesis of chlorophyll and is also essentially confined to the chloroplasts. An increase in RNA (ribonucleic acid) is also observed in the plastids. The pattern of changes in chlorophyll and protein is summarized in Fig. 4.

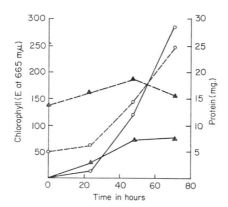

Fig. 4. The synthesis of chlorophyll and protein during chloroplast development in illuminated etiolated *Euglena*. Key: ————, chlorophyll; ———, protein; ○, plastids; ▲, small particles. (Adapted from Brawerman *et al.*, 1962.)

III. Carotenoids

A. Distribution of Carotenoids

1. chlorophyta

a. Plastid Carotenoids. The main plastid carotenoids of the chlorophytes, excluding the Siphonales, are reported to be the same as in the higher plants, namely, β-carotene (IV), lutein (3,3′-dihydroxy-α-carotene; V), violaxanthin (3,3′-dihydroxy, 5,6,5′,6′-diepoxy-β-carotene; VI), and neoxanthin (3,3′,5 (or 6)-trihydroxy-6(or 5)hydro-5′,6′-epoxy-β-carotene; VII); small amounts of

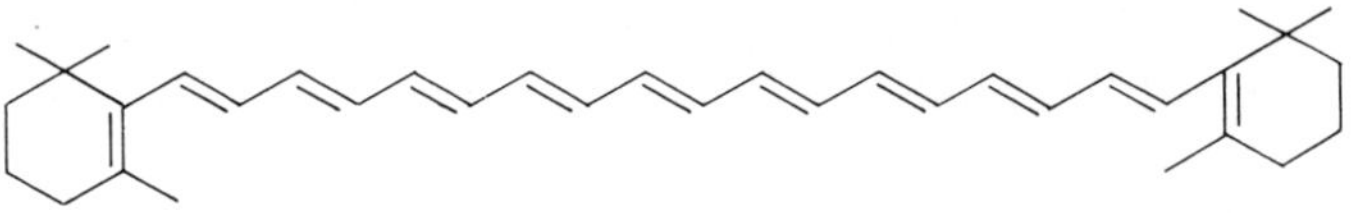

β-Carotene
(IV)

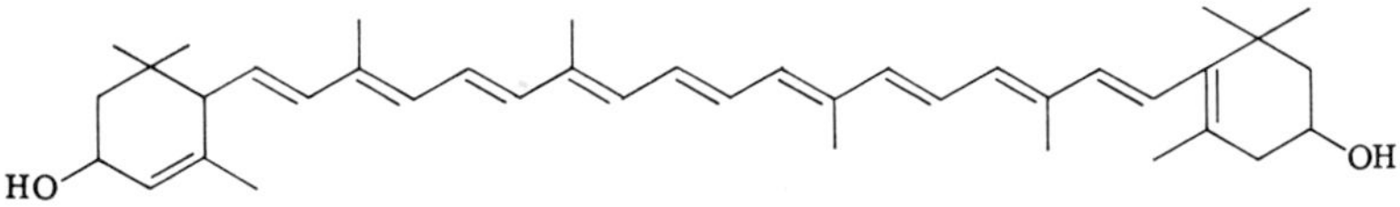

Lutein
(V)

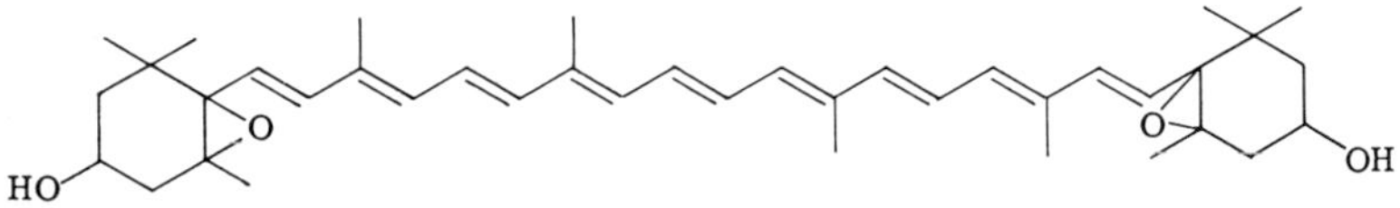

Violaxanthin
(VI)

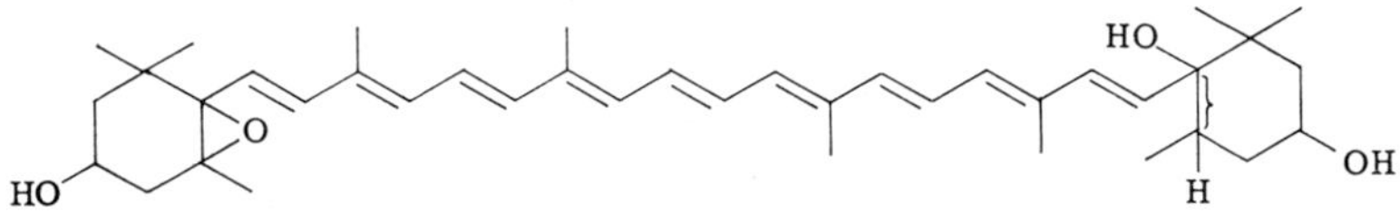

Neoxanthin
(VII)

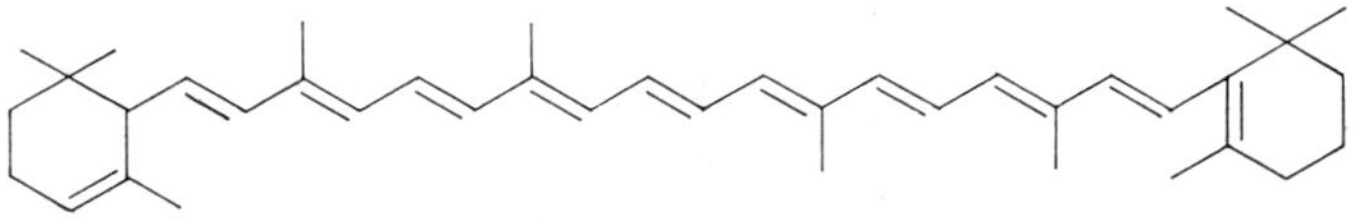

α-Carotene
(VIII)

α-carotene (VIII), and zeaxanthin (3,3′-dihydroxy-β-carotene) are also frequently present (Strain, 1951, 1958; Goodwin, 1952, 1962). The green flagellates are no exceptions to this general picture which is found in *Haematococcus
pluvialis* (Goodwin and Jamikorn, 1954a), *Chlamydomonas reinhardi* grown
in the dark (Sager and Zalokar, 1958), *Chlamydomonas agloeformis* and
Dunaliella salina (Strain, 1958), *Dunaliella teriolecta, Nannochloris atomus,
Chlorella stigmatophora,* and *Tetraselmis suecica* (Jeffrey, 1961). A complex
mixture of xanthophylls is present in *Chlamydomonas reinhardi* grown in the
light (Sager and Zalokar, 1958); as some of the xanthophylls appear to be
highly oxidized pigments, they may represent photochemical breakdown products in senescent or dead cells. In *Chlamydomonas reinhardi* the α:β-ratio is

1:20 (Sager and Zalokar, 1958) which is typical of the Chlorophyta and higher plants, but *C. agloeformis* contains "much α-carotene" (Strain, 1958). The ratio of xanthophylls to carotenes, generally about 3:1 in higher plants and 4.2:1 in *Chlorella pyrenoidosa* (Allen *et al.*, 1960b), is very variable in the green flagellates, ranging from 1:3 in *Chlamydomonas reinhardi* to 5.5:1 in *N. atomus*. A pale green mutant of *C. reinhardi* has been reported which contains only about 0.2–0.5% of the carotenoids present in the native strain; all the pigments present in this strain are carotenes, no xanthophylls could be detected (Sager and Zalokar, 1958). The concentrations of total carotenoids vary from 3.46 mg./g. dry weight in dark-grown *C. reinhardi* to 0.54 mg./g. dry weight in *N. atomus*. The concentration of carotenoids in light-grown *C. reinhardi* is only 1.42 mg./g. dry weight. This general situation was also observed in *Chlorella vulgaris* (Goodwin, 1954).

b. Extraplastidic Pigments. Under certain unfavorable nutritional conditions many flagellates go into a resting state and encyst. The process is often accompanied by the production of relatively large amounts of extraplastidic carotenoid pigments—known collectively as "hematochrome." As the chemical nature of these pigments is now clear this term can in most circumstances be discarded. The extraplastidic pigment in *Dunaliella salina* is β-carotene (Fox and Sargent, 1938), and in *Haematococcus pluvialis* (Tischer, 1944; Goodwin and Jamikorn, 1954a) and *Nannochloris atomus* (Jeffrey, 1961) it is astaxanthin (3,3'-dihydroxy-4,4'-dioxo-β-carotene). In both of the last two cases the pigment is esterified; plastid xanthophylls are always unesterified (Goodwin, 1952).

2. EUGLENOPHYTA

a. Plastid Pigments. The main carotenoids in *Euglena* species are β-carotene, antheraxanthin (5,6-epoxyzeaxanthin), and neoxanthin (Krinsky and Goldsmith, 1960; Davies, 1961). Earlier reports had indicated that lutein was the main pigment in *Euglena* (Goodwin and Jamikorn, 1954b); it is clear that the techniques then in use did not distinguish between lutein and antheraxanthin. There is no report that α-carotene is synthesized by *Euglena*, but traces of γ-carotene are reported (Krinsky and Goldsmith, 1960).

b. Extraplastidic Pigments. The euglenoids possess bright orange eyespots (stigma), and the pigmentation of the eyespot has frequently been ascribed to carotenoids; this remains to be proved, but it is possible that echinenone (4-oxo-β-carotene), hydroxyechinenone (3-hydroxy-4-oxo-β-carotene), and euglenarhodone (possible structure: 3,4-dioxo-β-carotene) are eyespot pigments. These pigments have been found in traces in normal *Euglena* cells by Krinsky and Goldsmith (1960) and echinenone was found in a chlorotic substrain of *Euglena gracilis* (strain HB-G) which contains no chloroplasts but which retains its eyespot (Goodwin and Gross, 1958). This strain also contains traces of "plastid" pigments, but echinenone is now the main pigment and it would seem that only echinenone has retained its original concentration following bleaching. However, in other bleached strains echinenone could not be detected. Recently a method has been developed for isolating the eyespots of *E. gracilis* strain Z; the pigments in the eyespots are β-carotene, cryptoxanthin, lutein and an unidentified compound (Batra and Tollin, 1964).

There are early reports that the red *Euglena heliorubescens* contains astaxanthin (Kuhn *et al.*, 1939; Tischer, 1941), and it was this that led to the belief that the bright red pigment, astaxanthin, was the pigment of all eyespots (Heilbron, 1942). It has never been possible to demonstrate the existence of astaxanthin in green *Euglena* (Krinsky and Goldsmith, 1960) or in bleached substrains, where conditions for detecting an eyespot pigment would be better (Goodwin and Jamikorn, 1954b; Goodwin and Gross, 1958; Wolken, 1961).

c. Pigments in Chlorotic Substrains. It has already been reported in the chlorophyll section that *Euglena* spp. when grown heterotrophically in the dark are colorless and that on illumination they rapidly turn green. Although all the chlorophyll disappears from dark-grown cultures, some carotenoids, about 20–25% always remains (Goodwin and Jamikorn, 1954b); however, carotenoids are synthesized along with chlorophylls when etiolated cells are exposed to light under conditions which do not allow cell multiplication (Kirk, 1962).

Provasoli *et al.* (1948) found that if *Euglena gracilis* is grown in the presence of streptomycin it becomes a permanently bleached strain, owing to the destruction of its ability to synthesize chloroplasts. Similar chlorotic strains can be produced by dihydrostreptomycin (Huzisige *et al.*, 1957) and other streptomycin-type antibiotics (Zahalsky *et al.*, 1962), by 3-amino-1,2,4-triazole (Aaronson and Scher, 1960), by antihistamine drugs (Gross *et al.*, 1955; Zahalsky *et al.*, 1962), by O-methylthreonine (Gray and Hendlin, 1962; Aaronson and Bensky, 1962), by heat (Pringsheim and Pringsheim, 1952), and by ultraviolet irradiation (Pringsheim, 1958). While chlorophyll synthesis is entirely inhibited in bleached strains, residual carotenoids are frequently

Phytofluene

(IX)

ζ-Carotene

(X)

present in small amounts (Goodwin and Jamikorn, 1954b; Goodwin and Gross, 1958); in some cases there are qualitative changes in the carotenoids and traces of the partly saturated polyenes phytofluene (IX) and ζ-carotene (X), which are precursors of the fully unsaturated carotenoids (see Goodwin, 1963), are observed (Goodwin and Gross, 1958).

The bleaching of *Euglena* by DL-O-methylthreonine is competitively inhibited by L-isoleucine, L-threonine, L-homoserine, α-aminobutyric acid, and α-oxobutyric acid; the last named was the most effective (Aaronson and Bensky, 1962). The inhibition of pigment synthesis by 3-amino-1,2,4-triazole is annulled by Fe^{++} or Fe^{+++} (Aaronson, 1960), and that by streptomycin by Mn^{++} (Kirk, 1962).

3. CHRYSOPHYTA; CHRYSOPHYCEAE

In 1942 Heilbron reported that β-carotene and fucoxanthin were the main carotenoid pigments present in a mixed culture of *Apistonema carteri*, *Thallochrysis litoralis*, and *Gloeschrysis maritima*. Almost 20 years elapsed before the next report appeared when Allen *et al.* (1960b) confirmed Heilbron's results using pure cultures of *Ochromonas danica* and *Prymnesium parvum*. Fucoxanthin represented some 75% of the total carotenoids, the remainder being mainly β-carotene together with traces of diatoxanthin and a pigment more strongly adsorbed than fucoxanthin. Fucoxanthin was also the main pigment in *Isochrysis galbana* (Dales, 1960; Jeffrey, 1961), *Sphaleromantis* sp. (Jeffrey, 1961), and *Pseudopedinella* sp., *Phaeaster* type, *Pavlova gyrans*, *Phaeocystis pouchetti*, *Chrysochromulina ericina*, *Dicrateria inomata*, and *Hymenomonas* sp. (Dales, 1960). Diatoxanthin was also present in *I. galbana* and *Sphaleromantis* sp. and diadinoxanthin in the former and dinoxanthin in the latter (Jeffrey, 1961). Dales (1960) also reported diadinoxanthin in *I. galbana* but Jeffrey could not detect this pigment.

Fucoxanthin, which is also the main carotenoid of Phaeophyceae, and thus probably the most abundant naturally occurring carotenoid, still defies all attempts of the organic chemists to unravel its structure. Diatoxanthin, diadinoxanthin, and dinoxanthin were first described by Strain (1944) and Strain *et al.* (1944); spectroscopically they are somewhat similar to zeaxanthin, lutein, and violaxanthin respectively, but they can be separated from the pigments by careful chromatography. Their structures are unknown.

β-Carotene was the only carotene present in *Ochromonas danica*, but was accompanied by a second pigment, possibly a *cis*-isomer of β-carotene in *Prymnesium parvum* (Allen *et al.*, 1960). On the other hand the eight chrysophyceae examined by Dales (1960) contained α- and γ-carotene in addition to β-carotene.

The xanthophyll:carotene ratio is high, ranging from 8.4:1 and 25.5:1 in *I. galbana* and *Sphaleromantis* sp. (Jeffrey, 1961) to 4.8:1 and 12.5:1 in

O. *danica* and P. *parvum*, respectively (Allen *et al.*, 1960b). The total concentration of carotenoids in these last two algae is 4.28 and 10.57 mg./g. dry weight respectively. Thus P. *parvum* becomes currently the richest known algal source of carotenoids, the previous best being 7.0 mg./g. dry weight recorded for *Euglena gracilis* var. *bacillaris* (Goodwin and Jamikorn, 1954b). The concentrations observed in *I. galbana* and *Sphaleromantis* sp. are lower: 3.59 and 2.65 mg./g. dry weight, respectively (Jeffrey, 1961).

4. CRYPTOPHYTA

The first report on the carotenoids of a member of this class was by Haxo and Fork (1959) who found that the main carotene was, surprisingly, α-carotene, and that the main xanthophyll was zeaxanthin or the closely related diatoxanthin. D. M. Thomas (1962) using a *Cryptomonas* sp. kindly supplied by Dr. M. B. Allen demonstrated that this strain also only produced α-carotene and that the main xanthophyll was not zeaxanthin but diatoxanthin. An unidentified pigment more strongly adsorbed than diatoxanthin was also detected. The xanthophyll:carotene ratio was 2.4:1 and 4.7:1 in *C. ovata* and *Cryptomonas* sp., respectively, and the total carotenoid concentration in the latter was 1.61 mg./g. dry weight. *Hemiselmis virescens*, however, does not follow the pattern observed in the *Cryptomonas* spp. The carotenoids present are β-carotene, lutein, diatoxanthin, and an unknown strongly adsorbed pigment; the xanthophyll-carotene ratio is 5.4:1 and the total carotenoid concentration 0.484 mg./g. dry weight (D. M. Thomas, 1962; Allen *et al.*, 1964). ε-Carotene (a carotene with two α-ionone residues) has recently been reported in *C. ovata* (Chapman and Haxo, 1963), it had previously been recorded only in members of two widely unrelated algal groups: in the marine green alga *Bryopsis corticulans* and the epiphytic marine diatom *Navicula torquatum* (see Strain, 1958).

5. PYRROPHYTA; DINOPHYCEAE

In 1927, Kylin reported a characteristic pigment, peridinin in *Peridinium* spp. It was also observed as the major pigment along with smaller quantities of dinoxanthin and diadinoxanthin in the fresh-water *Peridinium cinctum* (Strain *et al.*, 1944). A similar distribution was also observed in *Gymnodinium* sp. (Jeffrey, 1961). The structures of these pigments are unknown. β-Carotene is also present in the Dinophyceae and the xanthophyll:carotene ratio in *Gymnodinium* sp. is 7:1; the total carotenoid concentration is 0.80 mg./g. dry weight.

B. FORMATION OF CAROTENOIDS

The general pattern of carotenoid biosynthesis is now reasonably clear (see Goodwin, 1963). "Active isoprene," isopentenyl pyrophosphate, is formed

from acetate via β-hydroxy-β-methylglutaryl-CoA and mevalonate (Fig. 5).
Isopentenyl pyrophosphate is then converted into a C_{20} unit, probably geranyl-
geranyl pyrophosphate, which dimerizes to form phytoene, the basic C_{40}
polyene, which is then converted into β-carotene. The exact point of ring

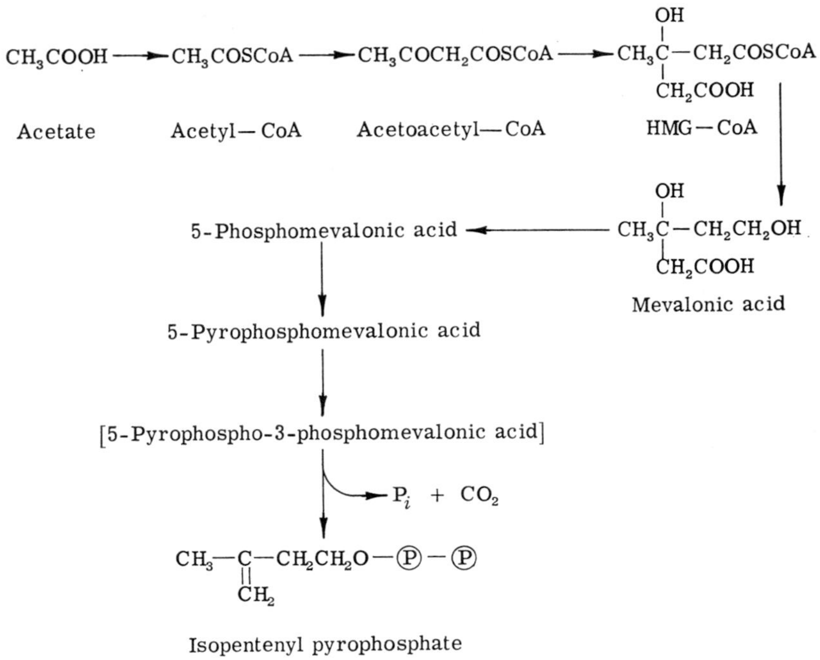

$$CH_3COOH \longrightarrow CH_3COSCoA \longrightarrow CH_3COCH_2COSCoA \longrightarrow \underset{\displaystyle \underset{CH_2COOH}{|}}{\overset{\displaystyle \overset{OH}{|}}{CH_3C}}-CH_2COSCoA$$

Acetate   Acetyl—CoA   Acetoacetyl—CoA   HMG—CoA

5-Phosphomevalonic acid $\longleftarrow$ $\underset{\displaystyle \underset{CH_2COOH}{|}}{\overset{\displaystyle \overset{OH}{|}}{CH_3C}}-CH_2CH_2OH$

Mevalonic acid

5-Pyrophosphomevalonic acid

[5-Pyrophospho-3-phosphomevalonic acid]

$\longrightarrow P_i + CO_2$

$$CH_3-\underset{\displaystyle \overset{\|}{CH_2}}{C}-CH_2CH_2O-\textcircled{P}-\textcircled{P}$$

Isopentenyl pyrophosphate

Fig. 5. The biosynthetic pathway for isopentenyl pyrophosphate.

formation in the final steps is still in doubt. Steele and Gurin (1960) degraded
the β-carotene produced by *Euglena gracilis* in the presence of [1-C^{14}]- and
[2-C^{14}]acetate. The distribution of label (Fig. 6) is in complete agreement

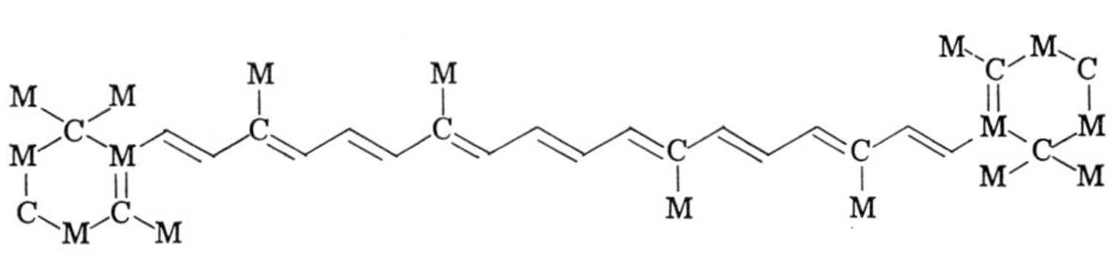

Fig. 6. The distribution of radioactivity in β-carotene synthesized by *Euglena
gracilis* grown in the presence of [1-C^{14}]acetate (C) and [2-C^{14}]acetate (M).
(Steele and Gurin, 1960.)

with the pathway outlined in Fig. 5, as was the distribution observed when
[2-C^{14}]mevalonate was the substrate. A further interesting observation made

by Steele and Gurin (1960) was that β-hydroxy-β-methylglutaric acid, although it stimulates carotenogenesis, is itself insignificantly incorporated into β-carotene. An explanation of this observation has not yet been advanced.

IV. Biliproteins

A. Distribution of Biliproteins

The chromoproteins, which for a long period have been known to occur in the blue-green and red algae, are termed biliproteins and their prosthetic groups phycobilins (ÓhEocha, 1960, 1964). The red pigments are phycoerythrins and the blue pigments phycocyanins, and they are termed R- or C-phycoerythrin and R- or C-phycocyanin according to whether they were obtained from the Rhodophyceae or the Cyanophyceae (Svedberg and Katsurai, 1929). This nomenclature is becoming increasingly difficult to apply unambiguously, since biliproteins are now known to occur in the Cryptomonads.

The red pigment from *Cryptomonas ovata* with a maximum at 565–568 mμ has a spectrum reminiscent of C-phycoerythrin but it also exhibits a shoulder at 600 mμ which is not present in C-phycoerythrin (Allen *et al.*, 1959; Haxo and Fork, 1959). The red pigment from *Rhodomonas lens* has a maximum at 556 mμ while those from *Hemiselmis rufescens*, *Cryptochrysis*, *Sennia* sp., and *Rhodomonas lens* are at 555 mμ, 554 mμ, 545 mμ, and 545 mμ, respectively (ÓhEocha and Raftery, 1959). However, all three contain the same prosthetic group, which also has the same spectral properties as the phycoerythrobilin obtained from R-, C-, and B-phycoerythrins (ÓhEocha, 1960); [β-phycoerythrin is obtained from the Rhodophyceae but has a different spectrum from R-phycoerythrin (Airth and Blinks, 1956)]. The nature of the pigment is still doubtful; some of its chemical properties are listed by ÓhEocha (1960).

Blue biliproteins have been obtained from *Hemiselmis virescens* (Allen *et al.*, 1959; ÓhEocha and Raftery, 1959), and, in trace amounts, from those cryptomonads (quoted above) which produce mainly red biliproteins (ÓhEocha and Raftery, 1959). The two strains of *H. virescens* which have been examamined synthesize two different biliproteins; the maxima for that from the Droop strain are 580, 620–625, and 646 mμ, while those for the Plymouth strain are at 588 and 615 mμ. Both pigments differ from R-phycocyanin (λ max 555, 615 mμ), C-phycocyanin (615 mμ), and allophycocyanin (650 mμ); [allophycocyanin occurs in small quantities in many blue-green and red algae (Haxo *et al.*, 1955)].

B. Formation of Biliproteins

Nothing is known of the biosynthesis of bile proteins in cryptomonads, or, for that matter, in other algae.

V. Pigmentation and Phylogeny of Phytoflagellates

A considerable amount of discussion has taken place regarding the significance of pigment studies as a means of evaluating the pattern of protistan evolution. Dougherty and Allen (1960) discussed this in detail and put forward a hypothetical scheme for the evolution of algal metaprostists. Goodwin (1962, 1963) considered this from the standpoint of carotenoid pigments only and produced a somewhat simplified scheme (Fig. 7). It will be useful to see how the more recent carotenoid work reported here fits into this scheme and whether it can accommodate the observations on chlorophyll and biliprotein distribution.

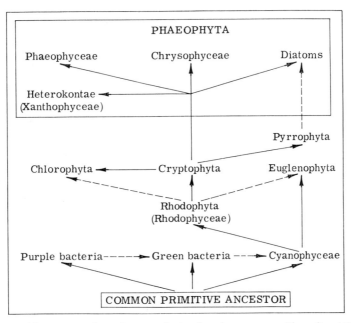

FIG. 7. Possible pattern of protistan evolution based on carotenoid studies (Goodwin, 1962.)

The following observations on carotenoid distribution justify this scheme: (a) the blue-green algae produce only β-carotene derivatives; (b) the red algae are more complex than the blue-green algae in that they produce both α- and β-carotene derivatives; (c) morphologically the Cryptophyta appear to be intermediate between the Rhodophyta and the Phaeophyta and this is supported by carotenoid studies; the xanthophylls of the Cryptophyta tend to be in a higher state of oxidation than those of the Rhodophyta and in a lower state than those of the Phaeophyta (D. M. Thomas, 1962; Allen *et al.*, 1964); (d) the Chrysophyceae synthesize fucoxanthin, a characteristic of all Phaeophyta except Heterokonts (Strain, 1958; D. M. Thomas, 1962); (c) the common synthesis of diadinoxanthin suggests a linkage between the Pyrrophyta and the Bacillariophyceae (diatoms), although the synthesis of peridinin by the Pyrrophyta and their failure to synthesize fucoxanthin emphasizes their difference; (f) the carotenoids of the Euglenophyta (β-carotene derivatives, including echinenone) clearly ally them more closely with the blue-green algae than with the Chlorophyta, which produce mixed (α- and β-type) carotenoids.

How well do the other photosynthetic pigments of the phytoflagellates fit into this pattern? The biliproteins occur in the Cryptophyta; this is consistent with their evolution from Cyanophyta via Rhodophyta, which is also suggested by carotenoid pigment distribution. With regard to chlorophyll distribution, chlorophyll *c* is found in all flagellates studied except the Chlorophyta and Euglenophyta, that is in the Cryptophyta, Dinophyceae, and Chrysophyceae, which clearly, as indicated in Fig. 7, must be on a different line from Chlorophyta and Euglenophyta. The existence of chlorophyll *a* and *b* in the Chlorophyta and Euglenophyta suggest a closer relationship than indicated in Fig. 7; however, their carotenoid distribution belie a close relationship and it is possible that, as indicated, they could have evolved as separate lines, both producing chlorophylls *a* and *b*, from the Rhodophyta, which essentially only synthesize chlorophyll *a* [the existence of chlorophyll *d* in Rhodophyta (Strain, 1958) still remains controversial (Allen *et al.*, 1960a)].

The scheme in Fig. 7 and the comments on the scheme must be considered as tentative; their main aim is to catalyze further investigations which will help to put this tiny edifice of "biochemical evolution" on a firmer basis.

VI. Nonphotosynthetic Flagellates

Only one heterotrophic phytoflagellate, *Polytoma uvella,* has been examined; its motile stage is yellow-orange while its resting, encysted, stage is somewhat darker red (Pringsheim and Mainx, 1926). The pigments have been examined by Links and his colleagues (Links, *et al.*, 1954; 1960; Links, 1955). The only carotene present in β-carotene, while the main xanthophylls present are echinenone and a weakly acidic pigment which has been termed polytomaxanthin [λ max 460–464 mμ (petroleum ether), 481 mμ (benzene), 500–502 (carbon disulfide)]. Its structure is unknown but it has similarities with euglenarhodone (Krinsky and Goldsmith, 1960). Twelve other minor components were present but astaxanthin was not detected. The observations have been generally confirmed by E. W. Thomas in the author's laboratory on a sample of *P. uvella,* kindly supplied by Dr. J. F. Ryley. Similar experiments by D. M. Thomas have demonstrated the probable presence of α-carotene and a series of ketocarotenoids in the pale yellow *Astasia ocellata*.

The xanthophyll:carotene ratio was about 4:1 and the concentration of total carotenoids between 0.3 and 0.4 mg./g. dry weight (Links *et al.*, 1960).

The general view is that *P. uvella* is descended from *Chlamydomonas* (Fritsch, 1948). The nature of the carotenoid pigments would not support this view; they are far more closely allied to the euglenoid pigments. Furthermore the major sterol in *P. uvella* is ergosterol or a closely related compound (Links, 1955; E. W. Thomas, 1961). This is also the main sterol in *Euglena gracilis* (Stern *et al.*, 1960) and a number of other non-photosynthetic flagellates (B. L. Williams, unpublished observations) but it is not a universal component of the sterols of the Chlorophyta; it is present in some strains of *Chlorella pyrenoidosa* (Klosty and Bergmann, 1952) but not in others (W. E. Davies and A. Dennis, unpublished observations).

REFERENCES

Aaronson, S. (1960). *J. Protozool.* 7, 289.

Aaronson, S., and Bensky, B. (1962). *J. Gen. Microbiol.* 27, 75.

Aaronson, S., and Scher, S. (1960). *J. Protozool.* 7, 156.

Airth, R. L., and Blinks, L. R. (1956). *Biol. Bull.* 111, 321.

Allen, M. B., Dougherty, E. C., and McLaughlin, J. J. A. (1959). *Nature* 184, 1047.

Allen, M. B., French, C. S., and Brown, J. S. (1960a). *In* "Comparative Biochemistry of Photoreactive Systems" (M. B. Allen, ed.), p. 33. Academic Press, New York.

Allen, M. B., Goodwin, T. W., and Phagpolngarm, S. (1960b). *J. Gen. Microbiol.* 23, 93.

Allen, M. B., Fries, L., Thomas, D. M., and Goodwin, T. W. (1964). *J G.en. Microbiol.*, 34, 259.

Batra, P. P., and Tollin, G. (1964). *Biochim. Biophys. Acta,* 49, 371.

Bogorad, L. (1960). *In* "Comparative Biochemistry of Photoreactive Systems" (M. B. Allen, ed.), p. 227. Academic Press, New York.

Brawerman, G., Pogo, A. O., and Chargaff, E. (1962). *Biochim. Biophys. Acta* 55, 326.

Brown, J. S. (1959). *Carnegie Inst. Wash. Year Book* 58, 330.

Brown, J. S. (1960). *Carnegie Inst. Wash. Year Book* 59, 330.

Brown, J. S. (1962). *Carnegie Inst. Wash. Year Book* 61, 352.

Brown, J. S., and French, C. S. (1959). *Plant Physiol.* 34, 305.

Brown, J. S. (1963a). *Photochem. and Photobiol.*, 2, 159.

Brown, J. S. (1963b). *Biochim. Biophys. Acta,* 75, 299.

Chance, B., and Sager, R. (1957). *Plant Physiol.* 32, 548.

Chapman, D. J., and Haxo, F. T. (1963). *Plant & Cell Physiol.* 4, 57.

Dales, R. P. (1960). *J. Marine Biol. Assoc. U.K.* 39, 693.

Davies, B. H. (1961), Ph.D. Thesis. University of Wales Aberystwyth.

Dougherty, E. C., and Allen, M. B. (1960). *In* "Comparative Biochemistry of Photoreactive Systems" (M. B. Allen, ed.), p. 129. Academic Press, New York.

Duysens, L .M. N., Amesz, J., and Kamf, B. M. (1961). *Nature* 190, 510.

Fox, D. L., and Sargent, M. C. (1938). *Chem. & Ind.* (*London*) 57, 1111.

Frank, S. R. (1946). *J. Gen. Physiol.* 27, 157.

French, C. S. (1957). *Proc. Instr. Control Symp. Instr. Soc. Am.* p. 83. (Sponsored by Northern Calif. Sect.)

French, C. S., and Elliott, R. F. (1958). *Carnegie Inst. Wash. Year Book* 57, 282.

Fritsch (1948).

Goodwin, T. W. (1952). "The Comparative Biochemistry of Carotenoids. Chapman & Hall, London.

Goodwin, T. W. (1954). *Experientia* 10, 23.

Goodwin, T. W. (1961). *Proc. 5th Intern. Congr. Biochem.*, *Moscow* 7, 294 (publ. 1963).

Goodwin, T. W. (1962). *In* "Comparative Biochemistry" (M. Florkin and H. S. Mason, eds.), Vol. 4, Part B. 643. Academic Press, New York.

Goodwin, T. W. (1963). "The Biosynthesis of Vitamins." Academic Press, New York.

Goodwin, T. W., and Gross, J. A. (1958). *J. Protozool.* 5, 292.

Goodwin, T. W., and Jamikorn, M. (1954a). *Biochem. J.* 57, 376.

Goodwin, T. W., and Jamikorn, M. (1954b). *J. Protozool* 1, 216.

Granick, S. (1949). *J. Biol. Chem.* 179, 505.

Gray, R. A., and Hendlin, D. (1962). *Plant Physiol.* 37, 223.

Greenblatt, C. L., and Schiff, J. A. (1959). *J. Protozool.* 6, 23.

Gross, J. A., Jahn, T. L., and Bernstein, E. (1955). *J. Protozool.* 2, 71.

Haxo, F. T., and Fork, D. C. (1959). *Nature* 184, 10.

Haxo, F. T., O'hEocha, C., and Norris, P. (1955). *Arch. Biochem. Biophys.* 54, 162.

Heilbron, I. M. (1942). *J. Chem. Soc.* p. 79.

Huzisige, H., Terada, T., Nishimura, M., and Uemura, T. (1957). *Biol. J. Okayama Univ.* 3, 209.

Jeffrey, S. W. (1961). *Biochem. J.* 80, 336.

Kirk, J. T. O. (1962). *Biochim. Biophys. Acta* 56, 139.

Klosty, M., and Bergmann, W. (1952). *J. Am. Chem. Soc.* 74, 1601.

Krinsky, N. I., and Goldsmith, T. H. (1960). *Arch. Biochem. Biophys.* 91, 271.

Kuhn, R., Stene, J., and Sörensen, N. A. (1939). *Ber. Deut. Chem. Ges.* 72, 1688.

Kylin, H. (1927). *Z. Physiol. Chem.* 166, 39.

Links, J. (1955). Ph.D. Thesis. University of Leyden, Netherlands.

Links, J., Verloop, A., and Havinga, E. (1954). *Rappt. Commun. Congr. Intern. Botan., 8th, Paris, 1954* 17, 35.

Links, J., Verloop, A., and Havinga, E. (1960). *Arch. Mikrobiol.* 36, 306.

Myers, J., and Graham, J. R. (1956). *J. Cellular Comp. Physiol.* 47, 397.

Nishimura, M., and Huzisige, H. (1959). *J. Biochem.* (*Tokyo*) 46, 225.

ÓhEocha, C. (1960). *In* "Comparative Biochemistry of Photoreactive Pigments" (M. B. Allen, ed.), p. 181. Academic Press, New York.

ÓhEocha, C., and Raftery, M. (1959). *Nature* 184, 1049.

ÓhEocha, C. (1964). *In* "Biochemistry of Plant Pigments" (T. W. Goodwin, ed.) 4, 57. Academic Press, London.

Pringsheim, E. G. (1958). *Rev. Algol.* [N.S.] 4, 41.

Pringsheim, E. G., and Mainz, F. (1926). *Planta* 1, 583.

Pringsheim, E. G., and Pringsheim, O. (1952). *New Phytologist* 51, 65.

Provasoli, L., Hutner, S. H., and Schatz, A. (1948). *Proc. Soc. Exptl. Biol. Med.* 69, 279.

Sager, R., and Zalokar, M. (1958). *Nature* 182, 98.

Schiff, J. A., Lyman, H., and Epstein, H. T. (1961). *Biochim. Biophys. Acta* 51, 340.

Smith, J. H. C. (1960). *In* "Comparative Biochemistry of Photoreactive Pigments" (M. B. Allen, ed.) p. 257. Academic Press, New York.

Smith, J. H. C., and Benitez, A. (1955). *Mod. Methods Plant Anal.* 4, 143.

Smith, J. H. C. and French, C. S. (1963). *Am. Rev. Plant Physiol.,* 14, 181.

Steele, W. J., and Gurin, S. (1960). *J. Biol. Chem.* 235, 2778.

Stern, A. I., Schiff, J. A., and Klein, H. P. (1960). *J. Protozool.* 7, 52.

Strain, H. H. (1944). *Ann. Rev. Biochem.* 13, 591.

Strain, H. H. (1951). *In* "Manual of Phycology" (G. M. Smith, ed.). Chronica Botanica, Waltham, Massachusetts.

Strain, H. H. (1958). "Chloroplast Pigments and Chromatographic Analysis." Penn. State Univ. Press, University Park, Pennsylvania.

Strain, H. H., Manning, W. M., and Hardin, G. (1943). *J. Biol. Chem.* 148, 655.

Strain, H. H., Manning, W. M., and Hardin, G. (1944). *Biol. Bull.* 86, 169.

Svedberg, T., and Katsurai, T. (1929). *J. Am. Chem. Soc.* 51, 3573.

Thomas, D. M. (1962). M.Sc. Thesis. University of Wales Aberystwyth.

Thomas, E. W. (1961). Unpublished observations.

Tischer, J. (1941). *Z. Physiol. Chem.* 267, 281.

Tischer, J. (1944). *Z. Physiol. Chem.* 281, 143.

Witt, H. T., Muller, A., and Rumberg, B. (1961). *Nature* 191, 194.

Wolken, J. J. (1958). *Brookhaven Symp. Biol.* 11, 87.

Wolken, J. J. (1961). "Euglena." Rutgers Univ. Press, New Brunswick, New Jersey.

Zahalsky, A. C., Hutner, S. H., Keane, M., and Burger, R. M. (1962). *Arch. Mikrobiol.* 42, 46.

Biochemistry of Acrasiales

BARBARA E. WRIGHT

The J. Collins Warren Laboratories of the Huntington Memorial Hospital of Harvard University, at the Massachusetts General Hospital, Boston, Massachusetts

		Page
I.	Introduction	341
II.	The Aggregation Process	343
	A. Evidence Relating to the Chemical Nature of the Chemotactic Agent	343
	B. Aggregateless Mutants	345
	C. Inhibitors and Stimulants of Aggregation	347
III.	Endogenous Changes in Respiration and Substrate Levels during Differentiation	347
	A. Respiration in the Absence and Presence of Glucose during Development	350
	B. Antigenic Changes Occurring during Differentiation	354
	C. Net Loss of Nitrogenous Compounds as a Function of Developmental Stage	355
	D. Net Gain in Carbohydrates during Morphogenesis	356
	E. Fatty Acid Biosynthesis	360
IV.	Protein Synthesis	362
V.	Enzyme Activities	363
	A. *In Vitro* Evidence	363
	B. A Comparison of *in Vivo* and *in Vitro* Evidence	366
VI.	Speculations on Control Mechanisms of Biochemical Differentiation in the Slime Mold	377
	References	379

I. Introduction

Sporulation of the cellular slime mold, *Dictyostelium discoideum,* is normally achieved as the result of a differentiation process involving many thousands of cells, some of which become transformed into a cellulose stalk and some of which become spores of the fruiting body or sorocarp. This sporulation process is accomplished entirely as a consequence of endogenous cellular metabolism in the absence of exogenous nutrients. The first figure summarizes the life cycle of the slime mold. The myxamebae multiply indefinitely in the pres-

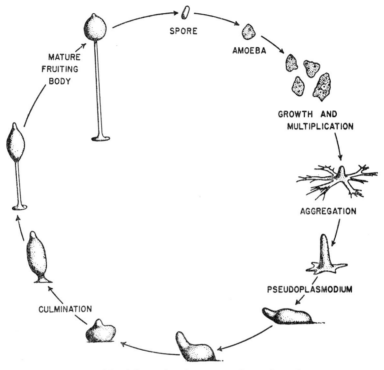

FIG. 1. The life cycle of *Dictyostelium discoideum.*

ence of nutrients, consisting of a rich medium and either live or dead bacteria. Only when the bacteria have been consumed can multicellular differentiation begin. Under the influence of a chemotactic hormone, the cells then aggregate to form a multicellular unit called a pseudoplasmodium. The front third of this mass represents the presumptive stalk cells, and the rear two-thirds the presumptive spore cells. The culmination process, in which pseudoplasmodia are transformed into sorocarps, involves extensive cellulose synthesis. As these cells differentiate, they also starve, and it is therefore not surprising that they lose weight and volume, that their respiration decreases, and that they partially deplete themselves of endogenous reserve materials. Unless stated otherwise, all of the work to be described concerns slime mold metabolism after starvation has begun, in the absence of any exogenous nutrients.

The purpose of this chapter is to describe what is known concerning the endogenous biochemical changes which accompany morphogenesis of the cellular slime mold, and to delve as deeply as possible into the underlying mechanisms controlling these biochemical changes.

II. The Aggregation Process

A. Evidence Relating to the Chemical Nature of the Chemotactic Agent

A recent review by Bonner (1959) summarizes the early experiments of Runyon, Bonner, and Shaffer demonstrating the existence of a chemotactic substance in the aggregation process. Shaffer developed an ingenious bioassay for the presence of the active substance in cell-free washings of aggregating amebae. Sensitive amebae could be shown to orient and move in the direction of a diffusion gradient of the chemotactic agent, called "acrasin" (Shaffer, 1953; Bonner, 1947). The activity of aqueous extracts of the chemotactic agent was very short-lived, due to a rapid inactivation by what appeared to be an extracellular enzyme. Treatments which would destroy or remove the hypothetical enzyme, such as methanol extraction, dialysis, boiling, exposure to acids or alkali, and ammonium sulfate precipitation resulted in the stabilization of acrasin activity (Shaffer, 1956a,b; M. Sussman et al., 1956). The way was then open to purify the chemotactic agent and determine its chemical nature. The possibility of its being a labile substance such as a protein was already excluded by the treatments mentioned above.

By chromatographing crude preparations of the chemotactic agent, Sussman and his associates (1956) separated several fractions with synergistic or antagonistic relationships, suggesting that acrasin may be a very complicated chemotactic complex. One of their fractions, which was active alone, was purified some thousand-fold by counter-current extraction (Sussman, M., 1958). Various analyses suggested to these workers that this material was still grossly impure.

Another approach to the problem was to find a source of acrasin other than the slime molds. Such an attempt led to the discovery that the urine of a pregnant woman was extremely active in the Shaffer test. A number of steroids also showed activity, although the response of the amebae was definitely weaker than it was to the urine (Wright, 1958). No correlation between the structure and activity of various steroids was obvious. On the assumption that acrasin might be a sterol-like compound, acid-hydrolyzed extracts of D. discoideum were fractionated using the Shaffer test as a guide. A sterol with relatively weak acrasin activity was isolated and identified (Heftmann et al., 1960).

The structure of this compound, Δ^{22}-stigmasten-3β-ol, is shown in Fig. 2. Unfortunately, difficulties with the assay system precluded further work on this problem.

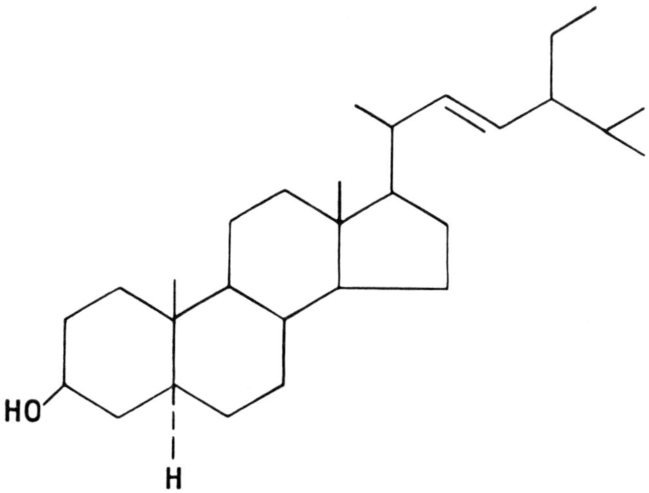

FIG. 2. Δ^{22}-Stigmasten-3β-ol.

Hostak and Raper (1960), employing quite a different type of assay with the slime mold *Acytostelium leptosomum,* found that both steroids and alkaloids could induce cell aggregation. Certain of the alkaloids tested exhibited the highest activity. Since both steroids and alkaloids are surface-active agents, these results may suggest a mechanism of aggregation by which the surface tension of the cell is lowered on the side closest to the source of the diffusion gradient, causing the cell to move in that direction. The main difficulties at present in pursuing this problem appear to be the absence of a really good assay system and the possibility that more than one component may be required for optimal chemotactic activity.

The isolation of Δ^{22}-stigmasten-3β-ol, representing some 0.3% of the dry weight of the slime mold, raised several interesting questions concerning its origin. For example, the possibility existed that it was synthesized by the bacteria on which the myxamebae were fed, especially in view of a report concerning the existence of such compounds in *Escherichia coli* (Dauchy and Kayser, 1958). Since it may be assumed that stigmastenol is synthesized via mevalonic acid, the incorporation of mevalonic acid-2-C^{14} into stigmastenol was investigated under various conditions (Johnson *et al.*, 1962). After incubation of *E. coli* with mevalonic acid-2-C^{14} for 5 hr. in the absence of slime mold, two radioactive species were obtained on alumina chromatography, neither of which was associated with the carrier stigmastenol (Fig. 3). The radioac-

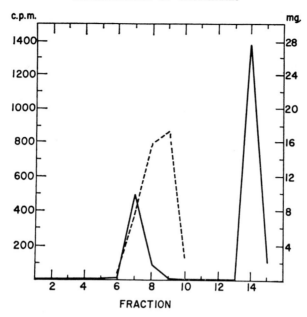

F<small>IG</small>. 3. *Escherichia coli* incubated with mevalonic acid-2-C^{14}. Solid line, radioactivity in counts per minute; broken line, weight of Δ^{22}-stigmasten-3β-ol in milligrams. (See Johnson *et al.*, 1962.)

tivity in the first peak (fraction 7) may be due to a sterol-like compound of bacterial origin; fraction 14 is an artifact resulting from the acid hydrolysis of mevalonic acid-2-C^{14}. When the slime mold was allowed to feed on dead *E. coli*, incubation with mevalonic acid-2-C^{14} during the vegetative stage gave the results plotted in Fig. 4. The radioactive species in fraction 7 was now absent, and stigmastenol was obtained in radiochemically pure form. Thus *E. coli* does not synthesize stigmastenol, nor does it contribute a precursor for the synthesis of the sterol by the slime mold. The latter conclusion is based on an experiment in which *E. coli* was grown in the presence of radioactive mevalonate, washed thoroughly, and fed as a dead preparation to the slime mold. No radioactivity could be detected in the isolated stigmastenol. Incorporation experiments at various developmental stages, coupled with data on the retention of radioactive stigmastenol during development, indicated that by far the most efficient period of sterol biosynthesis was the vegetative stage, and that relatively little turnover of stigmastenol occurred thereafter.

B. A<small>GGREGATELESS</small> M<small>UTANTS</small>

By the use of ultraviolet irradiation, R. R. Sussman and Sussman (1953) obtained a number of mutant strains of *D. discoideum* which no longer aggre-

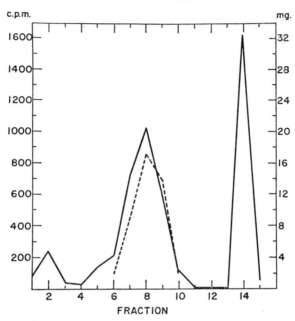

FIG. 4. *Dictyostelium discoideum* incubated with mevalonic acid-2-C[14] during the vegetative stage (dead *Escherichia coli*). Solid line, radioactivity in counts per minute; broken line, weight of Δ^{22}-stigmasten-3β-ol in milligrams. (See Johnson *et al.*, 1962.)

gated—a failure apparently not due to the lack of acrasin, for it was present in the aggregateless mutants (Ennis, 1957). It was found that surface contact with cells of the wild-type strain is essential for aggregateless cells to realize a normal morphogenetic development. Thus by immunological technique Gregg and Trygstad (1958) investigated the possible role of aberrant surface antigens in the behavior of the aggregateless mutants. The most definitive results were obtained in experiments with Agg 91 and Agg 89. These strains were shown to produce antisera of similar and reasonably high titer with homologous antigen (i.e., the antisera would agglutinate and clump homologous amebae). However, anti-wild-type sera failed to agglutinate Agg 91 and Agg 89 amebae, indicating that the surface antigens of the latter two variants have been altered or eliminated so that agglutination could not be effected. Furthermore, anti-Agg 91 and anti-Agg 89 sera failed to agglutinate wild-type amebae. Thus, these mutant strains, incapable of being agglutinated by anti-wild-type sera, produce antisera which lack antibodies necessary to agglutinate the normal strain of *D. discoideum*. In the case of these two mutants it appears likely that their failure to undergo normal development may well be associated with the alteration or elimination of certain surface antigens in the amebae.

C. INHIBITORS AND STIMULANTS OF AGGREGATION

A number of investigations have dealt with the effect of various compounds on the aggregation process (Hirschberg and Rusch, 1950, 1951; Bradley *et al.*, 1956; Kostellow, 1956; Wright and Anderson, 1959; Gerisch, 1961; Krichevsky and Wright, 1961, 1963). 2,4-Dinitrophenol, which inhibits aggregation reversibly, stimulates respiration and causes an increase in the inorganic phosphate levels in the cells (Gerisch, 1961; Hirschberg and Rusch, 1951). The action of this inhibitor is probably due to an uncoupling of oxidative phosphorylation, which is necessary for morphogenesis. A particularly interesting inhibitor is ethylenediamine tetra-acetic acid, since it interferes with the formation of normal fruiting bodies without inhibiting the cellular differentiation into spores and stalk cells. Thus biochemical differentiation into two cell types appears to be independent of the normal culmination process (Gerisch, 1961).

Many unrelated compounds stimulate the rate of morphogenesis, such as histidine (Bradley *et al.*, 1956), other amino acids, glucose, and inorganic salts (Slifkin and Bonner, 1952; Krichevsky and Wright, 1961, 1963). The variety in the nature of these stimulants suggested the possibility that their effect could be nonspecific and due, for example, to the buffer capacity of the compounds. This mechanism of action, as well as chelation and ionic strength effects, was ruled out (Krichevsky and Wright, 1963). The mechanism of action of glucose and histidine was examined in more detail. It was concluded that glucose, which stimulates the rate of morphogenesis (see Fig. 6), respiration (see Table III), and protein synthesis (see Fig. 7), is acting as a primary energy source. The effect of inorganic phosphate on morphogenesis is shown in Fig. 12. Since both glucose and phosphate are rate-limiting to multicellular development, it is curious that they accumulate in the cells as a consequence of "the metabolism of differentiation" (see Tables V and XIII). Histidine also stimulates the rate of protein synthesis, but does so in an indirect manner, and not as an energy source or as a limiting amino acid for protein synthesis. If the exogenous stimulants of differentiation act by different mechanisms and not via one central limiting reaction, it might be expected that their effects could be additive. At optimal concentrations of each, glucose plus histidine are additive in stimulating the rate of multicellular morphogenesis. At optimal histidine concentration, suboptimal levels of phosphate also have an additive stimulating effect (Krichevsky and Wright, 1963).

III. Endogenous Changes in Respiration and Substrate Levels during Differentiation

It is appropriate to preface this section with some cautionary notes. In discussing alterations in various cellular components over the course of development, it must constantly be borne in mind that we are dealing with an ever changing, starving system which is undergoing continuous and significant decreases with respect to weight, volume, protein content, etc. Experiments of White and Sussman (1961) showed an average loss per cell of 40–70% in dry weight over the course of differentiation, and a similar loss for three morphogenetic mutants. In the experiments concerning respiration of the slime mold based on dry weight, Liddel and Wright (1961) found an average loss in dry weight of 48% from the amebae to the 1-day-old sorocarp. Investigations designed to determine the intracellular molarity of various substrates (see below) revealed an average loss of 61% in cell volume throughout differentiation. The loss from the amebae to the pseudoplasmodium stage is approximately 20%. Thus, for example, we shall see that oxygen consumption based on cell number drops smoothly between the pseudoplasmodium and culmination stages of development. However, on the basis of dry weight (which is decreasing at a different rate than respiration), O_2 consumption is constant during this period. Depending upon the purpose of an investigation, it may be more meaningful to consider a particular change, such as respiration or the concentration of an amino acid, from the point of view of a single cell rather than in terms of molarity or dry weight.

Significant quantitative variations, from one experiment to the next, have been observed in the intracellular content of protein, free amino acids, glucose, etc. In the latter case, for example (see below), the exact time of harvest from the rich medium (i.e., only amebae, some residual bacteria; no bacteria, some aggregation) appeared to be critical to the subsequent glucose content of the differentiating cells. This may simply be due to the length of time the cells are in contact with the glucose-rich media. The number of washings necessary to free the amebae from bacteria prior to plating, as well as the ratio of cell to water volume during washing, is undoubtedly of importance to the intracellular content of water-soluble compounds, in part perhaps because of cell-membrane damage and permeability changes. It is also difficult to choose exactly comparable stages from one experiment to another, since the speed, the efficiency, and the degree of synchrony of differentiation all are also affected by the factors mentioned above.

Another problem to bear in mind in a differentiating system concerns errors resulting from the lack of specificity of an assay. For example, quantitative protein determinations often depend on the presence of peptide bonds or aromatic amino acids. The amino acid pool of the slime mold, which contains aromatic amino acids and probably a number of soluble peptides (Krivanek and Krivanek, 1959) is relatively large at the early stages of development, and decreases to a minimum at the pseudoplasmodium stage (see below). Thus the error in a protein value due to the amino acid pool is not a constant one during development. One solution to this problem is to analyze precipitated protein (Wright, 1960a). Table I indicates the extent to which a protein deter-mination (Folin and biuret) must be corrected at three stages of development. Values obtained from total crude extracts are compared to those made on the precipitated protein of a comparable aliquot at each stage (Gezelius, 1963).

Table I

PROTEIN DETERMINATIONS BEFORE AND AFTER ACID PRECIPITATION[a]

Stage	Crude extract	Acid precipitate	Percent
Ameba			
Biuret	17.1	13.3	78
Folin	17.1	13.9	81
Migrating pseudoplasmodium			
Biuret	22.6	20.6	91
Folin	24.0	21.5	90
Sorocarp			
Biuret	7.5	6.3	83
Folin	8.2	6.9	84

[a] Protein was precipitated with perchloric acid (3.5%) and redissolved in 0.5 M NaOH. See text.

The acid-soluble amino acid peptide pool fraction therefore represents 20% of the total Folin or biuret activity in the ameba extracts.

Most investigators following the incorporation of an isotope, for example, into cells of a differentiating system, would be aware that permeability of the

Table II

"PERMEABILITY" AS A FUNCTION OF DEVELOPMENTAL STAGE[a]

Exogenous compound[b] (specific radioactivity = 100)	Endogenous compound[b] (% exogenous specific radioactivity)		
	Ameba	Preculmination	Sorocarp
Methionine	8.3	66.4	28.2
Glucose	1.4	52.6	32.3
Glutamate	5.0	13.3	0.6

[a] See Wright and Anderson, 1960b; Wright and Bloom, 1961; Wright and Bard, 1963.

[b] These data were obtained by incubating cells in the presence of the exogenous radioactive substance, and thereafter isolating this material from the cells after proper washing procedures. The specific radioactivity values result either from a net accumulation of exogenous compound (as in the case of glucose) or from an exchange of the intracellular with the extracellular com-pound (as in the case of methionine).

isotope could affect their results. However, the literature indicates that a number of investigators are not fully aware of the consequences of *alterations* during development in cell permeability. In the case of the cellular slime mold, it is clear that the cells have a selectively permeable membrane, and that the permeability characteristics of the cells undergo significant changes as differentiation proceeds (Faust and Filosa, 1959; Wright and Anderson, 1960b; Wright and Bloom, 1961; Wright and Bard, 1963). Table II gives three examples of such changes in permeability for methionine, glucose, and glutamate.

Had alterations in the permeability of S^{35}-methionine during development not been investigated, data on the rate of protein synthesis would have indicated a 10-fold change as a function of differentiation rather than no change (Wright and Anderson, 1960b). Later sections of this chapter will consider the implications of these permeability changes with respect to substrate and dye permeation in histochemical studies, the rate of enzyme reactions measured *in vivo*, etc.

One more cautionary note is pertinent before presenting the available data on endogenous changes during differentiation. There are, of course, two major presumptive cell types—about one-third of the cells in a pseudoplasmodium became stalk and about two-thirds became spores. With few exceptions, for practical reasons, analyses are performed on all the cells present at a given stage of development. Values thus obtained therefore represent an average not only for all cells present but also for all regions of the multicellular body. Gregg *et al.* (1954) have shown that protein nitrogen losses occur predominantly in the presumptive stalk cells. Histochemical studies have indicated enzyme or, as we shall see, substrate localizations in the pseudoplasmodium. Thus the molarity of an endogenous compound, determined on total cell volume, may be manyfold in error if it is concentrated *in vivo* in one area of the cells of one presumptive type (e.g., at the apical tip during active cellulose synthesis at culmination).

Awareness of these many problems of interpretation must not of course discourage biochemical investigations; rather, they must encourage wherever possible the development of new techniques and methods for studying biochemical changes in the intact, differentiating cell.

A. Respiration in the Absence and Presence of Glucose during Development

Gregg (1950) first described the dependence of slime-mold differentiation on O_2, and studied the endogenous respiration of *D. discoideum*. In recent experiments, the endogenous respiration per cell has been found to be highest at the ameba stage and to decline linearly with time from the migration to the sorocarp stage. On a dry weight basis, a similar drop in the oxygen quotient (Q_{O_2}) from the ameba stage is also observed, followed by a plateau between the pseudoplasmodium and culmination states, with a final drop at the sorocarp stage (Liddel and Wright, 1961). These data are shown in Fig. 5.

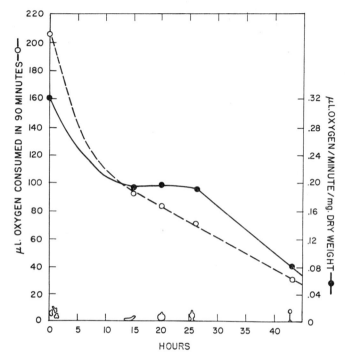

FIG. 5. Respiration based on dry weight and cell number. The slime mold was allowed to differentiate inside Dixon-Keilin flasks and respiration was measured at different stages of development. The left ordinate shows the total μliters of oxygen consumed over a 90-min. period. The right ordinate shows Q_{O_2} based on dry weight. The abscissa indicates the time elapsed from the start of the first determination and depicts the various stages of development (ameba, migrating pseudoplasmodium, preculmination, culmination, and sorocarp). (See Liddel and Wright, 1961.)

Maximal respiration at the ameba stage might be expected, since the cells have just finished engulfing bacteria and contain all the endogenous reserves which are to be the sole source of energy and of material for the synthesis of compounds essential in the remainder of its life cycle. In comparing these two curves, the most interesting section is the 10-hr. period from the migrating pseudoplasmodium to the culmination stage. The dashed curve indicates that, on the average, each cell consumes an ever decreasing amount of O_2, while the other curve shows that the decline in O_2 uptake is proportional to the decline in dry weight; i.e., their ratio is constant.

The data given in Table III were obtained by removing the cells from agar at four different developmental stages and determining their respiration in a

Table III

OXYGEN QUOTIENT (Q_{O_2}) AT FOUR STAGES OF DEVELOPMENT

Stage	$Q_{O_2}{}^a$	Standard deviation	No. of experiments	Average % stimulation by glucose	Standard deviation	No. of experiments
Ameba	0.271	0.011	9	0	0	11
Migrating pseudo-plasmodium	0.199	0.021	17	0	0	7
Preculmination	0.214	0.019	10	9.4	4.1	5
Young sorocarp	0.147	0.030	9	40	13.7	13

[a] Q_{O_2} (μliters O_2 uptake per minute per milligram dry weight) for 4 stages of development determined in a salt solution. Percentage of stimulation by glucose was determined by tipping glucose into the Warburg flask after 30 min. incubation. (See Liddel and Wright, 1961.)

salt solution in the absence and presence of glucose. The endogenous Q_{O_2} values check qualitatively with those obtained by measuring respiration directly on

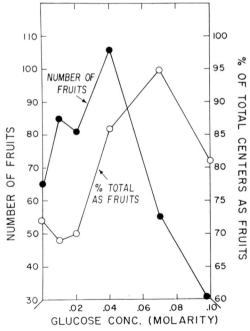

FIG. 6. The effect of glucose on the rate of morphogenesis, as measured by (a) the number of fruits and (b) percentage of differentiating bodies (i.e., eventual fruits) represented as fruits at the time of assay. (Krichevsky and Wright, 1963.)

the differentiating cells. Since glucose can stimulate respiration from the pre-culmination to the sorocarp stage of development, it would appear that sub-strate availability rather than low enzyme levels are limiting respiration. The sharp downward break in the endogenous Q_{O_2} curve at the culmination stage may indicate a critical depletion of endogenous oxidizable substrates. This de-ficiency might well play an important role in terminating the differentiation process. The influence of glucose on the rate of morphogenesis (Fig. 6) and the rate of protein synthesis (Fig. 7) can also be interpreted as an indication

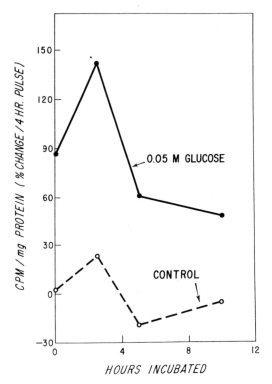

FIG. 7. The effect of glucose on the rate of protein synthesis. One-ml. samples of myxamebae were spread on a number of petri dishes of 2% agar. After differentiation had proceeded for 0, 2.5, 5, or 10 hr., C^{14}-mixed amino acids were added with and without glucose. Control and experimental samples were incubated at 4 or 8 hr. before trichloroacetic acid was added. The percentage change in specific radioactivity of the isolated protein was then determined. (Krichevsky and Wright, 1963.)

of limiting energy sources. The data on protein synthesis were obtained by exposing cells at various developmental stages between aggregation and sorocarp to a 4-hr. "pulse" of radioactive amino acids in the absence and presence of glucose (Krichevsky and Wright, 1963).

B. Antigenic Changes Occurring During Differentiation

A number of immunochemical investigations on differentiating systems has demonstrated quantitative and qualitative changes in antigens during morphogenesis. This is not surprising, since many structures found only in the more differentiated tissues of an organism are antigenic in nature. Consider, for example, cardiac myosin in the presumptive heart cells or alkaline phosphatase in presumptive bone tissue in the developing chick embryo (Ebert, 1953; Moog, 1952). There is also the large class of blood-group substances, which are nitrogen-containing carbohydrates (Boyd, 1947), and more unique structures such as an antigenic polysaccharide isolated from *Ascaris lumbricoides* (Campbell, 1936).

Recent studies by Gregg (1960) on cell-surface antigens at various developmental stages of *D. discoideum* have demonstrated that qualitatively identical surface antigens (obtained by washing the cells) are present from the time of aggregation to sorocarp formation. These may contain the "slime" deposited by the cells. This investigation also revealed antigenic material(s) unique to whole spores and in spore washings. The antisera obtained in these two cases appeared to be the same, suggesting that the activity of whole spores was due only to surface antigens. The spore-surface antigen(s) is (are) not present earlier in development, and may well be the same as that described by White and Sussman (1963b). Their material also was associated only with the spores and was not present in the earlier developmental stages; this antigen was purified and identified as a mucopolysaccharide (see below and Fig. 10). By homogenization and consequent release of intracellular antigens, Gregg demonstrated altogether 19 different antigens during the transition of the myxamobae to the mature spores (1961). The stalks were not analyzed. Table IV

Table IV

ANTIGENIC CHANGES DURING THE TRANSITION FROM THE
VEGETATIVE AMEBAS TO THE MATURE SPORES[a]

Antigen	Antigens shared, synthesized, and destroyed																		
Vegetative amebas	1	2	3	4	5	6	7	8	9									
Migrating pseudo-plasmodia				4	5	6	7	8	9	10	11	12	13					
Mature spores						6	7	8	9	10	11			14	15	16	17	18	19

[a] For experimental details see Gregg, 1961.

indicates the distribution of these antigens at three stages of development. As Gregg emphasizes, such data tell us nothing concerning the mechanism by which antigenic changes occur—e.g., *de novo* synthesis, complete or partial destruction, or alterations in the solubility or specificity of existing antigens. Takeuchi (1961) has also studied antigenic changes as a function of development.

C. Net Loss of Nitrogenous Compounds as a Function of Developmental Stage

Gregg, Hackney, and Krivanek first reported a net loss of protein nitrogen during development, particularly between the pseudoplasmodium and sorocarp stages (1954). Furthermore, this loss was shown to have occurred for the most part in the stalk cells, and to be accompanied by ammonia formation. A qualitative examination of the amino acid pool revealed a similar composition throughout development; of particular interest was the absence of phenylalanine, proline, histidine, and asparagine (Krivanek and Krivanek, 1959).

The loss of nitrogenous compounds has recently been confirmed by other methods and examined in greater detail (Wright and Anderson, 1960a). In these investigations the Carnegie procedure (Roberts *et al.*, 1955) was used to separate endogenous amino acid and protein fractions labeled with S^{35}-methionine. The three fractions shown in Fig. 8 were followed by total counts,

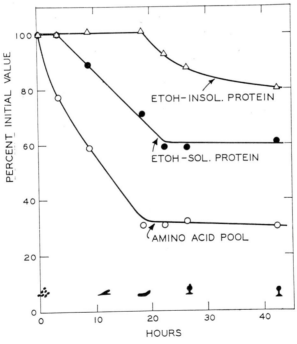

FIG. 8. The sequence of utilization of three classes of nitrogenous compounds during development. Stages of differentiation are indicated on the abscissa. (See Wright and Anderson, 1960a.)

and plotted as percent of the initial value for each fraction. At least for the first 25 hr. of differentiation, methionine content was shown to be a reliable index of the concentration of amino acids and protein present. Following a minimal value at the migrating pseudoplasmodium stage, the concentration of the amino acid pool is constant per cell and therefore increases on the basis of cell volume or of protein. A specific analysis of methionine content per cell aliquot revealed this behavior (Wright and Anderson, 1960b), whereas glutamate (and aspartate) were atypical and never decreased during development (see below). The results of White and Sussman (1961) confirmed the general picture shown in Fig. 8. In their study, the Carnegie fractionation procedure was also used, but all fractions were assayed by the Folin reagent and expressed as percent of the total Folin activity.

Like protein and amino acids, ribonucleic acid (RNA) is also utilized during development, and all of these nitrogenous compounds are degraded as a function of time also in various morphogenetic mutants (White and Sussman, 1961). Various microbes incapable of differentiation have been shown to utilize endogenous amino acids, protein, and RNA under starvation conditions (Halvorson, 1958; Mandelstam, 1958). It is quite clear that although differentiation does not *cause* the utilization of endogenous macromolecules, it *depends* upon it, in that the products of protein and RNA breakdown are required for biosynthetic steps involved in morphogenesis. The utilization of endogenous reserves is an important characteristic of most differentiating systems, and will be discussed in the last section (Wright, 1962).

It might be mentioned at this point that information is now available on the DNA base composition of *D. discoideum*. It has an unusually low percent of (guanine + cytosine) (Schildkraut *et al.*, 1962).

D. Net Gain in Carbohydrates during Morphogenesis

Histochemical studies by Bonner *et al.* (1955), confirmed by Krivanek and Krivanek (1958), have revealed an accumulation of a non-starch polysaccharide material specifically associated with the differentiation of the spore cells. After removal of starch or glycogen (by salivary digestion), the periodic acid-Schiff reaction (PAS) for polysaccharides was applied to cells and multicellular individuals at various stages of maturity. Toward the beginning of migration, the two presumptive cell types were indistinguishable. The slime sheath surrounding the pseudoplasmodium was PAS positive. At late migration and early culmination, however, there appeared a sharp line of demarcation between the two cell types, and finally the spore cells became very intensely stained. These non-starch polysaccharide materials may well represent some of the antigens described by Gregg (1960, 1961) and/or the antigenic mucopolysaccharide of the spore identified by White and Sussman (see below). Whatever its identity, Bonner *et al.* (1955) have demonstrated in an interesting experiment that the synthesis of the spore-cell polysaccharide is potentially reversible up until the terminal stages of sorocarp formation. In eight migrating pseudoplasmodia, that section of the individual was removed which included the division line between the two-cell types, with respect to PAS staining (see Fig. 9). In four of the

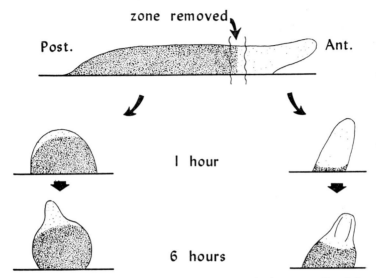

Fig. 9. A diagram illustrating the experiment in which a partially differentiated migrating cell mass is bisected and each portion is examined by the PAS technique after 1 and 6 hr. respectively. (See text, and Bonner *et al.*, 1955.)

pseudoplasmodia so treated, the separate anterior and posterior pieces were fixed 1 hr. following the operation; the remaining four were fixed after 6 hr. migration. Indications of reversal in staining characteristics could be seen after 1 hr., but in 6 hr. a fairly complete reversal was evident, and in some cases culmination was already in progress (see Fig. 9). Here we have an example of the biochemical basis for the multipotency of presumptive cell types in the earlier stages of differentiation: the reversible accumulation of a polysaccharide characteristic of one cell type.

Quantitative data on the increase in carbohydrate during development was obtained by Gregg and Bronsweig (1956), who demonstrated a doubling of total reducing sugar based on dry weight, a result confirmed by White and Sussman (1961).

1. CELLULOSE

The sorophore sheath and cell-wall substance of the fruiting body of the cellular slime mold is composed of cellulose (β-1,4 linkages). This has been demonstrated by staining reactions, X-ray diffraction pattern, analysis of hydrolysis products, osmotic and viscometric measurements (Brefeld, 1869; Raper and Fennell, 1952; Gezelius and Rånby, 1957; Mühlethaler, 1956; Gezelius, 1959).

2. GLUCOSE

The accumulation of free glucose, based on dry weight, has been demonstrated during morphogenesis of D. *discoideum* (Wright and Anderson, 1959). The intracellular molarity of glucose had to be known for studies on the metabolism of C^{14}-glucose (see below). Table V summarizes these results (Wright *et al.*, 1964), which confirm the earlier finding that the cellular

Table V

INTRACELLULAR GLUCOSE MOLARITY $(\times 10^3)^a$

Stage	Experiment			
	I	II	III	IV
Ameba	—	0.06	—	0.07
Aggregation	0.07	0.03	—	0.03
Preculmination	—	0.23	0.46	0.10
Culmination	0.13	0.27	0.55	—
1-Day sorocarp	0.04	—	—	0.09
2-Day sorocarp	—	—	0.03	—

a Each cell extract was deproteinized by perchloric acid and the perchlorate removed as the potassium salt. To remove an inhibitor(s), the supernatant was then passed successively over Dowex-50 and Dowex-1 before assay by the (special) Glucostat method (Worthington Biochem. Corp., 1962). Glucose was identified by, and quantitatively recovered from, paper chromatograms.

glucose concentration is maximal at the culminating stages of development. Following 10–12 hr. of starvation (usually the time required for the cells to aggregate on 2% agar at 17°C., if no aggregation is present at the time of harvest), the glucose value is minimal. At about this time, the soluble pool of easily available energy sources has reached a minimal size, and gluconeogenic activity coupled with protein degradation begins (see Wright and Anderson, 1960a; Liddel and Wright, 1961). During this endogenous carbohydrate synthesis, the intracellular glucose concentration reaches a peak value at the preculmination and culmination stages. Some of the possible causes of variability in glucose molarity from one experiment to another have been discussed previously. These data on intracellular glucose levels will be related to the dynamics of glucose metabolism *in vivo* in a later section. White and Sussman (1963a) have recently also confirmed the observation that glucose accumulates at culmination.

3. TREHALOSE

Clegg and Filosa (1961) have identified the nonreducing disaccharide trehalose in the spores of the cellular slime mold *D. mucoroides* as well as in *D. discoideum* (Clegg and Filosa, 1963). It constitutes more than 7% of the dry weight of spores, and is not present in the earlier stages of development. Since trehalose disappears during germination, these authors speculate that the disaccharide may be utilized as an energy source for this process.

4. GLUCOSE POLYMER

A water-soluble, nondialyzable polysaccharide was purified by White and Sussman (1963a) from immature fruiting bodies of *Dictyostelium discoideum*. It has been identified as a polymer composed only of glucose units and rich in α-1,4 linkages. The curve SGP (soluble glucose polymer) in Fig. 10 illustrates the developmental kinetics of this polysaccharide. The curve labeled IGP represents cellulose. *Dictyostelium mucoroides* also contains the soluble polysaccharide.

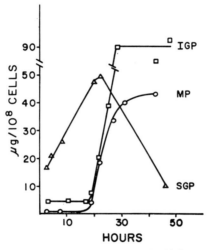

FIG. 10. The accumulation during development of cellulose (IGP), a soluble glucose polymer (SGP), and a mucopolysaccharide (MP). (See White and Sussman, 1963d.)

5. MUCOPOLYSACCHARIDE

This water-soluble, nondialyzable polysaccharide, identified by White and Sussman (1963b) contains galactose, galactosamine, and galacturonic acid. Since it is antigenic and associated only with the spores of the fruiting body, it may well be the spore-surface antigen described by Gregg (see earlier discussion). In Fig. 10 the increase in the amount of this mucopolysaccharide (MP) is correlated with the developmental stage. The antigen rises to 1–1.5% of the dry weight in young sorocarps.

This mucopolysaccharide as well as the glucose polymer, and of course cellulose, do not appear in mutants incapable of forming spore and stalk cells. In one interesting mutant unable to form normal sorocarps, Fr-17, these polysaccharides actually appear sooner than in the wild type, since this strain is characterized by an unusually high rate of cellular differentiation.

6. URIDINE DIPHOSPHOGLUCOSE

Uridine diphosphoglucose (UDPG) has been shown (e.g., Glaser, 1958) to be a precursor of cellulose in other systems, and UDPG synthetase is known to be very active during culmination in D. *discoideum* (Wright and Anderson, 1959). Concentration of this compound as a function of differentiation was therefore investigated. Table VI demonstrates that, like glucose and the glucose polymer, UDPG accumulates at culmination. Note that it is present in concentrations very comparable to glucose at all stages of development (see Table V). This is

Table VI

INTRACELLULAR UDPG MOLARITY $(\times 10^3)^a$

	Experiment				Glucose molarity for Exp. IV
Stage	I	II	III	IV	
Ameba	—	0.04	0.04	0.05	(0.07)
Aggregation	0.02	—	—	<0.01	(0.03)
Migrating pseudo-plasmodium	—	0.15	—	—	—
Preculmination	—	—	—	0.14	(0.10)
Culmination	0.13	—	1.0	—	—
1-Day sorocarp	—	—	0.04	0.08	(0.09)
2-Day sorocarp	<0.01	<0.01	—	—	—

^{a} Uridine diphosphoglucose was assayed quantitatively by UDPG dehydrogenase and identified chromatographically.

particularly clear in the last experiment, in which both glucose and UDPG were determined in the same extracts. UDPG was assayed with a specific dehydrogenase (Wright *et al.*, 1964) and its identity confirmed by chromatography.

The data thus far presented on endogenous changes during development are summarized in Table VII. Other data included in this table are discussed below.

E. FATTY ACID BIOSYNTHESIS

The total extracted (CHCl$_3$:CH$_3$OH 2:1) lipid contend of D. *discoideum* myxamebae was approximately 15% of the dry weight. Of this fraction, 40%

Table VII

ALTERATIONS IN CELLULAR CHARACTERISTICS DURING DIFFERENTIATION

	Stage of		Approx-imate % original value	Reference
	Max. conc.	Min. conc.		
"Precursors"				
Cell volume	Ameba	Sorocarp	40	Wright and Bard, 1963.
Dry weight	Ameba	Sorocarp	50	White and Sussman, 1961; Liddel and Wright, 1961.
Respiration	Ameba	Sorocarp	20	Gregg, 1950; Liddel and Wright, 1961.
Protein	Ameba	Sorocarp	70	Gregg et al., 1954; Wright and Anderson, 1960a; White and Sussman, 1961.
Amino acid pool	Ameba	Migrating pseu-doplasmodium	30	Wright and Anderson, 1960a; White and Sussman, 1961.
RNA	Ameba	Sorocarp	40	White and Sussman, 1961.
Intermediates				
Glucose	Culmination	Aggregation, Sorocarp	300	Wright and Anderson, 1959; White and Sussman, 1963b; Wright et al., 1964.
Glucose polymer	Culmination	Ameba, sorocarp	300	White and Sussman, 1963b.
UDPG	Culmination	Aggregation, sorocarp	200	Wright et al., 1964.
Products				
Reducing substance	Sorocarp	Amebae	100	Gregg and Bronsweig, 1956; White and Sussman, 1961.
Cellulose	Sorocarp	Amebae	Infinite	Brefeld, 1869. Raper and Fennell, 1952; Mühlethaler, 1956; Gezelius and Rånby, 1957.
Trehalose	Sorocarp	Amebae	Infinite	Clegg and Filosa, 1961.
Glutamate (aspartate)	Sorocarp	Amebae	500	Wright and Bard, 1963.
Orthophosphate	Sorocarp	Amebae	300	Gezelius and Wright, 1964;
Mucopolysac-charide	Sorocarp	Amebae	Infinite	White and Sussman, 1963a.

by weight consisted of neutral lipids. The phospholipids contain an unusually high percentage of mono- and polyunsaturated fatty acids, two of which had not previously been described (Davidoff and Korn, 1962a). Since work on the biosynthesis of the fatty acids of D. discoideum is rapidly progressing (Davidoff and Korn, 1962b), the field is ripe for correlations with respect to the differentiation process.

IV. Protein Synthesis

Although a net loss in cellular protein occurs during development, the rate of protein synthesis does not change significantly. This has been shown by studies on the incorporation of S^{35}-methionine into protein at various developmental stages (Table VIII). It would even appear that the rate of incorporation is minimal at preculmination and culmination—an observation which may be an artifact due to complexities not relevant to the present discussion (Wright and Anderson, 1960b). At preculmination the majority of the intracellular

Table VIII

PERCENT OF INCORPORATION OF S^{35}-METHIONINE
INTO PROTEIN PER 30 MINUTES[a]

| | Experiment | |
Stage	I	II
Amebae	—	7.6
Aggregation	4.5	—
Pseudoplasmodium	—	3.7
Preculmination	3.4	—
Culmination	2.9	—
Young sorocarp	—	4.4
Old sorocarp	6.6	—

[a] See Wright and Anderson, 1960b.

methionine molecules are labeled by exogenous (S^{35}) methionine (see Table II) and incorporation values obtained at this stage are considered to be the most reliable. This value, about 7% per hour, is shown to be comparable to the values for animal cells and bacteria in Table IX. The consequences of protein turnover have been thoroughly discussed by Mandelstam (1960). Relative to their growth rate under optimal conditions the two cell types capable of differentiation have a higher rate of protein turnover than do the bacteria. What might this mean? In the early stages of differentiation, under essentially resting conditions, cells of many types depend in part on the breakdown of endogenous protein materials as a source of energy and building blocks for synthetic purposes. Let us assume that this protein degradation is not selective—that is, it may occur at the same rate for a protein species which will eventually disappear

Table IX

COMPARISON IN RATES OF PROTEIN TURNOVER

Cell type	Percent increase cell mass per hour (optimal growth conditions)	Percent per hour incorporation (resting cells)	Reference
Animal cells	4	1.0	Eagle *et al.*, 1957.
Myxamebae	40	7.0	Wright and Anderson, 1960b.
Bacillus cereus	300	7.0	Urbá, 1959.
Escherichia coli	400	5.0	Mandelstam, 1958.

(in certain of the differentiated cells) as for an enzyme which must be maintained at its original concentration. A relatively high rate of protein turnover would thus allow for extensive protein utilization as well as for changes in protein composition, while providing the synthetic potential with which critical proteins may be maintained. Evidence will be presented for alterations during development in the concentration of an enzyme protein, but we do not yet know whether this is due to alterations in the rate of release, of synthesis, or degradation of the protein, or due to some combination of effects.

V. Enzyme Activities

A. *In Vitro* EVIDENCE

1. HISTOCHEMICAL

A number of enzymatic activities have been demonstrated by histochemical techniques: alkaline phosphatase, 5-nucleotidase, nonspecific dehydrogenase, lipase, tyrosinase, cytochrome oxidase, and amine oxidase (Bonner *et al.*, 1955; Krivanek, 1956; Krivanek and Krivanek, 1958; Takeuchi, 1960). The first three enzymes in particular exhibited high activity in cells of the pre-stalk area. When interpreting these results, it should be pointed out that they do not necessarily reflect either a differential enzyme distribution or activity in the cells of the multicellular individual. Serious artifacts can result from the fixation and other histochemical procedures used. For example, it is known that certain dehydrogenases of the slime mold are very labile to enzymatic destruction and are strongly protected by their substrates (see below). The incubation conditions for nonspecific dehydrogenase were very severe—30 min. at 37°C. Quite possibly under these conditions the differential presence of substrates in particular cell regions could result in various degrees of enzyme protection. Thus the histochemical results could be a reflection of a differential endogenous substrate (rather than enzyme) localization. As for the alkaline phosphatase results, it is now known that the orthophosphate concentration *in vivo* is such as to seriously inhibit the activity of this enzyme (see below). The tissue-fixation procedures used before analysis for this enzyme most probably removed the natural inhibitor (inorganic phosphate) present in the cells. Alternatively, there occurred a differential removal of free or loosely bound phosphate, thus allowing detection of the enzyme in some cellular regions only. The permeability changes which have been demonstrated as a function of developmental stage (see Table II) may well be more significant in one cell region than another, and will of course influence the entry of various substrates and stains as well as the exit of endogenous materials.

2. CELL-FREE EXTRACTS

A number of enzyme activities were surveyed in cell-free extracts at various stages of development (Krivanek, 1956; Wright and Anderson, 1959; Takeuchi, 1960). On the basis of protein (which decreases during differentiation) the following enzymes changed little in specific activity: lactic acid, glutamic acid, DPN-isocitric acid, TPN-malic acid, and glyceraldehyde phosphate dehydrogenases; glucose-6-phosphatase, alanine-α-ketoglutaric transaminase, succinic dehydrogenase, and cytochrome oxidase. Five enzymes showed significant increases in specific activity, the maxima occurring at preculmination: 6-phosphogluconic, DPN-malic, glucose-6-phosphate, and TPN-isocitric dehydrogenases and UDPG synthetase. Subsequent studies showed that the latter three enzymes of this group were subject to various degrees of a specific, rapid *in vitro* inactivation. However, this inactivation occurs only in extracts prepared at early stages of differentiation, but not in extracts prepared at preculmination (Wright, 1960a). The responsible agent was a heat-labile factor present only in extracts prepared from cells in the early stages of development. The destructive

Table X

SPECIFIC ACTIVITIES[a] OF ISOCITRIC DEHYDROGENASE

		Stage of differentiation		
Isocitrate	Hours preincubated	Early aggregation	Preculmination	Young fruit
Absent	0	2.83	3.72	2.21
	2.0	0.13	2.77	1.53
Present	0	3.84	3.86	3.12
	2.0	3.08	3.07	3.03

[a] $\triangle 340$ mμ./min./mg. protein. (See Wright, 1960a)

action of the enzyme presumed to be responsible for the inactivation of isocitric dehydrogenase, for example, can be prevented by isocitrate (Table X). At each of the three indicated stages of development, comparable aliquots of cells were harvested in the absence and presence of isocitrate. Extracts were prepared, and isocitric dehydrogenase activity was determined for each sample immediately and again after a 2-hr. incubation period at 21°. It can be seen that isocitrate prevented enzyme inactivation at early aggregation. *In vitro* much more endogenous material capable of reducing TPN (triphosphopyridine nucleotide) is present at preculmination than in the early stages (Wright, 1960b). Results comparable to those shown in Table X were obtained also for a glucose-6-phosphate dehydrogenase (Wright, 1960b). UDPG synthetase is subject to a less striking differential *in vitro* inactivation; UTP (uridine triphosphate) has a slight stabilizing effect on this enzyme. Because of the probable importance of UDPG in cellulose synthesis (Glaser, 1958), this enzyme was carefully re-examined under conditions circumventing differential inactivation. An increase in specific activity of 3-fold, peaking sharply at culmination, does in fact occur (see Table XI). Whether this is a cause or an effect of the increase in UDPG

Table XI

UDPG SYNTHETASE SPECIFIC ACTIVITY[a]

Stage	μmoles TPNH/min./mg. protein ($\times 10^3$)	
	Exp. 1	Exp. 2
Ameba	4.0	7.0
Aggregation	—	8.8
Migrating pseudoplasmodium	5.8	—
Preculmination	—	13.0
Culmination	14.2	—
1-Day sorocarp	5.2	10.2

[a] Assayed as described previously (Wright and Anderson, 1959) except that cells were harvested in 0.01 M tris, pH 7.5, 0.01 M with respect to UTP, frozen once, centrifuged and assayed immediately.

accumulation will be discussed below. Table XII summarizes our present knowledge concerning the specific activity of eight enzymes during development.

There is suggestive evidence in other developing systems—germinating seeds (Beevers and Walker, 1956) and mouse embryos (Noyes and Folk, 1927)—for differential enzyme inactivation *in vitro* as a function of the stage of differentiation. This phenomenon is apparently only an artifact of extracts and has no known significance with respect to biochemical mechanisms of differentiation

Table XII

ENZYME SPECIFIC ACTIVITIES

No change	Significant increase
Glucose-6-P dehydrogenase	Alkaline phosphatase
Glyceraldehyde-3-P dehydrogenase	UDPG synthetase
Lactic acid dehydrogenase	
Isocitric dehydrogenase	
Glutamic acid dehydrogenase	
Alanine-αKG transaminase	

in vivo. It does serve to emphasize the completely different chemical and physical environment of enzymes in extracts compared to enzymes in intact cells and to stress the dangers of extrapolating from results obtained *in vitro* to conditions *in vivo.*

B. A COMPARISON OF *in Vivo* AND *in Vitro* EVIDENCE

For the many reasons detailed earlier in this review, it was considered highly desirable, if not necessary, to obtain *in vivo* evidence relating to the actual activity of an enzyme in the differentiating cell. Three systems will be discussed in which an examination of circumstances existing *in vivo* were essential to an interpretation of results obtained *in vitro.*

1. ALKALINE PHOSPHATASE

In previous investigations (Krivanek, 1956; Wright and Anderson, 1959), the specific activity of this enzyme was shown to increase during development. A very stable enzyme with a pH optimum at 9.0 was found to increase in spe-

Table XIII

INTRACELLULAR INORGANIC PHOSPHATE[a] MOLARITY
DURING DEVELOPMENT

Stage	Molarity P_i	% Inhibition alkaline phosphatase
Ameba	0.003	25
Preculmination	0.003	25
Sorocarp	0.065	92

[a] P_i was assayed chemically. The percent of enzyme inhibition is that found *in vitro* at these levels of Pi (Gezelius and Wright, 1963).

cific activity during differentiation, and to be highly specific for AMP. Since inorganic phosphate is a known inhibitor of this enzyme, the phosphate molarity *in vivo* was determined by microbiological and chemical assay (Gezelius and Wright, 1963). Typical values at three stages of development are given in the first column of Table XIII. The extent to which these concentrations of orthophosphate inhibit the slime mold alkaline phosphatase is shown in the second column. Figure 11 indicates the increase in specific enzyme activity, based on

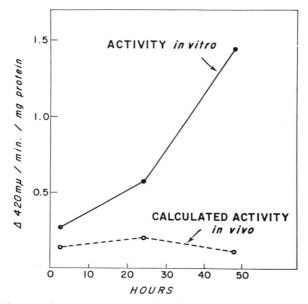

FIG. 11. The specific activity of alkaline phosphatase during development, with *p*-nitrophenyl phosphate as substrate. The calculated activity is based on the amount of orthophosphate present in the cells at various stages of differentiation. (See text, and Gezelius and Wright, 1963.)

precipitated protein, at three stages of development. The lower curve gives the predicted *in vivo* enzyme activity, based on the molarity of intracellular phosphate present at each stage. The data indicate that the observed increase of activity *in vitro* reflects an increase in enzyme concentration, but that the inhibition of the enzyme *in vivo* by inorganic phosphate results in maximal enzyme activity during preculmination. The intracellular accumulation of inorganic phosphate is interesting to consider from another point of view: exogenous phosphate over a concentration range of 10^{-2} to $10^{-3}M$ stimulates the rate of differentiation (Krichevsky and Wright, 1963). This is shown in Fig. 12.

Apparently some metabolic limitation (phosphorylation?) is relieved by the cellular accumulation of phosphate. The presence of exogenous phosphate or

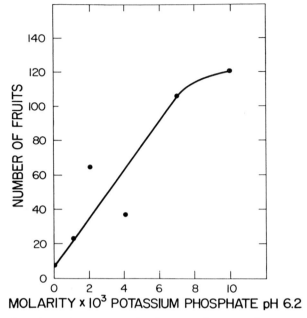

FIG. 12. The effect of inorganic phosphate on the rate of sorocarp formation, as measured by the number of fruiting bodies at the time of assay. (See Krichevsky and Wright, 1963.)

glucose does not affect the enzyme levels early in differentiation, but does so in the sorocarps.

2. GLUTAMATE OXIDATION

Glutamic acid dehydrogenase was chosen for detailed study because of its stability at all stages of development *in vitro* and because this enzyme should be particularly critical for an endogenous metabolism dependent upon the con-

Table XIV

SPECIFIC ACTIVITIES OF GLUTAMIC DEHYDROGENASE
AND ALANINE-α-KETOGLUTARIC ACID TRANSAMINASE[a]

Stage of differentiation	Dehydrogenase	Transaminase
Early aggregation	50.0	5.50
Preculmination	50.7	4.72
Young fruit	33.0	5.52

[a] DPNH formation ($\triangle 340$ mμ./min./mg. protein) was determined in the presence of cell-free extracts prepared at 3 stages of development. (See Wright, 1960a)

version of amino acids into Krebs-cycle intermediates. The Krivaneks have also stressed the importance of this reaction in the slime mold (1959, 1962). Table XIV gives data on the specific activity of this enzyme and a transaminase involving glutamate at three stages of differentiation. The activity of the dehydrogenase decreases somewhat. In connection with another study, this enzyme was purified from the slime mold and the K_M for glutamate was found to be 2.5×10^{-3} (Tomkins, 1960). Although this enzyme does not increase in concentration during differentiation, one might expect this pathway to increase in activity *in vivo*. The evolution of $C^{14}O_2$ from intact cells exposed to $1\text{-}C^{14}$-glutamate was therefore determined. In order to justify the use of this assay as the same system represented by the *in vitro* accumulation of DPNH in the presence of glutamate, a number of experiments were performed (Brühmüller and Wright, 1963).

It was found that CO_2 is not formed through a nonoxidative decarboxylation of the glutamate, since the reaction *in vivo* and *in vitro* is completely inhibited anaerobically at all stages of development, as shown in Table XV. Although

Table XV

DEPENDENCE OF $C^{14}O_2$ EVOLUTION FROM $1\text{-}C^{14}$-GLUTAMATE ON AEROBIOSIS *in Vivo* AND *in Vitro*

| | | In vivo | | In vitro | |
| | | C.p.m. per cell aliquot | Percent dependence | μmoles CO_2/hr./mg. protein ($\times 10^3$) | Percent dependence |
Stage	Atmosphere				
Ameba	Air	1,622	—	9.2	—
	N_2	140	91	0.3	97
Preculmination	Air	5,046	—	4.14	—
	N_2	96	98	0.2	95
Sorocarp	Air	702	—	2.84	—
	N_2	36	95	0.3	90

Anaerobiosis was insured by treatment with $Na_2S_2O_4$ in the presence of safranin. C^{14}-glutamate was present at a concentration of 2×10^{-4} M. Comparable cell aliquots *in vivo* were used at each developmental stage. (See Brühmüller and Wright, 1963.)

these data implicate glutamic acid dehydrogenase and therefore α-ketoglutarate (α-KG) in the reaction, more direct evidence was desirable. The rate of CO_2 evolution from both glutamate and α-KG was determined in fresh, undialyzed extracts at three stages of development—ameba, preculmination, and sorocarp

(Table XVI). The concentration of glutamate used is comparable to that found *in vivo* (see below). The rates of $C^{14}O_2$ evolution were remarkably similar, suggesting that α-KG may be the only precursor of CO_2 starting with glutamate.

Table XVI

In Vitro CO_2 Evolution from Glutamate and α-Ketoglutarate

	μmoles CO_2/hr./mg. protein ($\times 10^3$)		
1-C^{14}-substrate	A[a]	P[a]	S[a]
Glutamate (1×10^{-4} M)	6.5	2.6	1.0
α-KG (2×10^{-4} M)	4.5	2.2	1.0

[a] CO_2 evolution was determined at 3 stages of development: A = amoeba, P = preculmination, and S = sorocarp. (See Brühmüller and Wright, 1963.)

The most convincing data implicating α-KG as the only intermediate in CO_2 evolution from glutamate can be seen in Fig. 13. Here unlabeled α-KG is shown to competitively "inhibit" $C^{14}O_2$ formation from 1-C^{14}-glutamate.

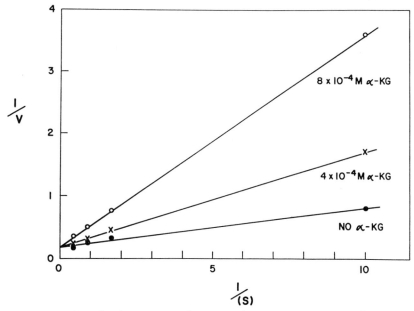

Fig. 13. A plot of 1/V against 1/(S) according to Lineweaver and Burk. The reaction is $C^{14}O_2$ evolution from 1-C^{14}-glutamate, and the inhibitor is unlabeled α-ketoglutarate. V = μmoles CO_2 per milligram protein per hour ($\times 10^3$) and (S) = μmoles glutamate per milliliter. (See Brühmüller and Wright, 1963.)

Turning now to the *in vivo* studies, conditions were found in which $C^{14}O_2$ evolution from $1\text{-}C^{14}$-glutamate was linear at all stages of development (Wright and Bard, 1963). After exposure of the cells to exogenous labeled glutamate, the intracellular glutamate was isolated in order to determine its specific radioactivity. Because of permeability changes as a function of differentiation, it had previously been found necessary to have this information to accurately calculate the activity of a reaction *in vivo* (Table II). It can be seen in Table XVII that

Table XVII

CO$_2$ Evolution from Glutamate *in Vivo*[a]

Stage	Cellular glutamate c.p.m. per μmole ($\times 10^{-3}$)	CO$_2$ c.p.m. per hour ($\times 10^{-3}$)	CO$_2$ μmole per hour
Ameba	38.0	24.0	0.64
Preculmination	100.0	80.0	0.80
Sorocarp	4.1	12.0	2.92

[a] Comparable cell aliquots were used at each stage of development. After exposure of the cells to exogenous labeled glutamate for 1 hr. the intracellular glutamate was isolated in order to determine its specific radioactivity. (See Wright and Bard, 1963.)

the intracellular glutamate became more highly labeled at preculmination than at the ameba and sorocarp stages of development. When the micromoles of CO$_2$ evolved per hour are calculated, based on the specific radioactivity of intracellular glutamate, it appears that the reaction increases during differentiation about 5-fold per cell aliquot or 7-fold on the basis of protein.

These data are in apparent conflict with the *in vitro* results (Table XIV) indicating a slight decrease in enzymatic activity at the later stages of development. Since the K_M of this enzyme is very high, and since preliminary observations suggested that intracellular glutamate was an atypical amino acid

Table XVIII

Intracellular Glutamate Concentration

Stage	μmole per cell aliquot	Molarity ($\times 10^4$)[a]	$(S)/K_M$[a]
Ameba	0.11	0.7	0.028
Preculmination	0.16	1.6	0.064
Sorocarp	0.48	8.0	0.320

[a] The molarity of glutamate inside the cell was calculated from the packed cell volume at each stage of development. The K_M of glutamic acid dehydrogenase is 2.5×10^{-3}. (See Wright and Bard, 1963.)

and accumulates during starvation, it appeared likely that the reaction rate *in vivo* could be influenced by substrate availability. Table XVIII indicates the changes in intracellular glutamate concentration during development, showing that the molarity increases 10-fold. The substrate to K_M ratio is given in the last column. These values increase from 0.03 to 0.3 in the sorocarp. When this value equals 1.0, the reaction is proceeding at one-half of its maximal activity. Thus, throughout development this reaction is substrate limited. Moreover, an increase in the $S:K_M$ ratio from 0.03 to 0.3 will theoretically account for the observed 6- to 7-fold increase in the rate of a reaction.

The efficiency with which intracellular glutamate is converted to CO_2 during development (Table XVII) with a comparable analysis for the formation of CO_2 from endogenous glucose (Wright and Bloom, 1961) is presented in Table XIX. Thus in contrast to the glutamate picture, the relative rate at which

Table XIX

THE CONVERSION OF ENDOGENOUS GLUCOSE
AND GLUTAMATE TO CO_2[a]

Stage	μmoles CO_2 per 15 min. *in vivo* from	
	Glucose	Glutamate
Ameba	0.30	0.16
Preculmination	0.06	0.20
Sorocarp	0.02	0.73

[a] See text.

glucose is converted to CO_2 *decreases* as differentiation proceeds. The metabolic machinery appears to become increasingly efficient at using amino acids as a source of energy, and less and less efficient at using carbohydrate. The apparent yield of CO_2 from intracellular glucose is greatest at the ameba stage and decreases by an order of magnitude during development. This circumstance might be anticipated in a system exhibiting an accelerated conversion of endogenous proteins to amino acids, Krebs-cycle intermediates, and glucose for two reasons: (a) These nonisotopic intermediates eventually supply the major source of the cells' requirements for energy. Glucose is used at an increasing rate for polymer synthesis and at a decreasing rate for energy (i.e., oxidized to CO_2). (b) The entrance of these nonisotopic materials, at an accelerated rate, into metabolic sequences would serve to dilute the specific radioactivity of like intermediates arising from C^{14}-glucose and lead to an apparent diminution in the yields of CO_2—that is, the specific radioactivity of the $C^{14}O_2$ would be lowered as differentiation proceeds.

3. GLUCOSE METABOLISM

Glucose can be degraded by several different pathways, some of which can be distinguished by using glucose specifically labeled in the 6 or 1 carbon (see Fig. 14). The ratio of the rate of $C^{14}O_2$ evolved from the 6 to the 1-C^{14} glucose is theoretically unity if triose phosphate isomerase is not limiting and if only the Embden-Meyerhof (EM) pathway is operating; this ratio decreases with increasing participation of the hexose monophosphate shunt (hms) pathway

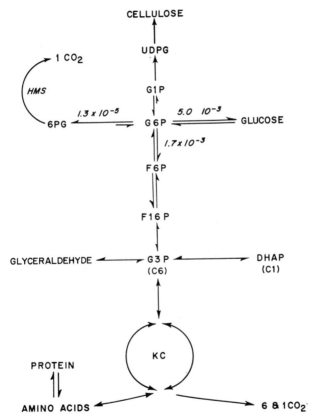

FIG. 14. Pathways of carbohydrate metabolism (see text).

(Katz and Wood, 1960). Using intact cells of *D. discoideum*, a C-6:C-1 ratio exceeding unity (1.3) had previously been reported, but no evidence was obtained to account for this unusual finding (Wright and Bloom, 1961). An extension of these studies has revealed that ratios between 2 and 3 can routinely be observed in *D. discoideum*, suggesting that these values result from a limiting triose phosphase isomerase reaction at high exogenous glucose concentrations (Wright and Brühmüller, 1963).

Figure 15 shows the μmoles of the $C^{14}O_2$ released from $1\text{-}C^{14}$ and $6\text{-}C^{14}$-glucose and gives the resulting C-6:C-1 ratios as a function of exogenous glucose concentration. This experiment was done at the sorocarp stage. The lower glucose concentrations, which do not appreciably affect the ratio, are of the

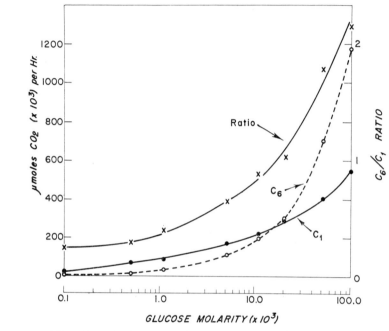

FIG. 15. The effect of glucose on the rate of CO_2 evolution in sorocarps. Glucose concentration is plotted on a logarithmic scale. The ratio of ($6\text{-}C^{14}$ to $(1\text{-}C^{14})CO_2$ from glucose labeled in the 6 or 1 position is derived from the μmoles of CO_2 plotted on the left ordinate. (See Wright and Brühmüller, 1963.)

order of the endogenous glucose levels of the spores ($10^{-4}M$; see Table V). In order to determine a "true" C-6:C-1 ratio, the amount of glucose used must be shown not to influence the pathways of glucose catabolism in the system being investigated; i.e., a plateau region such as that shown at the low glucose concentrations must be demonstrated. The fact that the exogenous glucose concentration can influence the C-6:C-1 ratio has not to our knowledge been reported in other systems. Thus in studies with animal tissues (e.g., Bloom, 1955) and microorganisms (for references, see Cheldelin, 1961), or with differentiating systems such as the sea urchin (Krahl, 1956) and rabbit ova (Fridhandler, 1961), only one concentration of exogenous glucose was used in

determining the C-6:C-1 ratio under various conditions or stages of development. Such studies are subject to the criticism that these ratios are not a true
reflection of the *in vivo* metabolism, but are in part due to the differential effect
of exogenous glucose on the various pathways leading to 1- and 6-$C^{14}O_2$. These
effects are further complicated by permeability differences in comparing tissues
or various stages of development.

It is now possible to relate these effects to the metabolism of differentiation.
The shape of the C-6:C-1 ratio curve shown in Fig. 15 is similar at all stages of
development except at preculmination, when the type of curve presented in Fig.
16 is obtained. The curve does not rise as quickly. However, in contrast to the

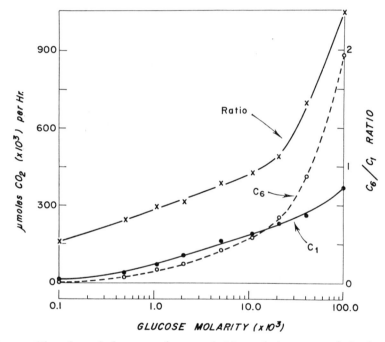

FIG. 16. The effect of glucose on the rate of CO_2 evolution at preculmination. (See
Wright and Brühmüller, 1963.)

sorocarp stage, even the lowest concentration of labeled glucose affects the
ratio. We are therefore influencing the pathways of glucose catabolism at
exogenous concentrations comparable to those present *in vivo* at preculmination. This result implies that the changes in intracellular glucose molarity that
normally occur during morphogenesis are such as to affect the pathways of
hexose metabolism. Table XX summarizes the results of three other experiments
in which the C-6:C-1 ratio was determined at three or four different exogenous
glucose concentrations as a function of developmental stage. The last column

Table XX

C-6:C-1 Ratios as a Function of Glucose Concentration[a]

Experiment	Stage	Extracellular glucose molarity ($\times 10^3$)				Ratio at $\frac{5.0}{0.1}$
		0.1	0.6	5.0	10.0	
		Ratios				
I	Ameba	0.43	0.69	1.1	1.0	2.6
	Aggregation	0.34	0.75	0.98	1.0	2.9
	Preculmination	0.38	0.44	0.56	0.53	1.5
	Culmination	0.40	0.58	0.84	0.96	2.1
	Sorocarp	0.22	0.37	0.96	1.2	4.4
II	Ameba	0.35	0.58	1.4	1.6	4.0
	Aggregation	0.12	0.27	0.99	1.2	8.3
	Preculmination	0.36	0.55	0.79	0.95	2.2
III	Ameba	0.47	0.72	0.94	—	2.0
	Aggregation	0.36	0.52	0.76	—	2.1
	Preculmination	0.39	0.41	0.50	—	1.3
	Sorocarp	0.22	0.32	0.63	—	2.9

[a] See text.

indicates the extent to which the ratio was increased between the concentration of 0.1 and $5.0 \times 10^{-3} M$ glucose. It can be seen that the greatest influence occurs at the time of the lowest intracellular glucose concentration, i.e., at aggregation and sorocarp. The least influence is seen at the periods of highest intracellular glucose levels, namely at preculmination and culmination. The amount of extracellular glucose required to influence the pathways of its catabolism might be expected to depend on the levels of intracellular glucose as well as on permeability differences from one stage to another. It is known that the cells are most permeable to glucose at preculmination (Wright and Bloom, 1961). *In vivo* glucose molarities are given in Table V. It can be seen from Table VI that the glucose levels reflect changing UDPG levels and may well also reflect glucose-6-phosphate levels, which could be critical in determining the relative importance of the EM and hms pathways. As is the case with the *in vivo* glucose levels, the degree of influence of exogenous glucose on the ratio varies a good deal from experiment to experiment, but within one experiment the relative influences are similar. The higher influence at each stage in Experiment II of Table XX may well be due to lower intracellular glucose levels in this particular batch of cells. At any rate, it is clear that the intensity and relative importance of the metabolic pathways on which the C-6:C-1 ratio depends can be easily influenced at all stages of development by altering the intracellular glucose or G-6-P levels.

Evidence has been presented that the shunt and EM pathways can be stimulated in a forward direction, so to speak; perhaps it is possible to mimic the metabolism of differentiation and reverse the EM pathway, *in vivo*, in the direction of gluconeogenesis. This may have been achieved by an unknown mechanism with exogenous glyceraldehyde, as shown in Table XXI. In the presence of

Table XXI

STIMULATION OF SHUNT ACTIVITY BY GLYCERALDEHYDE[a]

Molarity unlabeled glyceraldehyde ($\times 10^3$)	$C^{14}O_2$ (c.p.m.) from	
	1-C^{14}-glucose	6-C^{14}-glucose
—	730	569
10	785	443
30	1012	396
100	1342	239

[a] C^{14}-glucose was present at 2.1×10^{-3} M. See text.

low levels of C^1-labeled glucose, the presence of the unlabeled intermediate stimulates shunt activity. One interpretation of this result is that high glyceraldehyde levels bring about a partial reversal of the EM or shunt pathways, or in some manner stimulates the shunt directly. In the absence of data on the permeability of glyceraldehyde, the effective intracellular concentration of this compound is of course unknown.

VI. Speculations on Control Mechanisms of Biochemical Differentiation in the Slime Mold

Unlike most systems undergoing morphogenesis, in the cellular slime mold multicellular development is neither constantly nor intermittently dependent upon growth. There is no net increase in protoplasm, protein, or nucleic acid. Rather, these substances must all continuously decrease in this starving system. For this reason, perhaps, the biochemical mechanisms controlling various metabolic activities responsible for morphogenesis may be uniquely simple (and hence, fortunately, uniquely analyzable). It is even conceivable that all of the "informational RNA" necessary for the synthesis of the critical enzymes controlling morphogenesis exists in the myxamebae, and that the control mechanisms for biochemical differentiation therefore depend entirely on the accumulation and activation of enzymes and on sequential substrate availability (Wright, 1960a). Although this view is admittedly extreme, it is useful in its simplicity, and need not be abandoned until we have good evidence that a particular enzyme is synthesized only, for example, at the culmination stage of development.

Let us consider the variety of mechanisms which could be responsible for the accumulation of a substance such as UDPG or even cellulose during differentiation. Its accumulation of course implies nothing as to mechanism. In the extreme, but unlikely, case it might be synthesized at the same rate at all stages of development, and finally accumulate due to a decreased rate of degradation or utilization. Let us assume, however, that it is synthesized *de novo* in the terminal stages of development. This could be due to (a) the critical accumulation of the necessary precursors and/or cofactors, or (b) the new appearance or increased concentration of critical enzymes. In the latter case, again, enzyme accumulation could arise through lack of degradation or enhanced synthesis or both (as in the case of rat liver arginase; Schimke *et al.*, 1963); enzyme could also accumulate by activation of preformed protein. If an increased enzyme level is observed associated with the enhanced accumulation of the material in question (such as UDPG synthetase in the case of UDPG accumulation), it may be the result and not the cause of the higher synthetic activity. A high rate of substrate (e.g., UTP) turnover may protect the enzyme involved such that it is spared when other protein species are degraded (protein utilization is very rapid just before stalk formation). Furthermore, if an enzyme level increases, it by no means follows that this matters—i.e., that this enzyme was a limiting factor in the rate of the reaction it catalyzes. Generally speaking, substrates and not enzymes limit reactions *in vivo* (Vegotsky and Frieden, 1958), and a 3- to 4-fold increase in enzyme concentration may have less of an effect on the reaction than a comparable increase in concentration of the substrate. At any rate, although certain enzymes do increase in specific activity during slime mold differentiation, evidence that their concentration is critical in controlling rates of metabolic reactions *in vivo* is nil.

On the other hand, good evidence has been obtained in a number of differentiating systems for the importance of substrate control *in vivo* in the absence of changing enzyme levels (Wright, 1962). The most thoroughly analyzed case is that of glutamic acid dehydrogenase, a key enzyme in a gluconeogenic metabolism. Here it is clear that the accumulation of glutamate inside the cells results in an increased rate of its oxidation. Exogenous glucose can stimulate both respiration and CO_2 evolution; the many enzymes of the hexose monophosphate shunt and Embden-Meyerhof pathways are capable of many fold their normal *in vivo* activity throughout differentiation. It has been shown that the changes in intracellular glucose concentration normally occurring during development can influence the pathways of glucose catabolism. It is also possible to stimulate the rate of morphogenesis by the addition of exogenous glucose. Thus the direction and intensity of a number of pathways of hexose synthesis and utilization are very sensitive to control by endogenous substrate levels throughout development. This fact, as well as the observation that certain enzymes critical to differentiation do not change in concentration during development, indicates that *in vivo* many enzymes are not limiting the reaction they catalyze. It should be pointed out, however, that this conclusion is based on a study of specific reactions (e.g., glutamic acid dehydrogenase) and pathways (e.g., Embden-Meyerhof) which are of fundamental importance not only to differentiation but also to any living cell. It may well be that the area of cellulose synthesis, for example, is a more probable one in which to find the *de novo* synthesis of a specific enzyme associated with a particular stage of development.

It would be naive to think in terms of "one limiting factor" for differentiation. Clearly there are multiple conditions to be satisfied, and synchronized, before cellulose can accumulate. The eventual accumulation of cellulose is no more critical to slime mold differentiation than the accumulation (or rapid turnover) of UDPG or glucose-6-phosphate (G-6-P)—less so, in fact, since less depends on it. Glucose-6-phosphate is an early precursor for the synthesis of many end products of differentiation (see Table VII). Again, G-6-P accumulation is no more critical to slime mold differentiation than the turnover of Krebs-cycle intermediates, which are responsible for energy generation as well as G-6-P formation. Finally, it is of primary importance to know what mechanisms first initiate the utilization of endogenous proteins. While starvation proceeds, glucose and phosphate begin to accumulate in the cell. These compounds and many others stimulate the rate of morphogenesis when added extracellularly. The variety of these stimulants and the synergistic effects between some of them probably reflect the complexity of conditions to be satisfied for differentiation to proceed. This multiplicity of limiting factors and the necessity for their synchronism may well be responsible for the stability and reproducibility of morphogenesis.

This is publication No. 1158 of the Cancer Commission of Harvard University.

References

Beevers, H., and Walker, D. A. (1956). *Biochem. J.* **62**, 114–119.
Bloom, B. (1955). *Proc. Soc. Exptl. Biol. Med.* **88**, 317–318.
Bonner, J. T. (1947). *J. Exptl. Zool.* **106**, 1–26.
Bonner, J. T. (1959). "The Cellular Slime Molds." Princeton Univ. Press, Princeton, New Jersey.
Bonner, J. T., Chiquoine, A. D., and Kolderie, M. Q. (1955). *J. Exptl. Zool.* **130**, 133–158.
Boyd, W. C. (1947). "Fundamentals of Immunology." Wiley (Interscience), New York.
Bradley, S. G., Sussman, M., and Ennis, H. L. (1956). *J. Protozool.* **3**, 33–38.

Brefeld, O. (1869). *Abhandl. Senckenberg. Naturforsch. Ges.* 7, 85–107.
Brühmüller, M., and Wright, B. E. (1963). *Biochim. Biophys. Acta* 71, 50–57.
Campbell, D. H. (1936). *J. Infect. Diseases* 59, 266–270.
Cheldelin, V. H. (1961). "Metabolic Pathways in Microorganisms." Wiley, New York.
Clegg, J., and Filosa, M. F. (1961). *Nature* 192, 1077–1078.
Clegg, J., and Filosa, M. F. (1963). Personal communication.
Dauchy, S., and Kayser, F. (1958) *Bull. Soc. Chim. Biol.* 40, 1533–1538.
Davidoff, F., and Korn, E. D. (1962a). *Biochem. Biophys. Res. Commun.* 9, 54–58.
Davidoff, F., and Korn, E. D. (1962b). *Biochem. Biophys. Res. Commun.* 9, 328–333.
Eagle, H., Piez, K. A., and Fleischman, R. (1957). *J. Biol. Chem.* 228, 847–861.
Ebert, J. D. (1953). *Proc. Natl. Acad. Sci. U.S.* 39, 333–338.
Ennis, H. L. (1957). Ph.D. Thesis. Northwestern University.
Faust, R. G., and Filosa, M. F. (1959). *J. Cellular Comp. Physiol.* 54, 297–298.
Fridhandler, L. (1961). *Exptl. Cell Res.* 22, 303–316.
Gerisch, G. (1961). *Arch. Entwicklungsmech. Organ.* 153, 158–167.
Gerisch, G. (1962). *Exptl. Cell Res.* 26, 462–484.
Gezelius, K. (1959). *Exptl. Cell Res.* 18, 425–453.
Gezelius, K. (1963). Unpublished data.
Gezelius, K., and Rånby, B. G. (1957). *Exptl. Cell Res.* 12, 265–289.
Gezelius, K., and Wright, B. E. (1963). *Bacteriol. Proc.* p. 48.
Glaser, L. (1958). *J. Biol. Chem.* 232, 627–636.
Gregg, J. H. (1950). *J. Exptl. Zool.* 114, 173–196.
Gregg, J. H. (1960). *Biol. Bull.* 118, 70–78.
Gregg, J. H. (1961). *Develop. Biol.* 3, 757–766.
Gregg, J. H., and Bronsweig, R. D. (1956). *J. Cellular Comp. Physiol.* 48, 293–300.
Gregg, J. H., and Trygstad, C. W. (1958). *Exptl. Cell Res.* 15, 358–369.
Gregg, J. H., Hackney, A. L., and Krivanek, J. O. (1954). *Biol. Bull.* 107, 226–235.
Halvorson, H. (1958). *Biochim. Biophys. Acta* 27, 256–262.
Heftmann, E., Wright, B. E., and Liddel, G. U. (1960). *Arch. Biochem. Biophys.* 91, 266–270.
Hirschberg, E., and Rusch, H. P. (1950). *J. Cellular Comp. Physiol.* 36, 105–114.
Hirschberg, E., and Rusch, H. P. (1951). *J. Cellular Comp. Physiol.* 37, 323–336.
Hostak, M. B., and Raper, K. B. (1960). *Bacteriol. Proc.* p. 58.
Johnson, D. F., Wright, B. E., and Heftmann, E. (1962). *Arch. Biochem. Biophys.* 97, 232–235.
Katz, J., and Wood, H. G. (1960). *J. Biol. Chem.* 235, 2165–2177.
Kostellow, A. (1956). Ph.D. Thesis. Columbia University.
Krahl, M. E. (1956). *Biochim. Biophys. Acta* 20, 27–32.
Krichevsky, M. I., and Wright, B. E. (1961). *Bacteriol. Proc.* p. 86.
Krichevsky, M. I., and Wright, B. E. (1963). *J. Gen. Microbiol.* 32, 195–207.
Krichevsky, M. I., and Wright, B. E. (1963). *Proc. 8th Intern. Congr. Microbiol., Montreal, 1962* p. 17.
Krivanek, J. O. (1956). *J. Exptl. Zool.* 113, 459–480.
Krivanek, J. O., and Krivanek, R. C. (1958). *J. Exptl. Zool.* 137, 89–115.
Krivanek, J. O., and Krivanek, R. C. (1959). *Biol. Bull.* 116, 265–271.
Krivanek, J. O., and Krivanek, R. C. (1962). *Am. Zool.* 2, 421.
Liddel, G. U., and Wright, B. E. (1961). *Develop. Biol.* 3, 265–276.
Mandelstam, J. (1958). *Biochem. J.* 69, 103–109.
Mandelstam, J. (1960). *Bacteriol. Rev.* 24, 289–308.

Moog, F. (1952). *Ann. N.Y. Acad. Sci.* 55, 57–63.

Mühlethaler, K. (1956). *Am. J. Botany* 43, 673–678.

Noyes, H. M., and Folk, K. G. (1927). *J. Biol. Chem.* 72, 449.

Raper, K. B., and Fennell, D. I. (1952). *Bull. Torrey Botan. Club.* 79, 25–51.

Roberts, R. B., Abelson, P. H., Cowie, D. B., Bolton, E. T., and Britten, R. J. (1955). *Carnegie Inst. Wash. Publ.* 607.

Schildkraut, C. L., Mandel, M., Levisohn, S., Smith-Sonneborn, J. E., and Marmur, J. (1962). *Nature* 196, 795–796.

Schimke, R. T., Brown, M. B., and Smallman, E. T. (1963). *Ann. N.Y. Acad. Sci.* 102, 587–601.

Shaffer, B. M. (1953). *Nature* 171, 975.

Shaffer, B. M. (1956a). *Science* 123, 1172–1173.

Shaffer, B. M. (1956b). *J. Exptl. Biol.* 33, 645–657.

Slifkin, M. K., and Bonner, J. T. (1952). *Biol. Bull.* 102, 273–277.

Sussman, M. (1958). *In* "The Chemical Basis of Development." (W. D. McElroy and B. Glass, eds.) pp. 264–295. The Johns Hopkins Press, Baltimore, Maryland.

Sussman, R. R., and Sussman, M. (1953). *Ann. N.Y. Acad. Sci.* 56, 949–960.

Sussman, M., Lee, F., and Kerr, N. S. (1956). *Science* 123, 1171–1172.

Takeuchi, I. (1960). *Develop. Biol.* 2, 343–366.

Takeuchi, I. (1961). *Am. J. Botany* 48, 530–531.

Tomkins, G. (1960). Unpublished data.

Urbá, R. C. (1959). *Biochem. J.* 71, 513–518.

Vegotsky, A., and Frieden, E. (1958). *Enzymologia* 19, 143–150.

White, G. J., and Sussman, M. (1961). *Biochim. Biophys. Acta* 53, 285–293.

White, G. J., and Sussman, M. (1963a). *Biochim. Biophys. Acta* 74, 173–178.

White, G. J., and Sussman, M. (1963b). *Biochim. Biophys. Acta* 74, 179–187.

Worthington Biochem. Corp. (1962). Glucostat brochure, Freehold, New Jersey.

Wright, B. E. (1958). *Bacteriol. Proc.* p. 115.

Wright, B. E. (1960a). *Proc. Natl. Acad. Sci. U.S.* 46, 799–803.

Wright, B. E. (1962). *In* "Comparative Biochemistry" (M. Florkin and H. S. Mason, eds.), Vol. 6, Chapter 1. Academic Press, New York.

Wright, B. E. (1960b). Unpublished data.

Wright, B. E., and Anderson, M. L. (1959). *Biochim. Biophys. Acta* 31, 310–322.

Wright, B. E., and Anderson, M. L. (1960a). *Biochim. Biophys. Acta* 43, 62–66.

Wright, B. E., and Anderson, M. L. (1960b). *Biochim. Biophys. Acta* 43, 67–78.

Wright, B. E., and Bard, S. (1963). *Biochim. Biophys. Acta* 71, 45–49.

Wright, B. E., and Bloom, B. (1961). *Biochim. Biophys. Acta* 46, 342–346.

Wright, B. E., and Brühmüller, M. (1963). *Federation Proc.* 22, 584.

Wright, B. E., Brühmüller, M., and Ward, C. (1964). *Develop. Biol.* 9, 287–297.

The Physiology of Trichomonads

MARY S. SHORB

Poultry Science Department, University of Maryland, College Park, Maryland

	Page
I. Introduction	384
II. Carbohydrate Metabolism	385
A. Carbohydrates Used for Growth	385
B. Anaerobic Carbohydrate Metabolism	389
C. Carbohydrates and Aerobic Respiration	397
D. Inhibitors of Carbohydrate Metabolism	403
E. Enzymes in Carbohydrate Metabolism	407
III. Nitrogen and Lipid Metabolism	414
A. Enzymes of Nitrogen Metabolism	414
B. Enzymes for Steroid Conversions	415
IV. The Chemical Composition of Trichomonads	415
A. Glycogens in *Tritrichomonas foetus* and *Trichomonas gallinae*	415
B. Nucleic Acid Composition	416
C. Lipid Composition	417
D. Amino Acid Composition	417
E. Vitamins and Other Compounds	419
V. The Nutritional Requirements of Trichomonads	419
A. Vitamin Requirements	424
B. Requirement for Trace Minerals	425
C. Requirements for Components of Nucleic Acids	425
D. Amino Acid Requirements	425
E. Fatty Acid Requirements and Development of Defined Media	426
F. Sterol Requirement	429
G. Unidentified Requirements	430
VI. Cultural Methods	430
A. Culture Methods for Different Species	431
B. Methods for Bulk Growth or Continuous Flow Culture	434
C. Agar Plate Culturing of Trichomonads	434
D. Storage and Survival of Trichomonads under Various Conditions	437

                                                                    Page
VII. Factors Affecting Pathogenicity 440
     A. Strain Differences in Pathogenicity in Natural infections . 440
     B. Pathogenicity in Experimental Hosts 442
     C. Trichomonads in Tissue Culture 445
VIII. Immunology in Trichomonad Infections 446
     A. Antigens in Trichomonads 446
     B. Fluorescent Antibodies 447
IX. Antibiotics and Other Drugs as Metabolic Tools 448
     A. Reversal Studies on Antitrichomonal Activity 448
     B. Induced Changes in Cultural Characteristics 449
X. Summary 450
     References 450

I. Introduction

Much work has been done on improvement of cultural methods, on growth requirements and development of chemically defined media, on isolation of clones for more definitive study of strain and species differences, on immunological techniques (especially fluorescent antibodies for diagnostic procedures), and on infections and virulence. Some knowledge has been gained about chemical composition, but precise analysis awaits further work on the variables controlling chemical composition. A great volume of work has been carried out since 1951,* on the enzyme systems and carbohydrates for energy and growth.

* More than 700 references on trichomonads have appeared from 1950 through March 1963, the period chosen for coverage on the physiology of trichomonads. The review by Lwoff (1951) stopped with references during 1950 and many references were not included in the review by Hutner and Provasoli (1955). However, all references strictly pertaining to morphology, classification, new hosts, new species, epidemiology, and chemotherapy have been excluded. This chapter does not include all references reviewed. Some foreign articles could not be located for review. For the most part, the nomenclature of Honigberg (1963) has been used. Where different names were used by different authors for the same species, the following has been used in this text: *Trichomonas gallinae* (= *Trichomonas columbae, Trichomonas bosi*); *Tetratrichomonas gallinarum* (= *Trichomonas gallinarum, Pentatrichomonas gallinarum*); *Tritrichomonas foetus* (= *Trichomonas foetus*); *Tetratrichomonas buttreyi* (= *Trichomonas buttreyi, Trichomonas batrachorum*-type); *Monocercomonas colubrorum* (= *Trichomonas* [*Eutrichomastix*] *colubrorum*); *Hypotrichomonas acosta* (= *Trichomonas acosta*); *Pentatrichomonas hominis* (= *Trichomonas hominis, Trichomonas intestinalis*); *Trichomonas tenax* (= *Trichomonas elongata*); *Trichomitis marmotae* (= *Paratrichomonas marmotae*); *Tritrichomonas suis* (= *Trichomonas* sp. nasal, fecal, and *Tritrichomonas rotunda*); *Tritrichomonas eberti* (= *Trichomonas eberthi*); *Tritrichomonas enteris* (= *Trichomonas enteris*). *Trichomitis batrachorum* (= *Trichomonas batrachorum, Paratrichomonas batrachorum*); *Tritrichomonas augusta* (= *Trichomonas augusta*); *Tetratrichomonas ovis* (= *Trichomonas ovis*); *Tetratrichomonas prowazeki* (= *Trichomonas prowazeki*).

The references for media in common use are: STS, Kupferberg *et al.* (1948); CPLM, J. G. Johnson and Trussell (1943); Diamond's, Diamond (1957).

In examining the physiology of the trichomonads, energy metabolism is the logical starting point.

II. Carbohydrate Metabolism

A. CARBOHYDRATES USED FOR GROWTH

Reports on stimulation of growth of trichomonads by carbohydrates are summarized in Table I. The data from tables in reviews by Lwoff (1951) and von Brand (1952) have been compared with the results of Cole (1950), Read (1957), Twohy (1959), and Lee and Pierce (1960). Since cultures were grown on different media, and different criteria of growth were used, discrepancies are to be noted and so there seems little point in detailed comparisons. Except for the pentoses and the sugar alcohols, which fail to support growth, the mono-, di- and polysaccharides were used in some degree by all the species. Glucose, fructose, galactose, and maltose appear best utilized by all species, while lactose, sucrose, trehalose, glycogen, starch, and dextrin supported good to fair growth of some species. Some carbohydrates supported only fair to poor growth. Compounds which failed to support growth of various organisms (not shown in table) include: adonitol, phloridzin, salicin, aesculin, α-methylglucose, inositol, xylan, pectin, and sorbose (see references in Table I). The species varied in the number of carbohydrates used, *Tritrichomonas foetus* and *T. augusta* both using 21 carbohydrates in some degree, with *Trichomonas vaginalis* and *Monocercomonas colubrorum* using least. Read (1957) concluded that *Trichomonas vaginalis* and *T. gallinae* used best, for growth, glucose polymers having the glucose-4, 1-β-glucoside configuration. This was not related to effective concentration of substrate nor to the pH alterations of the medium. Samuels (1959) observed that several 6-carbon acids, both mono- and dicarboxylic (not specified by name), had intense growth-stimulating effects at 0.1 to 1.0 μg. per milliliter.

Of the Krebs-cycle intermediates, C^{14}-succinate as well as glucose-U-C^{14} were reported by Kunitake *et al.* (1962) to be incorporated during the growth of *Trichomonas vaginalis*. Lund and Shorb (1962) observed that while cholesterol was required for growth, acetate was also required by *T. gallinae*. Twohy (1959) found that acetate, pyruvate, and succinate produced insignificant growth of *Tritrichomonas augusta*.

Interesting observations have been made on how different sugars affect growth and length of life. Cole (1950) found that although trehalose produced a population peak only 55% of the glucose control, it was attained 48 hr. after the control peak was reached and the *Tritrichomonas foetus* culture lasted almost twice as long as the control. Total population with trehalose was slightly superior to glucose, possibly due to slow release of glucose from the compound.

Table I

Utilization of Carbohydrates for Growth by Trichomonads[a]

Carbohydrate	Monocercomonas colubrorum	Trichomonas vaginalis 5A	Trichomonas vaginalis	Tritrichomonas foetus BR	Tritrichomonas foetus	Trichomonas gallinae WS	Trichomonas gallinae	Hypotrichomonas acosta 3	Hypotrichomonas acosta 5	Hypotrichomonas acosta 6	Tritrichomonas augusta
	Ref. 1[b]	Ref. 1	Ref. 3	Ref. 1	Ref. 2	Ref. 1	Ref. 3	Ref. 5	Ref. 5	Ref. 5	Ref. 4
Monosaccharides											
Pentoses											
Ribose	—	—	—	—	—	—	—	±	±	—	—
Arabinose	0	0	0	0,?	?	0	±	±	±	—	0
Xylose	0	0	0	0,?	?	0	0	0	?	—	0
Rhamnose	0	0	—	0	?	0	—	?	?	—	—
Hexoses											
Sorbose	—	—	—	—	—	—	—	?	?	—	—
Glucose	+	+	±	+	+	+	+	+	+	+, s	+
Fructose	+	0,+	0	+	—	±,+	+	+	+, s	+, s	+
Galactose	+	0,+	±	+	±	+	±	+, s	+	+, s	+
Mannose	—	0	0	+	+	—	0	±	+, s	+, s	+
Disaccharides											
Maltose	+	+	+	0,+	+	±,+	+	±	+	+, s	+
Lactose	±,+	0	0	0,+	—	+	0	±	+, s	?	+
Sucrose	+	0	0	0,+	+	—	±	—	?	?	+
Trehalose	—	0	±	—	±	—	±	—	—	—	+
Melibiose	—	0	±	—	+	—	0	+	—	—	+
Cellobiose	—	0	—	—	?	—	±	—	+, s	0	+
Turanose	—	0	0	—	—	—	±	—	—	—	+

Polysaccharides										
Melezitose	—	—	—	—	±	—	—	—	—	+
Raffinose	+	—	?	?	+	0	+	0,+	—	0[c]
Glycogen[e]	+	0	+,s	±	+	+[c]	—	0,+	+	—
Starch[d]	+	+,s	±,s	?	+	+[d]	—	+,+	—	0
Dextrin	+	0	0	+	—	+	—	+,+	—	0
Inulin	0	—	—	—	—	±,+	—	±,+	—	0
Alcohols										
Mannitol	?	0	?	0	—	—	?	—	—	—
Inositol	—	—	?	?	0	—	—	—	0	—
Sorbitol	?	—	?	?	0	—	—	—	0	—
Dulcitol	?	—	—	—	0	—	—	—	0	—
Erythritol	?	—	—	—	—	—	—	—	—	—
Glycerol	?	—	—	—	—	—	—	—	—	—

[a] KEY TO SYMBOLS:

0, No growth.

+, Best growth.

±, Fair growth, 50% or less of best growth.

?, Poor growth or 10% of best growth.

s, Slow to very slow growth.

[b] References:

1. From Lwoff (1951) and von Brand (1952) reviews.

2. Cole (1950).

3. Read (1957).

4. Twohy (1959).

5. Lee and Pierce (1960); 1 to 2 weeks' growth. Lyxose and gluconic, glucuronic, and galacturonic acids gave no growth.

[c] Lwoff and Lee specify soluble glycogen.

[d] von Brand and Lee specify soluble starch.

Read (1956, 1957) attempted to adapt *Trichomonas gallinae* to a poorly utilized carbohydrate; after a single transfer the organisms showed an enhanced capacity for growth on galactose. However, after 48 transfers in sucrose medium he found no enhancement of growth on this substrate. Read (1957) also found that the fermentability of glucose and maltose in short experiments with nondividing cells was not significantly different. However in supporting growth maltose was a much more efficient substrate than glucose, yielding about 5 times as many cells with *Trichomonas vaginalis* and more than twice as many with *T. gallinae*. Cell counts of *T. gallinae* at 48 hr. were optimal with $10^{-2}M$ maltose, and were minimal between 10^{-4} to $10^{-5}M$. Twohy (1959), using *Tritrichomonas augusta*, observed that glucose as a carbohydrate source limited growth below 3.25 mmole, where a maximum population of 12.8×10^5 organisms per milliliter was obtained. The rate of growth was, however, largely independent of concentration. Cole (1950) found that a billion actively growing organisms of *Tritrichomonas foetus* strain BR used 554 mg. of glucose the first 24 hr. of growth and 207 mg. the second 24 hr., slightly higher than the amounts reported by Andrews and von Brand (1938).

Teras (1961) found *T. vaginalis* could be divided into three groups; those which produced gas from all sugars investigated, those which produced gas from maltose and mannitol, and a third group with no regularity in fermentation. Acid production was equal in the three groups. No relation between the fermentations and pathogenicity was detected.

Several reports have included studies on the products of anaerobic growth.

1. PRODUCTS OF ANAEROBIC GROWTH

Lactic acid was the major acid formed in STS medium (Kupferberg *et al.*, 1948) containing maltose and human serum, by anaerobic cultures of *Trichomonas vaginalis*, strain 2 (Kupferberg *et al.*, 1953). Carbon dioxide was produced anaerobically. The *T. vaginalis* culture took up labeled HCO_3^- during growth, and the product was almost entirely outside the cell. The products were later examined by paper chromatography by Wellerson *et al.* (1959, 1960) who detected lactic acid (labeled exclusively in the carboxyl carbon), malic acid, and a third unidentified acid. Wirtschafter and Jahn (1956) had earlier demonstrated some of the enzymes for lactic acid formation from glucose.

Suzuoki and Suzuoki (1951a) cultivated *Tritrichomonas foetus* anaerobically for 48 hr. on a beef extract, peptone, bovine serum, glucose medium and found 9 to 11 ml. of gas evolved per 50 ml. of medium. Analysis of the gas showed it to be largely H_2 (74–84%), N_2 (12–20%), methane (1.9–2.1%), and O_2 (2–6%). Suzuoki and Suzuoki (1951b) had shown that succinic acid made up 83% of the titrable acids, and lactic and pyruvic acids <10% each.

Lindblom (1961), growing Sanborn's strains of trichomonads in NIH thioglycolate broth with 1% beef serum, for 70–75 hr., demonstrated that succinic acid was the major acid (>50%) produced by *Tritrichomonas foetus*, *Tetratrichomonas gallinarum*, and the nasal *Tritrichomonas suis*. The fecal *T. suis* produced more lactic than succinic acid, although about 45% of the total acid was not accounted for. Pyruvic acid was found in small amounts in all cultures. The nasal form of *T. suis* produced much more total acid than the others. The lactic-pyruvic ratio was about 2.5 for the two swine forms, and about 1.0 for the other two species.

Trichomonas vaginalis, strain 5A, grown aerobically (authors' statement) on modified CPLM medium (J. G. Johnson and Trussell, 1943) containing thioglycolate, slowly metabolized uniformly labeled D-glucose-C^{14} (glucose-U-C^{14}) and succinate-2,3-C^{14} to CO_2 and to amino acids, which were then incorporated into protein (Kunitake *et al.*, 1962).

By far the greatest interest of many investigators has been the manometric study of the anaerobic glycolytic pathway and the metabolic products from carbohydrates.

B. ANAEROBIC CARBOHYDRATE METABOLISM

1. VARIATION IN MANOMETRIC STUDIES

The results of manometric studies on anaerobic gas and acid formation with various carbohydrates are shown in Table II. Direct comparison of findings is difficult because of the great variation in technique and in components in the experiments; the original papers should be consulted. Read and Rothman (1954, 1955) called attention to several factors causing variation. In studying the anaerobic metabolism of strains 2 and 5A, using washed cells harvested at different times during the cycle of population growth, they found strain differences in the Q_{acid} and Q_{gas} which changed throughout the cycle of growth. The metabolic peak corresponded to the initial portion of the logarithmic growth phase. The changes were shown to be a function of quality of the medium, age of the inoculum, strain and cultural history of the strain. In experiments with glucose as substrate, lactic acid accounted for only 33–50% of the total acid. They concluded that more work needed to be done on strain differences. About the same time an excellent paper appeared which explained much of the variability.

2. GLYCOGEN SYNTHESIS AND ITS INFLUENCE ON ENDOGENOUS
AND EXOGENOUS ANAEROBIC METABOLISM

Variability in endogenous metabolic measurements led Ryley (1955) to study glycogen reserves. Energy metabolism and motility of *Tritrichomonas foetus* was maintained aerobically or anaerobically at 37°C. for considerable periods by fermentation of intracellular glycogen reserves, supplemented by

Table II

End Products of Anaerobic Metabolism of Carbohydrates[a]

Organism	Strain	Substrate[b]	Q_{gas} (μl./10^8 cells/hour[c])				Q_{acid} (μl./10^8 cells/hour[c])			References
			CO_2	H_2	Other	Total	Total	Lactic	Other	
Trichomonas vaginalis	Izumida	None	104	—	65	169	—	—	—	Ninomiya and Suzuoki, 1952.
		Glucose	202	—	178[d]	380	—	—	—	Ninomiya and Suzuoki, 1952.
		Maltose	—	—	—	266	—	—	—	Ninomiya and Suzuoki, 1952.
		Pyruvate	313	—	131	444	—	—	—	Ninomiya and Suzuoki, 1952.
		Lactate	107	—	84	191	—	—	—	Ninomiya and Suzuoki, 1952.
		Others[e]	N	—	N	N	—	—	—	Ninomiya and Suzuoki, 1952.
Trichomonas vaginalis	2	Glucose	85	+	?	—	+	+	—	Kupferberg et al., 1953.
		Glucose	+	+	—	—	—	—	—	Read, 1953.
Trichomonas vaginalis	5A	None	—	—	—	—	28	13	—	Read and Rothman, 1955.
		Glucose	240	118	A	V	324	126	—	Read and Rothman, 1955.
		Sugars[f]; pH 6	+	+	—	—	+	—	—	Read, 1955.
		Citric acid cycle intermed.; pH 6[g]	N	N	—	—	N	—	—	Read, 1955.
		None	18[h]	20[h]	—	—	—	—	—	Read, 1957.
		Glucose	100[h]	100[h]	—	—	—	—	—	Read, 1957.
		Maltose	96[h]	104[h]	—	—	—	—	—	Read, 1957.
		Trehalose	60[h]	50[h]	—	—	—	—	—	Read, 1957.
		Glycogen	60[h]	75[h]	—	—	—	—	—	Read, 1957.
Trichomonas gallinae	WS	Sugars[f]; pH 7	+	+	—	—	+	—	—	Read, 1955.
		Citric acid cycle intermed.; pH 7[g]	+	+	—	—	+	—	—	Read, 1957.
		None	235	175	—	—	—	—	—	Read, 1957.
		Glucose	644	485	—	—	—	—	—	Read, 1957.
		None	16[i]	18[i]	—	—	—	—	—	Read, 1957.
		Glucose	100[i]	100[i]	—	—	—	—	—	Read, 1957.
		Galactose	105[i]	121[i]	—	—	—	—	—	Read, 1957.
		Fructose	110[i]	118[i]	—	—	—	—	—	Read, 1957.
		Xylose	61[i]	50[i]	—	—	—	—	—	Read, 1957.

Organism	Strain	Substrate							References
	WS (cont.)	Maltose	98^i	102^i	—	—	—	—	Read, 1957.
		Trehalose	100^i	98^i	—	—	—	—	Read, 1957.
		Sucrose	66^i	64^i	—	—	—	—	Read, 1957.
		Starch	97^i	102^i	—	—	—	—	Read, 1957.
		Glycogen	88^i	90^i	—	—	—	—	Read, 1957.
Tetratrichomonas gallinarum	Sanborn	Glucose	Op, V	—	—	—	—	—	Lindblom, 1961.
		Lactate	—	59^j	—	—	—	—	Lindblom, 1961.
		Pyruvate	—	10^j	—	—	—	—	Lindblom, 1961.
		Formate	—	30^j	—	—	—	—	Lindblom, 1961.
Tritrichomonas suis	Nasal Sanborn	Glucose	Op, V	—	—	—	—	—	Lindblom, 1961.
		Lactate	—	0^j	—	—	—	—	Lindblom, 1961.
		Pyruvate	—	19^j	—	—	—	—	Lindblom, 1961.
		Formate	—	0^j	—	—	—	—	Lindblom, 1961.
Tritrichomonas suis	Fecal Sanborn	Glucose	Op, V	—	—	—	—	—	Lindblom, 1961.
		Lactate	—	0^j	—	—	—	—	Lindblom, 1961.
		Pyruvate	—	7^j	—	—	—	—	Lindblom, 1961.
		Formate	—	0^j	—	—	—	—	Lindblom, 1961.
Tritrichomonas suis	Cecal PC-414	None	105	108	213	85	39	—	Doran, 1957.
		Glucose	313	145	458	345^k	131	—	Doran, 1957.
		Pyruvate	150	117	267	—	—	—	Doran, 1957.
		Lactate	173	119	292	—	—	—	Doran, 1957.
Tritrichomonas foetus	Tricho	None	200^l	100^m	—	—	—	—	Suzuoki and Suzuoki, 1951a, b.
		Glucose	450^l	234^m	409	—	—	—	Suzuoki and Suzuoki, 1951a, b.
		Pyruvate	—	150^m	—	—	—	—	Suzuoki and Suzuoki, 1951a, b.
		Formate	—	$128^{m,n}$	—	—	—	—	Suzuoki and Suzuoki, 1951a, b.
Tritrichomonas foetus	Belfast	None (Intracellular glycogen)	325	—	+	—	—	$+^o$	Ryley, 1955.

Table II—Continued

Organism	Strain	Substrate[b]	Q_{gas} ($\mu l./10^8$ cells/hour[c])				Q_{acid} ($\mu l./10^8$ cells/hour[c])			References
			CO₂	H₂	Other	Total	Total	Lactic	Other	
	Belfast (cont.)	Maltose	15[j]	—	—	—	—	—	—	Ryley, 1955.
		Glucose	100[j]	—	—	—	—	—	—	Ryley, 1955.
		Fructose	100[j]	—	—	—	—	—	—	Ryley, 1955.
		Galactose	<100[j]	—	—	—	—	—	—	Ryley, 1955.
		Lactose	<100[j]	—	—	—	—	—	—	Ryley, 1955.
Tritrichomonas foetus	PB-610 Nasal	None	36	—	77	113	77	31	—	Doran, 1957.
		Glucose	195	—	110	305	208[k]	92	—	Doran, 1957.
		Pyruvate	204	—	103	307	—	—	—	Doran, 1957.
		Lactate	178	—	92	270	—	—	—	Doran, 1957.
Tritrichomonas foetus	BP-1	None	34	—	71	105	67	31	—	Doran, 1957.
		Glucose	205	—	90	295	328[k]	139	—	Doran, 1957.
		Raffinose	42	—	82	124	—	—	—	Doran, 1957.
		Lactose	47	—	80	127	—	—	—	Doran, 1957.
		Pyruvate	182	—	93	275	—	—	—	Doran, 1957.
		Lactate	150	—	94	244	—	—	—	Doran, 1957.
Tritrichomonas foetus	BP-3	None	—	—	—	165	75	28	—	Doran, 1959.
		Glucose	—	—	—	230[j]	240	75	—	Doran, 1959.
Tritrichomonas foetus	BP-4	None	—	—	—	140	70	32	—	Doran, 1959.
		Glucose	—	—	—	242[j]	327	136	—	Doran, 1959.
Tritrichomonas foetus	A-1	None	—	—	—	235	97	37	—	Doran, 1959.
		Glucose	—	—	—	200[j]	390	164	—	Doran, 1959.
Tritrichomonas foetus	A-2	None	—	—	—	152	42	16	—	Doran, 1959.
		Glucose	—	—	—	220[j]	307	98	—	Doran, 1959.
Tritrichomonas foetus	Sanborn	Glucose	Op, V		—	—	—	—	—	Lindblom, 1961.
		Lactate		6[j]	—	—	—	—	—	Lindblom, 1961.

Organism	Strain	Substrate	Pyruvate	Formate								Reference
	Sanborn (cont.)		—	—								Lindblom, 1961.
			—	—								Lindblom, 1961.
Tetratrichomonas buttreyi	PC-287	None	—	—	47	0^j	54	101	—	36	16	—	Doran, 1958.
		Glucose	—	—	130	67^j	71	201	—	109^k	42	—	Doran, 1958.
		Maltose	—	—	135	—	70	205	—	—	—	—	Doran, 1958.
		Lactose	—	—	50	—	59	109	—	—	—	—	Doran, 1958.
		Raffinose	—	—	46	—	61	107	—	—	—	—	Doran, 1958.
		Pyruvate	—	—	117	—	82	199	—	—	—	—	Doran, 1958.
		Lactate	—	—	98	—	72	170	—	—	—	—	Doran, 1958.

[a] Key to symbols in body of table:
  +, Indicates product was formed by organisms.
  N, Not used.
  V, Variable amounts, depending on age of cells when harvested.
  Op, Optimum.
  A, No methane but a trace or no NH_3.
  ?, Not specified.
[b] For test conditions, refer to original papers. The substrates varied in concentration from 0.01 to 0.05 M. Buffers and pH differ, as well as gas phase, age of culture, and cultural conditions of cell preparations.
[c] Unless stated otherwise, all figures in the table are equal to microliters of gas or acid per 10^8 cells per hour. Variations are given in the following footnotes by alphabetical notation.
[d] Maximal at pH 6.2.
[e] Acetate, formate, succinate, fumarate, citrate, glutamate, gluconate not used.
[f] Metabolized, anaerobically, glucose, galactose, fructose, mannose, maltose, sucrose, trehalose, lactose, starch, glycogen.
[g] Materials tested were citrate, isocitrate, α-ketoglutarate, succinate, fumarate, malate, as well as β-hydroxybutyrate.
[h] Relative rate, with glucose as 100. Galactose, mannose, fructose, arabinose, xylose, lactose, sucrose not fermented.
[i] Relative rate, with glucose as 100. Mannose, arabinose, lactose not fermented.
[j] Percent stimulation over endogenous rate.
[k] Substrate at 0.05 M for anaerobic acid production, 0.01 or 0.02 M for other tests.
[l] mm^3 gas at 60 min.
[m] Relative amounts of H_2 evolved during 30 min., 10^7 cells as suspension.
[n] Glycerol, lactate, and DL-α alanine inactive.
[o] Acetic and succinic acids.

any extra substrates available. These substrates were degraded under both aerobic and anaerobic conditions to CO_2, a gas other than CO_2 (shown by Suzuoki and Suzuoki, 1951a,b, to be H_2), and succinic and acetic acids. The glycogen reserves depended in part on the carbohydrate in the culture medium. The intracellular glycogen disappeared on aerobic or anaerobic incubation of washed suspensions of organisms in the absence of extracellular substrate. In the presence of glucose, fructose, lactose, or galactose, although the metabolic rate (O_2 uptake, acid formation, or CO_2 output) was considerably increased, there was a net synthesis of glycogen. Maltose slightly spared utilization of intracellular glycogen. In a bicarbonate suspending medium, endogenous gas evolution had a $Q(N_2/CO_2)$ about 325 and was almost doubled in the presence of glucose or fructose; galactose and lactose had a smaller effect, and maltose stimulated by $\sim 15\%$. Since gas production was tied up with acid formation and perhaps with CO_2 fixation or assimilation, this was also studied in an analysis of the suspending medium under aerobic or anaerobic conditions. Aerobic conditions favored production of acetic acid at the expense of succinic acid, while anaerobic conditions and CO_2 in the gas phase favored glycogen breakdown and succinic acid production. Under neither condition was formic acid produced nor were detectable amounts of ethanol, glycerol, or pyruvic acid produced. Not more than 0.05 mole of lactic acid was produced per mole of hexose used.

With these facts in mind, the results of other investigators may be examined.

3. ACID AND GASEOUS PRODUCTS OF ANAEROBIC CARBOHYDRATE FERMENTATION

Most of the early work was on *Trichomonas vaginalis* (Table II). Ninomiya and Suzuoki (1952) showed that *T. vaginalis* evolved not only CO_2 but some other gases. The CO_2 evolution was increased by the addition of glucose or pyruvate, and total gas by several carbohydrates. Several citric acid cycle components were inactive. With *T. vaginalis*, strain 2, Kupferberg *et al.* (1953) were not able to demonstrate the production of any gas other than CO_2 in appreciable amounts and found a low Q_{CO_2} of 85, although Read (1953) observed that *T. vaginalis* metabolized glucose to H_2, CO_2, and unidentified acid(s). Read and Rothman (1955) show a variation of 161 to 334 with an average of 240 for Q_{CO_2} and an average Q_{H_2} of 118.

Read (1955, 1957), using anaerobic gaseous fermentation as the measure of carbohydrate utilization by *Trichomonas vaginalis* and *T. gallinae*, observed that the sugars utilized to produce CO_2 and H_2 were those which supported growth (Table I). However, as mentioned earlier, the relative quantitative differences in rates of utilization as determined by short fermentation experiments did not correspond to those obtained in growth experiments.

Trichomonas gallinae used all of the citric acid cycle intermediates tested; *T. vaginalis* did not.

Warren and Allen (1959; data not shown in Table II), found that anaerobic gas production of the Jones' Barn strain of *Trichomonas gallinae* was stimulated 2- to 3-fold by glutamic acid. The gas produced was adsorbed by KOH. The acid formed was γ-amino-*n*-butyric acid, while α-methyl-α-amino-*n*-butyric acid was tentatively identified, along with an amino acid complex.

Differences between species were also apparent when Lindblom (1957, 1961) measured the H_2 produced with lactate, pyruvate, or formate by *Tetratrichomonas gallinarum* and two strains of *Tritrichomonas suis* and *Tritrichomonas foetus*. *Tetratrichomonas gallinarum* used all three compounds for H_2 production while *Tritrichomonas foetus* used lactate and formate. The two forms of *T. suis* appeared to release H_2 from pyruvate but not from formate or lactate. Doran (1957) also studied the gas production of cecal *T. suis* (PC-414). Glucose was the most useful for CO_2 and other gas formation, although pyruvate and lactate were also used. Lactic acid constituted 43% of the total acid produced by this strain with glucose and 47% without glucose.

The most extensive manometric work has been done on *Tritrichomonas foetus*, beginning with Suzuoki and Suzuoki (1951a,b). Glucose stimulated the production of both CO_2 and H_2 by the "tricho" strain while pyruvate and formate increased the amount of H_2. They found that 73% of the total acid was succinic, and only 10% lactic, which might have been expected in the usual glycolytic pathway. Ryley's work (1955) on *T. foetus* has already been reviewed.

Doran has done comparable research on gaseous and acid end products. In the first study (1957), besides the cecal *Tritrichomonas suis*, PC-414, mentioned above, two other strains of trichomonads were used, *T. foetus* BP-1 and a nasal strain from swine, BP-610. Nearly two-thirds of the gas evolved by the three cultures in the presence of glucose was CO_2. Without substrate, less than half of the gas evolved by each of the trichomonads was CO_2. While the addition of glucose increased CO_2 evolution nearly 3-fold in the case of the cecal trichomonad (*T. suis* PC-414), it increased it nearly 6-fold with *T. foetus* and the nasal strain. Other gas(es) increased only slightly in the presence of glucose and other substrates. Raffinose and lactose had little effect on gas evolution and O_2 uptake in *T. foetus*. Pyruvate and lactate stimulated gas production and also O_2 uptake. Lactic acid constituted from 38 to 47% of the total acid produced with or without glucose as substrate. The total amount of acid produced anaerobically with these cultures was much higher than the amount produced aerobically. Based on the production of CO_2 and other gases, acid formation, and carbohydrate utilization, and comparison with other strains of *T. foetus* in later work Doran thought BP-610 might possibly be a highly adapted strain of *T. foetus* (Doran, 1959).

To determine whether metabolic strain differences actually could be demonstrated, four strains of *T. foetus*, kept under identical cultural conditions from the time of isolation were studied (Doran, 1959). The results on gas and acid production are shown in Table II (the carbohydrates utilized and aerobic metabolism will be discussed later, see Tables III and IV). The strains varied somewhat in amount of acid produced. Strain A-1, having the highest endogenous rate and the lowest proportional utilization of glucose, produced more acid than did the other three strains. The Q_{acid} and $Q_{lactate}$ of each strain were greater under anaerobic conditions than under aerobic conditions, either in the presence or absence of glucose, and were greater under both conditions in the presence of glucose than in its absence. Lactic acid accounted for 30–51% of the acid produced, and the four strains were alike as to the percentage produced under aerobic and anaerobic conditions. *Pentatrichomonas hominis* used glucose, galactose, maltose, and sucrose (Solomon, 1957; data not shown in Table II).

Tetratrichomonas buttreyi from swine was similar to *T. foetus* (Doran, 1958). With or without glucose, the Q_{acid} and $Q_{lactate}$ were nearly twice as much under anaerobic as under aerobic conditions, and lactic acid was 38–44% of the total acid, with or without glucose. Anaerobic gas increased over endogenous with glucose, maltose, pyruvate, lactate, but not lactose or raffinose. Glucose, maltose, and lactate increased the CO_2, while pyruvate increased gas other than CO_2. Acetate, malate, fumarate, citrate, gluconate, glutamate, and formate did not increase amounts of gas evolved, and some even inhibited total gas production (data not shown in Table II).

Two types of *Tritrichomonas augusta* were found by Concannon (1959) in respect to anaerobic utilization of carbohydrates. Glucose, maltose, and galactose were used best, and sucrose, fructose, and trehalose less by both types. The LISA type did not use mannose, turanose, nor melibiose; these were used by the MTM type. The latter type did not use lactose, inositol, sorbitol, or arabinose—all used by the former type. The endogenous rate of MTM type was higher than that of LISA type.

In *Tritrichomonas augusta* grown in continuous-flow cultures with generation times of 10.3 to 49.5 hr., Twohy and Tucker (1961) observed that these cultures were consistent in rate of total gas evolution, irrespective of growth rate, both under endogenous conditions and with glucose. Although the study was incomplete, fairly consistent values for H_2, CO_2 and acid production were obtained at the faster rates of growth. Production of H_2 equaled or nearly equaled CO_2 production, which was a marked increase over values from conventional cultures.

It is apparent that all the species anaerobically metabolize the hexoses, some of the disaccharides, and vary in ability to use other carbohydrates and the citric acid cycle intermediates. They all produce CO_2 and H_2 or some other gas, as well as acid which is, for the most part, only about one-fourth to one-half lactic. Succinic acid is formed anaerobically by resting cells and is the major acid formed during growth. Some species can use pyruvate and lactate for anaerobic gas production. It would be of interest to examine the use of carbohydrates in aerobic metabolism.

C. CARBOHYDRATES AND AEROBIC RESPIRATION

The earliest manometric work on O_2 uptake by *Tritrichomonas foetus* (Suzuoki and Suzuoki, 1951b) and by *Trichomonas vaginalis* (Ninomiya and Suzuoki, 1952) was followed by several papers in which conflicting results were reported. Much of the difficulty in comparing the effect of various carbohydrates on O_2 uptake was due to the differences in growth conditions, number of organisms used, pH, concentration of substrate, buffer systems, ratio of O_2 to air, method of measurement of O_2 uptake, and different methods of reporting results. Some of the variation is illustrated below.

1. FACTORS INFLUENCING ENDOGENOUS RESPIRATION

The endogenous respiratory rates of different species, as reported by the authors or extrapolated from information given, are shown in Table III. The growth medium used by all workers was made from crude materials with glucose or maltose as the carbohydrate source. Except in the earliest work mentioned above, the washed cultures were standardized at 10^8 cells and the Q_{O_2} was reported as cubic millimeters of oxygen consumed per hour. The endogenous rates for the two strains of *T. vaginalis* reported by three investigators varied from 70 to 150 mm.^{3} of O_2 per 100 million organisms. The cause of some of this variation was the difference in the ratio of O_2 to air used in the manometric tests.

a. Oxygen Tension and Respiration. The stimulation of oxygen uptake in the absence of glucose by 100% oxygen as the gas phase was first reported by Ninomiya and Suzuoki (1952) for *Tritrichomonas foetus* "tricho." The stimulation came within 60 min. Oxygen uptake with glucose was slightly inhibited after 120 min. For *Trichomonas vaginalis* however, the high O_2 tension increased endogenous respiration while inhibiting almost completely the O_2 uptake with glucose. They suggested the O_2 toxicity might be due to accumulation of H_2O_2 because *T. vaginalis* had no catalase. However, some organisms, especially *Tritrichomonas foetus,* as shown by them and several later workers, contain catalase (see discussion under enzyme systems in Section II,E,3). It is hard to believe that accumulation of H_2O_2 could account for the O_2 toxicity in view of the work described by Doran (1956a, 1957, 1958). With glucose as the substrate, *Tetratrichomonas buttreyi* and the cecal form of *Tritrichomonas suis*(?) consumed more O_2 when the organisms were suspended in a mixture containing 5% O_2 than in air. *Tritrichomonas foetus* and the

Table III

AEROBIC ENDOGENOUS RESPIRATION OF TRICHOMONADS

Culture	Strain	Q_{O_2} mm.³ O_2 per 10⁸ cells per hour	Reference
Trichomonas vaginalis	5A	96	Read and Rothman, 1955.
	5A	70	Wirtschafter *et al.*, 1956.
	Izumida	≈95 (5% O_2)	Wirtschafter *et al.*, 1956.
		≈150 (100% O_2)	Ninomiya and Suzuoki, 1952.
Tritrichomonas foetus	"Tricho"	≈60 (at 30 min., 5% O_2)	Ninomiya and Suzuoki, 1952.
		≈90 (at 30 min., 100% O_2)	Ninomiya and Suzuoki, 1952.
	Belfast	176 (113–255)/mg. N/hr.	Ryley, 1955.
	BP-1	120	Doran, 1957.
	PN-610	130	Doran, 1957.
	BP-3	95 ± 2.5	Doran, 1959.
	BP-4	101 ± 5	Doran, 1959.
	A-1	184 ± 5.5	Doran, 1959.
	A-2	91 ± 3.4	Doran, 1959.
Tritrichomonas suis	Cecal PC-414	210	Doran, 1957.
	Fecal	Wide variation	Lindblom, 1961.
	Nasal	Wide variation	Lindblom, 1961.
Tetratrichomonas buttreyi	PC-287	82	Doran, 1958.
Tetratrichomonas gallinarum		Wide variation	Lindblom, 1961.

nasal form PN-610 consumed less O_2 during the 1- to 2-hr. intervals in the same gas mixture and then increased consumption after 3 hr. Pure O_2 inhibited oxidation of glucose; the inhibition increased with time for all four organisms. However, the endogenous respiration was not inhibited by pure O_2 but O_2 was stimulatory for the three porcine forms.

b. Intracellular Glycogen and Endogenous Respiration. Ryley (1955) with *Tritrichomonas foetus* Belfast strain observed from a series of 18 experiments an endogenous rate averaging 176, the range being 113–255 per milligrams of nitrogen (representing 10⁸ cells) per hour (Table III). The variation was due to synthesis of large amounts of intracellular glycogen, partially derived from the nitrogenous components of the medium, but there was a greater synthesis in the presence of added carbohydrate (Manners and Ryley, 1955). Without substrate, in aerobic respiration, Ryley (1955) showed a loss of glycogen in *T. foetus;* he concluded that its energy metabolism centered around its intracellular glycogen reserves, supplemented by any extracellular substrates. Therefore the conditions under which cells were grown would influence the endogenous respiration rate and the rates derived from various conditions and substrates used in manometric tests. This fact was not taken into consideration in some of the earlier investigations.

c. *Strain and Species Differences in Endogenous Respiration.* Doran carefully studied *Tritrichomonas foetus* respiration. All strains were grown in Diamond's medium with maltose as the carbohydrate. In one paper (Doran, 1959), four cultures were maintained on identical conditions from isolation to the time of the experiments. He showed strain differences in endogenous respiration (Table III), strain A-1, having a particularly high rate of 184, double that of two other strains. *Tritrichomonas suis,* cecal strain PC-414, had a Q_{O_2} of 210, the highest for any species (Doran, 1957). Lindblom (1957, 1961) reported wide variation in endogenous respiration for two strains of *T. suis* and for *Tetratrichomonas gallinarum.* Doran (1958) found a low rate of 82 for *Tetratrichomonas buttreyi* PC-287.

Other variables reported have been in respiratory quotients and in CO_2 fixation. This might be explored before discussing O_2 uptake with various carbohydrates.

d. *Respiratory Quotients.* Kupferberg *et al.* (1953) first reported a decline in the respiratory quotients (RQ) of *Trichomonas vaginalis,* strain 2 from 1.08 at 0 to 60 min., to 0.92 for the 120- to 180-min. period. This was not confirmed by Read and Rothman (1955) for *T. vaginalis.* They reported an RQ of 1.06 to 1.16 for the first hour and 1.08 to 1.14 for the third hour. Doran (1958) found the RQ of *Tetratrichomonas buttreyi* by the "direct" and "indirect" methods to be 1.06 for the first hour and 1.09 for the second and third hours. Lindblom (1961) investigated the RQ of *Tritrichomonas foetus,* *Tetratrichomonas gallinarum,* and the fecal and nasal strains of *Tritrichomonas suis.* Using a Tris-maleate buffer at pH 6.4 he observed the RQ's to be, respectively, 0.90, 0.82, 0.99, and 0.80. However, with a phosphate buffer at the same pH, the RQ's for the four organisms were respectively, 1.17, 1.10, 1.30, and 1.24. It is obvious that the buffer systems used in manometric studies will influence results. In addition, convincing work by two groups offered proof that CO_2 was fixed.

e. *Carbon Dioxide Fixation.* Kupferberg *et al.* (1953), after observing the decline in the RQ with time, suggested the fixation of CO_2 by *Trichomonas vaginalis.* This was confirmed by the use of radioactive carbon and the demonstration of a radioactive carbon fixation product. Wellerson *et al.* (1959, 1960) isolated and identified the product as lactic acid and found all of the radioactivity in the carboxyl carbon. Ryley (1955) found CO_2 fixed in pyruvate, while succinate and acetate were excreted by *Tritrichomonas foetus.*

With these facts in mind, it is not hard to understand why such variable results have been reported in studies on the effect of carbohydrates on O_2 uptake.

2. EFFECT OF CARBOHYDRATES ON OXYGEN UPTAKE

No attempt is made here to discuss the optimum or the limiting conditions of the manometric tests used by the various investigators. The original references should be consulted for details. Table IV summarizes the work on the effect of several carbohydrates on O_2 uptake. Most investigators presented their data as percent stimulation over endogenous uptake, although the Japa-

Table IV

EFFECT OF SUBSTRATES ON OXYGEN UPTAKE[a]

	Amount of stimulation[b]					
Substrate	Trichomonas vaginalis (3)[c]	Tetra-trichomonas gallinarum (1)[c]	Tetra-trichomonas buttreyi (1)[c]	Tritri-chomonas foetus (9)[c]	Tritri-chomonas suis (3)[c]	Tritri-chomonas augusta (2)[c]
Arabinose	—	—	0	0–±	0	—
Xylose	—	—	0	0	0	±
Glucose	2+–3+	+	+	+–3+	+–3+	—
Fructose	+	±	I	+–3+	+–2+	—
Galactose	—	±	0	±–3+	±–3+	±
Mannose	—	±	±	±–2+	±–2+	±
Sorbose	—	—	—	0	—	—
Lactose	—	I	I	0–+	±–+	±–+
Sucrose	—	0	±	±–2+	0–±	—
Maltose	2+	±	±	±–3+	0–+	±
Trehalose	—	—	0	±	±	—
Cellobiose	—	—	—	—	—	±–+
Raffinose	—	—	0	0–±	±	—
Inulin	—	—	±	±	±	—
Dextrin	—	—	—	±	—	—
Glycogen	—	—	—	0–±	—	±
Starch	—	—	—	0–±	—	—
Glycerol	—	I	—	I–0–±	I	—
Sorbitol	—	—	0	0	0	±–+
Glucose-1-phosphate	—	—	—	—	I	—
Fructose-1,6-diphosphate	—	0	—	—	0–±	—
Gluconate	0	—	—	—	—	—
Phosphoglycerate	—	I	—	—	I	—
Lactate	+	I	0	0–±	I–0–±	—
Formate	0	±	—	0–±	I	—
Acetate	0	I	0	0–±	I–0	—

Table IV —*Continued*

	Amount of stimulation[b]					
Substrate	*Trichomonas vaginalis* (3)[c]	*Tetra-trichomonas gallinarum* (1)[c]	*Tetra-trichomonas buttreyi* (1)[c]	*Tritri-chomonas foetus* (9)[c]	*Tritri-chomonas suis* (3)[c]	*Tritri-chomonas augusta* (2)[c]
Propionate	—	—	—	±	—	—
Pyruvate	+–3+	±	0	0–±	I–±	—
Citrate	0	0	0	I–0	I–0	—
α-Ketoglutarate	0	I	0	I–0	I–0	—
Succinate	0–+	I	0	I–0	I–0	—
Fumarate	0	I	0	I–0	I–0	—
Malate	±–+	±	0	I–0–±	I–0	—
Oxalacetate	0	I	—	I	I	—
DL-α-Alanine	0	—	—	0	—	—
DL-β-Alanine	—	—	—	0	—	—
L-Aspartate	—	—	—	0–±	—	—
Asparagine	—	—	—	±	—	—
L-Glutamate	0	—	—	0–±	—	—
Glutamine	—	—	—	±	—	—
L-Tyrosine	—	—	—	0	—	—
Glycine	—	—	—	0	—	—
Butyrate	0	—	—	±	—	—
Ethanol	—	—	—	0	—	—
References[d]	*1, 7, 8, 11*	*6*	*4*	*3, 5, 6, 9, 10*	*3, 6*	*2*

[a] Key to symbols in body of table:

  0, No stimulation

  ±, 10–50%

  +, 50–99%

  2+, 100–149%

  3+, 150–200%

  I, O_2 uptake lower than endogenous by 10 or more %

[b] Stimulation over endogenous respiration.

[c] ( ) Total number of strains used in the various studies.

[d] References:

  1. Baba *et al.*, 1957.

  2. Concannon, 1959.

  3. Doran, 1957.

  4. Doran, 1958.

  5. Doran, 1959.

  6. Lindblom, 1961.

  7. Ninomiya and Suzuoki, 1952.

  8. Read and Rothman, 1955.

  9. Ryley, 1955.

  10. Suzuoki and Suzuoki, 1951b.

  11. Wirtschafter *et al.*, 1956.

nese investigators (Suzuoki and Suzuoki, 1951b; Ninomiya and Suzuoki, 1952) used O_2 uptake with glucose as 100% and other workers gave actual O_2 uptake measurements. The total number of strains used in the various studies is shown in each column heading.

In general, carbohydrate utilization for respiration resembles that for growth and anaerobic metabolism. The monosaccharide hexoses were the most stimulatory, with disaccharides next. However, the polysaccharides were generally poorly utilized as compared with their activity for growth. Intermediates or compounds entering into the glycolytic pathway and citric acid cycle were used poorly or not at all, except that *Trichomonas vaginalis* was reported by some workers (Ninomiya and Suzuoki, 1952; Wirtschafter *et al.*, 1956; Baba *et al.*, 1957) to be stimulated 50% or more by lactate, pyruvate, succinate, and malate. Rhamnose, isocitrate, β-hydroxybutyric acid, and the sugar alcohols (except glycerol by one strain of *Tritrichomonas foetus* and sorbitol by *T. augusta*) were not used (not shown in Table IV). Many of the intermediates and some sugars inhibited O_2 uptake.

Although the number of carbohydrates studied was incomplete for every species, it appears that the respiration of *Tritrichomonas foetus* and *T. suis* is stimulated to the greatest degree and by the largest number of sugars. Oxygen uptake by strain BP-1 *T. foetus* was stimulated by glucose to 194% (Doran, 1957) and the nasal strain of *T. suis*, to 166% (Lindblom, 1961). On the other hand, *Tetratrichomonas buttreyi* failed to use or was inhibited by some sugars which stimulated O_2 uptake of the two previously mentioned flagellates (Doran, 1958).

Quantitative differences in O_2 uptake between strains within a species were apparent in the careful study made by Doran (1959). While four strains of *Tritrichomonas foetus*, cultured under identical conditions, utilized glucose, galactose, mannose, and fructose at a high rate and lactose, sucrose, fructose, maltose, and trehalose at a lower rate, one strain, A-1, consistently used the four monosaccharides at a lower rate than did the other three strains, although it had an endogenous rate 83–90% higher than the other strains. Strain A-1 most closely resembled the nasal trichomonad of swine, PN-610 (Doran, 1957). Doran (1959) believed lactose and raffinose might be used to distinguish strains. The nasal strain from swine, PN-610 used both sugars, strain BP-1 failed to use both sugars, and strain BP-4 did not use raffinose. Concannon (1959) distinguished two strains of *Tritrichomonas augusta* on the basis of difference in utilization of lactose, cellobiose, and sorbitol. Ryley (1955) pointed out differences in *T. foetus* strains, especially in maltose, lactose, sucrose, and glycerol utilization when comparing the reactions of his strain with that used by Suzuoki and Suzuoki (1951b). Lindblom (1961) also observed species variation in lactose, maltose, and sucrose use. He believed that carbohydrate utilization might be useful for strain and species differentiation, but thought more comparative work was needed. This is provided in the studies of isolated enzyme systems and the action of enzyme inhibitors on trichomonad metabolism.

D. Inhibitors of Carbohydrate Metabolism

Various metabolic inhibitors have been used in studies on O_2 uptake with or without added carbohydrates, on anaerobic gas or acid formation, and on motility. Since these studies were carried out under variable conditions, Table V summarizes—in a general way only—the findings of several workers with commonly used inhibitors. In some cases, the activity of a particular compound is shown as ranging from inhibition to stimulation (in Table V see 8-Hydroxyquinoline, Azide, 2,4-Dinitrophenol, arsenate or arsenite effect on O_2 uptake with *Tritrichomonas foetus*). This may indicate strain differences, differences in levels of inhibitor, or differences in substrates in the various tests. The original references in the footnotes of Table V should be consulted for details.

As can be seen from Table V, direct comparison of activity of the various inhibitors for the several species is almost impossible. Those inhibitors—iodoacetate, arsenite, fluoride, and perhaps azide—which act on the —SH or glycolytic enzymes were the most potent in inhibiting both anaerobic fermentation and O_2 uptake in most organisms. Iodoacetate inhibition indicates that glycolysis normally goes past the triphosphate stages yet Lindblom (1961) found fluoride (an enolase inhibitor) inhibited only *Tritrichomonas foetus* and *Tetratrichomonas gallinarum,* the organisms he found to form pyruvate from phosphoglyceric acid. This suggested to him that these two organisms produce pyruvate (and perhaps lactate) by conventional means via an anaerobic pathway.

Arsenate, malonate, and hydrogen peroxide are mainly lacking in inhibitory action (Table V), and this suggests the presence of catalase (except for *Trichomonas vaginalis* and perhaps *T. gallinae*) and the lack of a complete citric acid cycle. Arsenate stimulation (Lindblom, 1961) was thought by him to be compatible with a triosephosphate oxidizing system since this ion increases the available esterifying material, and oxidation of the arseno-phosphoglyceraldehyde may not require arsenate acceptors, thus not limiting the rate of reaction.

Cyanide in general did not inhibit O_2 uptake [except for *Tritrichomonas foetus* (Doran, 1956b; Suzuoki and Suzuoki, 1951b), and *Trichomonas vaginalis* (Lindblom, 1961)] although reported to inhibit to some extent anaerobic fermentation by *T. vaginalis* (Read, 1953; Read and Rothman, 1955) and *Tritrichomonas foetus* (Doran, 1957, 1959; Ryley, 1955). Read (1953) and Read and Rothman (1955) found carbon monoxide had no effect in aerobic O_2 consumption of *Trichomonas vaginalis* but inhibited anaerobic gas formation in the dark, which was reversed by light, suggesting that a heavy

Table V

EFFECT OF INHIBITORS ON ANAEROBIC GAS FERMENTATION,

Inhibitor	Enzyme or sites inhibited	Trichomonas vaginalis	
		Anaerobic gas fermentation	O₂ uptake[b]
Iodoacetate	Glycolysis, —SH enzymes 3-phosphoglyceraldehyde dehydrogenase	0, y, +	—
Iodoacetamide	—SH enzymes	—	—
8-Hydroxyquinoline	Glycolysis, enolase	—	—
Phenyl mercuric acetate	—SH enzymes	+	—
Arsenite	—SH enzymes, succinic dehydrogenase	+	+
Dipyridyl	Aldolase, non-heme iron	—	—
Glyceraldehyde	Glycolysis	0	—
Arsenate	Organic phosphate bond	0	0
Fluoroacetate	Isocitric dehydrogenase	—	—
Fluoride	Glycolysis, enolase, metals, citric acid cycle	+	+
β-Phosphonopropionate	Succinic dehydrogenase or oxidase	0	—
Malonate	Succinic dehydrogenase, citric acid cycle	—	0, +
Arsenoacetate	Succinic oxidase	0	—
2,4-Dinitrophenol	Oxidative phosphorylation	+	—
Cyanide	Cytochrome oxidase, metallo-enzymes	0, +	0
Azide	Iron porphyrin	—	0, +
Carbon monoxide	Cytochrome oxidase, haemprotein	0, +	0
Hydroxylamine	Iron porphyrin	—	—
Hydrogen peroxide		—	+
References[c]		1, 8, 9, 10 11, 12, 15	8 10 12

[a] Key to symbols in body of table:

    0, No inhibition

    ±, 10% inhibition

    +, more than 15% inhibition

    S, Stimulatory

    y, Inhibition, with iodoacetate and chloromercuribenzoate, of anaerobic gas production with glucose, but not with pyruvate, as substrate (Ref. 8).

[b] Endogenous or with carbohydrate substrate.

MOTILITY, AND OXYGEN UPTAKE BY TRICHOMONADS[a]

Tritrichomonas foetus			Tritrichomonas suis (nasal)	Tritrichomonas suis (fecal)		Tetratrichomonas buttreyi	Tetratrichomonas gallinarum	Trichomonas gallinae	
Anaerobic gas fermentation	Motility	O₂ uptake[b]	O₂ uptake[b]	Motility	O₂ uptake[b]	O₂ uptake[b]	O₂ uptake[b]	Anaerobic gas fermentation	Motility
+	+	+	+	—	+	+	+	+	—
—	—	+	0	—	0, +	—	+	—	—
+, ±	±, 0	S, 0, +	0	0	0	±	+	—	—
+	—	—	—	—	—	—	—	+	—
+	±, +	±, +, S	0	—	0, +	+	+	0	—
+	0, ±	0	—	—	—	—	—	—	—
—	—	—	—	—	—	—	—	0	—
+	0	S, 0	S, 0	—	S, 0	—	+	0	—
—	0	±	—	—	±	—	—	—	—
0, +	+	0, +	0	—	0	±	+	+	—
—	—	—	—	—	0	—	—	—	—
—	0, +	0, S	0	—	0	0	0	—	+
—	—	—	—	—	—	—	—	—	—
+, ±	0, +	0, +, S, ±	0, S	0	0, S	0	+	+	—
0, +	0, +	0, +	0	0	0	0	0	—	—
±, +	+	0, S, +	0	—	0, +	±	0	—	—
—	—	—	—	+	±	—	—	—	—
+	±, +	0, ±, +	0	+	0	0	+	—	—
—	+	0	0	—	0	—	0	—	—
3, 5, 11, 13	3, 5, 7, 13	2, 3, 5, 6, 7, 8, 13, 14	6	3	2, 3, 6	4	6	11	13

[c] References:

1. Baernstein, 1954, 1955.
2. Doran, 1956b.
3. Doran, 1957.
4. Doran, 1958.
5. Doran, 1959.
6. Lindblom, 1961.
7. Ninomiya and Suzuoki, 1951.
8. Ninomiya and Suzuoki, 1952.
9. Kupferberg et al., 1953.
10. Read, 1953.
11. Read, 1957.
12. Read and Rothman, 1955.
13. Ryley, 1955.
14. Suzuoki and Suzuoki, 1951b.
15. Wellerson, Jr. and Kupferberg, 1962.

metal system was involved in anaerobic gas formation. On the other hand Kupferberg *et al.* (1953) found anaerobic acid formation not inhibited to a significant extent by cyanide or CO.

Some species and strains were not inhibited by most of the compounds, the nasal *Tritrichomonas suis* being notable in this respect. In some work in which comparable conditions were maintained in all the tests (Ryley, 1955; Doran, 1957, 1958, 1959; Lindblom, 1961) differences in inhibitor effect among strains and species were noted. Motility was found to be coupled to O_2 uptake by Ryley (1955) for *Tritrichomonas foetus*. Respiration and motility were uncoupled by arsenite, fluoride, hydroxylamine, and azide. Doran (1959) observed that iodoacetate abolished motility of four strains of *T. foetus*, but had less inhibitory effect on O_2 uptake of two strains while fluoride, arsenite, azide, and hydroxylamine reduced or abolished motility of all strains although producing insignificant inhibitory effects on endogenous O_2 consumption. Ninomiya and Suzuoki (1951) also noticed O_2 uptake with *T. foetus* was not inhibited by several inhibitors although they stopped motility.

Some work with isolated enzyme systems (not shown in Table V) is more definitive. Wirtschafter *et al.* (1956) found iodoacetate was an effective inhibitor of pyruvate oxidation by *Trichomonas vaginalis* but fluoracetate, fluoride, parapyruvate, malonate, and arsenite were ineffective. Seaman (1953) reported that β-phosphonopropionate and arsenoacetate effectively inhibited succinic dehydrogenase from *T. vaginalis*. Baernstein (1961) observed that malic dehydrogenase from *T. vaginalis* was inhibited by p-mercuribenzoate but not by iodoacetate, iodoacetamide, or arsenite. These latter three compounds did not inhibit lactic dehydrogenase from the same organism (Baernstein, 1959). Lactic dehydrogenase from *T. vaginalis* was inhibited by p-chloromercuric benzoate (Ninomiya and Suzuoki, 1952). Aldolase from *T. vaginalis* was inhibited by pyrophosphate (Wellerson, Jr. and Kupferberg, 1962) and EDTA (ethylenediaminetetraacetic acid) and 2,2'-dipyridyl, but not by iodoacetate (Baernstein, 1954, 1955). The inhibition was reversed by ferrous or cobaltous salts. Aldolase from *Tritrichomonas foetus* was inhibited by 2,2'-dipyridyl (Ryley, 1955) but this inhibitor had little effect on the respiration or fermentation of whole cells or acid formation from hexose diphosphate by homogenates.

Inhibition by some steroids has been reported. Baba *et al.* (1957) observed that cortisone and hydrocortisone inhibited endogenous O_2 uptake by *T. vaginalis* at low concentrations. At high concentrations these compounds also inhibited glucose decomposition, although cortisone at low concentrations accelerated it. Succinate and fructose oxidation were inhibited while the inhibition of O_2 uptake by gluconic, citric, α-ketoglutaric, and fumaric acids was increased by both steroids.

The work on enzyme inhibitions has suggested that trichomonads break down carbohydrates through the usual glycolytic pathway, but the pathway to terminal respiration is not through the usual Krebs cycle. Enzymes reported to be contained in trichomonads are discussed in the next section.

E. Enzymes in Carbohydrate Metabolism

The sugars utilized and the activity of enzyme inhibitors, especially on isolated enzyme reactions, give evidence that the anaerobic carbohydrate metabolism in trichomonads must occur in the conventional Embden-Meyerhof scheme of glycolysis. This is further proven by the demonstration of enzymatic reactions carried out by resting cells or homogenates of trichomonads, about 17 having been reported.

1. ENZYMES OF THE GLYCOLYTIC PATHWAY

The key enzymes reported in trichomonads (Ninomiya and Suzuoki, 1952; Wirtschafter, 1954b; Wirtschafter and Jahn, 1956; Baernstein, 1954, 1955, 1959, 1961; Doran, 1957, 1959; Doscher, 1960; Kunitake et al., 1962; Read, 1953, 1957; Wellerson, Jr. and Kupferberg, 1962; Wellerson et al., 1959, 1960) are shown in Table VI. The experiments of Ryley (1955) with the isolated enzyme systems of *Tritrichomonas foetus* and Lindblom (1961) with four organisms are especially extensive. Most of the enzymes active in the metabolism of sugars to lactic acid have been shown to be present although there is some variation in the enzymes reported in different species and strains. The reactions are carried through to pyruvate by *T. foetus* and *Tetratrichomonas gallinarum* (Lindblom, 1961) and by *Trichomonas vaginalis* (Wellerson, Jr. and Kupferberg, 1962). Seven intermediates of the system were identified by Wirtschafter and Jahn (1956); glucose-1-phosphate, fructose-6-phosphate, glucose-6-phosphate, fructose-1,6-diphosphate, 2-phosphoglyceric acid, 3-phosphoglyceric acid, and phosphoenolpyruvate with *T. vaginalis*. The lack of inhibitory activity by fluoride and 8-hydroxyquinoline suggested a lack of the glycolytic enzyme enolase in the cecal *Tritrichomonas suis* (Doran, 1957).

Evidence that some part of the hexose shunt is present comes from the reports on glucose-6-phosphate dehydrogenase and phosphoriboisomerase (Wellerson et al., 1960; Doscher, 1960). All of the organisms have active aldolase, characterized by Baernstein (1955) as a cobalt-activated system. Hexokinase and enzymes involved in phosphorylative carbohydrate degradation to pyruvate and through conversion by lactic dehydrogenase to lactic acid have been reported. The latter enzyme has been purified and described by Baernstein (1959, 1961). The enzymes of *Trichomonas vaginalis* and *Tritrichomonas foetus* have been most fully investigated. *Tetratrichomonas gallinarum* and *Tritrichomonas suis*, both nasal and fecal, appear to lack some of the glycolytic enzymes (Doran, 1956b, 1957; Lindblom, 1961). The inability to demonstrate triosephosphate isomerase activity (Lindblom, 1961) in *Tritrichomonas foetus*, *T. suis*

Table VI

Enzymes in the Carbohydrate Metabolism of Trichomonads[a,b]

Enzyme	Trichomonas vaginalis	Trichomonas gallinae	Pentatrichomonas hominis	Tetratrichomonas gallinarum	Tetratrichomonas buttreyi	Tritrichomonas suis (nasal)	Tritrichomonas suis (fecal)	Tritrichomonas foetus
Amylase	(+, 1)[a,b]							+, 18
Maltase	—							+, 18
Glucose dehydrogenase				—, 13		—, 13	—, 13	—, 13
Phosphoglucomutase	+, 22, 25			—, 13		—, 13	—, 13	+, 13, 18
Glucose-6-phosphate dehydrogenase	+, 21, 29			+, 13		+, 13	+, 13	+, 13
Phosphoriboisomerase	+, 21, 29							—
Phosphoglucoisomerase (Phosphohexoisomerase)	+, 22			+, 13		+, 13	+, 13	+, 13
Phosphorylase	—, 22							+, 18[A]
Aldolase	+, 2[B], 3, 22, 23			+, 13		+, 13	+, 13	+, 13, 18[B]
Hexokinase	+, 22, 23			+, 13		++, 13	++, 13	++, 13, 18
Phosphofructokinase	+, 22			+, 13		+, 13	+, 13	+, 13
α-Glycerophosphate dehydrogenase	+, 25							—
Keto isomerase								+, 18
Triose phosphate dehydrogenase	+, 22							
Triose phosphate isomerase	(+, 14)			—, 13		—, 13	—, 13	+, 18[C]
Glycerol dehydrogenase						—, 13	—, 13	—, 13
Phosphoglyceromutase and enolase				—, 13		—, 13	—, 13	—, 13
Enolase	+, 22			+, 13		—, 13	—, 13	+, 13
Pyruvate kinase	+, 22						—, 8	

Enzyme								
Lactic dehydrogenase	+, 4[D], (14), 25, 22	—	—	—	-, 9	—	—	+, 10, (14)
Carboxylase	-, 20, 21	—						—
Alcohol dehydrogenase	-, 22	—						—
Citric acid cycle enzymes								
Pyruvate dehydrogenase	-, 16, 26; +, (14), 24, 26	(+, 16); (+, 16)	(+, 28)		-, 9; (-, 9)	-, 7, 8; (+, 8)	-, 7, 8	-, 7, 8, 13; +, 7, 8, 10; (-, 14)
Aconitase	-, 5	(+, 16)						—
Isocitrate dehydrogenase	-, 5, 26	(+, 16)						—
α-Ketoglutaric dehydrogenase	—	(+, 16)						—
Succinoxidase	+, 27		(+, 28)					—
Succinic dehydrogenase	-, 16, 26							—
Fumarase	-, 5							—
Malic dehydrogenase	++, 5[E], 11, 26	(+, 16)	(+, 28)	+, 13	+, 13	+, 13	-, 13	-, 13
"Malic enzyme"	-, 23; +, 22			+, 13				
Cytochrome oxidase					-, 13	-, 13	-, 13	-, 13
Flavin protein terminal oxidase	+, 6, 12, 14, 15	+, 6					+, 6	-, 18, 19; +, 6
DPN oxidase	+, 5, 25							
DPNH oxidase	+, 5, 20, 25							
Iron porphyrin	+, 15							
Cytochrome, type a								-, 19
Cytochrome, type a₃	(+, 17)							‾
Cytochrome, type b								+, 19[F]
Cytochrome, type c								-, 19
Cytochrome, not specified	-, 20							
Catalase	-, 12, 14, 17, 18	-, 18		+, 13	+, 9	+, 8, 13	+, 8, 13	-, 18; ++, 14, 18; +, 8, 13, 19

Table VI—Continued

Enzyme	Trichomonas vaginalis	Trichomonas gallinae	Pentatrichomonas hominis	Tetratrichomonas gallinarum	Tetratrichomonas buttreyi	Tritrichomonas suis (nasal)	Tritrichomonas suis (fecal)	Tritrichomonas foetus
Peroxidase	—	—	—				+, *19*	+, *14, 19*
Formic dehydrogenase	—	—	—	+, *13*	—	+, *13*	+, *13*	—, *18*
Formic hydrogenlyase	—	—	—	+, *13*	—	—, *13*	—, *13*	+, *13*
Hydrogenase	—	—	—	—	—	—	—	—, *19*
Dehydrogenlyase	—	—	—	—	—	—	—	—, *19*

a References indicated by italic numerals in table (see list of references for complete information):

1. Adler, 1953.	*21.* Wellerson *et al.*, 1960.
2. Baernstein, 1954.	*22.* Wellerson, Jr. and Kupferberg, 1962.
3. Baernstein, 1955.	*23.* Wirtschafter, 1954b.
4. Baernstein, 1959.	*24.* Wirtschafter *et al.*, 1955.
5. Baernstein, 1961.	*25.* Wirtschafter and Jahn, 1956.
6. Baernstein, 1963.	*26.* Wirtschafter *et al.*, 1956.
7. Doran, 1956b.	*27.* Seaman, 1953.
8. Doran, 1957.	*28.* Solomon, 1957.
9. Doran, 1958.	*29.* Doscher, 1960.
10. Doran, 1959.	*b* Key to symbols:
11. Kunitake *et al.*, 1962.	—, No activity
12. Kupferberg *et al.*, 1953.	+, Activity
13. Lindblom, 1961.	++, Vigorous activity
14. Ninomiya and Suzuoki, 1952.	( ), Presumptive or indirect activity
15. Read, 1953.	[A], Some phosphate combined with fructose
16. Read, 1957.	[B], Metallo-aldolase
17. Read and Rothman, 1955.	[C], Triose phosphate oxidizing system
18. Ryley, 1955.	[D], Only L(+) lactate used, enzyme linked to DPN
19. Suzuoki and Suzuoki, 1951b.	[E], Linked to L(−) malate and DPN
20. Wellerson *et al.*, 1959.	[F], Muscle type b cytochrome

and *Tetratrichomonas gallinarum* is interesting. These organisms may have an active α-glycerophosphate dehydrogenase as reported for *T. vaginalis* (Wirtschafter and Jahn, 1956).

The lack of phosphorylase activity (which catalyzes the formation of glycogen) in the presence of a very high glycogen content (20.8%) suggested the possibility of an alternate route (Wellerson, Jr. and Kupferberg, 1962).

2. ENZYMES OF THE OXIDATIVE PATHWAY

That trichomonads lack some of the citric acid cycle enzymes is also fairly well established. *Trichomonas vaginalis* possesses malic dehydrogenase, characterized by Baernstein (1961). It apparently lacks all other of the cycle enzymes (Read, 1957) except pyruvate dehydrogenase (Wirtschafter *et al.*, 1956, Wirtschafter and Jahn, 1956; Ninomiya and Suzuoki, 1952) although Kunitake *et al.* (1962) conclude from their work that there is indirect evidence for a tricarboxylic acid cycle. Although preparation of cell-free systems for the cycle was not successful, a small but significant fraction of the labeled succinate appeared as $C^{14}O_2$. The pathway from pyruvate to malate and succinate may be lacking in *T. vaginalis* since Wellerson *et al.* (1960) found that labeled CO_2 appeared only in the carboxyl group of lactate and none in malate or succinate. However, Wellerson, Jr. and Kupferberg (1962) found evidence for "malic" enzyme and, as pointed out by Baernstein (1963), succinate is a source of electron donors and a major end product (Section II). Wirtschafter *et al.* (1956) in tracer studies with 2-C^{14}-pyruvate showed that although several unidentified compounds incorporated activity during the course of pyruvate metabolism, none of the labeled compounds corresponded to any of the citric acid cycle intermediates. *Tritrichomonas foetus* contains some part of the cycle, since CO_2 is fixed in pyruvate, while acetate and succinate are excreted (Ryley, 1955). Since pyruvate is oxidized by some trichomonads, pyruvate dehydrogenase must also be present in *T. foetus* and nasal *T. suis* (Doran, 1957, 1959), while all citric acid cycle enzymes were lacking in fecal *Tritrichomonas suis*, *Tetratrichomonas buttreyi*, and *T. gallinarum* (Doran, 1957, 1958; Lindblom, 1961). The fact that *Trichomonas gallinae* uses all (Read, 1957), and *Pentatrichomonas hominis* (Solomon, 1957) uses some of the members of the cycle, suggests that an alternate path from the usual cycle is operating. Kunitake *et al.* (1962) also conclude from their work on the metabolism of glucose-U-C^{14} and succinate-2,3-C^{14} to CO_2 and amino acids, by *Trichomonas vaginalis* grown aerobically, that a tricarboxylic acid cycle operates. However, their attempts to carry out the cycle reactions were unsuccessful.

Lindblom (1961) has proposed an interesting scheme for possible interrelationships in carbohydrate metabolism, shown in Fig. 1, which accounts for the accumulation of acid end products, CO_2 fixation and production of H_2

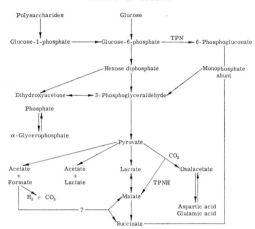

FIG. 1. Possible interrelationships in the carbohydrate metabolism of trichomonads. (From Lindblom, 1961.)

and CO_2. The original paper should be consulted for a discussion of details of this scheme.

3. ENZYMES IN THE ELECTRON TRANSPORT SYSTEM

Many anaerobes lack a cytochrome system. Instead, flavin nucleotides function in the transport of hydrogen. Baernstein (1963) has reviewed the studies on the terminal respiration of trichomonads and evidence for the electron transport system (Suzuoki and Suzuoki, 1951b; Ninomiya and Suzuoki, 1952; Ryley, 1955; Read, 1957; Wellerson et al., 1959). All attempts to demonstrate cytochromes have been negative except for the report by Suzuoki and Suzuoki (1951b) which indicated cytochrome b in Tritrichomonas foetus. Studies involving enzymes in terminal respiration (see Table VI for enzymes and references) suggests that a system other than cytochrome is involved. In fact, Wellerson et al. (1959) have isolated both riboflavin and flavin mononucleotide from Trichomonas vaginalis cells.

Baernstein (1963) summarizes the evidence for electron transport mechanism in Tritrichomonas foetus, Trichomonas vaginalis, and Trichomonas gallinae thus:

> "Trichomonads have a limited capacity for oxygen utilization which is insensitive to cyanide and results in hydrogen peroxide accumulation except when catalase is also present. A flavoprotein terminal oxidase is indicated, but the importance of the oxygen utilization is not known. Some strains produce hydrogen gas which is probably linked to electron transport. The organisms are essentially anaerobic and therefore depend upon coupled reactions mediated by pyridino and flavoproteins

resulting in the production of reduced compounds. All three organisms depend on conventional glycolysis supplemented with other systems linked to NADP and to succinate to furnish electron donors. Electron transport in anaerobic metabolism is limited to dehydrogenase couplings and to the excretion of the reduced compounds. In some strains anaerobic production of hydrogen supplements the usual mechanisms of electron transport."

The scheme for electron transport, as depicted by Baernstein, is shown in Fig. 2.

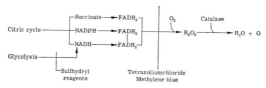

FIG. 2. Electron transport in trichomonads. (From Baernstein, 1963.)

A few other enzyme systems have been studied in trichomonads, one which is particularly interesting being concerned with blood-group substances.

4. ENZYMES DECOMPOSING BLOOD-GROUP SUBSTANCES

Enzymes of possible significance in pathogenicity and parasitism are described in a series of papers by Watkins and co-workers. Watkins (1953) demonstrated several enzymes from the Belfast and Manley strains of *Tritrichomonas foetus* which act on human blood-group substances A, B, H, Le^a and Le^b, leading to their serological inactivation. *Trichomonas vaginalis* was without this activity. The *Tritrichomonas foetus* extracts did not destroy the serological properties of the specific polysaccharide from the *Shigella* bacillus, the type XIV pneumococcus polysaccharide or the specific substance isolated from *T. foetus* by Feinberg and Morgan (1953). The enzymes also appeared to be different from those in *Clostridium welchii*. A partially purified enzyme preparation inactivated the H-specific structures and those responsible for M and N specificity but was without action on A, B, P, or S receptors on the erythrocyte surface. Enzymes responsible for inactivation of the H and M receptors could be differentiated by inhibition tests (Watkins and Morgan, 1954). Crude extracts, in contrast to the partially purified preparations above, contained enzymes which rapidly destroyed the serological activity of the water-soluble A and B mucoids. The enzymatic hydrolysis of each blood-group substance was inhibited by a different sugar component and presumably a different enzyme was involved (Watkins and Morgan, 1955). Watkins (1959) describes the characteristics of *T. foetus* extracts which destroy the serological properties of A, B, H, and Le^a blood-group substances, resulting in the production of about 20% reducing sugars and a liberation of D-fucose, galactose, and N-acetyl hexosamine. In addition, the *T. foetus* preparation hydrolyzed compounds of known structure containing α- or β-galactoside, α- or β-glucoside, N-acetyl-α- or β-glucosaminide, N-acetyl-α- or β-galactosaminide, α-L-fucoside or α-L-rhamnoside linkages.

Tyler and Watkins (1960) examined the stepwise degradation of the blood-group H mucopolysaccharide by a *Tritrichomonas foetus* enzyme and the results were consistent with the idea that the blood-group specificity is destroyed by removing terminal nonreducing sugars, the first sugar removed by the H enzyme being fucose.

Watkins *et al.* (1962) observed that stepwise enzymatic degradation of group B substance, first with a purified B-decomposing enzyme from *T. foetus,* followed by treatment with an H-decomposing enzyme from *T. foetus,* gave a material with a higher blood-group Le^a activity than the original material. Watkins (1962) described the activity of three preparations from *T. foetus.* Preparation I destroyed the serological activity of A, B, and Le^a substances, but not H serological activity. Preparation II destroyed the H serological activity but not that of A, B, or Le^a, and preparation III, prepared by electrophoresis at pH 7.0 destroyed B and Le^a serological activity but not H or A.

Ikeda (1955) also found *Tritrichomonas foetus* enzymes acted on O, A, and B substances from human stomach linings. Another enzyme of interest was described by Green *et al.* (1951) who observed β-glucuronidase activity with axenic cultures of *T. vaginalis* in the presence of menthol glucuronide.

One may speculate on the fate of various polysaccharides in the animal body during infection with the pathogenic strains of trichomonads. It is also of interest to consider enzyme systems other than those involving primarily carbohydrates. These might also influence pathogenicity and infection.

III. Nitrogen and Lipid Metabolism

Little has been done in the field of nitrogen and lipid metabolism of trichomonads, perhaps because the growth medium is complex and many crude source materials must be added. A few studies have been made on enzymes of nitrogen metabolism.

A. Enzymes of Nitrogen Metabolism

Lwoff (1951) said there are no proteolytic enzymes in trichomonads. However, Watkins (1959) mentions that in the work with blood-group substances, no account was taken of the proteolytic enzymes in *Tritrichomonas foetus.* Unpublished work of Pusztae and Morgan in that laboratory indicated certain proteolytic enzymes could cause an extensive or limited loss of serological activity. Watkins suggests that an examination of purified *T. foetus* enzymes for peptidases should be made. Evidence for protein-synthesizing enzymes is found in the work of Kunitake *et al.* (1962) in the radioactive amino acids found in the proteins of *Trichomonas vaginalis*. Warren and Allen (1959) studied glutamic decarboxylase and the amino acids of *T. gallinae* when it was observed that the addition of glutamic acid increased gas production 2- to 3-fold. These observations will be discussed in more detail in the sections on chemical composition and nutritive requirements. Only one paper has discussed enzymes involved with lipid substrates.

B. Enzymes for Steroid Conversions

Sebek *et al.* (1957) found that organisms of the family Trichomonadidae could convert certain steroids and the conversions were like those carried out by mammalian tissues and by various microorganisms. *Trichomonas gallinae* affected the 3-ketosteroids of the pregnane and allopregnane series at C-3. Thus, pregnane-3, 11, 20-trione and allopregnane-3, 11, 20-trione were reduced to their 3-hydroxylated analogs. *Trichomonas gallinae* also possesses a dehydrogenating system specific for C-17, as oxygen functions were reduced or oxidized only at C-17 in steroids of the 3-keto-4-androstene and estratriene series.

Much more work has been done on the nutritive requirements of trichomonads than on isolated nitrogenous or lipoidal enzyme systems. Less work has been done on the chemical composition of the organisms, which will be examined next.

IV. The Chemical Composition of Trichomonads

Few reports have appeared on the chemical composition of trichomonads. The most work has been done on the glycogens.

A. Glycogens in *Tritrichomonas foetus* and *Trichomonas gallinae*

Feinberg and Morgan (1953) isolated a glycogen-like polysaccharide from dried *Tritrichomonas foetus* cells in a yield of 5–10% during a study of an immunologically specific substance. It appeared homogeneous by ultracentrifuge and electrophoretic analysis, and was thought to be a polysaccharide-amino acid complex containing 10 amino acids and 5 or 6 sugars.

Further study of the polysaccharides from *Tritrichomonas foetus* and *Trichomonas gallinae* (Manners and Ryley, 1955) indicated they were branched α-1:4 glucosans which resembled, but were not identical with, animal glycogens rather than amylopectin in branching characteristics. The "glycogens" from *Tritrichomonas foetus* and *Trichomonas gallinae* had unit-chain lengths of 15 and 9 glucose residues respectively, and β-amylolysis limits of 60 and 51%. The polysaccharides have a rotation of $[\alpha]\frac{18}{D} + 197$ or $199°$, stain yellow-brown with dilute iodine, are degraded by salivary α-amylase, and have molecular weights of about 3×10^6. They are white powders, freely soluble in water, giving opalescent solutions. The cell glycogen content of *Tritrichomonas foetus* grown with glucose lies between 10 and 30% (dry weight basis), although one value of 55% was observed. Without glucose, the glycogen content was 8.1%. With 1% glucose, 6 times the yield of organisms was obtained with a glycogen content of 17.4%. Increasing the glucose content of the medium to 2–6% reduced growth by half, and gave cells with a glycogen content of about 14%. Similar values for intracellular glycogen were obtained with *Trichomonas gallinae*.

Ryley's study (1955) focuses attention on the glycogen reserve of the parasite as the center of its catabolic activities. The cytochemical studies (Wantland *et al.*, 1962) on *Trichomonas tenax* showed glycogen as large, oval, and irregularly shaped clear areas of 2 to 3 μ, containing purple-red to bright red granules. Total amounts of glycogen varied with the strain and diminished during periods of acceleration in reproductive activity.

B. NUCLEIC ACID COMPOSITION

Hamada (1954) found that the strain of *Trichomonas vaginalis*, which infected pretreated mice, changed morphologically and showed characteristic immunological reactions. It was in close agreement with *Tritrichomonas foetus* in immunological reactions but clearly different from the original strain and *T. foetus* in the nucleic acid content. Hamada (1956) describes the deoxyribonucleic acid (DNA) content in several trichomonads. The washed organisms were obtained from pure cultures and one strain was from the abdominal cavity of a mouse infected with *Trichomonas vaginalis*. Schneider's diphenylamine reaction was used, the DNA measured with the Helger spectrophotometer at 610 mμ, and results expressed as DNA-P in micrograms per cell. Pure cultures grown for 48 hr. on V bouillon (Hamada, 1953) and 4×10^8 cells were used for the test. *Trichomonas vaginalis* had an average DNA-P of 1.58×10^{-8} μg. per cell, another strain pathogenic to mice, had 3.35×10^{-8} μg. per cell while *Tritrichomonas foetus* "tricho" had 5.48×10^{-8} μg. per cell. Cells of *Trichomonas vaginalis* from 24- to 60-hr. cultures were almost constant in DNA-P content. The DNA-P content of *T. vaginalis* taken from infected mice was also constant, $6.1–6.7 \times 10^{-8}$ DNA-P μg. per cell, after 3, 4, or 5 days infection, while the DNA from *Tritrichomonas foetus* "tricho" taken from infected mice was constant at 12.03×10^{-8}. They believed this indicated species difference.

Wantland *et al.* (1962) in cytochemical studies on *Trichomonas tenax* found a relatively heavy concentration of DNA in nuclear wall chromatin, the network of chromatin throughout the nucleus, and the tripartite endosome. When trichomonad cultures are grown on completely synthetic media, these components of the cells will be a fertile field for comparative studies.

C. Lipid Composition

Lipid composition also offers a great field for exploration since few detailed studies have been made on the composition of lipids of parasitic protozoa. Shorb (1961) stated that the fatty acids in the total lipid extract of *Trichomonas gallinae* reflected the kinds and amounts of fatty acids found in the basal medium; oleic and palmitic acids were the most concentrated, along with a complex mixture of fatty acids similar to those from the Trypticase supplement. The same comment can be made about Monocercomonas (Lee and Shorb, 1962). However, Halevy (1963) investigated the lipid content of 2 strains of *Tritrichomonas foetus* grown on modified Diamond's medium containing peptone, yeast extract, and 10% inactivated horse serum. In one experiment 79.6–83.3% of the radioactive acetate was found in the phospholipids, 14.3–17.1% in glyceride fatty acids, and 3.3–3.7% in sterol esters. No sterol synthesis was demonstrated although analysis of the lipids of *T. foetus* showed that the sterol content was half that of the phospholipids, and 100-fold that of glycerol. Analysis of the medium showed about 60% of the lipid to be sterol and cholesterol esters; therefore, the medium would appear to be the source of sterols. Perhaps the different results as to lipid content rests in the different media employed by the two investigators. It appears that some parasitic protozoa lack the enzymatic mechanism for the synthesis of some essential lipids, whereas free-living protozoa such as *Tetrahymena pyriformis* have a remarkable lipid-synthesizing mechanism (Shorb, 1961).

Wantland *et al.* (1962) demonstrated lipids in the cytoplasm as small, light gray-blue, spherical or oval areas from 1 to 2 μ in diameter occurring most frequently toward the posterior end of the flagellate, also in the marginal areas of both the parabasal body and axostyle. Cholesterol was observed in the cytoplasm as small pale violet or red spherical areas from 0.5 to 1.5 μ in diameter.

D. Amino Acid Composition

Several papers have dealt with the amino acid composition of trichomonads. All the organisms were grown on media containing crude supplements such as serum. Although the organisms were washed before extracting the amino acids, the question of adsorption of the amino acids from the medium remains (A. E. Johnson, 1962). The amino acids found are listed in Table VII. Smith and Spriggs (1959) measured the free amino acids from *Trichomonas vaginalis* 5LA in ethanol extracts of cells grown in CPL medium minus agar, in unidimensional chromatography. Warren and Allen (1959) used alcoholic extracts of washed suspensions of the Jones' Barn strain of *Trichomonas gallinae* in-

Table VII

The Amino Acid Composition of Trichomonads[a]

Amino acid	Tritrichomonas foetus			Tritrichomonas suis	Tetratrichomonas gallinarum	Trichomonas gallinae Strain JB	Trichomonas gallinae Strain JB	Pentatrichomonas hominis	Pentatrichomonas sp. Strain Pig cecum	Trichomonas vaginalis Strain 5A	Trichomonas vaginalis
Alanine	+++	+++	+++	+++	+++	+++	+++		++	++	+	2.6*
Arginine	++	?	?	++	++	++	++	++	++	++	?	1.7
Aspartic acid	++	+	++	++	++	++	++		++	++	+	0.3
Cystine	+	+	+	+	+	+	+			++	?	—
Glutamic acid	+++	+++	+++	+++	+++	+++	+++		+++	+++	?	1.0
Glycine												2.2
Cysteine	±	±	±	±	±	±	±		±	±	—	—
Histidine	+	+	+	+	+	+	+	?	+	+	—	0.04
Isoleucine											—	0.1
Methionine	++	++	++	++	++	++	++	?	++	++	—	—
Leucine	++	++	++	++	++	++	++		++	++	++	2.0
Lysine	+	+	+	+	+	+	+		+	+	+	0.6
Ornithine											—	—
Phenylalanine	++	++	++	++	++	++	++	?	++	++	—	0.1
Proline	+	+	+	+	+	+	+	+	+	+	—	0.4
Serine	+	+	+	+	+	+	+		+	+	—	0.2
Threonine	+	+	+	+	+	+	+		+	+	—	0.1
Tyrosine	+	+	+	+	+	+	+	?	+	+	+	0.1
Valine	+	+	+	+	+	++	+		+	+	—	0.6
γ-Amino-n-butyric acid												—
α-Methyl-α-amino-n-butyric acid												—
Unknown #9						+						—
Unidentified amino acids	+	—	+	+	+	+	+		+	+		—
Cysteic acid (?)	±	—	±	—	±	—	—		—	±		—
References[b]	1	3	4	1	1	1	6	2	1	1	5	7

[a] Key to symbols:
*, Micromoles in total protein
?, Tentative identification
±, Lowest amounts
++, Highest amounts
(4), Unidentified amino acids

[b] References:
1. Mehra et al. (1960).
2. Swenson (1960).
3. A. E. Johnson (1960).
4. A. E. Johnson (1962).
5. Smith and Spriggs (1959).
6. Warren and Allen (1959).
7. Kunitake et al. (1962).

cubated anaerobically with glutamic acid, and measured the amino acids formed. Mehra *et al.* (1960) employing paper and column chromatography, used hydrolyzates of whole cells of several trichomonads. Swenson (1960) studied the free amino acids from the supernatant of boiled water extracts from the Jones Barn strain of *T. gallinae*. A. E. Johnson (1960, 1962) identified the free amino acids in a water extract of protoplasm of organisms grown on CPLM agar-free medium. In none of these papers were quantities determined. Kunitake *et al.* (1962) grew *T. vaginalis* in CPLM medium with glucose-U-C^{14}, identified the amino acids in total protein, and gave results as μmoles of amino acids (Table VII). They identified 15 amino acids—alanine, glycine, leucine, arginine, and glutamic acid being highest. These amino acids were also identified by the other workers. Much work remains to be done on the proteins and amino acids when these organisms can be grown on defined minimal media, the unidentified spots posing interesting problems.

If it were true, as Lwoff (1951) stated, that *Tritrichomonas foetus* does not contain proteolytic enzymes this fact would definitely enter into the picture of parasitism and nitrogen metabolism. Other work refutes this statement (see Section III,A). Perhaps all amino acids are synthesized from simpler compounds which would explain the importance of the glycolytic pathway for these organisms. As A. E. Johnson (1962) pointed out, nitrogen metabolism of these organisms is complex as indicated by the large numbers of amino acids present in the free state. It is evident from the work of Kunitake *et al.* (1962) that *Trichomonas vaginalis* can snythesize amino acids during glucose metabolism, and proteins are obviously synthesized during growth.

E. Vitamins and Other Compounds

Wellerson *et al.* (1959) isolated riboflavin and flavin mononucleotide from *Trichomonas vaginalis*. A concentration of 75 mg. per gram of cell (dry weight) was not greatly different from that reported for bacteria.

Intermediates in cell metabolism have been mentioned in connection with specific enzymes, in the section on enzymes.

Obviously the chemical composition of these flagellates will bear further study. Studies on the nutritional requirement and growth of the organisms in synthetic media will further this type of investigation.

V. The Nutritional Requirements of Trichomonads

Some of the early work on trichomonad requirements for ascorbic acid, linoleic acid, pantothenic acid, and unknown factors has been reviewed by Lwoff (1951) and von Brand (1952); for cholesterol, by Lwoff (1951), von Brand (1952), and van Wagtendonk (1955); and for monoribonucleotides or

Table VIII

Defined Media Used in Growth Studies with Trichomonads

Ingredient	Medium [a]					
	Sp	S	SL	SLM	7E	5E
	(Unless otherwise noted data given in mg./100 ml.)					
Amino acid mix #9 [b]	—	—	—	—	—	250
DL-α-Alanine	—	25	40	—	25	—
L-Arginine hydrochloride	—	25	80	25	40	—
L-Asparagine	20	—	80	—	—	—
DL-Aspartic acid	—	50	40	50	20 (L-)	—
L-Cystine	150(·HCl)	1	2	1	10 (diethyl ester·2HCl)	—
L-Cysteine hydrochloride	—	100	200	200	150	—
L-Glutamic acid	—	50	160	100	100	—
Glycine	—	50	160	50	100	—
DL-Histidine hydrochlorid	—	20 (L-, HCl·H$_2$O)	120	20 (L-, HCl)	300 (L-, HCl·H$_2$O)	—
Homocysteine thiolactone hydrochloride	—	—	—	—	—	—
DL-Isoleucine	—	5	80	—	5	—
DL-Leucine	—	5	120	5	20 (L-)	—
DL-Lysine hydrochloride	—	20 (−HCl)	60	20	5 (L-HCl)	—
DL-Methionine	—	6	40	6	100	—
DL-Phenylalanine	—	4	80	4	25	—
L-Proline	—	—	15 [c]	—	5	—
DL-Serine	—	—	80	—	100	—
DL-Threonine	—	10	40	10	10 (L-)	—
DL-Tryptophan	—	2	120	2	10	—
L-Tyrosine	—	5	20	5	5 (ethyl ester·HCl)	—
DL-Valine	100	6	80	6	10	—
Maltose	—	—	1000	—	—	—
Glucose	—	—	—	1000	100 [d]	500
Sucrose	—	1.5	—	—	—	—

	1	2	3	4	5	6
Ribose	0.4	—	0.8	—	—	—
Mannitol	—	—	4.8	1	300	150
Na$_2$ glycerophosphate·5H$_2$O	—	—	—	—	—	—
Potassium glycerophosphate	0.1	—	—	—	—	—
Glycerol	—	—	—	—	100	—
Sodium acetate, anhydrous	480 (·3H$_2$O)	960	—	—	100 (3H$_2$O)	—
Thiomalic acid	—	40	40	40	—	25
Ascorbic acid	—	—	350	80	—	40
Pyromellitic acid	350	0.8	350	—	—	—
Ribonucleic acid (Na salt)	20	—	—	—	—	—
Adenine	10[e]	0.8	0.8	20	—	8
Adenylic acid	—	—	—	—	—	—
Guanine	10[e]	0.8	0.8	20	—	8
Guanylic acid	—	—	—	—	—	—
Uracil	10[e]	0.8	0.8	20	—	8
Uridylic acid	10[e]	0.8	0.8	20	—	8
Cytidylic acid	—	0.8	0.8	20	—	8
Orotic acid	0.3	—	0.3	—	—	—
Thymine	1	—	1	—	—	—
Putrescine dihydrochloride	0.04	—	0.04	[0.2]	—	[0.08]
K$_2$HPO$_4$	50	120	—	20	—	—
KH$_2$PO$_4$	50	120	—	20	—	—
K$_3$PO$_4$ × H$_2$O	50 (−H$_2$O)	—	240	40	—	—
K$_3$ citrate·H$_2$O	—	240	—	—	—	—
Ringer's solution	95 ml.	—	—	10	—	—
(NH$_4$)$_2$SO$_4$	—	—	10	20	—	—
MgCO$_3$	—	—	—	10	—	—
Metal mix 44	0.5 ml.[f]	—	—	10[g]	—	6[g]
Metal mix 50[g]	—	10	10	—	—	—
MgSO$_4$·7H$_2$O	75	10	—	—	—	—
CaCl$_2$·2H$_2$O	—	5	—	—	—	—
H$_3$BO$_3$	(0.0001)	2	0.00057	(0.01)	—	—
FeSO$_4$·7H$_2$O	(0.005)	0.88	0.025	(0.1)	—	—
FeCl$_3$·6H$_2$O	—	0.125	—	—	—	—
ZnSO$_4$·7H$_2$O	(0.0125)	0.31	0.0545	(0.5)	—	—
MnSO$_4$·H$_2$O	(0.0025)	—	0.0077	(1)	—	—
CuSO$_4$·5H$_2$O	(0.0005)	0.064	0.00195	(0.1)	—	—

Table VIII—*Continued*

Ingredient	Medium[a]					
	Sp	S	SL	SLM	7E	5E
		(Unless otherwise noted data given in mg./100 ml.)				
CoSO₄	—	(0.00025)	0.096	0.000655	(0.05)	—
(NH₄)₆Mo₇O₂₄·4H₂O	—	—	0.123	—	(0.04 Mo)	—
EDTA	—	0.00125	—	0.00125	—	—
Vanadium	—	—	—	—	(0.005)	—
Vitamin mix 13 (= 12)[h]	—	—	—	—	30[i]	2 ml./100[i]
Vitamin B₁₂	0.001	0.0001	0.0048	0.0048	[0.0005]	[0.0002]
Nicotinic acid	0.032	0.4	0.15	0.15	0.2 + [0.5]	[0.2]
Thiamine hydrochloride	0.016	0.6	0.075	0.075	[0.5]	[0.2]
Riboflavin	0.08	0.04	0.39	0.39	[0.05]	[0.02] (Na phosphate)
Thioctic acid	200 units		—	—	[0.02] DL	[0.008]
Calcium pantothenate	0.032	0.3	0.15	0.15	4. + [0.5]	4. + [0.2]
p-Aminobenzoic acid	0.016	0.01	0.075	0.075	[0.05]	[0.02]
Pyridoxine hydrochloride	0.064	—	0.306	0.306	[0.1]	[0.04]
Pyridoxal hydrochloride	0.016	—	0.075	0.075	[0.1]	[0.04]
Pyridoxamine dihydrochloride	0.016(·HCl)	0.1	0.075	0.075	—	—
Pyridoxamine phosphate	—	—	0.05	—	—	—
Folic acid	0.008	0.025	0.0125	0.0125	[0.02]	[0.008]
Leucovorin (folinic)	—	0.002 (Ca·5H₂O)	0.02	0.02	[0.001] (Ca·5H₂O)	[0.0004] (Ca·5H₂O)
Biotin	0.008	0.001	0.0342	0.0342	[0.0025]	[0.001]
Choline	0.8 (Cl)	1 (·H₂ citrate)	1.6 (Cl)	1 (Cl)	7.5	3 (·H₂ citrate)
i-Inositol	0.8	1	1.6	1	5	[2]
p-Hydroxybenzoic acid	—	—	(1)[k]	(1)[l]	[0.05]	[0.02]
D-α-Tocopheryl acetate	—	—	—	—	0.2	—
DL-Tocopherol	0.24[d]	0.4	—	—	—	—
Methylene blue	—	—	—	—	—	—
Cholesterol	—	2.5	2.5	2.5	0.5	0.5

[a]	SP	S	SL	SLM	7E	5E
Oleic	—	—	—	—	(1.65)[k]	(1.65)[l]
Palmitic	—	—	—	—	(1.50)[k]	(1.50)[l]
TEM-4T[m]	200[o]	100	2	1[n]	—	—
Tween 80	100	2000	—	—	5	5
Agar	1000	—	100[p]	100[p]	100[p]	—
Trypticase	—	—	—	—	—	—
Serum	—	5	—	—	—	—
pH to	7.6	6.0	6.5–7.5	—	7.0, 7.2[k]	7.0
With	KOH	—	KOH	—	NaOH	NaOH

[a] Medium used by:
  SP, Sprince et al. (1953).
  S, Sanders (1957).
  SL, Shorb and Lund (1959).
  SLM, Lund and Shorb (1962).
  7E and 5E, Lee et al. (1962a).
[b] Given in Lee and Pierce (1960) as a modification (not specified) of amino acid mix 8 (p. 407).
[c] Required when Trypticase is omitted.
[d] May be omitted.
[e] Bases may be used.
[f] Metal mix 44, given as the amount of metal ions per 100 ml., 0.5 ml. would contain (amount metal ions) given in table.
[g] Given in Lee and Pierce (1960). Mix contains amount (mg/100 ml. metal ions) as indicated in table.
[h] Vitamin mix 13 contains the same final concentrations of vitamins as vitamin mix No. 12 (Lee and Pierce, 1960) taken from Hutner, et al. (1957).
[i] 30 mg. mix 12 contains the amounts given in square brackets in 7E medium.
[j] 2 ml. of mix 12 contains the amounts given in square brackets in 5E medium.
[k] Amount used with Trichomonas gallinae SLTc.
[l] Amount used with Tritrichomonas suis PN1-75.
[m] TEM-4T, a diacetyl tartaric acid ester of tallow monoglyceride, Hachmeister, Inc., Pittsburgh, is replaced by oleic plus palmitic acids (amounts given in table) for Trichomonas gallinae SLT and Tritrichomonas suis, PN1-75.
[n] 1 mg. ascorbyl palmitate is substituted for Monocercomonas colubrorum.
[o] Omitted by Shorb and Lund (1959).
[p] Ionagar #2, Consolidated Labs., Inc., Chicago Heights, Illinois.

the corresponding free bases by Hutner and Provasoli (1955). Carbohydrates supporting growth have already been discussed (Table I). Development of chemically defined media for growth of trichomonads from poikilotherms and for some parasites from warm-blooded animals has been actively pursued. Several of these organisms have been grown in almost defined media. The formulas of the most defined media are shown in Table VIII. The requirement for a few specific metabolites has been studied.

A. Vitamin Requirements

1. water-soluble vitamins

Jones and Smith (1957, 1959) have shown a requirement by *Trichomonas gallinae* for nicotinamide, choline, pyridoxamine, calcium pantothenate, pyridoxine, folic acid, and biotin when these were omitted from the basal medium (Sp, Table VIII) of Sprince *et al.* (1953). Shorb and Lund (1959) included all the vitamins which improved the growth of *T. gallinae* in developing their chemically defined medium (SL, Table VIII). None of these was studied as to essentiality by omission from the basal medium since nonsynthetic supplements were required.

An exceptionally high calcium pantothenate requirement (4 mg./100 ml.) by the trichomonads from poikilotherms was observed by Lee *et al.* (1962a,b). This may reflect a lack of calcium in their media 5E and 7E (Table VIII). Calcium does not appear in their formula. They have also included *p*-hydroxybenzoic acid and relatively large amounts of nicotinic acid, choline, and inositol.

2. fat-soluble vitamins

A requirement for tocopherol or coenzyme Q and related compounds was reported by Shorb and Lund (1962) for a variant strain SLTc of *Trichomonas gallinae,* when grown on their synthetic medium supplemented with solvent-extracted Trypticase plus cholesterol, and oleic and palmitic acids. Compounds which fulfilled this requirement were: d-α-tocopheryl-polyethylene glycol 1000 succinate (0.45 μg. per milliliter of medium for half maximum growth); α-tocopherylquinone (0.75 μg.), d-α-tocopheryl acetate (1.8 μg.), dl-α-tocopherol (4.5 μg.), d-γ-tocopherol (6.9 μg.), d-α-tocopherol (7.1 μg.), coenzyme Q_{10} (2.0 μg.) or a water-soluble form of coenzyme Q_{10} with Emulphor and dimethylacetamide (0.05 μg.), coenzyme Q_9 (0.6 μg.), ubichromenol (0.8 μg.) plastoquinone (0.8 μg.), coenzymes Q_3 (2.3 μg.), Q_4 (2.7 μg.), 7,8-dimethoxy-2,5-dimethyl-2(4′, 8′, 12′-trimethyltridecyl)-6-chromanol (6.0 μg.) and 2,3-dimethoxy-5-methylbenzoquinone (1.0 μg.). TEM-4T (see footnote, Table VIII), unextracted Trypticase, and several crude lipid-rich materials were active as well as the Emulphor, a polymerized vegetable oil. Two samples of vitamin K_1, containing oxidation products, were active (0.6 and 1.5 μg.). d-α-Tocopheryl succinate (unpublished), coenzyme Q_2, menadione, succinate, and several antioxidants and water solubilizers, such as propyl gallate, butylated hydroxytoluene, butylated hydroxyanisole, Santoquin, DPPD, Sustane 3, polyethylene glycol, sodium taurocholate, sodium hexametaphosphate, Triton X100, and dimethylacetamide were inactive. Since the requirement could not be satisfied by just any antioxidant or water solubilizer, and very small amounts of some compounds were needed, it would appear that the requirement was for a function perhaps associated with the quinones. The coenzyme Q complex is a part of the electron-transport system in animals and plants.

B. Requirement for Trace Minerals

Sanders' (1957) medium (S, Table VIII) is high in magnesium ions compared with the other media. Shorb and Lund (1958, 1959, 1963) in developing SL medium, were able to replace agar by increasing the trace minerals to the levels shown in formula SL (Table VIII). The SL medium is the only one including Ca as a part of the mineral mix. Lee et al. (1962a,b) observed that the upper temperature limits of growth of the trichomonads from poikilotherms may be raised by increasing the trace elements and amino acids. Vanadium is included in their trace minerals. In the final analysis, the agar in medium 7E and 5E, and the Trypticase needed with SL and SLM media for some species, may be eliminated by judicious juggling of trace mineral and amino acid levels.

C. Requirements for Components of Nucleic Acids

Sanders (1957) used the Na salt of ribonucleic acid (RNA) in the medium, minus serum, which he devised for *Tritrichomonas foetus*. Shorb and Lund (1958, 1959) reported that a factor in some RNA preparations was required by *Trichomonas gallinae* even though the SL medium contained four or more of the component bases or acids; *Tritrichomonas foetus* and *Tritrichomonas suis* PN-175 grew on medium S with RNA and TEM-4T (see footnotes, Table VIII). Lee and Pierce (1960) found that *Hypotrichomonas acosta* could not use the free bases but required the nucleotide in high concentration. No attempt was made by them or others to reexamine the antagonism between nucleosides and nucleotides described for *Trichomonas vaginalis* by Sprince et al. (1953).

D. Amino Acid Requirements

Weiss and Ball (1947) early reported on the requirements of *Tritrichomonas foetus* for amino acids in the synthetic medium of Kidder and Dewey (1945) supplemented with a folic acid concentrate. They found that *T. foetus* required arginine, glycine, tryptophan, histidine, isoleucine, leucine, lysine, threonine, methionine, phenylalanine, proline, serine, and valine. Serum contained some factor capable of improving the medium, and casein, lactalbumin, and wheat-germ protein digests improved growth. Shorb and Lund (1963) were unable to repeat this work with *T. foetus* BP 1, using synthetic folic acid.

Smith (1955) studied the effect of cysteine on the growth of *Trichomonas vaginalis* strain 5A in a medium containing 19 amino acids, RNA, and 5% human serum, under aerobic and anaerobic conditions. On second serial transfers of the cysteine-less cultures, growth of aerobic cultures and of anaerobic cultures was 76 and 98% less than the cysteine-containing controls. This indicated a need for cysteine for growth as well as for its reductant property. A need for glutamine was also indicated for *T. vaginalis* in the work of Eugere *et al.* (1956). Serum treated with an ion-exchange resin of a carboxylic acid type would not support growth unless glutamine or the eluate from the column was also added. A requirement for proline was noted by Shorb and Lund (1959) with *T. gallinae*. When fatty acids are supplied as TEM-4T (Shorb and Lund, 1963) optimum growth occurs with lower levels of Trypticase (0.05–2.0%) in the presence of proline compared with 0.3–2.0% Trypticase without proline.

Lee *et al.* (1962a) have developed an amino acid medium (7E, Table VIII), in which 3+ growth ($\sim$15–50 $\times$ 10^4 organisms per milliliter; Lee and Pierce, 1960) was obtained on first subculture with strain S5 of *Tritrichomonas augusta,* and lesser growth with other strains. The change in amino acid concentration and other constituents given in medium 5E (Table VIII) produced better growth with the *Monocercomonas* and *Hypotrichomonas* cultures than did the amino acid mix in medium 7E. The essentiality of each amino acid was not demonstrated by omission of single acids. For other trichomonads, *Trichomonas gallinae, Tetratrichomonas gallinarum, Tritrichomonas foetus* and *Tritrichomonas suis* PN-175, a crude supplement, such as serum or Trypticase was required, in addition to amino acids (Shorb and Lund, 1959, 1962).

E. Fatty-Acid Requirements and Development of Defined Media

Attempts to eliminate serum from the growth medium served as the real starting point for advances in the development of chemically defined media.

The work of Sprince, Kupferberg, and co-workers on serum fractions required by *T. vaginalis* has been reviewed by Lwoff (1951) and Hutner and Provasoli (1955) and their final medium, Sp (Sprince *et al.,* 1953) is shown in Table VIII. Guthrie (1946) and Guthrie and Snell (1950) replaced serum, in Difco veal-infusion broth, with ascorbic acid or thioglycolate, cholesterol, 9 B vitamins, adenine, guanine, uracil, and xanthine, for *Tritrichomonas foetus.* Casein, beef, and liver products substituted for veal infusion if the medium contained the above chemicals plus casein hydrolyzate, glucose, trace minerals, tryptophan, cystine, citrate, and agar.

Clausen (1953) fractionated horse serum and found an essential water-soluble, nondialyzable, and heat-stable (at pH 8) factor for *T. foetus,* with characteristics of seromucoid. Cholesterol was present but by itself did not support growth in 2% glucose broth. Sanders (1957) used an amino acid, vitamin, metal mix medium (S, Table VIII) containing a small amount of agar and Trypticase. Potassium thiomalate and pyromellitic acid were the reducing and buffering compounds. Serum was replaced by cholesterol and Tween 80. Tween 20, 40, and 60 were less effective than Tween 80. The degree of dispersion of cholesterol markedly affected growth. Agar was not essential. Choline H₂ citrate and potassium glycerophosphate improved growth.

Shorb and Lund (1958, 1959) further clarified the lipid requirements. Serum could be replaced by a saturated 99+% pure fatty acid, e.g., palmitic, plus an unsaturated pure fatty acid, such as oleic, for *Tritrichomonas foetus* and *T. suis* PN-175 but not for *Trichomonas gallinae* in Sanders' medium (S, Table VIII), modified by omitting Tween 80, when cholesterol, Trypticase, and RNA were added as supplements. The same fatty acids replaced serum for growth of *T. gallinae* SL in medium SL (Table VIII) in the presence of cholesterol, Trypticase, and RNA, but these supplements together would not support growth of *Tetratrichomonas gallinarum*. Serum stimulated the growth of all of the organisms over that of the above supplements. TEM-4T, a diacetyl tartaric acid ester of tallow monoglyceride, was very effective in supplying the fatty acid mixtures in a water-soluble form. The impurity of fatty acids from several sources was pointed out.

Wyss *et al.* (1960) tested the water-soluble and ether-soluble fractions of bovine serum on the growth of *Tritrichomonas foetus* in Sanders' medium. The water-soluble fraction (WF) contained a required factor, not identified, in addition to components in the ether fraction. WF contained lipid factors; it supported growth at the 1.0% level without cholesterol or the ether fraction. The ether fraction, in the presence of WF, was replaceable by stearic, elaidic, or oleic acid. In the presence of cholesterol the oleic effect was antagonized. Without cholesterol, linoleic and linolenic acids were toxic, but with cholesterol in certain proportions, effects were good. Although the fatty acids were specified as "puriss.," no analysis of purity was given. Possibly the unsaturated fatty acids used were partially oxidized or contained other toxic materials which might account for the inhibition. Frank and Reiner (1954) had previously reported on the toxicity of C_6 to C_{12} fatty acids and on some inhibition with oleic. Lauric acid and sodium lauryl sulfate have been used in trichomoniasis (Frank and Reiner, 1954; Carrow, 1955; O'Brien and Thoms, 1955).

Lund and Shorb (1962) in a synthetic medium (SLM, Table VIII) composed of constituents taken from Sanders' and SL medium, obtained good growth of *Tritrichomonas suis* PN-175 with a supplement containing 50 μg. of TEM-4T, 100 μg. of cholesterol and 10 mg. per milliliter of Trypticase. This strain has grown well through 6 serial transfers on the same medium containing oleic and palmitic acids, d-α-tocopheryl acetate, cholesterol with Trypticase at 10 mg. per milliliter. The Trypticase contained about 0.002% methanol-chloroform extractable material, mostly fatty acids. TEM-4T is an impure source of fatty acids (Shorb and Lund, 1963) and perhaps non-saponifiables (Holz *et al.*, 1961). Shorb and Lund (1962) using solvent-extracted Trypticase as the only nondefined substance, grew *Trichomonas gallinae* SLTc, a tocopherol-requiring strain, on first subculture, with pure oleic and palmitic acids, d-α-tocopheryl polyethylene glycol 1000 succinate, and cholesterol as the lipid source. With these supplements, the Trypticase needed for minimal to optimal (5×10^6 organisms per milliliter) growth was 0.5 to 4 mg. per milliliter (Shorb and Lund, 1963). This last example represents possibly the best growth of a trichomonad from warm-blooded animals on nearly defined medium.

Perhaps the trichomonads first to be grown on a completely synthetic medium will be from poikilotherms inasmuch as they may represent lower forms than those from warm-blooded animals. Samuels (1959) substituted 2% sheep serum for agar in STS medium in attempts to secure a chemically defined medium for *Tritrichomonas augusta*. Propyl gallate replaced cysteine for maintenance of reducing conditions. Amino acids, vitamins, nucleic acid precursors, and lipids reduced the serum requirement to 0.25% and casein digest to 0.8%. Several 6-carbon acids, both mono- and dicarboxylic, had intense growth-stimulating effects at 0.1–1.0 μg. per milliliter. These acids were not specified by name and no further reference to them has been found.

Lee and Pierce (1960) grew *Hypotrichomonas acosta* in Diamond's medium in which horse serum was replaced with 0.001% of TEM-4T + 0.0005% of cholesterol, and the yeast extract with ribonucleotides. Trypticase was reduced from 2% to 0.25% for strains 3 and 5 by the addition of vitamins, amino acids, and metal mixes. Lee *et al.* (1960) found that, on a defined medium similar to that used by Lee and Pierce (1960), Trypticase could be replaced for *T. augusta*, strain 5 and *Monocercomonas* strain Ns-L:PRR through 3 serial transfers, by mixtures of amino acids and metals. Lee *et al.* (1961) reported further work on the comparative growth of 17 strains of trichomonads from poikilotherms in the defined medium in which *T. augusta* (S5 and S103) and strain Ns-L:PRR of *Monocercomonas* sp. grew well. All of the remaining strains multiplied with 0.025% Trypticase enrichment with maximal growth at 0.25–0.5% Trypticase. The four strains of *H. acosta* and *Trichomitis batrachorum* grew poorly on this medium even in the presence of 1% Trypticase. Lee *et al.* (1962b) discuss in a general way the problems encountered in culturing trichomonads from poikilotherms. The complete composition of the medium (7E, Table VIII) which produced growth with some of these organisms was given in their next paper (Lee *et al.*, 1962a). The medium was chemically pure except for agar (0.1%) and TEM-4T (0.002%) or ascorbyl palmitate (0.001%), the former containing several saturated and unsaturated fatty acids (Shorb and Lund, 1959) and the latter several saturated fatty acids (Lee and Shorb *in* Lee *et al.*, 1962b). In medium 7E growth of *Tritrichomonas augusta,* especially strain S5, was 3+ (15–50 × 10^4 organisms per milliliter; Lee and Pierce, 1960), in the first subculture without Trypticase. *Trichomitis batrachorum* cultures showed little growth (which might actually be only the carry-over of the large numbers of organisms inoculated) unless 0.025% Trypticase was added. Two strains of *Monocercomonas* showed no response to Trypticase over that obtained without Trypticase. They grew better in medium 5E (Table VIII) without Trypticase (for the first three transfers, Lee, 1963). There was a difference between strains as shown by the TEM-4T requirement by *Monocercomonas* sp. and the requirement for saturated fatty acids only by *M. colubrorum.*

F. STEROL REQUIREMENT

The papers by Cailleau were reviewed by Lwoff (1951) and van Wagtendonk (1955). Two studies since that time have appeared on the cholesterol requirement of *Trichomonas gallinae.* Mandel and Honigberg (1957) found that 0.001% of cholesterol or its analog, dihydrocholesterol, yielded similar response curves with optimal growth of 4 × 10^5 flagellates, in replacing serum, which produced 1.5 × 10^6 trichomonads at the 1.0% level. Growth with thioglycolate medium alone was 5 × 10^3, all at 48 hr., 37°C. Increasing toxicity was observed in higher levels of either sterol. The two sterols in combination elicited an additive response below those of their single optimal concentrations; their toxicities became evident when the sum of the concentrations exceeded the optimal concentration of either. These observations argued for a similar site of action for both substances. Attempts to isolate strains adapted to one or the other sterol were not successful. Perhaps the organism converted one sterol to another with a single specific effect, since Sebek *et al.* (1957) showed that *T. gallinae* had enzymes interconverting certain steroids (discussed in the section on enzymes).

Lund and Shorb (1960, 1962) reinvestigated the sterol requirements of a variant of *T. gallinae* (SLT) and *Tritrichomonas suis* PN-175, using a chemically defined medium except for Trypticase and fatty acids supplied as TEM-4T. The sterol requirement for *T. gallinae* was fulfilled by cholesterol, 7-dehydrocholesterol, cholestanol (dihydrocholesterol) [but not brassicasteryl acetate, erroneously reported active by Hutner & Holz (1962)], and to a lesser degree, by ergosterol, β-sitosterol, zymosterol, and zymosterol acetate. Cholestanol and β-sitosterol inhibited at certain concentrations. Subsequent gas-liquid chromatography of the sterols showed that only cholesterol and zymosterol acetate contained 1 peak, the other sterols contained 2 to 4 peaks. Repurified cholestanol (99.5% pure, supplied by Dr. W. E. Robbins, U.S.D.A., Beltsville, Maryland) was active and showed no inhibition of growth, while repurified β-sitosterol (95% pure, from Dr. Robbins) was inactive. Also inactive were diethylstilbestrol, estrone, dehydroepiandrosterone, progesterone, testosterone, deoxycorticosterone acetate, cortisone acetate, compound A, 5,6-dihydroergosterol, Δ^7 cholestenol, dihydroergosterol acetate, stigmasterol, sodium taurocholate, cholic acid, methyl deoxycholate, deoxycholic acid, and methyl cholate. Fat-soluble vitamins as well as precursors in cholesterol synthesis, acetate, mevalonic acid, mevalonic acid plus liver extract, and squalene did not replace cholesterol. Acetate was required for growth of *T. gallinae* in the presence of cholesterol in contrast to acetate toxicity with *Tritrichomonas suis* PN-175. For the latter organism, acetate was omitted from the SLM medium although present as a contaminant in the Trypticase supplement (Lund and Shorb, 1962). *Tritrichomonas suis* PN-175 utilized cholesterol, cholestanol, 7-dehydrocholesterol, and the impure β-sitosterol. A small amount of sterol-replacing material was present in fat-solvent extracts of Trypticase.

Holz *et al.* (1961) pointed out that Tweens and presumably other lipids prepared from commercial grades of lipids are contaminated with unsaponifiable material. Further study of the sterol requirements of trichomonads would appear in order when these organisms can be grown in an absolutely chemically pure medium, using pretested pure sterols. Much needed are pure sources of cholesterol and water-soluble fatty acids protected from oxidation to be used with otherwise completely chemically pure basal media. In fact, the whole complex question of lipid growth requirements needs to be reexamined on this basis. Lipid requirements may represent only a physiochemical absorption phenomenon although the manner of obtaining food (Adler *et al.*, 1952; Samuels, 1957b), would suggest that ingestion of lipid materials is not the problem. More likely, some parasitic flagellates no longer synthesize essential lipid materials, such as the fatty acids, sterols, and fat-soluble vitamins. Perhaps some of the questions of growth requirements may be answered in the work on the trichomonads from poikilotherms.

G. Unidentified Requirements

In the preceding discussion, it is evident that crude supplements such as agar, serum, crude lipids, ribonucleic acid, and Trypticase are required by all trichomonads, even though amounts of these supplements are being continually reduced by the addition of known compounds or the alteration of constituents in the basal medium. The extent to which unidentified factors are required is apparent in the composition of the media for stock cultures.

VI. Cultural Methods

Some improvements in cultural methods include the addition of certain antibiotics to curb yeast and mold contamination, the axenic cultivation of many flagellates previously not so cultured, continuous-flow cultivation of *Tritrichomonas augusta*, new or improved storage techniques, development of agar-plate methods which permits cloning cultures, and the study of such cloned cultures. Many cultural methods for various species of trichomonads have been published. Those which improve diagnosis or result in axenic cultures are discussed below.

A. Culture Methods for Different Species*

An improved culture medium for *Trichomonas gallinae* (Diamond and Herman, 1952; Diamond, 1954, 1957) consisted of Trypticase, yeast extract, maltose, L-cysteine hydrochloride, L-ascorbic acid, agar, inactivated sheep serum, potassium penicillin G, and streptomycin. This medium permitted establishment and maintenance of axenic cultures of *Tetratrichomonas gallinarum*, a *T. gallinarum*-like form, *Tritrichomonas eberthi*, *Trichomonas gallinae*, *Tritrichomonas foetus*-like trichomonad from the nasal passages of swine and *Tetratrichomonas buttreyi* from the swine cecum; *Tritrichomonas foetus*, *Tetratrichomonas buttreyi* from calf feces; *Pentatrichomonas hominis* from man and a wild rat; and *Trichomonas vaginalis*. Methylene blue inhibited growth of the *Tetratrichomonas buttreyi* and *Pentatrichomonas hominis*. The only trichomonad which failed to grow in this medium was *Trichomonas tenax*. Diamond later (1960, 1962) axenically cultivated *T. tenax* in anaerobic fluid medium from primary cultivation with *Trypanosoma cruzi*. *Trypanosoma cruzi* died out when the mixed culture was grown in autoclaved, modified Diamond's medium supplemented with nonautoclaved horse serum and chick-embryo extract.

Few studies have been as complete as Diamond's. Nonaxenic growth of *Trichomonas tenax* was obtained in meat broth plus antibiotics (Wegner, 1953) or in egg-yolk infusion and CPLM medium (Honigberg *et al.*, 1957) with a single strain of bacteria. De Carneri (1955) and Solomon (1957) cultured *P. hominis* axenically on a complete medium, like CPLM, with antibiotics, but not in STS medium, while Shaffer and Biegeleisen (1951) used a medium preconditioned by growth with an anaerobic strepto-bacillus. Nakamura (1961a) used a two-phase medium of egg and blood in Ringer's solution with starch for a nonaxenic culture of *P. hominis*, in which fumagillin eliminated *Entamoeba histolytica* but not bacteria. Petrovic (1950) cultivated 5 trichomonad species on 19 different media. *Trichomonas gallinae* was maintained for the longest period on liquid-solid phase rice bouillon-agar-serum; *T. tenax* did best in agar-serum and agar-ascites; *Pentatrichomonas hominis* and *P. hominis* var. *muris* in agar-ascites and agar-rice bouillon-serum; *Trichomonas vaginalis* in agar-serum. Lom (1957) gave a preliminary note on the

---

* See footnote in Introduction, Section I, for references on commonly used media designated as CPLM, STS, Diamond's, etc. throughout this section.

cultivation of *Tetratrichomonas limacis*. Gabel (1954) maintained gastric mucin cultures of *Trichomitis marmotae* for longer than 3 months.

Culture methods for *Tritrichomonas foetus* include studies on salt tolerance (Jaskowski, 1950); inhibition of growth of *T. foetus* when an alcoholic solution of cholesterol was added to Schneider's medium (Galuszka, 1960); 100% positive diagnostic cultures on Schneider's medium with nystatin (Galuszka, 1962); 89% positive cultures in Plastridge's medium (1943) with Difco beef extract (Fitzgerald *et al.*, 1954b). *Tritrichomonas suis* and other trichomonads from swine were cultured on the same medium (Hammond and Fitzgerald, 1953). *Tritrichomonas enteris* (see Levine, 1961) from ceca of sheep was cultivated readily at 37°C. in Diamond's, CPLM medium, and bovine cecal extract medium (Andersen and Levine, 1962). A trichomonad closely resembling *Trichomonas pavlovi* (see Levine, 1961) from the rumen and cecum of calves in Utah grew in Diamond's, modified Plastridge's, and cecal-extract media (Jensen and Hammond, 1962).

Several methods for improving the isolation and culture techniques for *Trichomonas vaginalis* have been advanced, using various liquid media and serum (Lash, 1950; Asami, 1952; Magara *et al.*, 1953a,b; Kiseleva and Voskresenskaya, 1956). Hartman (1951) found *T. vaginalis* would grow in suitable media not over 1-cm. deep when the CO_2 in the atmosphere was between 10 and 25%. Lawlis (1952) observed that 6 of 17 bacterial organisms, grown in monoculture with *T. vaginalis,* inhibited growth *in vitro* and the filtrate from *Micrococcus epidermidis* failed to support *T. vaginalis* growth comparable to controls. Pray (1952), in a similar study of monobacterial cultures, showed that bacteria inhibiting growth and early death of the flagellate removed the maltose essential to the flagellate. Other cultures stimulated growth.

Wirtschafter (1954a) maintained *Trichomonas vaginalis* without subculturing for 23 days when 0.2 ml. of a 48-hr. culture of the trichomonads in CPLM medium was overlaid on a slant of Bacto NIH agar, the plug in the tube sealed with Parafilm, and the tube incubated at 37°. Flooding of the culture slant on the 20th day with 2.0 ml. of CPLM medium produced, by the twenty-third day, a very abundant growth of *T. vaginalis* normal in appearance and very active.

Sorel (1954) cultured *Trichomonas vaginalis* in the presence of a *Candida;* Kozłowska (1956) found that contamination with the pathogenic fungus *Scopulariopsis brevicaulis* increased growth of *Trichomonas vaginalis*. *Scopulariopsis brevicaulis* not only grows well in the presence of arsenic, but is used as an indicator for traces of arsenic. This observation would be important when arsenic compounds are used as therapeutic means. Commensal effects might well be also associated with other drugs. Barretto *et al.* (1957, 1958) observed that *T. vaginalis* was associated with *Candida* sp. and Doderlein's bacillus or both in about 25% of their cases; cultures in Kupferberg's medium gave better diagnostic results than direct examination. De Carneri (1956a) also found *T. vaginalis* associated with *Candida*—an organism unaffected by most antibacterial antibiotics. By using a W-shaped tube and antibiotics, he freed the culture of bacteria and fungi. He also (1956c) maintained pure axenic cultures of *T. vaginalis* and *Pentatrichomonas hominis* in Difco thioglycolate medium plus 3% horse serum for the former and 10% for the latter, the protozoa surviving about a month. The effect of chloramphenicol derivatives (de Carneri, 1956d) on these cultures was negligible. Varga (1962) found a saline-glucose medium valuable in the cultural diagnosis of *Trichomonas* and *Monilia* vaginitis. Kuczyniska (1962) compared three media for diagnostic purposes, the most convenient being Pavlova's (1938), while Johnson-Trussel-Jahn's (1945) was best for experimental purposes. The addition of penicillin and streptomycin did not guarantee pure cultures of *T. vaginalis*. Honigberg (1957) incorporated 300 μg. per milliliter of nystatin, penicillin, dihydrostreptomycin, and sometimes chloramphenicol into suitable media. No strain of *T. vaginalis* or *T. gallinae* appeared affected by the treatment. Furthermore the strains had the same pathogenicity to mice and tissue cultures before and after exposure to nystatin. This medium facilitated isolation of *T. gallinae* directly from the mouth of pigeons. From chickens, McDowell (1953) cultured *Tetratrichomonas gallinarum* nonaxenically in 0.2% gastric mucin in Ringer's solution. It was parasitized by *Sphaerita,* occasionally by *Nucleophaga. Tritrichomonas eberthi* was cultured only with *Tetratrichomonas gallinarum* and often showed a high percentage of infection with *Sphaerita.* Several reports on cultural methods for trichomonads from cold-blooded animals have appeared. Lee (1958, 1960) isolated two strains of *Hypotrichomonas acosta* in axenic culture in a modification of Diamond's medium, using polymyxin B, dihydrostreptomycin, and chloramphenicol. The isolated strains did not grow as well on this medium as did monoxenic or dioxenic cultures. Samuels (1958) kept two strains of *Tritrichomonas augusta* in STS medium with 5% sheep serum for approximately 2 years. Penicillin, streptomycin, and nystatin were used initially to eliminate bacteria and fungi. Continuous culture was possible at 8° to 35°C. and a pH range of 6 to 8. At 26°, serum concentration has little if any effect; at 35° serum inhibited. Axenic cultures of *T. augusta* were obtained through the use of the Noguchi tube by Concannon and Lacaillade (1958). The migration medium employed in each tube consisted of Drbohlav's modified Ringer's fluid, agar, inactivated serum, streptomycin, and penicillin G. The sidearm was inoculated with approximately 0.2 ml. of feces from a heavily parasitized amphibian. In 18 hr. axenic protozoa were collected. *Tritrichomonas augusta* isolates were maintained in antibiotic-free, simplified Trypticase agar, and 0.5 ml. of inactivated serum.

Tetratrichomonas prowazeki (strain 885) was cleared of all bacteria on

CPLM medium containing 5% normal horse serum, penicillin, streptomycin, and sulfathiazole (Honigberg, 1958a). It could be maintained for many weeks without transfer on CPLM and BBL fluid thioglycolate (both with 5% horse serum), but under these conditions the protozoan counts were relatively low. The addition of 0.1% Wilson's granular mucin, Type 1701W, permitted growth and made 48-hr. transfers feasible. At room temperature on mucin-containing media the culture might reach, on CPLM at least, >350,000 organisms per milliliter and could be kept for several weeks without transfer. Serial transfers on CPLM without agar under anaerobic conditions failed. Honigberg (1958b) was successful in clearing a dixenic culture of *Trichomitis batrachorum* on CPLM (pH 7.5) containing 5% horse serum with 300 µg. per milliliter of tetracycline phosphate. Addition of Wilson's mucin, stimulated growth, but the cultures had to be kept for several weeks before adequate counts (at best 100,000 organisms per milliliter) were obtained. Inclusion of both mucin and embryo extract in CPLM with serum greatly improved growth (>300,000 organisms per milliliter). Akatov (1955) maintained trichomonads in houseflies, a possible vector in transmission of disease.

B. Methods for Bulk Growth or Continuous Flow Culture

McEntegart (1952) and Feinberg (1953) developed media for bulk growth of trichomonads while Samuels and Beil (1962) developed a serum-free autoclavable medium which supported axenic culture of 10 trichomonads. The latter medium contains Trypticase, yeast extract, glucose, and citric, ascorbic, and thiomalic acids, liver solution NF (Armour), liver infusion (Difco), light cream, and cholesterol; all were necessary for growth of *Pentatrichomonas hominis* and some *Trichomonas vaginalis* cultures.

Twohy's (1961) continuous culture of *Tritrichomonas augusta* offers interesting prospects for several types of research. It was grown in a relatively simple continuous-culture Novick apparatus employing a system of "external control." Glucose at low concentration in a modified Diamond's medium controlled the population of trichomonads. Various rates of flow through the constant-volume growth chamber gave corresponding rates of growth. Twohy and Tucker (1961) described the characteristics of cultures grown under these conditions (see Section II,B,3 on metabolism).

C. Agar Plate Culturing of Trichomonads

Most valuable developments from the standpoint of definitive studies on morphology, strain variations, genetics, metabolism, nutrition, transfaunation, immunity and pathogenicity, chemotherapy and drug resistance, are the reports on the methods of culturing trichomonads on agar plates. This permits isolation of clones and study of pure lines of cultures from a single protozoan. Methods of culture and application are described below in some detail.

While axenic cultures of *Trichomonas vaginalis* in agar stabs were used by Kato and Tanabe (1953) and Magara *et al.* (1953b), Asami *et al.* (1955) were first to report on plate culture of *T. vaginalis;* they used a modification of the anaerobic plate method of Fortner (1928). In this method, a culture of *Escherichia coli* was grown in one-half of a divided Petri dish. On the other side, *T. vaginalis* was grown on the surface or within a solid medium made of meat extract, peptone, glucose, 20% human serum, and 2% agar. After sealing the dish and incubating at 37°C. for 48 hr., small colonies appeared on the surface. Serial transfers of the cultures in this environment were not successful, possibly due to lack of surface moisture. Stab cultures in deep 0.5% agar medium were successful and colonies appeared within 24 hr. as small white spots.

More successful plate methods are described by Ivey (1961) who utilized Diamond's medium for pour plates with Ionagar at 0.45%. Tubes of medium were cooled, 1.0 ml. of serum, 1.0 ml. of antibiotics containing a final concentration of 100 units penicillin, 100 μg. streptomycin, 25 μg. nystatin, and the inoculum, contained in 0.5 ml. of regular Diamond's medium, were added to each tube. Plates were poured, cooled, and a Petri dish blotter was inserted to control excess moisture. The plates were incubated using standard Brewer-jar technique. Colonies of *T. vaginalis* developed, 0.2 to 2.0 mm., in about 5 days. Clone growth occurred in medium containing Ionagar in the range 0.35 and 0.55%. Prolonged exposure of organisms to O_2 and/or a temperature of 25°C. injured clone development.

Samuels (1962a) gives detailed directions for preparing agar cultures of trichomonads in plates, Burri tubes, and sealed slides. He found CPLM agar at pH 6.0–6.5 was successful for *Trichomonas* spp. and *Pentatrichomonas* spp., and Diamond's medium at pH 7.0 for *Tritrichomonas* spp. The method consists of pouring 20 ml. of 1.6% agar in appropriate medium from 20- or 25-mm. tubes into sterile glass or plastic 100-mm. Petri dishes. Just before pouring, 0.2 ml. of a solution containing 5000 units per milliliter of penicillin and 5000 μg. per milliliter of streptomycin were added to each tube. Immediately after pouring, each plate was placed in an airtight box with a 5-g. piece of frozen CO_2. The plates were held there to harden and absorb CO_2 for at least 15 min. No serum was used in this layer. An overlay medium (10 ml.) with 0.8% agar was melted, warmed penicillin-streptomycin and inactivated sheep serum were added along with diluted organisms in 0.5 ml. of liquid, and the mixture poured rapidly over the previously prepared layer. The plates were again set in the CO_2 atmosphere box to harden and absorb. Incubation was carried out in sealed desiccators with NaOH-pyrogallol and frozen CO_2. Colonies for replating were dug from the agar, placed in tubes, and medium added to a total volume of 5 ml. Unless the colony was freed from the agar—by mashing with a wooden dowel stick—the organisms usually did not emerge even on inoculation to broth. Antibiotics were used in primary broth transplants. Techniques for Burri tubes and slides were also described.

Results ranged from well isolated colonies to confluent growth. *Trichomonas gallinae* DP-3 plated readily from a few organisms, while a very large number of strain SL had to be used; DP-3 colonies at the interface between the two agar layers tended to spread widely, often making it difficult to be sure of purity for isolation. SL colonies were small in general and showed little spreading, even at the interface. In any plate there was some variation of colonial morphology. Colonies near the free agar surface were small (inhibited by early exposure to oxygen or partial drying?). Colonies at the interface were likely to show some spreading. Colonies in slide cultures stopped growth earlier and never reached the size of those in plates or tubes. Flattened organisms from colonies a single layer thick were of value since pinocytosis was observed at their margins. The central spindle chromosomes were visible and the whole mitotic sequence could be observed.

By plating specimens directly from patients, it was possible in a single step to colonize *Trichomonas vaginalis* and to recover axenic clones. Clonal colonies were successfully developed from axenic cultures of three strains of *T. vaginalis*, *T. gallinae* (two strains), *Tetratrichomonas gallinarum* (one strain), *Tritrichomonas augusta* (five strains), *T. foetus* (four strains), *T. suis*(?) (six strains), *Pentatrichomonas hominis* (one strain) and an undescribed porcine form. Clonal cultures of *Tritrichomonas augusta* were compared with parent stocks for antigenic homogeneity and rate of change. Since sexual phenomena are unknown in these organisms, by using selected mutants, it should be possible to test unequivocally whether, and under what conditions, genetic recombinations occur. These techniques have also been used successfully in antibiotic testing (Samuels and Stouder, 1962).

Filadoro and Orsi (1958), using CPLM medium with serum, penicillin, and streptomycin on 2% agar, incubated in a CO_2 atmosphere, developed a quantitative agar-plate diffusion assay of trichomycin. Samuels and Stouder (1960) obtained visible colonies of *Trichomonas vaginalis* in 2 to 5 days in agar plates of CPLM or Diamond's medium under anaerobic incubation with added CO_2. A number of antibiotics and synthetic drugs were tested for activity against *T. vaginalis*, using impregnated paper discs as for bacteria. Zones of inhibition were found at 50 μg. per disc with fourteen compounds, and at 10 μg. per disc with eleven of those. After growth in subinhibitory concentrations of the antibiotic, thiolutin (Pfizer), colonies of one strain of *T. vaginalis* resisted at least ten times the normal inhibitory amount. Preliminary results indicate that a resistant mutant had been selected. Further applications in drug testing were reported by Samuels (1961b, 1962b) and Samuels and Stouder (1962).

West *et al.* (1962) also employed the overlay-plating technique for *Tritrichomonas foetus* and other protozoa. For *T. foetus*, the base layer consisted of 2% Bacto-Tryptose, 1% yeast extract-bacteriological (Oxo), 0.5% glucose, 0.2% L-cysteine HCl, 0.02% L-ascorbic acid, and 1% Ionagar at pH 7.0. The 10 ml. of overlay medium contained in addition to the basal broth, 0.3% Ionagar, 0.05% L-arginine HCl, 0.05% inositol, and 3% gelatin, along with 0.1 ml. of a penicillin-streptomycin solution, 1 ml. of inactivated horse serum, and 2 ml. of inoculum. Anaerobic conditions in the plates were obtained by the simple method of fastening a mixture of 3 parts of pyrogallol, 3 parts K_2CO_3, and 15 parts of diatomaceous earth in a filter-paper envelope on the inner surface of a Petri dish lid. This was sealed to a Petri dish bottom containing the inoculated medium and test discs by use of warm paraffin. After incubation for 3 days at 37° in an inverted position, zones of inhibition could be seen around selected antibiotics.

Concurrently with improvements of isolation and purification methods came improvements in methods of preserving cultures.

D. Storage and Survival of Trichomonads under Various Conditions

1. survival of *Tritrichomonas foetus* in stored semen

Artificial insemination may favor the widespread dissemination of trichomonad infection (Joyner and Millar, 1952). Fitzgerald *et al.* (1953, 1954a) found that *Tritrichomonas foetus* from cultures survived in egg yolk-buffer mixes with antibiotics for an average of 5.9 days. In three trials where semen was present and examination for trichomonads was made culturally, *T. foetus* survived 8.7 days. The average duration of sperm activity was 7.3 days. In 7 trials, with *T. foetus* from vaginal samples, the average survival was 9.6 days. Use of semen from an infected bull, diluted 1 to 15 in egg yolk-buffer mixture containing sulfanilamide, streptomycin, and penicillin did not result in infection. Since bull semen can be satisfactorily stored at −79° in the presence of glycerol, it was thought (Joyner, 1954) such storage might kill trichomonads in the semen. He added active trichomonads to semen or seminal plasma and subjected them to dilution in egg yolk-citrate and temperature storage. *Tritrichomonas foetus* did not survive at some concentrations of glycerol tolerated by bovine spermatozoa: they could be eliminated from infected semen by overnight storage at 5° in 20% glycerol, or, preferably, by freezing to −79° in the presence of 10% glycerol.

2. PRESERVATION BY FREEZING OF TRICHOMONAD CULTURES

Papers soon appeared on the effect of the suspending medium and freezing condition on *Tritrichomonas foetus*. McWade and Williams (1954) found *T. foetus* could survive in prepared milk semen extender frozen to −79° and maintained at that temperature for as long as 125 days. Leidl and Mahrla (1954) recovered the organisms from serum broth frozen to −99°. Levine and Marquart (1954, 1955) found recovery of *T. foetus* best when frozen at the rate of 1° per minute to −76° in CPLM medium with 5–10% glycerol. Enzyme inhibitors were ineffective in preventing slow death of organisms during storage at −25° (Levine et al., 1955, 1958) and high salt concentration was deleterious. Joyner and Bennett (1956) reconfirmed the failure of *T. foetus* to survive freezing in 10% glycerol in egg yolk-citrate diluent where sperm survived; the organisms survived when the suspending medium was egg yolk-phosphate or milk. However, Blackshaw and Beattie (1955) found survival of *T. foetus* in 5 and 7.5% glycerol, in some cases with a citrate buffer, when frozen immediately after glycerol was added.

Levine, McCaul, and Mizell (1957, 1959) froze *Tritrichomonas foetus* in the presence of glycerol at different phases of the growth curve. The protozoa were much more vulnerable when frozen during initial and logarithmic phases than at the peak of the growth curve or for some time thereafter. Fitzgerald and Levine (1957, 1961) noted that after growth in CPLM medium survival was better if protozoa were stored in a chest-type freezer at a constant −21° than if stored in an upright freezer in which the temperature varied cyclically. Survival was better when the protozoa were equilibrated with glycerol at room temperature (24°) before freezing than when equilibrated at 4°, indicating a critical zone to be passed through rapidly if they are to survive. When cultivated in CPLM medium buffered with glycylglycine or triethanolamine, they survived better frozen in the presence of 1M glycerol than when cultivated in plain CPLM medium. In phosphate-buffered medium, they grew poorly and few survived freezing. Fitzgerald and Levine review 4 factors in storage death: (1) dehydration denaturation of proteins, with high salt concentration contributing to protein denaturation; (2) slow metabolism; (3) damage by crystal growth through recrystallization upon storage; (4) temperature fluctuation during storage.

Levine and Andersen (1961) and Levine et al. (1962) observed as many protozoa alive after 512 days as at 8 days when stored at −95° whereas at −28° the protozoa continued to die off. These protozoa had been grown in Diamond's medium without agar or phosphates for ∼26 hr., an equal quantity of 2.0M glycerol was added to the culture medium, and 1-ml. amounts of the protozoan suspensions were sealed in glass tubes. Knowledge gained in the studies with *T. foetus* has been applied to the culture storage of other flagellates.

Storage of stock strains of axenic cultures of *Trichomonas vaginalis*, *Tritrichomonas foetus*, and *Trichomonas gallinae*, or *Pentatrichomonas hominis* with mixed bacterial flora was studied by McEntegart (1954) who had observed loss of strain characteristics upon frequent *in vitro* passage. All strains of trichomonads grew in the presence of 5% glycerol, some to a limited extent in 10%, none in 15%. The best method was storage at $-79°$ following slow freezing, the protozoa being suspended in a medium containing 10% glycerol. *Trichomonas gallinae* survived even without glycerol for 6 months. *Trichomonas vaginalis* remained viable for 4 months but deteriorated in storage and died out after 6 months. *Pentatrichomonas hominis* in 10% glycerol was viable after 6 months at $-79°C.$, but in the presence of 5% glycerol did not survive beyond 4 months. *Tritrichomonas foetus* could not be preserved under any test conditions. More recently McEntegart (1959) reported successful cultures were obtained from *Trichomonas vaginalis* which had been stored in a CO_2 cabinet for 26 months with 5% glycerol. In four samples, active organisms were few and frail. Two years was close to the extreme period of survival for *T. vaginalis* under those conditions. He suggests that cultures may be kept for as long as a year with confidence of survival. Molinari (1956) observed that *P. hominis* would not survive even 30 sec. at $-180°$ due probably to ice-crystal formation.

Satti and Honigberg (1959) found that *Trichomonas gallinae* ($\sim10^6$ organisms per milliliter) survived up to at least 4 hr. of freezing at $-150°$ in tap or glass-distilled water pH 7.2, and at least 16 hr. in Gey's or Earle's balanced salt solution (BSS). After prolonged freezing, although no motile organisms were seen, rich cultures of trichomonads could be obtained on thioglycolate medium. Incubation periods for visible growth increased in proportion to the time during which the organisms were frozen. *Trichomonas vaginalis* ($\sim10^6$ organisms per milliliter) survive for at least 1.5 hr. in Earle's BSS at $-15°$. Honigberg and King (1962) found survival of *T. vaginalis* best in 9% glycerol with Gey's BSS at $-72°$. When the freezing time was about 1.5 hr., 38% of the parasites were recovered after 4 and 5 weeks, producing rich cultures from 0.5 ml. inocula within 48 hr. on suitable media. The JB strain of *T. gallinae* was more resistant to prolonged maintenance at $-19°$ than the *T. vaginalis* culture. Following either quick (2 hr.) or slow (8.5 hr.) freezing, 40–45% of the parasites survived 4 weeks at $-19°$ while 8% of the trichomonads were viable at 34 weeks. Whereas Honigberg and others have used CO_2 for freezing, Diamond *et al.* (1962) used liquid N_2 at $-196°$. Trophic stages of *T. vaginalis* and *T. gallinae* survived for 10 months and *Tritrichomonas foetus* and *Pentatrichomonas hominis* for 5 months without noticeable decay. Further work with this technique should be of interest.

3. SURVIVAL OF TRICHOMONADS UNDER NATURAL OR CULTURAL CONDITIONS

Trichomonas vaginalis survived as long as 6 hr. in a droplet of vaginal discharge placed on the surface of an enamel block and so Kessel and Thompson (1950) believed that the organisms would survive in a fomite long enough for transfer to another individual. Whittington (1951) exposed *T. vaginalis* to fluctuating temperatures below 37° in culture medium, in undiluted and in diluted vaginal exudate. Some strains survived 1–3 days at temperatures between 4 and 1.5°; one strain survived freezing between −4 and 0°. *Trichomonas vaginalis* survived 24 hr. in Ringer's solution (Barretto *et al.*, 1957). Guida *et al.* (1960) mention a modified Reick medium in which *Tritrichomonas foetus* survived as long as 16 days with no special incubation conditions, permitting samples to be sent from afar for examination. De Carneri (1956b) proposed a method of storing trichomonads in monobacterial cultures. *Pentatrichomonas hominis* kept for 1 month at 25° in a rich biphasic medium of horse serum and rice starch associated with *Escherichia coli. Escherichia coli* is later removed with antibiotics. McLoughlin (1957a) found that *Tetratrichomonas gallinarum* failed to survive as long as 48 hr. in droppings kept at room temperature but did survive as long as 5 days at a continuous 6°.

Further studies of conditions of survival of these parasites would be of interest as they would be concerned in transfaunation and pathogenicity. Certainly conditions of survival outside the natural host could influence infection of a new host. No attempt is made here to review the extensive literature on transfaunation. Several very excellent papers have appeared on this subject.

VII. Factors Affecting Pathogenicity

Approximately half of the references in the last decade on trichomonads have been concerned with epidemiology and chemotherapy in human and animal infections. Only those reports are considered here which have some experimental basis or show physiological factors influencing pathogenicity.

A. STRAIN DIFFERENCES IN PATHOGENICITY IN NATURAL INFECTIONS

1. COURSE OF NATURAL INFECTION

Differences in pathogenicity in strains of *Trichomonas gallinae* have been known since Stabler first isolated the virulent Jones' Barn (JB) strain in 1948. This strain has maintained its pathogenicity through 300 serial passages in pigeons (Stabler, 1953, 1957). Only 7 of the infected pigeons lived, and the survival time for those dying was 7.6 days. Infection and death result from the implantation of a single individual (Stabler and Kihara, 1954a,b). Honigberg

(1961a) measured the growth rates of three strains of *T. gallinae* and found a positive correlation between rates of growth and degree of virulence for pigeons as well as for mice. The generation time for the virulent JB strain was 3.5 hr.; for TG strain, 3 hr. and 50 min., and 5 hr. 50 min. for the less virulent YG strain. In contrast, the growth rates of three strains of *T. vaginalis* were inversely proportional to the virulence of the strains in the experimental host (mouse).

2. HISTOPATHOLOGY OF *Trichomonas gallinae* INFECTION IN PIGEONS

Histopathological changes in the pigeon infected with *Trichomonas gallinae* described by Mesa *et al.* (1961) consist of inflammation and ulceration of the oropharyngeal mucosa, following a peculiar palisading of the parasites on the surface. They migrate to the pharyngeal glands, penetrate underlying tissues, and reach the liver. Enlarging, nonliquefying abscesses in the liver appeared to be the cause of death. These investigators suggest that the JB strain of *T. gallinae* possesses a hepatic toxicity comparable with that of *Staphylococcus aureus* in man. Frost *et al.* (1961) found that the epithelial cells in liver sections from a pigeon infected with this strain contained trichomonads.

Infection of birds by routes other than the mouth have been indicated, since livers were infected when the organisms were given by mouth to esophagotomized pigeons (Jaquette, 1950). McLoughlin (1957b) was able to infect 9-week-old poults with *Tetratrichomonas gallinarum* DT-79 rectally but only young birds (1 week old) were infected *per os*. Infections in humans also can occur in unnatural sites since Walton and Bacharach (1963) have noted the rare occurrence of trichomonads (possibly *Trichomonas tenax*) in the respiratory tract of man.

The pathogenicity of *Trichomonas vaginalis* has been the subject of many reports. Experiments to detect biochemical differences in this species have necessarily been made in experimental animals although a few reports of the vaginal biochemical changes help explain the pathological changes in trichomonad infections.

3. BIOCHEMICAL AND PATHOLOGICAL CHANGES IN
   NATURAL *Trichomonas vaginalis* INFECTIONS

Asami and Nakamura (1955) found that the amount of glycogen in the vaginal mucosa varied inversely with the number of organisms in the vaginal discharge. They suggested that vigorous consumption of glycogen by *Trichomonas viginalis* facilitated the invasion of bacteria into the vagina with resulting vaginitis.

Although smears from humans normally show the host phagocytes engulfing the parasites, Frost *et al.* (1961) observed *Trichomonas vaginalis* in the cytoplasm of a nonphagocytic, huge, "reactive" columnar epithelial cell at the squamo-columnar junction in endocervical biopsy material—the first report of invasion of tissues—and established the fact that this species contains truly pathogenic strains. These authors pointed out that this organism has long been considered a saprophyte with a predilection for the surface of the squamous epithelium (Koss and Wolinska, 1959).

B. Pathogenicity in Experimental Hosts

1. *Trichomonas gallinae* and *Trichomonas vaginalis* infections in mice

While many animals have been used in experimental infections with trichomonads, the mouse has perhaps been the most widely used. Honigberg (1961a) has reviewed in detail previous work on experimental infections in mice with several trichomonads and in particular with *Trichomonas gallinae* and *T. vaginalis*.

Honigberg and Braunthal (1957) and Honigberg (1959) statistically analyzed the volumes of lesions in subcutaneous inoculations of mice with three strains of *Trichomonas gallinae* in axenic cultures. Significant differences in the mean volumes of the lesions reflected the pathogenicity of the strain in the natural host, the pigeon. Only the Jones Barn strain seemed more pathogenic to mice than the most pathogenic strain of *Trichomonas vaginalis*, three strains of which were also tested. A mild strain of *T. gallinae* was significantly less virulent to mice than the least virulent strains of the human parasite. When maintained in culture, attenuation of virulence was more marked in *T. gallinae* than in *T. vaginalis* (Honigberg, 1961a). The presence of agar, methyl cellulose, and mucin (in order of decreasing activity) enhanced the development of subcutaneous lesions in mice while gelatin had little influence over that of organisms grown in basal medium only. A low-virulence strain of *T. gallinae*, YG, maintained in medium without agar for 9 weeks, failed to produce any lesions in 30 inoculations. These observations applied to *T. vaginalis* also. His data suggested that, although environmental conditions played an important role in modifying pathogenicity, virulence was basically an expression of characteristics inherent in the strains of *T. gallinae* and *T. vaginalis*. Honigberg and Read (1960) tried to change experimentally the virulence of a relatively nonpathogenic strain YGA of *T. gallinae* by incubating it twice with a cell-free homogenate of the Jones Barn strain. Evidence of enhanced virulence was suggested by increased size of lesions produced in mice. Addition of deoxyribonuclease to the homogenate cell mixture blocked the transformation. Interpretation of this paper is clouded by the rather large standard deviation of lesion size.

Subcutaneous lesions produced in mice by axenic cultures of *Trichomonas gallinae*, JB strain, revealed healthy parasites within macrophages in edematous tissue at a considerable distance from the periphery of the abscesses or, with the virulent C_1 strain of *T. vaginalis*, near the abscesses (Frost *et al.*, 1961).

The subcutaneous control lesions receiving aliquots of sterile culture medium at pH 6 or 7 (Honigberg and Frost, 1961), rapidly passed the acute phase within the first 8 hr. and within 1 week the tissue became relatively normal and pocketed off for resolution the foreign-body reaction within the site of injection. Lesions produced by *T. gallinae* or *T. vaginalis* did not reach the resolution phase during the 14 days of observation. Edema became massive outside the site of injection where histiocytic activity became great by the second day. At the margin of the injection site, fibrocytic activity and new capillary growth was high within 7 days; however, lesions soon spread past this abortive reparative zone. Spreading edema accompanied dissemination of the organisms and well preserved trichomonads were present within host cells at great distances from the initial lesion. In this fashion, the lesion was actively progressing and spreading during the 14-day observation period.

Inoculation of *Trichomonas vaginalis* into mice by other routes resulted in similar findings. Following the report of Iwai (1957) that abscesses contained *T. vaginalis* parasites on subcutaneous, intraperitoneal, or intrapleural inoculation, Reardon and Jacobs (1958) and Reardon *et al.* (1961) tested two strains of *T. vaginalis* by intraperitoneal injections into mice. One pure culture (C_1) was derived from a severe case of vaginitis, another (R) from a relatively mild infection. The inoculation of 1×10^6 organisms or higher of C_1 strain regularly produced death in six strains of mice. Only slight differences were observed in susceptibility of the mouse strains to C_1 parasites. R strain parasites in parallel experiments did not kill.

Teras (1961) also found *Trichomonas vaginalis* strains had what was characterized as "strong, medium or weak" pathogenicity in white mice. Massive invasion of trichomonads into the abdominal organs and alterative-exudative changes in the latter characterized strongly pathogenic strains. Strains of medium pathogenicity produced some changes of alterative-exudative as well as productive character, whereas invasion of trichomonads into abdominal organs, with the exception of liver and pancreas, was noticed rarely. Weakly pathogenic strains did not invade the abdominal organs and changes were proliferative ones. *Trichomonas vaginalis* strains differed in their biochemical activity to sugars (see Section II), but no relation between this activity and pathogenicity could be detected. There was a certain link between the pathogenicity of the strains in animals and sensitivity to some remedies. Strains of stronger pathogenicity both *in vitro* and *in vivo* were markedly more resistant to Osarsole (acetarsone), sanasine, and uropirine than strains of weaker pathogenicity. Differences between strains of *T. vaginalis* were clearly demonstrated by the agglutination reaction and the complement fixation. By cross-agglutination, it was found that the titer of the agglutinins largely depended on the strains of the protozoa used. The hypothesis that the species of trichomonads parasitizing the human genitourinary tract consists of different types, even subspecies, was presented.

Mice pretreated with washed erythrocytes from young chickens before intra-peritoneal inoculations with *T. vaginalis* had a 70% mortality rate while those inoculated from peritoneal fluid from fatal infections of pretreated mice had 100% mortality (Inoki and Hamada, 1953).

Wantland *et al.* (1958, 1962) have shown that *Trichomonas tenax* can cytolyze epithelial cells, erythrocytes, and leucocytes, and are frequently present in cases of pyorrhea.

2. PATHOGENICITY EXPERIMENTS WITH OTHER TRICHOMONADS

Early work on pathogenicity of *Tritrichomonas foetus* has been reviewed by Levine (1961), Buttrey (1955, 1956), Tumka (1961), and Hibler *et al.* (1959, 1960) on trichomonads from swine, *Tritrichomonas suis*, *T. rotunda*, and *Tetratrichomonas buttreyi*, n.sp.; and by Andersen and Levine (1962) and Andersen *et al.* (1962) for *Tetratrichomonas ovis* from sheep. Buttrey (1957, 1960) observed changes of virulence of protozoa from swine on subculturing. Although trichomonads have been found associated with atrophic rhinitis in pigs (Switzer, 1951a,b; Spindler *et al.*, 1953; Levine, Marquardt, and Beamer, 1954; Brion and Cottereau, 1954; Fitzgerald *et al.*, 1954c), there is no proof that they are the primary cause of the disease. Hibler *et al.* (1959) found the swine trichomonads had low host or organ specificity, although Buttrey (1955) found no migration between their respective habitats of the nasal and digestive tract forms. Aside from the immunological studies reviewed in the next section and the biochemical characteristics reviewed in previous sections, there has been little experimental work on the basis of pathogenicity with the above species. Lynch *et al.*, (1954, 1955) and Schnitzer *et al.* (1950) infected white mice sub-cutaneously with *Tritrichomonas foetus* for drug testing. While many other excellent studies on transfaunation and routes of infection have been carried out (see Levine, 1961; Saxe, 1954a,b; Saxe *et al.*, 1952; Inoki *et al.*, 1952; Shaw and Buttrey ,1958a,b; Fitzgerald *et al.*, 1954b, 1955, 1958a,b; Hammond and Leidl, 1956a,b, 1957; Hammond *et al.*, 1957) only those studies which demon-strate differences in virulence among strains, or a predilection for certain sites of infection in the unnatural host, suggests a biochemical or physiological basis for infectiveness. Shaw and Buttrey (1958a,b) found physiological differences between the porcine-nasal, the gastrocecal species, and *T. foetus* in ability to survive passage through the digestive tract of the chick. Rubin and Cordray (1958) observed loss of virulence for intravaginal infection of hamsters by *T. foetus* kept for 2.5 years on artificial medium, while a freshly isolated strain, BP-3, was much more infective. The work of Kean and Weld (1955) and Weld and Kean (1956, 1958a,b) is of interest in this respect. The anterior chamber of the eye of the rabbit was used for 14 continuous serial passages of *Trichomonas vaginalis*. The protozoa had an affinity for the lens and lens substance; they were found in histological sections up to 41 days after injection. These organisms disappeared rapidly after injection, reappearing in cultures of the aqueous humor at a later time. The invasion of the lens was usually associated with the return of the parasites to the anterior chamber. If the injection of cultures into the anterior of the chamber avoided injuring the lens, no infection and no acute inflammatory reaction developed. Human sera and sera from several animal species had the capacity to kill and disintegrate *T. vaginalis*, a property lost on heating.

Other routes of infection and other animals (reviewed by Kradolfer, 1954) have been proposed or used, mainly in connection with tests for chemotherapeutic agents, and will not be discussed here. Similarly, factors such as host diet and stress in host animals have not been discussed because they have been inadequately studied or are difficult to evaluate as affecting pathogenicity. However, one method particularly useful in studying pathogenic differences and toxicity is that of tissue culture.

C. Trichomonads in Tissue Culture

Kotcher and Hoogasian (1957) carried out experiments with chick embryo explants with HeLa and human synovial cells infected with *T. vaginalis;* the tissues did not die as reported by Hogue (1943). Tissue death which did occur resulted from invasion of the tissues by the protozoan and resulted from mechanical injury rather than toxic products. Culture filtrates did not cause death.

Honigberg and McLure (1960) used monolayer cultures of chick liver. The JB strain of *T. gallinae* multiplied very fast, was not destroyed by macrophages, and appeared capable of multiplying within the cell, ultimately destroying the cell. It damaged noninfected macrophages and suppressed division of fibroblasts. The mildly virulent strain YG multiplied relatively slowly in cell culture, contained many abnormal individuals, appeared to be digested by macrophages, and did not damage macrophages or fibroblasts. There was no evidence of the presence of a true exotoxin.

Honigberg (1961b) studied the effect of two strains of *T. vaginalis,* TVC (Cavanagh-Honigberg) and TVC_1 (Jacobs), on avian and mammalian cell cultures in living as well as in fixed and stained preparations. In chick liver cultures, trichomonads could be seen in macrophages soon after inoculation. As the infection progressed, some of the fibroblast-like cells contained the parasites within their cytoplasm. In HeLa cell cultures the parasites seemed to cause a progressive cytopathogenicity. By the end of a 24-hr. period the entire cell culture was destroyed and the trichomonads could be seen in the cell debris and seemed to feed on it. The extracellular flagellates did not appear to be feeding on living cells, although the parasites were capable of invading the cytoplasm of such cells. Filtrates of actively growing trichomonad cultures had no apparent cytopathogenic effects on either the chick liver or HeLa cell cultures. However at the 1962 Society of Protozoologists Symposium, Honigberg (1962) stated that filtrates of TVC_1 strain appeared to cause more damage to the tissue culture cells than the *T. gallinae* strains.

The effects of swine nasal trichomonads on swine kidney cell cultures were reported by Switzer (1959). The nasal trichomonads reached maximal population density 4 or 5 days after introduction into the tissue cultures causing cell degeneration and a pH decrease of 0.2 to 0.4 units below that of the uninoculated control tubes. Cell degeneration was probably due either to exhaustion of nutrients or to accumulation of metabolic by-products and was not due to direct action of the trichomonads on the cells. Trichomonads could be maintained by serial passage in the tissue cultures.

Many papers have dealt with the immunity of animals against different species of trichomonads. Only those papers suggesting differences in antigenic structure—hence chemical or physiological differences—or new means of identification by the use of fluorescing antibodies, have been reviewed in the next section.

VIII. Immunology in Trichomonad Infections

A. Antigens in Trichomonads

Menolasino and Hartman (1954) produced several different antibodies in rabbits against somatic and flagellar antigens of *Trichomonas vaginalis* and *Tritrichomonas foetus*, revealing a complex antigenic structure in these protozoa. They concluded that the two species were similar antigenically. McEntegart (1956) by cross-agglutination and cross-absorption tests with *Trichomonas vaginalis* and two strains of *Tritrichomonas foetus*, concluded the three strains were serologically distinct. Schoenherr (1956) also found *Trichomonas vaginalis*, *Tritrichomonas foetus*, *Trichomonas gallinae* and *T. ardin-delteili* could be differentiated serologically by means of cell-fragment and precipitation reactions. Serum of women, cows, and golden hamsters with chronic trichomonas infections had no detectable antibodies.

Sanborn (1955) used living cultures of *Tritrichomonas suis* from the cecum of a hog affected with atrophic rhinitis, a trichomonad from the nose, and *T. foetus* for antibody production in rabbits. Agglutination tests showed highest titers with homologous sera and antigens, indicating the three strains were different. Cross-agglutination titers were much lower, in most cases no higher than that with control antisera from a rabbit immunized with the medium. Agglutination tests with serum from hogs with atrophic rhinitis showed possible antibodies against the unidentified trichomonad in 4 out of 9 hogs.

Warren and Chandler (1958) successfully immunized white mice with antigen collected from *in vitro* protein-free cultures of *T. gallinae* (Jones Barn strain). Complete protection was observed in 50% of the challenged animals.

The remainder of the immunized group showed varying protection as evidenced by the time required for appearance of lesions and size of lesions when compared with normal controls. Pooled sera from convalescent animals agglutinated washed suspensions of *T. gallinae* grown *in vitro,* in dilutions as high as 1:320. Normal mouse serum was without effect. Electrophoretic studies revealed a lowered serum protein level in convalescent sera and albumin: γ-globulin ratios were lowered in sera with high agglutinating titers.

Samuels (1957a) observed lysis of *Tritrichomonas augusta* by fresh serum and agglutination with heated serum. The "natural" agglutinins against *T. augusta* were found in the γ- and β-globulin fractions by paper electrophoresis (Chun-Hoon and Samuels, 1959). Anti-*T. augusta* rabbit serum agglutinated at 1:1280, in contrast to the "natural" activity of 0–1:2. These immune sera possessed precipitating activity at 1:32 in capillary tube tests against soluble material from lyophilized organisms. "Natural" antibody did not precipitate under the same test conditions.

Chun-Hoon and Samuels (1960) produced anti-*T. augusta* 101 rabbit sera with agglutinating titers as high as 1:4096. The antisera precipitated whole-trichomonad antigen in capillary tube and agar gel double diffusion tests. Four-fold concentrations of normal sera did not have precipitating antibody although agglutinating titer rose. At least four antigens were involved. Cross-absorption agglutination tests were conducted between *T. augusta* 101 and four other strains; *T. foetus,* three strains; *T. suis* (?), four strains; and *Trichomonas vaginalis,* two strains. "Normal" lamb and calf sera and rabbit antisera were used. Absorption with *Tritrichomonas augusta* reduced the titer, but had no effect on titers against other species; reciprocal absorptions with others did not affect titers against strain 101. Differences appeared between strains 101, 103, and 104 of *T. augusta,* but strain 5 appeared identical with 101.

Nakamura (1961b) applied the agar-gel technique in studying *Pentatricho-monas hominis* antibodies in human, rabbit, and guinea pig sera. Fluorescing antibodies have also been used in immunological studies.

B. FLUORESCENT ANTIBODIES

Search for serological variants of *Trichomonas vaginalis* in vaginal discharges led to the preparation of a specific antibody labeled with fluorescein (McEntegart *et al.,* 1958). Such an antibody has the property of coating the corresponding antigen which can then be identified by ultraviolet fluorescence microscopy. By means of anti-*T. vaginalis* serum from rabbits, the globulin fraction of the serum was separated, conjugated to fluorescein isocyanate, and the conjugate then purified by repeated ethanol fractionation and absorption, twice with dried liver powder. Having established that the homologous Liverpool strain of *T. vaginalis* could be stained specifically by the anti-*T. vaginalis* fluorescing antibody, the known wide antigenic differences between *T. vaginalis* and

Tritrichomonas foetus was demonstrated by the same means, using three films on one microscope slide, one each of the pure cultures of *Trichomonas vaginalis* and *Tritrichomonas foetus,* and one of mixed culture. After acetone fixation, the films were covered with one pool of conjugated anti-*T. vaginalis* globulin. The three films showed bright specific fluorescence for *T. vaginalis,* mixed dull and bright fluorescence, and dull auto-fluorescence. With conjugated anti-*Tritrichomonas foetus* (var. Belfast) there was a reversal of the bright and dull fluorescence in the mixed films. The "3-spot test" with Lanceley's Liverpool 52 strain of *Trichomonas vaginalis* showed it to be serologically distinct from the original Liverpool strain as it fluoresced less brightly than the original. The technique was more difficult to apply to vaginal smears, with confusing bright auto-fluorescence of cellular and other elements and nonspecific staining of leucocytes.

Hayes and Kotcher (1960) studied the identification of *Trichomonas vaginalis* from vaginal secretions by wet preparation, Papanicolaou staining, culture in thioglycolate medium, and fluorescent-antibody technique. There were 33.3% positive tests for *T. vaginalis* by the wet preparations, 40% by the culture method, 13% by Papanicolaou stain and 39.6% by the fluorescent antibody technique. The fluorescent antibody procedure required $\sim$2 hr. for demonstration of *T. vaginalis* compared to 48 to 72 hr. by the culture method. Ginel (1962) followed the infection of pure cultures of *T. vaginalis* in guinea pigs by daily clinical observation and cytological and fluorescence studies.

IX. Antibiotics and Other Drugs as Metabolic Tools

Although antibiotics against trichomonads have been screened by the disc-plate technique and by artificially infected animals, few studies have been made on reversal of the antibiotic effect in studies on their mode of action.

A. REVERSAL STUDIES ON ANTITRICHOMONAL ACTIVITY

In mice infected with *Trichomonas vaginalis* (Schnitzer and Kelly, 1954), local treatment with inactive doses of pararosaniline HCl markedly antagonized an active dose of acriflavine. The interference phenomenon of Browning and Gulbransen (1922) applies therefore to *T. vaginalis.*

Michaels (1962) studied the mode of inhibitory action of certain 3- and 5-nitropyridines and pyrimidines on *Trichomonas vaginalis.* The compounds with the greatest *in vitro* activity, and the only ones active *in vivo,* were 5-nitropyridines and pyrimidines with a single substituent at C-2. The *in vitro* inhibitory activity was reversed by structurally related compounds, e.g., 2-acetamido-5-nitropyridine. All inhibitors were thought to be acting similarly. In work with 2-amino-5-nitropyrimidine, which caused extreme prolongation of generation time, the effect was reversible on removal of the inhibitor without subsequent effect on the lag phase or generation time of surviving cells. Other experiments indicated that the inhibitor acted by arresting mitosis at the prophase. This activity was similar to that of 2,4-dinitrophenol, which also blocks mitosis at the prophase by inhibiting phosphorylation. With both drugs, there was an excess of diphosphopyridine nucleotide, thought to accumulate as the result of prophase blockage. Orlowska and Mordarski (1962) have compared the activity of several mitotic toxins against *T. vaginalis* without reversal studies.

Cuckler *et al.* (1955), studying *in vitro* the effect of aminitrazole on *Trichomonas vaginalis* and *T. foetus,* found that a series of B vitamins, also large amounts of thiamine, purines, and pyrimidines, would not reverse antitrichomonad activity Samuels (1962b), testing metronidazole inhibition of *T. vaginalis,* found reversal of the drug activity by liver infusion and by a mixture of purines, which also stimulated growth. Samuels (1961b) had previously tested the nitrothiazoles, nitroimidazoles, and related compounds for inhibition and found mutants resistant to 1-(2-hydroxyethyl)-2-methyl-5-nitroimidazole. However, 2-amino-5-nitrothiazole (Enheptin) treatment did not induce Enhaptin-fast strains of *T. gallinae* JB (Stabler and Mellentin, 1953).

Resistant strains obviously either produced a drug antagonist or metabolized a drug to a nontoxic form. Indeed, change in cultural characteristics seems typical of trichomonads under several conditions.

B. Induced Changes in Cultural Characteristics

Mention has already been made of changes in pathogenicity during cultivation (Rubin and Cordray, 1958; Honigberg, 1959) and changes in utilization of galactose for growth (Read, 1956, 1957; see Section II,A). Flick (1954) found that age of culture, variable division rate, and bacterial flora of cultures were environmental factors affecting the percent of organisms with characteristic flagellar numbers in *Pentatrichomonas hominis*. Wirtschafter (1954c) also produced multinucleated forms of *Trichomonas vaginalis* grown in CPLM medium without agar. Cultures showing an oxidized state produced 50–80% giant cells. The trend was reversed by growing cultures in reduced conditions. Lund and Shorb (1962) obtained variants of *T. gallinae* SL which did not require the RNA factor in ribonucleic acid and this same strain, which required tocopherol or coenzyme Q_{10} (Shorb and Lund, 1962), lost its requirement after about 50 serial transfers on the SL medium with oleic and palmitic acids, tocopheryl acetate, and extracted Trypticase as supplements (Shorb and Lund, 1963).

Samuels (1959) found that *Tritrichomonas augusta* adapted to successive experimental steps in developing defined media. He had previously observed deviations during division and development (Samuels, 1954) affecting the nuclear or motor system which he thought might constitute evolutionary mechanisms. Mutants resistant to thiolutin were developed in agar plates (Samuels and

Stouder, 1960). A more detailed study (Samuels, 1961a,b) was made on the resistance of *Trichomonas vaginalis* and *T. gallinae* in the disc assay of drugs. In drug-treated plates, only colonies survived which had been previously selected for drug resistance. Another type of variability of *T. vaginalis* was noted; in broth medium, the organisms spread like amebae. Such changes as discussed above, point to new fields of investigation.

X. Summary

The pathway of carbohydrate metabolism is generally well established as being glycolytic, with presumably the pentose shunt also functioning. The pathway through or around the citric acid cycle, and the terminal respiratory system, especially the evolution of H_2, will bear more investigation. It would be especially interesting if some of the manometric studies were repeated using cloned cultures of differing pathogenicity, of differing resistance to antibiotics, or with different nutritional requirements. With cloned cultures, the work on chemical composition and nutritional requirements might be reinvestigated, especially in the lipid requirements. The metabolism of trichomonads will be more clearly defined when these organisms can be grown on a completely defined medium, with pretested chemically-pure growth substances. Interrelationships of medium ingredients could then be studied. Especially interesting would be a study of the enzymes in nitrogenous and lipid metabolism. These biochemical differences would then be of value in transfaunation, and in pathological and immunological studies, and perhaps classification of organisms could be based concisely on these characteristics.

ACKNOWLEDGMENTS

The help of Dr. D. J. Doran, Dr. J. J. Lee, and Mrs. Pauline G. Lund in reading the manuscript is gratefully acknowledged. Unpublished work by the author was supported in part by grants from Merck & Co. and the National Institutes of Health (# E3411).

REFERENCES

Adler, S. (1953). *Acta Med. Orient.* 12, 204.
Adler, S., Back, A., and Sadovsky, A. (1952). *Nature* 170, 903.
Akatov, V. A. (1955). *Veterinariya* 32, 84.
Andersen, F. L., and Levine, N. D. (1962). *J. Protozool.* 9, Suppl., 18.
Andersen, F. L., Levine, N. D., and Hammond, D. M. (1962). *J. Parasitol.* 48, 589.
Andrews, J., and von Brand, T. (1938). *Am. J. Hyg.* 28, 138.
Asami, K. (1952). *Kitasato Arch. Exptl. Med.* 25, 149.
Asami, K., and Nakamura, M. (1955). *Am. J. Trop. Med. Hyg.* 4, 254.
Asami, K., Nodake, Y., and Ueno, T. (1955). *Exptl. Parasitol.* 4, 34.
Baba, T., Nagata, K., and Nakajima, T. (1957). *Gunma J. Med. Sci.* 6, 22.

Baernstein, H. D. (1954). *Federation Proc.* 13, 177.
Baernstein, H. D. (1955). *Exptl. Parasitol.* 4, 323.
Baernstein, H. D. (1959). *J. Parasitol.* 45, 491.
Baernstein, H. D. (1961). *J. Parasitol.* 47, 279.
Baernstein, H. D. (1963). *J. Parasitol.* 49, 12.
Barretto, M., Filho, H. Z., de Oliveira, P. V., Marques, W. Mendonca, J., Saquis, J., Guimarães, J., and Vila, E. (1957). *Rev. Assoc. Med. Brasil.* 3, 231.
Barretto, M., Zago, H., de Oliveira, P., Marques, W., Mendonca, J., Saquis, J., Guimarães, J. and Vila E. (1958). *Rev. Assoc. Med. Brasil.* 4, 126.
Blackshaw, A. W., and Beattie, H. E. R. (1955). *Australian Vet. J.* 31, 214.
Brion, A., and Cottereau, P. (1954). *Compt. Rend. Soc. Biol.* 148, 1415.
Browning, C. H., and Gulbransen, R. (1922). *J. Pathol. Bacteriol.* 25, 395.
Buttrey, B. W. (1955). *J. Protozool.* 2, Suppl., 2.
Buttrey, B. W. (1956). *J. Protozool.* 3, 8.
Buttrey, B. W. (1957). *J. Protozool.* 4, Suppl., 5.
Buttrey, B. W. (1960). *Proc. S. Dakota Acad. Sci.* 39, 102.
Carrow, L. A. (1955). *Quart. Bull. Northwestern Univ. Med. School* 29, 326.
Chun-Hoon, H., and Samuels, R. (1959). *J. Protozool.* 6, Suppl., 23.
Chun-Hoon, H., and Samuels, R. (1960). *J. Protozool.* 7, Suppl., 6.
Clausen, J. K. (1953). *Nature* 171, 1067.
Cole, B. A. (1950). *Proc. Helminthol. Soc. Wash. D.C.* 17, 65.
Concannon, J. N. (1959). *J. Protozool.* 6, Suppl., 23.
Concannon, J. N., and Lacaillade, C. (1958). *J. Protozool.* 5, Suppl., 20.
Cuckler, A. C., Kupferberg, A. B., and Millman, N. (1955). *Antibiot. Chemotherapy* 5, 540.
de Carneri, I. (1955). *Nature* 176, 605.
de Carneri, I. (1956a). *Am. J. Trop. Med. Hyg.* 5, 210.
de Carneri, I. (1956b). *Am. J. Trop. Med. Hyg.* 5, 677.
de Carneri, I. (1956c). *Riv. Parassitol.* 17, 247.
de Carneri, I. (1956d). *Farmaco (Pavia), Ed. Sci.* 11, 926.
Diamond, L. S. (1954). *Exptl. Parasitol.* 3, 251.
Diamond, L. S. (1957). *J. Parasitol.* 43, 488.
Diamond, L. S. (1960). *J. Parasitol.* 46, 43.
Diamond, L. S. (1962). *J. Protozool.* 9, 442.
Diamond, L. S., and Herman, C. M. (1952). *J. Parasitol.* 38, Suppl., 11.
Diamond, L. S., Meryman, H. T., and Kafig, E. (1962). *In* "Culture Collections: Perspectives and Problems," Proc. of the Specialists Conference on Culture Collections, Ottawa (S. M. Martin, ed.), p. 189. Univ. of Toronto Press, Toronto, Canada.
Doran, D. J. (1956a). *J. Protozool.* 3, Suppl., 13.
Doran, D. J. (1956b). *J. Protozool.* 3, Suppl., 13.
Doran, D. J. (1957). *J. Protozool.* 4, 182.
Doran, D. J. (1958). *J. Protozool.* 5, 89.
Doran, D. J. (1959). *J. Protozool.* 6, 177.
Doscher, G. E. (1960). Master's Thesis. Rutgers University, New Brunswick, New Jersey.
Eugere, E., Lynch, V., and Thoms, R. K. (1956). *J. Parasitol.* 42, Suppl., 23.
Feinberg, F. G. (1953). *Nature* 171, 1165.
Feinberg, F. G., and Morgan, W. T. J. (1953). *Brit. J. Exptl. Pathol.* 34, 104.
Filadoro, F., and Orsi, N. (1958). *Antibiot. Chemotherapy* 8, 561.

Fitzgerald, P. R., and Levine, N. D. (1957). *J. Protozool.* 4, Suppl., 5.

Fitzgerald, P. R., and Levine, N. D. (1961). *J. Protozool.* 8, 21.

Fitzgerald, P. R., Hammond, D. M., and Miner, M. L. (1953). *J. Parasitol.* 39, Suppl., 11.

Fitzgerald, P. R., Hammond, D. M., and Miner, M. L. (1954a). *Am. J. Vet. Res.* 15, 36.

Fitzgerald, P. R., Hammond, D. M., and Shupe, J. L. (1954b). *Vet. Med.* 49, 409.

Fitzgerald, P. R., Hammond, D. M., and Shupe, J. L. (1954c). *Cornell Vet.* 44, 302.

Fitzgerald, P. R., Johnson, A. E., Thorne, J., and Hammond, D. M. (1955). *J. Parasitol.* 41, Suppl., 17.

Fitzgerald, P. R., Johnson, A. E., Hammond, D. M., Thorne, J. L., and Hibler, C. P. (1958a). *J. Parasitol.* 44, 597.

Fitgerald, P. R., Johnson, A. E., Thorne, J. L., and Hammond, D. M. (1958b). *Am. J. Vet. Res.* 19, 775.

Flick, E. W. (1954). *Exptl. Parasitol.* 3, 105.

Fortner, J. (1928). *Zentr. Bakteriol., Parasitenk., Abt. I. Orig.* 108, 155.

Frank, H. G., and Reiner, L. (1954). *J. Immunol.* 72, 191.

Frost, J. K., Honigberg, B. M., and McLure, M. T. (1961). *J. Parasitol.* 47, 302.

Gabel, J. R. (1954). *J. Morphol.* 94, 473.

Galuszka, J. (1960). *Wiadomosci Parazytol.* 7, 501.

Galuszka, J. (1962). *Wiadomosci Parazytol.* 8, 315.

Ginel, W. (1962). *Wiadomosci Parazytol.* 8, 217.

Green, L. W., Burt, J. C., Hesseltine, H. C., and Odell, L. D. (1951). *Am. J. Obstet. Gynecol.* 61, 446.

Guida, H. G., Medeiros, P. M., and Pizelli, G. N. (1960). *Publ. Inst. Zootec.* (*Rio de Janeiro*) 35, 3.

Guthrie, R. (1946). Ph.D. Thesis. Univ. Minnesota.

Guthrie, R., and Snell, E. E. (1950). *Bacteriol. Proc.* 44.

Halevy, S. (1963). *Proc. Soc. Exptl. Biol. Med.* 113, 47.

Hamada, Y. (1953). *Osaka Daigaku Igaku Zasshi* 5, 429.

Hamada, Y. (1954). *Osaka Daigaku Igaku Zasshi* 6, 340.

Hamada, Y. (1956). *Med. J. Osaka Univ.* 6, 1101.

Hammond, D. M., and Fitzgerald, P. R. (1953). *J. Parasitol.* 39, Suppl., 11.

Hammond, D. M., and Leidl, W. (1956a). *J. Protozool.* 3, Suppl., 1.

Hammond, D. M., and Leidl, W. (1956b). *J. Parasitol.* 42, 22.

Hammond, D. M., and Leidl, W. (1957). *Am. J. Vet. Res.* 18, 461.

Hammond, D. M., Fitzgerald, P. R., and Johnson, E. (1957). *J. Parasitol.* 43, 695.

Hartman, E. (1951). *J. Parasitol.* 37, Suppl., 10.

Hayes, B. S., and Kotcher, E. (1960). *J. Parasitol.* 46, Suppl., 45.

Hibler, C. P., Hammond, D. M., Caskey, F. H., Johnson, A. E., and Fitzgerald, P. R. (1959). *J. Protozool.* 6, Suppl., 7.

Hibler, C. P., Hammond, D. M., Caskey, F. H., Johnson, A. E., and Fitgerald, P. R. (1960). *J. Protozool.* 7, 159.

Hogue, M. J. (1943). *Am. J. Hyg.* 37, 142.

Holz, G. G., Jr., Wagner, B., Erwin, J., and Kessler, D. (1961). *J. Protozool.* 8, 192.

Honigberg, B. M. (1957). *J. Parasitol.* 43, 43.

Honigberg, B. M. (1958a). *J. Protozool.* 5, Suppl., 15.

Honigberg, B. M. (1958b). *J. Protozool.* 5, Suppl., 15.

Honigberg, B. M. (1959). *J. Parasitol.* 44, 51.

Honigberg, B. M. (1961a). *J. Parasitol.* 47, 545.

Honigberg, B. M. (1961b). *Abstr. 1st Intern. Conf. Protozool., Prague, 1961* p. 62.

Honigberg, B. M. (1962). Personal communication.

Honigberg, B. M. (1963). *J. Protozool.* 10, 20.

Honigberg, B. M., and Braunthal, S. D. (1957). *J. Parasitol.* 43, Suppl., 40.

Honigberg, B. M., and Frost, J. K. (1961). *Abstr. 1st Intern. Conf. Protozool., Prague, 1961* p. 63.

Honigberg, B. M., and King, V. M. (1962). *J. Protozool.* 9, Suppl., 18.

Honigberg, B. M., and McLure, M. T. (1960). *J. Protozool.* 7, 6.

Honigberg, B. M., and Read, C. P. (1960). *Science* 131, 352.

Honigberg, B. M., Mandel, M., Lee, J. J., and Braunthal, S. D. (1957). *J. Protozool.* 4, Suppl., 5.

Hutner, S. H., Baker, H., Aaronson, S., Nathan, H. A., Rodriguez, E., Lockwood, S., Sanders, M., and Petersen, R. A. (1957). *J. Protozool.* 4, 259.

Hutner, S. H., and Holz, G. G., Jr. (1962). *Ann. Rev. Microbiol.* 16, 192.

Hutner, S. H., and Provasoli, L. (1955). *In* "Biochemistry and Physiology of Protozoa" (S. H. Hutner, and A. Lwoff, eds.), Vol. 2, p. 39. Academic Press, New York.

Ikeda, T. (1955). *Gunma J. Med. Sci.* 4, 279.

Inoki, S., and Hamada, Y. (1953). *J. Infect. Diseases* 92, 1.

Inoki, S., Hamada, Y., Chuma, E., and Fujiwara, J. (1952). *Osaka Daigaku Igaku Zasshi* 4, 1.

Ivey, M. H. (1961). *J. Parasitol.* 47, 539.

Iwai, S. (1957). *Japan. J. Parasitol.* 6, 136.

Jaquette, D. S. (1950). *Poultry Sci.* 29, 157.

Jaśkowski, L. (1950). *Proc. 2nd Meeting Polish Parasitol. Soc., Paławy, June, 1950* p. 109.

Jensen, E. A., and Hammond, D. M. (1962). *J. Parasitol.* 48, 30.

Johnson, A. E. (1960). *J. Parasitol.* 46, Suppl., 45.

Johnson, A. E. (1962). *Exptl. Parasitol.* 12, 168.

Johnson, J. G., and Trussell, R. E. (1943). *Proc. Soc. Exptl. Biol. Med.* 54, 245.

Johnson, J. G., Trussell, M. H., and Jahn, F. (1945). *Science* 102, 126.

Jones, I., and Smith, B. F. (1957). *J. Parasitol.* 43, Suppl., 42.

Jones, I., and Smith, B. F. (1959). *Exptl. Parasitol.* 8, 509.

Joyner, L. P. (1954). *Vet. Record* 66, 727.

Joyner, L. P., and Bennett, G. H. (1956). *J. Hyg.* 54, 335.

Joyner, L. P., and Millar, P. G. (1952). *Vet. Record* 64, 1.

Kato, T., and Tanabe, T. (1953). *Sanka to Fujinka* 20, 185.

Kean, B. H., and Weld, J. T. (1955). *Proc. Soc. Exptl. Biol. Med.* 89, 218.

Kessel, J. F., and Thompson, C. F. (1950). *Proc. Soc. Exptl. Biol. Med.* 74, 755.

Kidder, G. W., and Dewey, V. C. (1945). *Physiol. Zool.* 18, 136.

Kiseleva, M. L., and Voskresenskaya, G. V. (1956). *Lab. Delo*, Vol. 2, p. 14.

Koss, L. G., and Wolinska, W. H. (1959). *Cancer* 12, 1171.

Kotcher, E., and Hoogasian, A. C. (1957). *J. Parasitol.* 43, Suppl., 39.

Kozłowska, D. (1956). *Wiadomosci Parazytol.* 2, Suppl., 31.

Kradolfer, F. (1954). *Exptl. Parasitol.* 3, 1.

Kuczyniska, K. (1962). *Wiadomosci Parazytol.* 8, 191.

Kunitake, G., Stitt, C., and Saltman, P. (1962). *J. Protozool.* 9, 371.

Kupferberg, A. B., Johnson, J. G., and Sprince, H. (1948). *Proc. Soc. Exptl. Biol. Med.* 67, 304.

Kupferberg, A. B., Singher, H. O., Lampson, G., Levy, L., and Romano, A. H. (1953). *Ann. N.Y. Acad. Sci.* 56, 1006.

Lash, J. J. (1950). *Am. J. Trop. Med.* **30**, 641.

Lawlis, J. F., Jr. (1952). *Butler Univ. Botan. Studies* **10**, 153.

Lee, J. J. (1958). *J. Protozool.* **5**, Suppl., 21.

Lee, J. J. (1960). *J. Protozool.* **7**, 393.

Lee, J. J. (1963). Personal communication.

Lee, J. J., and Pierce, S. (1960). *J. Protozool.* **7**, 402.

Lee, J. J., and Shorb, M. S. (1962). Unpublished data.

Lee, J. J., Pierce, S., and Samuels, R. (1960). *J. Protozool.* **7**, 6.

Lee, J. J., Pierce, S., and Gurski, D. R. (1961). *J. Protozool.* **8**, Suppl., 5.

Lee, J. J., Pierce, S., Hutner, S. H., Smith, B. J., and Gurski, D. R. (1962a). *J. Protozool.* **9**, 445.

Lee, J. J., Smith, B. J., and Hutner, S. H. (1962b). *J. Protozool.* **9**, Suppl., 10.

Leidl, W., and Mahrla, A. (1954). *Fortpflanz. Zuchthyg. u. Haustierbesam.* **4**, 101.

Levine, N. D. (1961). "Protozoan Parasites of Domestic Animals and of Man." Burgess, Minneapolis, Minnesota.

Levine, N. D., and Andersen, F. L. (1961). *J. Protozool.* **8**, Suppl., 5.

Levine, N. D., and Marquardt, W. C. (1954). *J. Protozool.* **1**, Suppl., 4.

Levine, N. D., and Marquardt, W. C. (1955). *J. Protozool.* **2**, 100.

Levine, N. D., Marquardt, W. C., and Beamer, P. (1954). *J. Am. Vet. Med. Assoc.* **125**, 61.

Levine, N. D., Houlahan, D. A., and Mizell, M. (1955). *J. Protozool.* **2**, 4.

Levine, N. D., McCaul, W. E., and Mizell, M. (1957). *J. Protozool.* **4**, Suppl., 5.

Levine, N. D., Mizell, M., and Houlahan, D. A. (1958). *Exptl. Parasitol.* **7**, 236.

Levine, N. D., McCaul, W. E., and Mizell, M. (1959). *J. Protozool.* **6**, 116.

Levine, N. D., Andersen, F. L., Losch, M. B., Notzold, R. A., and Mehra, K. N. (1962). *J. Protozool.* **9**, 347.

Lindblom, G. P. (1957). *J. Protozool.* **4**, Suppl., 18.

Lindblom, G. P. (1961). *J. Protozool.* **8**, 139.

Lom, J. (1957). *Cesk. Parasitol.* **4**, 219.

Lund, P. G., and Shorb, M. S. (1960). *J. Protozool.* **7**, 5.

Lund, P. G., and Shorb, M. S. (1962). *J. Protozool.* **9**, 151.

Lwoff, M. (1951). *In* "Biochemistry and Physiology of Protozoa" (A. Lwoff, ed.), Vol. 1, p. 148. Academic Press, New York.

Lynch, J. E., English, A. E., Morrison, J., and Maven, I. (1954). *Antibiot. Chemotherapy,* **4**, 899.

Lynch, J. E., Holley, E. C., and Margison, J. E. (1955). *Antibiot. Chemotherapy* **9**, 508.

McDowell, S. J. (1953). *J. Morphol.* **92**, 337.

McEntegart, M. G. (1952). *J. Clin. Pathol.* **5**, 275.

McEntegart, M. G. (1954). *J. Hyg.* **52**, 545.

McEntegart, M. G. (1956). *J. Pathol. Bacteriol.* **71**, 111.

McEntegart, M. G. (1959). *Nature* **183**, 270.

McEntegart, M. G., Chadwick, C. S., and Nairn, R. C. (1958). *Brit. J. Venereal Diseases* **34**, 1.

McLoughlin, D. K. (1957a). *J. Parasitol.* **43**, 307.

McLoughlin, D. K. (1957b). *J. Parasitol.* **43**, 321.

McWade, D. H., and Williams, J. A. (1954). *Mich. State Univ., Agr. Exptl. Sta., Quart. Bull.* **37**, 248.

Magara, M., Amino, E., and Yokouti, E. (1953a). *Am. J. Trop. Med. Hyg.* **2**, 267.

Magara, M., Yokouchi, K., and Amino, E. (1953b). *San-fujinka no jissai* **2**, 1260.

Mandel, M., and Honigberg, B.M. (1957). *Anat. Record* 128, 586.

Manners, D. J., and Ryley, J. F. (1955). *Biochem. J.* 59, 369.

Mehra, K. N., Levine, N. D., and Reber, E. F. (1960). *J. Protozool.* 7, 12.

Menolasino, N. J., and Hartman, E. (1954). *J. Immunol.* 72, 172.

Mesa, C. P., Stabler, R. M., and Berthrong, M. (1961). *Avian Diseases* 5, 48.

Michaels, R. M. (1962). *J. Protozool.* 9, 478.

Molinari, V. (1956). *Bull. Soc. Pathol. Exotique* 49, 254.

Nakamura, M. (1961a). *J. Parasitol.* 47, 368.

Nakamura, M. (1961b). *J. Protozool.* 8, Suppl., 18.

Ninomiya, H., and Suzuoki, Z. (1951). *J. Japan. Biochem. Soc.* 23, 116.

Ninomiya, H., and Suzuoki, Z. (1952). *J. Biochem. (Tokyo)* 39, 321.

O'Brien, J. E., and Thoms, R. K. (1955). *J. Am. Pharm. Assoc., Sci. Ed.* 44, 245.

Orlowska, V., and Mordarski, M. (1962). *Wiadomosci Parazytol.* 8, 197.

Pavlova, E. (1938). *Med. Parazitol. i Parazitar. Bolezni* 7, 119.

Petrovic, Z. (1950). *Arhiv Bioloskih Nauka (Beograd)* 2, 33.

Plastridge, W. N. (1943). *J. Bacteriol.* 45, 196.

Pray, E. G. (1952). *J. Parasitol.* 38, 398.

Read, C. P. (1953). *Anat. Record* 117, 649.

Read, C. P. (1955). *J. Parasitol.* 41, Suppl., 16.

Read, C. P. (1956). *J. Parasitol.* 42, 23.

Read, C. P. (1957). *J. Parasitol.* 43, 385.

Read, C. P., and Rothman, A. H. (1954). *J. Parasitol.* 40, Suppl., 21.

Read, C. P., and Rothman, A. H. (1955). *Am. J. Hyg.* 61, 249.

Reardon, L. V., and Jacobs, L. (1958). *J. Parasitol.* 44, 21.

Reardon, L. V., Ashburn, L. L., and Jacobs, L. (1961). *J. Parasitol.* 47, 527.

Rubin, R., and Cordray, D. (1958). *Am. J. Vet. Res.* 19, 249.

Ryley, J. F. (1955). *Biochem. J.* 59, 361.

Samuels, R. (1954). *J. Protozool.* 1, 8.

Samuels, R. (1957a). *J. Protozool.* 4, 5.

Samuels, R. (1957b). *J. Protozool.* 4, 110.

Samuels, R. (1958). *J. Protozool.* 5, Suppl., 9.

Samuels, R. (1959). *J. Protozool.* 6, Suppl., 20.

Samuels, R. (1961a). *Abstr. 1st Intern. Conf. Protozool., Prague, 1961* p. 187.

Samuels, R. (1961b). *J. Protozool.* 8, Suppl., 5.

Samuels, R. (1962a). *J. Protozool.* 9, 103.

Samuels, R. (1962b). *J. Parasitol.* 48, 30.

Samuels, R., and Beil, E. A. (1962). *J. Protozool.* 9, Suppl., 19.

Samuels, R., and Stouder, D. J. (1960). *J. Protozool.* 7, 5.

Samuels, R., and Stouder, D. J. (1962). *J. Protozool.* 9, 249.

Sanborn, W. R. (1955). *J. Parasitol.* 41, 295.

Sanders, M. (1957). *J. Protozool.* 4, 118.

Satti, M. H., and Honigberg, B. M. (1959). *J. Parasitol.* 44, 51.

Saxe, L. H. (1954a). *J. Parasitol.* 40, Suppl., 20.

Saxe, L. H. (1954b). *J. Protozool.* 1, 220.

Saxe, L. H., Friend, A., and Devaney, B. M. (1952). *J. Parasitol.* 38, Suppl., 14.

Schnitzer, R. J., and Kelly, D. R. (1954). *Proc. Soc. Exptl. Biol. Med.* 85, 123.

Schnitzer, R. J., Kelly, D. R., and Leiwant, B. (1950). *J. Parasitol.* 36, 343.

Schoenherr, K. E. (1956). *Z. Immunitaetsforsch.* 113, 83.

Seaman, G. R. (1953). *Exptl. Parasitol.* 2, 366.

Sebek, O. K., Rosselet, J. P., Jr., and Michaels, R. M. (1957). *Bacteriol. Proc.* p. 133.

Shaffer, J. G., and Biegeleisen, J. Z. (1951). *Am. J. Hyg.* **53,** 139.

Shaw, R., and Buttrey, B. (1958a). *J. Protozool.* **5,** Suppl., 9.

Shaw, R., and Buttrey, B. (1958b). *Proc. S. Dakota Acad. Sci.* **37,** 35.

Shorb, M. S. (1961). *Abstr. 1st Intern. Conf. Protozool., Prague, 1961* p. 205.

Shorb, M. S., and Lund, P. G. (1958). *J. Protozool.* **5,** Suppl., 15.

Shorb, M. S., and Lund, P. G. (1959). *J. Protozool.* **6,** 122.

Shorb, M. S., and Lund, P. G. (1962). *J. Protozool.* **9,** Suppl., 20.

Shorb, M. S., and Lund, P. G. (1963). Unpublished data.

Smith, B. F. (1955). *J. Parasitol.* **41,** Suppl., 16.

Smith, B. F., and Spriggs, A. S. (1959). *J. Protozool.* **6,** Suppl., 31.

Solomon, J. M. (1957). *J. Parasitol.* **43,** 39.

Sorel, C. (1954). *Presse Med.* **62,** 602.

Spindler, L. A., Shorb, D. A., and Hill, C. H. (1953). *J. Am. Vet. Med. Assoc.* **122,** 151.

Sprince, H., Goldberg, R., Kucker, S., and Lowy, R. S. (1953). *Ann. N.Y. Acad. Sci.* **56,** 1016.

Stabler, R. M. (1948). *J. Parasitol.* **34,** 147.

Stabler, R. M. (1953). *J. Parasitol.* **39,** Suppl., 12.

Stabler, R. M. (1957). *J. Parasitol.* **43,** Suppl., 40.

Stabler, R. M., and Kihara, J. T. (1954a). *J. Parasitol.* **40,** 25.

Stabler, R. M., and Kihara, J. T. (1954b). *J. Parasitol.* **40,** 706.

Stabler, R. M., and Mellentin, R. W. (1953). *J. Parasitol.* **39,** 637.

Suzuoki, Z., and Suzuoki, T. (1951a). *Nature* **168,** 610.

Suzuoki, Z., and Suzuoki, T. (1951b). *J. Biochem. (Tokyo)* **38,** 237.

Swenson, P. A. (1960). *J. Protozool.* **7,** 26.

Switzer, W. P. (1951a). *Vet. Med.* **46,** 478.

Switzer, W. P. (1951b). Thesis. Iowa State College, Ames, Iowa.

Switzer, W. P. (1959). *Am. J. Vet. Res.* **20,** 1010.

Teras, J. (1961). *Abstr. 1st Intern. Conf. Protozool., Prague, 1961* p. 221.

Tumka, A. F. (1961). *Veterinariya* **39,** 37.

Twohy, D. W. (1959). *J. Protozool.* **6,** Suppl., 20.

Twohy, D. W. (1961). *J. Protozool.* **8,** Suppl., 5.

Twohy, D. W., and Tucker, P. A. (1961). *J. Protozool.* **8,** Suppl., 5.

Tyler, H. M., and Watkins, W. M. (1960). *Biochem. J.* **74,** 2P.

van Wagtendonk, W. J. (1955). *In* "Biochemistry and Physiology of Protozoa" (S. H. Hutner and A. Lwoff, eds.), Vol. 2, p. 76. Academic Press, New York.

Varga, A. (1962). *Obstet. Gynecol.* **20,** 91.

von Brand, T. (1952). "Chemical Physiology of Endoparasitic Animals," p. 95. Academic Press, New York.

Walton, B. C., and Bacharach, T. (1963). *J. Parasitol.* **49,** 35.

Wantland, W. W., Wantland, E. M., Remo, J. W., and Winquist, D. L. (1958). *J. Dental Res.* **37,** 949.

Wantland, W. W., Wantland, E. M., and Weidman, T. A. (1962). *J. Parasitol.* **48,** 305.

Warren, L. G., and Allen, K. W. (1959). *J. Protozool.* **6,** Suppl., 20.

Warren, L. G., and Chandler, A. C. (1958). *J. Parasitol.* **43,** 21.

Watkins, W. M. (1953). *Biochem. J.* **54,** xxxiii.

Watkins, W. M. (1959). *Biochem. J.* **71,** 261.

Watkins, W. M. (1962). *Immunology* **5,** 245.

Watkins, W. M., and Morgan, W. T. J. (1954). *Brit. J. Exptl. Pathol.* **35,** 181.

Watkins, W. M., and Morgan, W. T. J. (1955). *Nature* 175, 676.

Watkins, W. M., Zarnitz, M. L., and Kabat, E. A. (1962). *Nature* 195, 1204.

Wegner, Z. (1953). *Bull. State Inst. Marine Trop. Med. Gdansk* 5, 208.

Weiss, E. D., and Ball, G. H. (1947). *Proc. Soc. Exptl. Biol. Med.* 65, 278.

Weld, J. T., and Kean, B. H. (1956). *Am. J. Pathol.* 32, 1135.

Weld, J. T., and Kean, B. H. (1958a). *Proc. Soc. Exptl. Biol. Med.* 98, 494.

Weld, J. T., and Kean, B. H. (1958b). *Exptl. Parasitol.* 7, 391.

Wellerson, R., Doscher, G., and Kupferberg, A. B. (1959). *Ann. N.Y. Acad. Sci.* 83, 253.

Wellerson, R., Doscher, G., and Kupferberg, A. B. (1960). *Biochem. J.* 75, 562.

Wellerson, R., Jr., and Kupferberg, A. B. (1962). *J. Protozool.* 9, 418.

West, R. A., Jr., Barbera, P. W., Kolar, J. R., and Murrell, C. B. (1962). *J. Protozool.* 9, 65.

Whittington, M. J. (1951). *Am. J. Hyg.* 49, 400.

Wirtschafter, S. K. (1954a). *J. Parasitol.* 40, 100 abst.

Wirtschafter, S. K. (1954b). *J. Parasitol.* 40, 360.

Wirtschafter, S. K. (1954c). *J. Parasitol.* 40, 100 abst.

Wirtschafter, S. K., Jahn, T. L., and Saltman, P. (1955). *J. Protozool.* 2, Suppl., 9.

Wirtschafter, S. K., and Jahn, T. L. (1956). *J. Protozool.* 3, 83.

Wirtschafter, S. K., Saltman, P., and Jahn, T. L. (1956). *J. Protozool.* 3, 86.

Wyss, W., Kradolfer, F., and Meier, R. (1960). *Exptl. Parasitol.* 10, 66.

Nutrition and Physiology of the Trypanosomatidae*

HELENE N. GUTTMAN AND FRANKLIN G. WALLACE

Department of Biology, Haskins Laboratories, New York, New York
New York University, New York, New York and
Department of Zoology, University of Minnesota, Minneapolis, Minnesota

		Page
I.	Introduction	460
II.	General Morphological Features of Trypanosomatids	460
III.	Genera of Trypanosomatidae	462
	A. *Crithidia*	462
	B. *Blastocrithidia*	462
	C. *Trypanosoma*	462
	D. *Leishmania*	462
	E. *Leptomas* and Related Genera	463
IV.	Growth in Defined Media	464
	A. Purine Requirements	464
	B. Pteridine Requirements	465
	C. Methionine Requirement	474
	D. Lipid Requirements	475
	E. Carbohydrate Requirements	475
V.	Growth of Trypanosomes	477
	A. *Trypanosoma cruzi*	477
	B. *Trypanosoma mega*	479
	C. Other Trypanosomes	480
	D. Organisms in Diphasic Media	481
	E. Experimental Morphogenesis	482
VI.	Growth in Tissue Culture	484
	A. Embryonated Avian Eggs	484
	B. Invertebrate Tissue	485
	C. Vertebrate Tissue	485

* Aided in part by grants (E-1088 and AI-02373) from the U.S.P.H.S.

Page

VII. Miscellaneous Experiments 486
    A. Sexual Reproduction 486
    B. Akinetoplasty 486
    C. Chemical Composition of Trypanosomatids 488
    D. Nucleic Acid Synthesis 490
    References 491

I. Introduction

In the Trypanosomatidae, use of the same terms to denote both gross morphology and genera has led to a confusion of interpretations for the same term. Awakened interest in the chemical changes concomitant with evolution in the Trypanosomatidae points to the desirability of unambiguous terminology so that chemical data may be assigned to logical positions in postulated evolutionary sequences. Because of the nomenclatorial tangles we will sketch the morphological features that delimit genera.

II. General Morphological Features of Trypanosomatids

The single flagellum is a nearly constant feature in the insect trypanosomatids although absent in certain attached stages or cysts. The flagellum always arises in the reservoir and emerges from the body through the reservoir mouth (Fig. 1).

The kinetoplast is a relatively large, deeply stained body just below the base of the flagellum and the base of the reservoir. It has been called kinetonucleus, micronucleus, basal body, or blepharoplast. We will use *kinetoplast* as suggested by Wenyon (1926). Kinetoplasts are peculiar to Trypanosomatidae and should not be confused, as they sometimes are, with blepharoplasts, organelles associated with all flagella. Kinetoplasts stain as do mitochondria (Janicki, 1915; Alexieff, 1917; Causey, 1925; Lwoff and Lwoff, 1931) and are Feulgen positive (Janicki, 1915; Bresslau and Scremin, 1924; Robertson, 1927; Cosgrove and Anderson, 1954).

The term blepharoplast was introduced by Webber (1898) to describe a portion of the flagellar element of *Zamia* antherozoids. Since it was initially used for a plant structure, blepharoplast must refer to the most general and ubiquitous flagellar element, i.e., the 9-fibered element at the base of the flagellum, anterior to the kinetoplast. The blepharoplast fibers appear to be continuous with the peripheral fibers of the axoneme. Differentiation from the axoneme proper requires well detailed electron micrographs (cf. Fig. 1 in Clark and Wallace, 1960; and also chapter by Pitelka and Child, this volume).

Contractile vacuoles are customarily considered absent from parasitic protozoa although they had been seen by Bütschli (1887), Wenyon (1926), and others. More recently, their presence has been noted by Cosgrove and Kessel (1958), and Clark (1959). The latter showed that the contractile vacuole is a constant feature of the flagellar complex with one vacuole or more opening into the side of the reservoir.

The single nucleus is most frequently found in the middle third of the body length (Fig. 1).

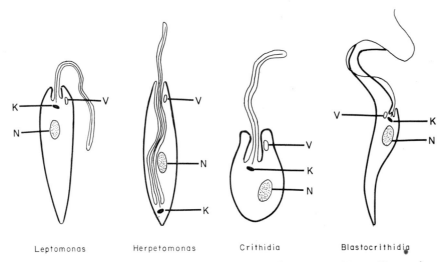

Leptomonas   Herpetomonas   Crithidia   Blastocrithidia

Fig. 1. The undisputed lower Trypanosomatidae genera. Key: N = nucleus; k = kinetoplast; V = contractile vacuole.

The genera of the Trypanosomatidae have been variously defined by morphological features alone (Fig. 1). In time metabolic features will clarify generic and species distinctions.

One host may be simultaneously infected with more than one species of trypanosomatid. Although this was pointed out by Léger (1902) and later reemphasized by Wallace (1943), many workers in the intervening period—and even later—have described different species isolated from one host as being stages in a single life cycle (e.g., Patton, 1908; Woodcock, 1914). Life-history data as criteria for classification of the insect trypanosomatids have contributed little besides confusion to the nomenclature and taxonomy of this group. Faulty species descriptions have abetted the creation of a somewhat spurious taxonomy. To clarify the characteristics—morphological and biochemical—we urge the use of cloned cultures for studies of morphology, especially life histories.

We accept five genera in the Trypanosomatidae as undisputed, plus one or two additional genera (among the insect trypanosomatids) still in need of clarification.

III. Genera of Trypanosomatidae

A. *Crithidia*

Members of the genus *Crithidia* (Léger, 1902) (Fig. 1) are relatively small (4–10 μ long) monoxenous parasites of insects with truncate anteriors. The body is relatively wide and often constricted slightly in the anterior third to produce a vase-like shape. The reservoir is funnel shaped with a cytostome which often occupies most of the anterior end. The kinetoplast is large, lateral, and relatively posterior, often near or beside the nucleus. A contractile vacuole lies in or near the wall of the reservoir on the side opposite of the kinetoplast. A fibrous organization (electron micrographs) in a somewhat loose meshwork, nearly filling the kinetoplast, is characteristic. Members of this genus have been at times erroneously called *Strigomonas* (Lwoff and Lwoff, 1931) or *Herpetomonas* (Noguchi and Tilden, 1926).

B. *Blastocrithidia*

The genus *Blastocrithidia* (Laird, 1959) (Fig. 1) is made up of monoxenous parasites of insects, long (15.1–53.5 μ) and quite slender (1.5–2.0 μ). A short reservoir opens laterally. A contractile vacuole is found lateral to or just posterior to the base of the reservoir. The kinetoplast is just posterior to the base of the reservoir and located just anterior or lateral to the nucleus. The fibrous organization of the kinetoplast is similar to that in *Crithidia*.

The single flagellum emerges from the mouth of the reservoir and is attached to the body of the organism, anterior to the reservoir, along the outer edge of an undulating membrane.

C. *Trypanosoma*

The *Trypanosoma* are hetereoxenous parasites of invertebrates and vertebrates with a morphologically complex life cycle. In the trypanosome, the morphological form "characteristic" of the genus, the reservoir is considerably posterior to the nucleus. The kinetoplast is posterior to the base of the reservoir, containing a mass of electron-dense, antero-posterior fibers which form a compact, sharply defined zone across the kinetoplast. The flagellum is attached to the body by an undulating membrane.

D. *Leishmania*

The *Leishmania* are heteroxenous parasites of invertebrates and vertebrates with a morphologically complex life cycle. The alternatives are (*a*) a form with a free flagellum and (*b*) the characteristic leishmanial form whose flagellum is never fully emergent. The fine structure of the kinetoplast is like that of *Trypanosoma*.

E. *Leptomonas* AND RELATED GENERA

Members of the genus *Leptomonas* (Kent, 1880) are lanceolate, the kinetoplast is near the anterior end of the body, and the flagellum emerges through a short, narrowly-opening reservoir. Similar parasites found in lactiferous plants are known as *Phytomonas* (Donovan, 1909). Presumed stages of *Phytomonas* have been found in plant-feeding insects but until very recently it has been unclear whether they were really developmental stages of the plant parasites or were *Leptomonas*. There is no direct evidence that trypanosomatids found in plants also multiply their indefinitely. No distinct morphological characteristics separate *Phytomonas* from other genera. Even if substantiated, variation in host is a rather tenuous basis for creating a special genus. For example, the finding that human-pathogenic reoviruses are antigenically cross-reactive with the plant-pathogenic wound-tumor viruses (Streissle and Maramorosch, 1963) is forcing reassessment of the classification of these morphologically similar viruses. Serological cross-reactivity among crithidias seems dependent only upon whether the host was a hemipteron or dipteron (McGhee and Hanson, 1963). *Strigomonas oncopelti*, parasitic in *Oncopeltus fasciatus* and allegedly from *Asclepias* (Noguchi and Tilden, 1926), fits the qualification for *Crithidia* sp.; *Phytomonas elmassiani* (Migone) recently isolated by Vickerman (1962) from both *Pergularia extensa* and *Oncopeltus famelicus*, may be a *Leptomonas*.

Leptomonas and *Herpetomonas* were diagnosed by Kent (1880). Both genera include lanceolate flagellates with a kinetoplast near the anterior end and a flagellum which emerges through a short, narrow-apertured reservoir opening at the anterior end of the organism. No biochemical differences to distinguish these genera have been reported possibly because of the paucity of authenticated cultures.

Among the recent studies, Wallace and Clark (1959) assigned some recent isolates of flagellates to *Herpetomonas*. They noted that most of the organisms fitted the description which serves for both *Leptomonas* and *Herpetomonas* but that some 5% of the organisms had reservoirs which extended posterior to the nucleus and kinetoplasts in the posterior portion of the body (Fig. 1).

We therefore suggest that cultures now assigned to *Herpetomonas* be tested to determine whether they are in fact two-membered—containing the two morphological types separable as *Leptomonas* and *Herpetomonas*—or whether the form with deep reservoir and posterior kinetoplast is spontaneously produced from the form with shallow reservoir and anterior kinetoplast. Cultures containing both morphological types should be assigned to the genus *Herpetomonas* only in the latter case.

IV. Growth in Defined Media

Since the report by Cowperthwaite *et al.* (1953) of the first chemically defined medium for a member of the Trypanosomatidae, several other hemoflagellates have been grown in defined media. These organisms include several *Crithidia* sp., one *Leishmania,* and one *Blastocrithidia.* The organisms and media are given in Tables I and IIA,B,C.

Table I

TRYPANOSOMATIDAE FOR WHICH CHEMICALLY DEFINED
MEDIA ARE AVAILABLE

Species	
Crithidia fasciculata (*Anopheles* strain)	ATCC 12745
C. fasciculata (*Culex pipiens* strain)	ATCC 12857
C. fasciculata (*Culex pipiens* strain, Nöller isolate)	ATCC 12858
C. luciliae	ATCC 14765
Crithidia sp. from *Euryophthalmus davisi*	ATCC 14766
Crithidia sp. from *Syrphid*	
C. (*Strigomonas*) *oncopelti*	ATCC 12982
Blastocrithidia culicis	ATCC 14806
Leishmania tarentolae	

The only organism with strikingly different minimal requirements is *Crithidia oncopelti* (Table IIB)—but that organism contains an endosymbiote (Pyne, 1961; Gill and Vogel, 1962, 1963). Since *C. oncopelti,* freed of its endosymbiote, cannot grow in medium IIB (H. Vogel, personal communication; Table IIB) one might expect that the true requirements for *C. oncopelti* are similar to those of other lower trypanosomatids.

A. PURINE REQUIREMENTS

Requirements for at least one purine derivative have been demonstrated for most of the organisms. Characteristically the lower trypanosomatids have a wide ability to interconvert purines and their derivatives but their precise enzymatic capabilities for this have not been systematically studied. Purine-interconversion ability may prove to be a good marker for tracing family affinities. Since it has already been shown that an unusual intermediate, 4-NH_4-5-imidazole carboxamidine is a common adenine precursor for the trypanosomatids (Aaronson and Nathan, 1954; Nathan and Cowperthwaite, 1955; Nathan, 1958a), detailed investigations of adenine biosynthesis are also in order.

B. Pteridine Requirements

Most of the water-soluble vitamins are required. Vitamin B_{12} is absent from the list. Members of the B_{12} family are produced by trypanosomatids (Nathan and Funk, 1959; Nathan et al., 1960). No requirement for thioctic acid has been demonstrated for any trypanosomatid. *Leishmania tarentolae* is the only organism shown to have a choline requirement but choline may be omitted if pyridoxal is included in the medium (Trager, 1957). Organisms grown with suboptimal amounts of choline either lacked flagella or only had stubby ones. There have been no reports of similar experiments with other trypanosomatids.

Pteridine metabolism in the Trypanosomatidae will be given detailed treatment. The peculiar folic acid metabolism of *C. fasciculata* (*Anopheles* strain) [*] was apparent from the first report (Cowperthwaite et al., 1953) of a requirement for unphysiologically high levels of folic acid. The failure of then known products of folic acid metabolism to bypass the nutritional requirement for folic acid presaged that there was at least one other function of folic acid besides those known in 1953. These workers showed that several natural products were active in replacing folic acid in the growth medium under conditions where the activity of the natural material was considerably more than could be predicted by the folic acid content of the natural material.

A potent replacement for folic acid was the supernatant from *Ochromonas malhamensis* cultures. A more realistic idea of the role of folic acid in the nutrition of *C. fasciculata* was gained when it was shown (Nathan and Cowperthwaite, 1955) that *O. malhamensis* supernatants could be acid-hydrolyzed so that the folic acid activity (for *Streptococcus faecalis*) was destroyed: this treatment inactivated the supernatant (for *C. fasciculata*) unless physiological quantities of folic acid were added (Table III). Experiments with the hydrolyzates revealed that *C. fasciculata* required only the usual amounts of folic acid (Table III) plus a second factor, *Crithidia* factor, probably related to folic acid. The active material in *O. malhamensis* hydrolyzates is present in such small quantities that it still has not been isolated in sufficient amounts to crystallize.

Commercial "purified" preparations of adenosine and guanosine also were a source of *Crithidia* factor. Simple recrystallization of guanosine from hot water freed guanosine from all *Crithidia* factor activity: all activity plus a small amount of guanosine was transferred to the mother liquor. From this concentrate, *Crithidia* factor was purified chromatographically and the characteristic ultraviolet spectrum traced.

Crithidia factor from guanosine was assigned the structure: 2-NH_2-4-OH-pteridine with an aliphatic substituent in the 6-position (Nathan and Cowperthwaite, 1955). The general structure was substantiated by Patterson et al.

[*] Then called *Herpetomonas* (*Strigomonas*).

Table II

DEFINED MEDIA FOR SEVERAL TRYPANOSOMATIDAE

IIA. *Medium Suitable for Organisms 1–8 in Table* I

Component	Concentration mg./100 ml. final medium[a]
L-Arginine HCl	50.0
L-Glutamic acid[b]	100.0
L-Histidine HCl	30.0
DL-Isoleucine	10.0
DL-Leucine	10.0
L-Lysine·HCl	40.0
DL-Methionine	10.0
DL-Phenylalanine	6.0
DL-Tryptophan	8.0
L-Tyrosine	6.0
DL-Valine	5.0
EDTA	60.0
B (as H_3BO_3)	0.05
Ca (as $CaCl_2$)[c]	0.05
Co (as $CoSO_4 \cdot 7H_2O$)	0.25
Cu (as $CuSO_4 \cdot 5H_2O$)	0.25
Fe (as $Fe(NH_4)_2(SO_4)_2 \cdot 6H_2O$)	0.1
Mn (as $MnSO_4 \cdot H_2O$)	14.0
$MgSO_4 \cdot 7H_2O$	65.0
K_3PO_4	15.0
Zn (as $ZnSO_4 \cdot 7H_2O$)	5.0
Adenine[d]	1.0
Sucrose[e]	1,500.0
Biotin	0.001
Ca pantothenate	0.3
Folic acid[f]	0.1
Nicotinic acid	0.3
Pyridoxamine dihydrochloride	0.1
Riboflavin	0.06
Thiamine hydrochloride	0.6
Hemin[g]	2.5
Triethanolamine (TEA)[g]	500.0

[a] The final pH of the medium should be pH 7.8–8.0. Any necessary adjustments should be made with H_2SO_4 or KOH.

The medium may be stored as a 4X concentrate. If such storage is desirable, the vitamins should be excluded from the medium formulation and added only before use.

[b] The A grade of California Biochemical Corp. is free of contaminating methionine. Glutamic acid is an absolute requirement for *C. fasciculata* (Nöller strain), *B. culicis*, and *C. oncopelti*.

[c] Prepare by acidifying $CaCO_3$ with HCl.

IIB. *Medium Suitable for Endosymbiote-Containing Strain of* Crithidia oncopelti[a]

Component	Concentration mg./100 ml. final medium
K_3PO_4	20.0
$MgSO_4 \cdot 7H_2O$	80.0
Ca (as $CaCl_2$)	0.3
Cu (as $CuSO_4 \cdot 5H_2O$)	0.04
Fe [as $Fe(NH_4)_2(SO_4)_2 \cdot 6H_2O$]	0.2
Zn (as $ZnSO_4 \cdot 7H_2O$)	0.1
Mn ($MnSO_4 \cdot H_2O$)	0.1
Cu ($CuSO_4 \cdot 5H_2O$)	0.008
Co ($CoSO_4 \cdot 7H_2O$)	0.01
B (as H_3BO_3)	0.01
Mo [as $(NH_4)_6 Mo_7O_{24} \cdot 4H_2O$]	0.005
NaCl	50.0
Triethanolamine	500.0
L-Arginine	30.0
L-Glutamic acid	100.0
L-Histidine	20.0
DL-Methionine	20.0
Thiamine hydrochloride	0.1
Nicotinic acid	0.1
Calcium pantothenate	0.1
Pyridoxamine dihydrochloride	0.1
Biotin	0.001
p-Aminobenzoic acid[b]	0.001
Sucrose[c]	1,000.0

[a] *Crithidia oncopelti*, cured of endosymbiotes will not grow in this medium (Vogel, 1963). Preliminary experiments indicate that it will grow in medium IIA (Guttman, 1964a, unpublished).

[b] Adenine (Newton, 1957) or $4NH_2$ -5-imidazole carboxamidine will substitute (Nathan, 1958a).

[c] Other sugars may be substituted.

---

[d] Any purine base, riboside, or most ribotides will do.

[e] Other sugars may substitute (Guttman, 1963b).

[f] For explanation see Sections IV, B and C in text on *Crithidia* factor.

[g] Prepare stock solution of hemin at 5.0 mg./ml. in 50% (w/v) TEA. When preparing the medium, half of the required TEA is added. This brings the base to pH 7. Only then is hemin added. With the addition of hemin in TEA, the other half of the TEA automatically is added.

Component	Concentration mg./100 ml. final medium
NaCl	200.0
Na$_2$HPO$_4$	125.0
KH$_2$PO$_4$	50.0
Hemin	2.5
DL-Alanine	70.0
L-Arginine hydrochloride	30.0
DL-Aspartic acid	120.0
L-Glutamic acid	190.0
Glycine	10.0
L-Histidine	15.0
L-Isoleucine	60.0
L-Leucine	150.0
L-Lysine hydrochloride	125.0
DL-Methionine	30.0
DL-Phenylalanine	40.0
L-Proline	50.0
DL-Serine	40.0
DL-Threonine	50.0
DL-Tryptophan	20.0
L-Tyrosine	40.0
DL-Valine	50.0
Riboflavin	0.2
Thiamine hydrochloride	0.2
Pyridoxine hydrochloride	0.2
Pyridoxal	0.2
Pyridoxamine dihydrochloride	0.2
Calcium pantothenate	0.8
p-Aminobenzoic acid	0.3
Nicotinamide	0.5
Biotin	0.02
Inositol	0.3
Folic acid	0.16
Choline chloride	0.3
Adenine	0.17
Guanine	0.17
Xanthine	0.17
Uracil	0.17
Cytidylic acid	0.05
Glucose	500.0
CaCl$_2$	2.6
MgSO$_4$·7H$_2$O	100.0
ZnSO$_4$·7H$_2$O	2.2
FeSO$_4$·7H$_2$O	1.0
MnSO$_4$·4H$_2$O	0.4
CuSO$_4$	0.05
CoSO$_4$·7H$_2$O	0.044
H$_3$BO$_3$	0.011

[a] This medium is prepared as 8 separate sterile solutions. The 8 solutions are mixed together aseptically just prior to inoculation. For details of concentration of stock solutions and compounding directions see Trager (1957).

Table III

SEPARATION OF *Crithidia* FACTOR AND FOLIC ACID ACTIVITIES
FROM *Ochromonas malhamensis* CULTURE SUPERNATANTS

$\mu g.$[a] Supernatant/ml. C. fasciculata basal medium[b]	Growth of *C. fasciculata* expressed as percentage of full growth		
		Supernatant hydrolyzed 1 hr. in 1 N HCl	
	No further treatment	No further additions	Plus folic acid 0.1 mμg./ml.
None	0	0	—
0.3	4	4	6
1.0	16	2	16
3.0	86	8	81
10.0	100	6	100

[a] Based on dry-weight determinations.

[b] Medium as in Nathan and Cowperthwaite, 1955.

(1955) who proved that the structure of *Crithidia* factor in human urine is 2-NH$_2$-4-OH, 6-(1-*threo*)1',2'-dihydroxypropyl pteridine; they named it biopterin.

There are several 2-NH$_2$-4-OH pteridines with aliphatic substituents in the 6-position (unconjugated pteridines) which have growth-factor (*Crithidia* factor) activity for *C. fasciculata*. The several unconjugated pteridines which spare the folic acid requirement so that it may be reduced from 1.0 μg. to 0.001 μg./ml. are characterized by possessing a 6-substituent at least 2 carbons long which bear at least two L-cis hydroxy groups. The whole family of active unconjugated pteridines is termed *Crithidia* Factor.

Probably all the *Crithidia* factors described when the first active compounds were identified are isolation artifacts and the naturally occurring factors are somewhat modified. As with folic acid, the parent *Crithidia* factors are probably either di- or tetrahydropteridines. The ease with which naturally occurring reduced pteridines are oxidized has been repeatedly pointed out by Ziegler (cf. Ziegler-Gunder, 1956). That these reduced pteridines (in this particular case isolated from *Drosophila* eyes) serve as *Crithidia* factors has been shown (Ziegler and Nathan, 1961).

Before discussing *Crithidia* factor synthesis and function, it is appropriate to summarize the roles of the conjugated pteridines (folic and folinic acids) in the Trypanosomatidae. All defined media (save the one in Table IIB) and many partially defined media for both lower and higher trypanosomatids contain conjugated pteridines, but only for the several *Crithidia* spp. has the role of pteridines been charted.

Once the folic acid requirement for *C. fasciculata* had been resolved into two requirements—one for a *Crithidia* factor and the other for folic acid itself—the function of folic acid was studied. It was found (Nathan *et al.*, 1956) that "folic acid" served as a cofactor in thymine synthesis: in the presence of *Crithidia* factor and thymine the folic acid requirement was bypassed (see also Table IV); an indefinite number of serial culture generations are obtainable in media containing no folic acid. A nongrowth-limiting function for folic acid in *Crithidia* was recently revealed (Guttman, 1964b) when growth curves for synthetic and natural (from human blood serum) *Crithidia* factors were compared. It can be seen (Figs. 2A and 2B) that there is both a lower slope and reduced total growth when folic acid is absent from the thymine-containing medium. The curves become superimposable when traces of folic acid are added (Fig. 2B). The role of folic acid here remains to be elucidated.

In media in which folic acid is the sole source of pteridine, *Crithidia* factor is produced from folic acid (Table IV). Although the reactions by which *Crithidia* factor is produced from this pteridine pool are still not clear, one of the cofactors in this sequence has been shown to be a vitamin B_6 derivative. As is the case with all organisms save the bacteria and some yeasts, it is not yet possible to bypass a B_6 requirement for *C. fasciculata*. It was impossible to even spare this requirement with a wide selection of known products of B_6 metabolism until a *Crithidia* factor was added to the medium (Nathan and Funk, 1959). Thus B_6-containing enzyme system mediates some important step in splitting folic acid and fabricating a *Crithidia* factor.

Wacker *et al.* (1959) were unsuccessful in showing conversion of C^{14}-folic acid to biopterin by cell-free extracts of *C. fasciculata*. Their short report contained no data, only an evaluation of results. One might expect that experiments using either whole cells or homogenates in which particulates are retained and perhaps a B_6 cofactor would be more fruitful.[*]

Under some circumstances *C. fasciculata* spp. synthesize *Crithidia* factors from non-pteridine precursors. To demonstrate synthesis during growth, Nathan and Funk (1959) grew *C. fasciculata* in a medium which contained, as major carbohydrate substrate, a compound such as sorbitol which is not a participant in the synthesis of *Crithidia* factor and also added 2,4,5-triamino-6-OH-pyrimidine plus any one of several sugars (Table IV) which served as intermediates in pteridine synthesis. The microbiological synthesis of the pteridine ring with concomitant production of the 6-C substituent is essentially the method used by the organic chemist.

To summarize, *Crithidia* factor is required for growth of at least several insect hemoflagellates; it may be supplied (*a*) as such; (*b*) as a conjugated

---

[*] Note added in proof: Kidder *et al.* (1964) briefly reported production of $2-C^{14}$ labeled *Crithidia* factor from $2-C^{14}$ labeled folic acid by *C. fasciculata* during growth. This report confirms the pathway proposed by Nathan *et al.* (1956).

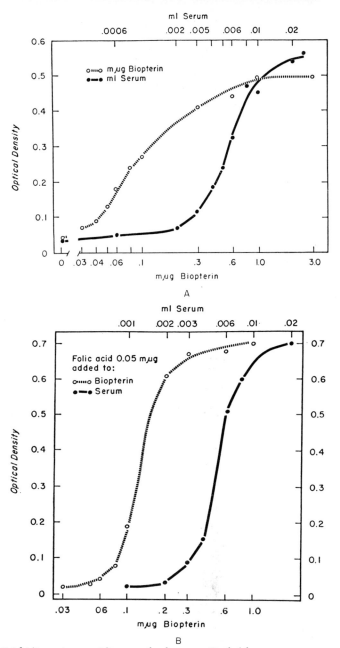

FIG. 2. Crithidia-active pteridine standard curves. Pooled human serum or commercial biopterin was used as standard. A. Differences in the slopes of curves and maximum response in unsupplemented medium. B. Effect of supplementation with traces of folic acid on the standard curves.

Table IV

PTERIDINE FUNCTIONS IN *Crithidia* SPP.

Pteridine functions satisfied by	Concentration required for full growth	Metabolic function in synthesis of
Folic acid	0.06–0.1 mg./100 ml.	Thymine, unknown factor, and *Crithidia* factor
Leucovorin	0.3–0.6 mg./100 ml.	Thymine, unknown factor, and *Crithidia* factor
Folic acid plus *Crithidia* factor	0.01–0.1 μg./100ml. 0.01–0.1 μg./100ml.	Thymine and unknown factor Vitamin B_{12} plus at least one other factor
Leucovorin plus *Crithidia* factor	0.01–0.1 μg./100ml. 0.01–0.1 μg./100ml.	Thymine and unknown factor Vitamin B_{12} plus at least one other factor
Thymine (or thymidine) Folic acid[a] plus *Crithidia* factor	1.0–3.0 μg./100ml. 0.005 μg./100ml. 0.01–0.1 μg./100ml.	Nucleic acids Unknown factor Vitamin B_{12} plus at least one other factor
Folic acid (or leucovorin) plus 2,4,5-triamino,6-hydroxypyrimidine and Glucose[b]	0.01–0.1 μg./100ml. 0.5 mg./100ml. 0.1–1.0 mg./100 ml.	Thymine and unknown factor *Crithidia* factor

[a] Organisms grow well without this supplement. See text Fig. 2, and Guttman (1964b) for further details.

[b] The following also serve: L-rhamnose, D-mannose, D-galactose, gluconolactone, and sucrose. To demonstrate *Crithidia*-factor synthesis, the organisms must be grown in a medium containing sorbitol as its substrate carbohydrate.

pteridine, part of which the organism can convert to a *Crithidia* factor (conversion from a pteridine pool); or (c) as non-pteridine precursors from which *Crithidia* factor can be synthesized (*de novo* synthesis).

The mechanism by which *Crithidia* distinguishes between pteridines which may or may not serve as *Crithidia* factors is probably located, at least in part, in the cell membrane. In a combination of growth (Ziegler and Nathan, 1961) and incubation (Nathan and Ziegler, 1961) studies, *Crithidia* only took up those *Drosophila* eye pteridines which can serve as *Crithidia* factors, i.e., isodrosopterin, inert as a growth factor, was not taken up by whole *C. fasciculata* cells but its isomer drosopterin, active as a growth factor, was readily taken up.

The function of unconjugated pteridines is only now being clarified. It was shown (reviewed by Kaufman, 1962) that $2\text{-NH}_2\text{-}4\text{-OH-}6,7\text{di-CH}_3$ tetrahydropteridine mediated the conversion of phenylalanine to tyrosine. This reaction is ruled out as the one which demands the presence of *Crithidia* factor because both phenylalanine and tyrosine are required by *Crithidia*. That *Crithidia* factor may be implicated in some growth-limiting hydroxylations cannot yet be ruled out. Although the hydroxylation of tryptophan to 5-OH tryptophan usually does not require a cofactor, we have at times shown a sparing of the *Crithidia* factor requirement by 5-OH tryptophan. A short report has recently implicated unconjugated pteridines in still another reaction: the oxidation of glyceryl ethers (Tietz *et al.* 1963).

Although there is no reason to believe that this is the growth-limiting function of *Crithidia* factor, one might speculate that at least one function of *Crithidia* factor involves lipids: lipids are conspicuously omitted from the current *Crithidia* media (Table II).

A nongrowth-limiting function for *Crithidia* factor—and pteridines in general—in *Crithidia* spp. is in the synthesis of vitamin B_{12} and congeners. *Crithidia fasciculata* (both *Anopheles* and *Culex pipiens* strains) and *C. oncopelti* only produce materials with B_{12} activity for *Ochromonas malhamensis* ("true" B_{12} activity) and for *Euglena gracilis* ("total" B_{12} activity) when

Table V

PRODUCTION OF VITAMIN B_{12}-LIKE ACTIVITY BY TRYPANOSOMATIDS

| | mμg. Vitamin B_{12}/liter of whole culture | | | |
| | C. fasciculata[a] | | C. oncopelti[b] | |
Pteridines added to growth medium	Euglena assay	Ochromonas assay	Euglena assay	Ochromonas assay
Folic acid 0.1 mg./100 ml.	4.0	4.6	Not tested	Not tested
Folic acid 0.05 mg./100 ml.	Not tested	Not tested	67.5	45.0
Folic acid 0.01 μg./100 ml. plus 2-NH$_2$, 4-OH, 6-trihydroxypropyl pteridine 0.1 μg./100 ml.	6.4	5.2	67.5	45.0
2-NH$_2$, 4-OH, 6-trihydroxypropyl pteridine 0.1 μg./100 ml.	5.2	0.7	Not tested	Not tested
None	0	0	0	0

[a] Vitamin B_{12} activity in both cells and culture supernatant.

[b] Vitamin B_{12} activity only in cells.

grown in pteridine-containing media (Nathan and Funk, 1959; Nathan *et al.*, 1960). The dependence on pteridine presence for B_{12} synthesis is especially striking in *C. oncopelti* (Table V), an organism which is usually grown in pteridine-free media. The role of pteridines as regulators of cell metabolism, probably independent of coenzyme function in the particular biosynthetic sequence, is unknown.

The production by *C. fasciculata* of more *Ochromonas*-B_{12}-activity (so-called true or human B_{12} activity) than *Euglena*-B_{12}-activity (so-called total B_{12}-activity) has its parallel in human metabolism: sera from patients with a variety of liver diseases (Rachmilewitz and Grossowicz, 1956) show the same phenomenon. Thus *C. fasciculata* provides a readily controllable system in which to study some factors which go awry in liver disease.

C. METHIONINE REQUIREMENT

The requirement for methionine is being investigated in some detail. At least some organisms, 1–8, in Table I require methionine for growth (Guttman, 1962). Some but not all of these trypanosomatids can synthesize methionine from homocysteine during growth (Guttman, 1963a; Table VI). Synthesis of

Table VI

METHIONINE SYNTHESIS FROM HOMOCYSTEINE THIOLACTONE BY TRYPANOSOMATIDS

Organism	Ability to synthesize methionine at 23–26°
Crithidia fasciculata (*Anopheles*)	Synthesis only at 28°
C. fasciculata (*Culex pipiens*)	+
C. fasciculata (*Culex pipiens*) Nöller strain	0
Crithidia sp. from *Syrphid*	0
C. luciliae	+
Crithidia sp. from *Europhthalmus davisi*	+
B. culicis	+

methionine is temperature sensitive with a cut-off point at 32–33°. The cofactor requirements for methionine synthesis in these organisms have not yet been identified. Methionine synthesis only occurs when the culture medium contains unphysiologically high levels of folic acid plus *Crithidia* factor (see Section IV,B,1 for details of pteridine metabolism). The possibility existed that folic acid could serve as a precursor of another pteridine vitamin particularly concerned with methylation. However hydrolysis of folic acid (see Table III for conditions) under conditions which completely destroys it does not diminish ability of the hydrolyzate to serve as a source of methylation cofactors (Guttman, 1962). It thus appears that the true cofactor is one of the impurities present in commercial folic acid. It is not any one of the following which have been excluded by test: *p*-aminobenzoic acid, *p*-aminobenzoylglutamic acid, pteroic acid, rhizopterin, and the following: 2-NH_2, 4-OH pteridines; 6-dihydroxypropyl (biopterin); 6,7-di OH (leucopterin); 6-OH (xanthopterin); 6-hydroxy-methyl; 6-CHO; 6-COOH; and the tetrahydro 6,7-dimethyl pteridine which is the cofactor for phenylalanine hydroxylase (Kaufman, 1962).

D. Lipid Requirements

No trypanosomatid growing in defined media (Table I) has a proven lipid requirement under normal conditions of laboratory culture. When *C. fasciculata* (*Anopheles* or *Culex pipiens* strains), *Crithidia* sp. from *Euryophthalmus* or *B. culicis* are grown at temperatures above their usual 22–27°C. supplements must be added to the medium (Nathan *et al.*, 1958; Guttman, 1963b). Between 32.5 and 33.3° (it varies slightly from experiment to experiment) growth ceases unless a lipid supplement from egg yolk is added. The combination lecithin plus cholesterol instead of egg yolk yields somewhat less growth (Guttman, 1962).

Some lower trypanosomatids not yet in growing partly defined media have lipid requirements (Guttman, 1964a). Lipid requirements of *Trypanosoma* spp. are covered in Section V.

E. Carbohydrate Requirements

All defined media for trypanosomatids and most undefined media contain a sugar. Glucose is most frequently used but sucrose, which does not caramelize when autoclaved with the required high pH (7.6–8.1) media, is a good substitute. Both glucose and sucrose are utilized for growth by all trypanosomatids growing in defined media at room temperature but utilization differences emerge as incubation temperature increases (Nathan *et al.*, 1958; Table VII) and are only erased by nutritional supplementation. Cosgrove (1963) showed that *C. luciliae*, and by implication several other trypanosomatids, probably contain hydrolases for sucrose and several other oligosaccharides. The presence of exohydrolases was excluded. One might expect that the hydrolases are membrane-associated or are quite close to the membranes. Cytochemical tests could resolve this question. One should also determine whether the auxiliary factors required for sucrose utilization (Table VII) at elevated temperatures serve to annul temperature damage to a particularly labile sucrase.

Early studies by Noguchi (1926) showed serological (agglutination tests) similarities among trypanosomatids. More recently McGhee and Hanson (1963) found several differences between their agglutination tests and Noguchi's, but for our purposes it suffices to note that they found gross cross-reactions among surface antigens of crithidias from hemiptera, while crithidias from diptera

Table VII

Effect of Temperature on Carbohydrate Utilization
by *Crithidia fasciculata* (*Anopheles* strain)[a]

Additions	Temp. 24–27°		Temp. 28–30°		Temp. 32.4°	
	Sucrose 2.0%	Glucose 1.0%	Sucrose 2.0%	Glucose 1.0%	Sucrose 2.0%	Glucose 1.0%
(1) None[b]	1.1	1.1	0.74	0.67	0.10	0.06
(2) Ca (as Cl): 15.0 mg./100 ml.	—	—	1.46	1.42	0.32	0.87
$MgSO_4 \cdot 7H_2O$: 0.1%	—	—	—	—	—	—
Fe (as SO_4): 0.5 mg./100 ml.	—	—	—	—	—	—
Cu (as SO_4): 0.04 mg./100 ml.	—	—	—	—	—	—
(3) L-Glutamic acid: 0.3%	—	—	1.38	1.28	0.96	1.43
Na_2 succinate·$6H_2O$: 0.1%	—	—	—	—	—	—
DL-Lactate: 0.2%	—	—	—	—	—	—
(4) No. 2 + No. 3	—	—	1.35	1.33	1.3	1.3

[a] Data of Nathan *et al.*, 1958.

[b] Unsupplemented medium of Nathan and Cowperthwaite (1954) used. Medium in Table VII was supplemented with glutamic acid and metals in response to these results.

cross-reacted among themselves. McGhee and Hanson (1963) suggested that differences between the cross-reacting crithidias might be revealed by techniques which revealed internal antigens. We expect that immunoelectrophoretic fine structure will also be different. McGhee and Hanson (1963) pointed out obvious differences between growth characteristics of some of the cross-reacting crithidias.

On the basis of serology and fermentation Noguchi (1926) fused the organisms now called *C. fasciculata* (*Anopheles*) and *C. fasciculata* (*Culex pipiens* strain) into *Herpetomonas culicidarum*. Many differences between the two organisms were overlooked by these limited tests. Differences in ability to synthesize methionine (Table VI) and differences in catalase content and effect of temperature on catalase content were shown by Wertlieb and Guttman (1963). Differences in carbohydrate utilization for growth (Guttman, 1963b) reveal the scope of tests needed to separate *Crithidia* strains biochemically.

Noguchi (1926) ascribed great significance to similarities of fermentative acid production from a small number of sugars—a method successful as one basis for speciation among bacteria. Among the protozoa, Seaman (1951) has shown failure to correlate fermentative acid production with utilizability of carbohydrates for growth of *Tetrahymena pyriformis*. In tests detailed elsewhere (Guttman, 1963b), differences in ability to utilize carbohydrates for growth between not only the *Anopheles* and *Culex pipiens* strains of *C. fascicu-*

lata but also among three other crithidias and *Blastocrithidia culicis,* all in defined media, are given.

Ryley (1955, 1956, 1962) and Cosgrove (1959) used increase in respiration rate in the presence of various substrates to evaluate carbohydrate metabolism of crithidias and some trypanosomes. Cosgrove (1959) pointed out the rather high endogenous O_2-consumption of *C. fasciculata* (*Anopheles* strain) and so expressed results as a combination of abolition of endogenous O_2 consumption and increase in respiration rate by carbohydrates. It is difficult to evaluate results expressed as abolition of endogenous respiration in terms of ability of a trypanosomatid to use a carbohydrate as a major substrate or as an aid in speciation, for, as already pointed out (reviewed by von Brand, 1951), composition of the medium in which respiratory experiments are done have a considerable effect on O_2-consumption.

Another method of evaluating carbohydrate metabolism is to trace the disappearance of carbohydrate from the medium. This ostensibly straightforward approach has many pitfalls. Uptake of carbohydrate is most frequently measured as disappearance of carbohydrate from a nongrowth medium (Ryley, 1962; Cosgrove, 1963). This method imposes limitations on uptake of carbohydrates which may require accessory factors for some transportase function. One might draw an analogy with bacteriophages which require the presence of attachment factors. The interpretation of carbohydrate utilization by nongrowing suspensions of organisms which had been grown in a glucose-containing medium is subject to constraints frequently imposed by glucose on utilization of a second carbohydrate (see diauxie section in Monod, 1942). Even if the previous growth medium does not affect utilization of a carbohydrate by cell suspensions, a conversion factor is required to determine how efficient carbohydrate uptake by suspensions must be (if it is strictly analogous) to be equivalent as a measure of carbohydrates utilizable as growth-supporting substrate. These problems would be obviated by doing parallel growth and kinetic uptake experiments in the same medium.

V. Growth of Trypanosomes

A. TRYPANOSOMA CRUZI

The most progress in defining media for trypanosomes was made by Citri and Grossowicz (1954, 1955). Since both investigators have changed their research interests, their work is detailed here. Citri and Grossowicz's medium for *Trypanosoma cruzi* is given in Table VIII. The three undefined components are casein hydrolyzate, serum albumin, and ribonucleic acid (RNA). They noted that oleic acid (contained in Tween 80) is not a growth requirement but was added to increase cell permeability. The presence of oleate, which was

Table VIII

PARTLY DEFINED MEDIUM FOR *Trypanosoma cruzi*[a]

Component	mg./100 ml.
NaCl	400.0
$Na_2HPO_4 \cdot 12H_2O$	300.0
KH_2PO_4	50.0
Casein hydrolyzate (enzyme digest)	1,000.0
Glucose	200.0
Hemin	1.0
p-Aminobenzoic acid	0.01
Biotin	0.02
Choline	0.3
Folic acid	0.25
Inositol	15.0
Nicotinamide	1.5
Pyridoxine	0.2
Pyridoxal	0.2
Pyridoxamine	0.2
Riboflavin	0.1
Thiamine	0.1
Vitamin B_{12}	0.00001
RNA	8.0
Cytidylic acid	2.0
Creatine	2.0
Creatinine	2.0
Tween 80[b]	1.0
Crystalline serum albumin[b]	200.0

[a] Data of Citri and Grossowicz (1955). This medium also adequate for *T. acomys*, *Leishmania tropica*, and *C. fasciculata*.

[b] These two components not required for growth. Tween 80 increases permeability and serum albumin detoxifies the oleic acid component of Tween 80.

somewhat toxic, forced a requirement for serum albumin as a detoxicant.

One would expect to replace RNA with one or more purines (pyrimidine-requiring trypanosomatids have still to be reported) and to replace casein hydrolyzate with amino acids alone, or in combination with metals, or metals and some lipid since activity of several casein hydroylzate preparations at times is partly due to these accessory factors. One might also expect that pantothenate, a conspicuous omission from the roster of vitamins, will be required in a revised medium.

Although Citri and Grossowicz (1955) did not state how long their cultures were grown before growth was assessed, one can assume that it was done at the end of log or beginning of stationary phase. Their counts, expressed as organisms $\times$ 10^7/ml. were: *T. cruzi*, 5.0; *T. acomys*, 5.1; *L. tropica*, 3.2, and *C. fasciculata*, 9.6. All organisms grew to the indicated densities upon serial transfer in the medium in Table VIII establishing the adequacy of the medium.

One dissent has been registered about the quality of the medium in Table VIII by Boné and Parent (1963) who claim unsatisfactory growth with the Citri-Grossowicz medium. Therefore they used a hardly defined medium previously designed in their laboratory (Boné and Steinert, 1956) and supplemented it further. They previously claimed the supplemented medium was suitable (Boné and Steinert, 1956). Their best medium, reported able to sustain their strain of *T. cruzi* at a density of 5–7 $\times$ 10^7 organisms/ml. [the same figure Citri and Grossowicz (1955) obtained with their medium] contained the following in grams per liter: Bacto-Tryptose, 15; glucose, 2; thiamine, 0.001; folic acid, 0.003; hemin; 0.02; Na stearate,* 0.025; NaCl, 4; $Na_3PO_4 \cdot 12H_2O$, 5; KCl, 0.4.

Growth increase in the Boné-Parent medium is far from spectacular when one compares the number of organisms inoculated (2.5–3.5 $\times$ 10^6/ml.) to the best growth achieved: it is only a 20- to 30-fold increase. Even though Boné and Parent (1963) have maintained their *T. cruzi* strain through serial transfer, one wonders whether growth and serial transfer from small inocula is possible.

Boné and Parent (1963) did clarify an aspect of lipid metabolism of *T. cruzi*: they confirmed the observation of Citri and Grossowicz (1955) that Tween 80 (oleic acid-containing) is somewhat toxic for *T. cruzi*. Boné and Parent's *T. cruzi* strain required a lipid which could be supplied by high concentrations (50.0 mg./100 ml.) of egg yolk lecithin or phosphatidyl inositol. From these clues, they identified the lipid growth factor as stearic acid (see Table IX for

Table IX

LIPID GROWTH FACTORS FOR A STRAIN OF *Trypanosoma cruzi*[a]

Active	Concentration (mg./100 ml.)	Inhibitory	Inactive
Stearic acid	2.5	Lauric acid	Linoleic acid
Sodium stearate	2.5	Myristic acid	Arachidic acid
Tween 60[b]	6.0	Palmitic acid	
Behenic acid	10.0	Palmitoleic acid	
Egg yolk lecithin[c]	50.0	Linolenic and oleic acid	
Phosphatidyl inositol[c]	50.0	Arachidonic acid	
		Butyl ester of stearic acid	

[a] According to Boné and Parent (1963).

[b] Best growth achieved is lower than in the presence of sodium stearate.

[c] Activity presumed due to stearic acid content.

* A freshly prepared colloidal solution was used for each batch of medium: stearic acid, 20 mg. + distilled H_2O, 98.3 ml. + 0.1 N NaOH, 1.7 ml., heated at 70° and stirred for 30 min.

list of active, inactive, and inibitory lipids). Failure of Citri and Grossowicz (1955) to uncover a lipid requirement may have been due to the presence of an active lipid in one or another of their undefined components or, less likely, a lack of a lipid requirement by their *T. cruzi* strain.

There are few other trypanosomes growing in liquid media (see Section V,B). We emphasize this method of growing trypanosomatids because under these conditions large-scale experiments on defining medium are simplified.

B. Trypanosoma mega

A medium for *T. mega* (isolated from the African toad, *Bufo regularis*) was designed by Boné and Steinert (1956). Their deceptively simple medium is composed of the following in grams per liter: Bacto-Tryptose, 15; Oxoid liver infusion, 1.0; glucose, 2.0; hemin, 0.02; NaCl, 4.0; $Na_3PO_4 \cdot 12H_2O$, 5.0; KCl, 0.4 (compare this with the Boné-Parent–*T. cruzi* medium in Section V,A). No further refinements of this medium have been reported. Other aspects of *T. mega* metabolism are covered in Section VI.

C. Other Trypanosomes

The Deanes (M. P. and L. M. Deane, 1961) added *T. conorrhini* to the list of organisms growing in liquid media. Although their medium supported growth of organisms newly harvested from blood-agar slants, success of serial cultivation is doubtful. The Deanes' medium is composed of: 100 ml. Hank's saline with phenol-red indicator, 2.5% enzymatic hydrolyzate of lactalbumin (in 10 ml. Hank's saline) and 20 ml. calf serum. Conspicuous absences include vitamins and nucleic acid derivatives (serum probably contains enough for one culture generation), carbohydrates, and hemin. The latter factors probably are carried over from the inoculum. One approach to defined media construction for *T. conorrhini* and perhaps other trypanosomes and leishmanias is to identify factors required to supplement the Deanes' medium and make it adequate for serial maintenance of the organisms.

Trypanosoma theileri and *Leishmania donovani* are good candidates for medium definition. Ristic and Trager (1958) grew *T. theileri* at two temperature ranges (25–28° and 37°) in a cow-blood lysate medium which also contained whole blood cells. The best growth reported was 5×10 organisms/ml. compared to 5×10^7 organisms/ml. for *T. cruzi* grown in other media (Section V,A). At 37°, *T. theileri* cultures contain crithidial forms with a small percentage of trypanosomes. The same blood lysate medium was used by Trager (1953) to grow leishmania-like forms of *L. donovani* at 37°.

Wallace (1956) and later Lehmann (1962) grew *T. ranarum* in a monophasic version* of Diamond and Herman's (1954) diphasic SNB-9 medium

---

* The liquid medium contained NaCl, 4.95 g.; Neopeptone (Difco) 18.0 g.; water, 900.0 ml.; and 5% (v/v) defibrinated rabbit blood.

(see footnote page 480). Wallace (1956) improved the growth by substituting yeast extract for Neopeptone.

Warren (1960) grew *Schizotrypanum cruzi* in a medium composed of brain-heart infusion and filtrate of coagulated whole blood. He found that endogenous respiration increased with culture age.

D. Organisms in Diphasic Media

Diphasic media constitute another starting point for defining media. Such media are invaluable for maintaining human pathogens *in vitro* and for producing fair quantities of organisms for studies not requiring defined media. Rather than giving an exhaustive list of those trypanosomes growing in diphasic media, we will give some characteristics of media and precautions useful for work with other organisms as well.

Before work on defining media began, many trypanosomatids—especially the human pathogens—were being isolated and maintained in one or another diphasic medium. The ancestor of most of these media is NNN medium (NaCl 0.6 g.; agar 1.4 g.; and water 90 ml.). One early medium, called Leptospira medium by Noguchi and Tilden (1926), was used for growth of several insect trypanosomatids in quantities sufficient for subsequent use as antigens for the production of rabbit antisera. Noguchi and Tilden's (1926) medium was: 0.9% NaCl, 80 ml.; fresh rabbit serum, 100 ml.; 2.0% agar (pH 6.5–7), 100 ml.; rabbit hemoglobin (to prepare: defibrinate blood, then add 3 parts distilled water) 10 ml.

In 1949 Sampath and Little designed a medium for *T. cruzi* which contained some defined elements in addition to agar and red blood cells. The problem of defining *T. cruzi* media is virtually solved (see Section V,A) and so problems encountered there will be helpful in work with other organisms. Citri and Grossowicz (1955) told how extra components had to be added to their medium to counteract toxicity by another component. Wallace (1956) speculated that the function of agar in the Diamond and Herman's (1954) medium he used for *T. ranarum* was to detoxify some blood component—probably complement.

Wallace's speculation, expanded to include other toxic blood components, may explain Vickerman's observation (personal communication) that some trypanosomatids, growing in blood media, require human blood of a particular type. Perhaps expanded use of polyvinyl sulfuric acid (PVSA), an anticoagulant which reduces effects by complement (Weinman, 1953), will obviate some of the toxic effects. In laboratories using blood donors who have survived trypanosome or leishmania infections, presence of antibodies is a further complication.

There is little agreement among trypanosome workers about the efficacy of different media. Differences in balance between toxic factors and growth factors are undoubtedly involved besides differences in the strains used in the several laboratories.

Diamond and Herman's (1954) SNB-9 medium* has been used to maintain many trypanosomatids isolated from insects, amphibia, and warm-blooded hosts.

Tobie *et al.* (1950) described a diphasic blood agar for *T. rhodesiense* and *T. gambiense*. Tobie (1958) grew *T. congolense* in the same medium after she grew this organism in a liquid blood-containing medium. Lehmann (1960) grew *T. rhodesiense* and *T. brucei* in diphasic media and Weinman (1960) grew *T. rhodesiense* and *T. gambiense* in a diphasic isolation medium.

Another problem is loss of cultivability of some trypanosomes after serial passage through laboratory animals (Reichenow, 1934). Weinman (1953) suggested that failure to complete a life cycle which is "fixed in nature" may be the cause. But such a failure would also prevent continued animal passage. Rather, we would expect that during animal passage the organisms either acquired additional growth requirements or became sensitive to a component in the growth medium.

E. EXPERIMENTAL MORPHOGENESIS

Little is known of the factors required to maintain polymorphic Trypanosomatidae in culture in the form they have in their highest animal host. Some experiments on factors which enhance the proportion of trypanosomes among the amembranous forms have been done. Is the increase in percentage of trypanosomes due to transformation or conversion of a population of mixed morphology from one composed of 90% amembranous forms to one composed of 90% trypanosomes? Such a phenomenon is not unique: such changes in *Brucella* (Braun, 1946) and *Pneumococcus* (Firshein and Braun, 1960) have been detailed. While we do not question the existence of life cycles in *Trypanosoma* and *Leishmania,* we suggest that recently cloned cultures be used for all *in vitro* morphogenesis experiments.

Franca (1911) claimed that amembranous forms of *T. rotatorium* from the digestive tract of a leech transformed into trypanosomes when transferred to constantly agitated frog serum. Agitation rather than the presence of serum was considered the essential factor. The first in a series of papers on induced morphological changes in noncloned *T. mega* appeared in 1956 (Steinert and

---

* SNB-9 medium contains: agar, 18 g.; NaCl, 4.95 g.; Neopeptone (Difco), 90 ml., distributed 5 ml./16 × 125 mm. screw-capped tube. Add 0.5 ml. defibrinated rabbit blood after the other components have cooled to 48°C. Solidify as slants. Overlay with 0.5 ml. of the liquid components.

Boné, 1956). In this and a later paper, Steinert (1958b) described a serum factor which, at rather high concentration, encouraged morphological change. Most work was done with the factor from calf serum. The serum was toxic until complement was inactivated. The factor is probably a globulin (Steinert and Boné, 1956) and is stable to both RNase and DNase (Steinert, 1958b). Steinert (1958a) described similar morphological changes caused by the addition of 0.04% urea. Where morphological changes were reported, at best 50% trypanosomes were produced by the serum treatment and 10% trypanosomes were produced by the urea treatment. Photomicrographs were taken of the trypanosomes resulting from the transformation but neither experiments with cloned cultures nor time-lapse photographs showing conversion of amembranous forms to trypanosomes have been offered.

There have been no reports of effects of raising the incubation temperature upon the morphology of *T. mega;* experiments of this sort have been done with other organisms. The same criticisms hold for these experiments to be described as for the *T. mega* serum and urea experiments. But regardless of whether the population change in the direction of increased numbers of trypanosomes is transformation or alteration in proportion of population components, the observations are of considerable biological importance.

The Deanes (1961) grew *T. conorrhini* in a calf serum-containing medium (Section V,C) and also on blood agar. The blood-agar medium only supported growth at 28° but the serum medium supported growth at both 28° and 37°. At the lower temperature the organisms appeared as they do in their invertebrate host: either in crithidial stages or small metacyclic trypanosomes. At 37° they found "almost a pure culture of mature and dividing trypanosomes."

Trejos *et al.* (1963) isolated *Schizotrypanum cruzi* from acute Chagas' disease patients. The organisms were grown in L-cell cultures incubated at 26° or 37°. As in the *T. conorrhini* experiments, organisms incubated at the lower temperature resembled the forms usually found in the hind gut of the invertebrate host; both intra- and extracellular forms of organisms grown at the highest temperature resembled those in infected mammals.

Nathan *et al.* (1958) grew cloned *Crithidia* sp. at temperatures extending from 26° to 33°. As expected for *Crithidia,* there were no profound morphogenetic changes although organisms grown at the higher temperature were rounded and had stumpy flagella. Later incubation of the 33° cultures at 26° for a few hours rendered these cultures indistinguishable from cultures kept continuously at 26° (Nathan, 1958b).

Whether temperature is the crucial determinant of the appearance of *Leishmania* bodies remains a lively issue, not to be solved until *Leishmania* and *Crithidia* can be grown *in vitro* at body temperature.

VI. Growth in Tissue Culture

A. EMBRYONATED AVIAN EGGS

Reports on infection of chick and duck eggs with insect trypanosomatids have only appeared recently.

McGhee (1957) isolated trypanosomatid from *Euryophthalmus davisi*. In initial culture it appeared to be a mixture of what now would be considered *Blastocrithidia* plus amembranous forms. After a few serial transfers only the amembranous forms—now called *Crithidia* sp. from *Euryophthalmus davisi*—could be seen. [It has never been established whether *E. davisi* was doubly infected; the possibility was suggested by McGhee (1959).] McGhee (1957) infected chorioallantoic membranes of 9-day-old chick embryos. Incubation at $30° \pm 2°$ both maintained the embryo and provided favorable growth conditions for the trypanosomid. The *Crithidia* sp. survived at least 5 serial transfers on chick chorioallantoic membranes. Some of the parasites were extracellular while others were seen within phagocytes. The hemoflagellates survived incubation of the embryos at $37°$ for 10 days.

McGhee (1959) infected chorioallantoic membranes of embryonated duck eggs* with culture forms of *Leishmania tarentolae*. Parasites were never detected within phagocytes. Under similar conditions, he could not infect the duck eggs with *Phytomonas* (*Crithidia*) *elmassiani*. He also infected allantoic fluid with *Crithidia* sp. from *Euryophthalmus*. The parasites grew at $30°$ and survived at $38°$ if the infected eggs were incubated at $30°$ for 2 days before transfer to the higher temperature.

Wallace and Clark (1959) also grew *Crithidia* sp. from *Euryophthalmus davisi* and also two other *Crithidia* sp., *C. fasciculata* and *C. luciliae* in embryonated eggs. Infections of yolk sacs, chorioallantoic membranes, and allantoic fluid were successful at $25-31°$. Parasites did not survive in embryonated eggs incubated at $37°$ † or unembryonated eggs incubated at $31°$. *Blastocrithidia culicis* grew on chorioallantoic membranes of embryonated eggs incubated at $25-31°$ but the embryos were always killed when 2×10^7 trypanosomatids were inoculated. A similar-sized inoculation of *Crithidia* spp. proved less than 50% lethal.

Biocca (1938) infected chick-embryo allantoic fluid with *T. brucei*; in 1940 Geiman did similar experiments with *Leishmania tropica*. Lethal effects on chick embryos of *Leishmania* spp. reported by Jones *et al.* (1944) presaged the results of Wallace and Clark (1959) with insect trypanosomatids.

We will not detail reports of infection of embryonated eggs with trypano-

---

* Incubated at $30°$ subsequent to infection.

† They did not try incubating the parasitized eggs at $30°$ before increasing the temperature to $37°$.

somes or leishmania since a detailed review has recently appeared (Pipkin, 1960).

B. INVERTEBRATE TISSUE

Growth of trypanosomatids in insect tissue cultures was delayed until the recent development of methods for cultivation of dipteran tissue. Methods for growing various pupal and young adult tissues of *Glossina palpalis* for a fair length of time were developed by Trager (1959a,b). Three trypanosomes, *T. vivax*, *T. brucei*, and *T. congolense*, were grown in several of the tissues. Of special note are the first *in vitro* cultures of *T. vivax*. The special conditions required were inoculation of parasites from chronically infected blood into 2-day-old tissue cultures which had been incubated at 30°–32°C. After initiation of the parasitized culture, incubation temperature is no longer critical: any temperature between 27° and 32° will do. The trypanosomes were identical in form with infective stages retrieved from naturally infected vectors. Some, but not all, cultures of parasitized tissues survived a 19-hr. incubation at 38° and these *T. vivax* could infect sheep. This variability of survival is unexplained. More than survival at 38° is involved for maintenance of *T. brucei* infectivity, for parasites kept at 38° for 19 hr. were not infective.

The trehalose content of *Glossina* tissue (10–19 mg./100 g. tissue; Geigy *et al.*, 1959) has been suggested as a factor controlling development of *T. rhodesiense* and *T. gambiense* into infective forms (Weinman, 1960). Both species developed into infective forms in blood-agar medium containing trehalose, but their so-called sensitivity to trehalose was lost after several subcultures during a period of about 2 months. One cannot tell from the published report whether loss of sensitivity means inability to form infective stages after (*a*) serial transfer in blood-agar medium and then transfer to similar medium containing trehalose or (*b*) continuous transfer in trehalose-containing blood agar. Differences in trehalose metabolism among tissue culture isolates used by Trager (1959a,b) to grow *Trypanosoma* sp. may account, in part, for variability of the ability of his parasites to form infective stages in tissue culture.

Weinman (1960) suggested that the presence of trehalose in the milieu is only one factor involved in formation of infective stages of trypanosomes; another remains to be identified. Might the second factor be an inducible one? If so, we can visualize gradual depletion of the infection-enabling factor during the course of *in vitro* cultivation.

C. VERTEBRATE TISSUE

Use of vertebrate tissue to grow trypanosomatids has a fairly long history. The pioneering experiments were those of Erdman (1915) who used rat organ explants embedded in plasma clots or plasma clots alone to grow *T. brucei*. Pipkin (1960) gave a historical account of experiments on development of trypanosomatids in tissue culture; the methods reviewed by him provide techniques for studying intra- and extracellular development of parasites and for developing screening systems for trypanocides. Whether trypanosomatids will parasitize a particular cell line is probably determined in part by the synthetic capacities of the cells in culture; Demarchi and Nicoli (1960) suggested that ability to synthesize hematin—a trypanosomatid growth factor—partly determines ability of the parasites to multiply.

VII. Miscellaneous Experiments

A. Sexual Reproduction

Wenyon (1926) pointed out the absence of proof for sexuality in the Trypanosomatidae. Since then attempts to show sexual reproduction in trypanosomes have been made by Elkeles (1944) with *T. cruzi*, Vanderplank (1944, 1947) with *T. rhodesiense*, Fiennes (1945) with *T. congolense*, and Fairbairn *et al.* (1946) with several species; none of these observations and experiments was convincing. Wenrich (1954) reiterated the lack of conclusive evidence for sexuality in trypanosomes.

Amrein (1957) and Amrein and Fulton (1959) mixed strains of *T. gambiense* or of *T. rhodesiense* which were resistant to different trypanocides and then tested for development of cross-resistant strains. Appearance of such cross-resistance would have signified exchange of genetic material; cross-resistant strains did not develop. Fulton (1960) was noncommittal: he cited the various opinions on sexual exchange or genetic material. Stephen (1962) found evidence of binary fission but no evidence of syngamy or other forms of sexual reproduction in *T. simiae* or *T. congolense*. There have been no reports on attempts to show exchange of genetic material in *Leishmania* or lower Trypanosomatidae.

Fulton (1960) was skeptical about trypanosomal transformation. However, the experiments of Inoki's group deserve repetition. Inoki and Matsushiro (1960) sought to detect transformation in *T. gambiense* through transfer of pararosaniline resistance. Inoki *et al.* (1961a,b) extended the transformation experiments to *T. evansi* and to the transfer of pararosaniline resistance between *T. gambiense* and *T. evansi*, and claimed positive results.

B. Akinetoplasty

Kinetoplasts (see Section II for synonyms) had long been known in trypanosomes when Bresslau and Scremin (1924) showed that kinetoplasts, like nuclei, are Feulgen positive. *Trypanosoma evansi* and *T. equiperdum*, two species whose life cycles lack stages in insect hosts, spontaneously lose their kinetoplasts in nature (reviewed by Hoare, 1954). Reichenow (1940) suggested that kinetoplastic trypanosomes cannot infect intermediate hosts. Therefore any mutant akinetoplastic trypanosomes are weeded out when the trypanosomes infect the insect vector.

Werbitzki (1910) and later Jírovec (1929) induced akinetoplasty in trypanosomes with acridine dyes such as acriflavine. Mühlpfordt (1959) did similar experiments with *T. evansi, T. equiperdum, T. brucei,* and *T. gambiense* but he could not induce akinetoplasty in *T. cruzi* with acriflavine.

Inoki's group investigated the mode of action of dyes in the production of akinetoplasty in *T. gambiense* and *T. evansi.* Hoare (1954) proposed that naturally produced akinetoplastic *T. evansi* resulted when kinetoplast division did not match cell division. Inoki (1957) suggested that acriflavine, rosaniline, and pararosaniline induced akinetoplasty in *T. gambiense* by inhibiting kinetoplast division. Such action had been proposed by Lavier (1927). However Inoki *et al.* (1961a) showed that acriflavine selects for akinetoplastic *T. evansi* by inhibiting division of only kinetoplastic forms. The differences in modes of action in the two species deserve further study.

Trager and Rudzinska (1964) produced 70–86% akinetoplasty in *Leishmania tarentolae* grown in a defined medium by providing the organisms with an optimal level of riboflavin (2.0 μg.%) plus acriflavine (33–60 μg.). Electron micrographs of akinetoplastic *L. tarentolae,* showed that the kinetoplast-limiting membrane was still intact.* The connecting mitochondrion was also still apparent although most of the cristae were lost. They did not check for retention of Janus green staining. These results make necessary a modification of the term akinetoplasty to loss of highly polymerized deoxyribonucleic acid (DNA) from the kinetoplast envelope rather than complete loss of the kinetoplast. Whether some akinetoplastic organisms also lose the kinetoplast envelope remains to be determined. If kinetoplast envelopes are found in akinetoplastic *T. gambiense* produced by Inoki's (1957) method, a revision will be required in his suggestion that acriflavine inhibits *T. gambiense*-kinetoplast division.

Reduction of *akinetoplasty* to mean only loss of DNA (= loss of Giemsa stainability and loss of electron-dense inclusions in the kinetoplasts) requires us to investigate the limits of DNA loss: are small DNA polymers also lost? Are all the DNA bases still present or is there a selective loss of one base which prevents further DNA synthesis? The intimate connection between riboflavin and acriflavine levels for induction of akinetoplasty in *L. tarentolae* (Trager and Rudzinska, 1964) suggests a sensitive flavin-enzyme site.

Investigations of the metabolic role of the kinetoplast envelope are also needed. The electron micrographs of Trager and Rudzinska (1964) and others

---

* Note added in proof: Mühlpfordt (1963a,b) found similar results with *T. cruzi* and several insect trypanosomatids. He concurs that organisms which contain kinetoplast envelops devoid of Giemsa-staining DNA, should not be termed akinetoplastic.

(see Section II) and the Janus green staining results of Shipley (1916) and others (see Section II) show continuity between the DNA-containing portion of the kinetoplast and at least one mitochondrion. If all the cell's mitochondria originate from the kinetoplast envelope, much the same way that mitochondria in higher plants are formed from chloroplast-limiting membranes (Wildman *et al.*, 1962), then one would expect that failure to maintain akinetoplastic trypanosomatids may be related to metabolic inactivation of the remaining kinetoplast envelope. Such organisms may survive under obligately anaerobic conditions. Possibly, some mitochondria are produced by pinching off nuclear membranes: Linnane *et al.* (1962) think yeast mitochondria originate in the nucleus. Thus alterations in metabolic function of nuclear membranes from akinetoplastic trypanosomatids must also be considered.

We have begun experiments on chemical induction of akinetoplasty in *Crithidia* and *Blastocrithidia* spp. grown in defined media. Akinetoplastic organisms will be tested for ability to infect insects (methods of Wallace and Johnson, 1961) and for other metabolic changes. It was first thought that akinetoplastic trypanosomes (in this case *T. evansi*) "behaved normally" (Hoare and Bennett, 1938) but Ray and Malhotra (1960) showed that Prothridium-induced akinetoplastic *T. evansi* have a prolonged generation time.

C. CHEMICAL COMPOSITION OF TRYPANOSOMATIDS

Desowitz (1959) and Williamson and Desowitz (1961) electrophoretically separated proteins from homogenates of *T. vivax, T. brucei, T. gambiense,* and *T. rhodesiense.* Three of the four protein fractions were found in all samples, the most mobile fourth fraction appeared as a diffuse trail in most but not all samples. None of the proteins were identified.

Williamson and Desowitz (1961) analyzed the amino acid composition of the four already mentioned species and also of *Crithidia oncopelti, T. cruzi* (culture forms), *T. lewisi, T. equinum,* and stilbamidine-resistant *T. rhodesiense.* Then they determined the protein amino acid and free amino acid patterns of the organisms and tested the theory of Schueler (1947) that the isoelectric point of some protein may shift with acquisition of drug resistance. No unusual proportions were found among the protein amino acids nor were there any statistically significant differences between amino acids with free ionizing end groups from stilbamidine-sensitive or stilbamidine-resistant *T. rhodesiense.* The free amino acids accounted for a small fraction of the total amino acids present. Alanine was the predominant component of the free amino pool: it accounted for about half of the total, except in *T. brucei* where the pool was 90% alanine.

Hack *et al.* (1962) found neutral lipids, phosphatidyl ethanolamine, phosphatidyl choline, and at least two inosities in *C. fasciculata* (ATCC 12857), *C. luciliae, B. culicis, T. cruzi,* and *L. donovani.* All but the latter two organisms contain cardiolipid. All the trypanosomatids lacked glycolipids and phosphatidyl glycerol, components common to *Chlamydomonas sphagnophila, Euglena gracilis,* and *Chlorella pyrenoidosa.*

Halevy (1962) identified glycerol, sterols, and sterol esters in *L. culicidarum* (probably *Crithidia fasciculata, Anopheles* strain), *H. muscidarum, L. tropica,* and *T. cruzi.* He explained his finding as an ergosterol-type sterol instead of cholesterol (previously reported by von Brand *et al., 1959*) as possible results of differences in strains or of cultural conditions. Halevy (1962) measured C^{14}-acetate incorporation into the various lipid fractions. It is difficult to evaluate the finding of increased incorporation into the sterols and sterol esters of *L. culicidarum* and *M. muscidarum* (as compared with *L. tropica* and *T. cruzi*) since cultures of the latter two organisms used for analysis were grown three times as long as the other two organisms. The growth phases of the cultures when they were harvested were not indicated.

D. NUCLEIC ACID SYNTHESIS

The nonspecific purine requirement for growth of all trypanosomatids listed in Table I save for *C. oncopelti* has been discussed (Section IV,A). The enzymatic capacities of *C. oncopelti* are difficult to determine because it contains an endosymbiote. Since there has been no census of enzymes involved in purine synthesis in these organisms, one can only approximate the location of the lesion in biosynthesis reflected as "a purine requirement."

Williamson and Rollo (1952) pointed out the requirement of *T. rhodesiense* for preformed adenine rather than for adenine precursors. Several crithidias can synthesize enough purine to satisfy their growth requirements from an imidazole precursor (Section IV,A) but they cannot synthesize purine from glycine (Nathan, 1954).

Boné and Steinert (1956) could not show incorporation of glycine-2-C^{14} or formate C^{14} into nucleic acids of *T. mega* although both acids could be traced into proteins. In contrast, Boné and Steinert (1956) reported rapid incorporation of adenine-8-C^{14} into *T. mega* nucleic acids; RNA was preferentially labeled (3–10 times more than DNA) and adenine was incorporated faster into adenine ribotides (4–5 times faster than into guanine ribotides) and adenine deoxyribotides (about twice as fast as into guanine deoxyribotides).

Fernandes and Castellani (1958) also saw no incorporation of glycine into *T. cruzi* nucleic acids. They have not expanded upon their report (1958) of a small amount of glycine incorporation into acid-soluble adenine which was unaffected by azaserine, an adenine-synthesis inhibitor. Their finding that stylomycin (puromycin) somewhat inhibited adenine incorporation into the acid-soluble adenine fraction (only when fairly large amounts of adenine-C^{14} were supplied) but did not affect incorporation into the nucleic acid adenine may support Yarmolinsky and Haba's (1959) suggestion that stylomycin may inhibit amino acid transfer during protein synthesis (stylomycin resembles the terminal adenylic amino acid of transfer RNA). Fernandes and Castellani (1958) also reported without interpretation that the combination of high levels of stylomycin plus low levels of adenine-C^{14} gave enhanced incorporation into acid-soluble adenine. In apparent contradiction of their 1958 paper, Castellani and Fernandes (1962) reported that stylomycin (and several analogs of stylomycin) inhibited incorporation of adenine into both nucleic acid adenine and nucleic acid guanine.

Pizzi (1961) found that 1-β-hydroxyethyl-2-methyl-5-nitroimidazole inhibited $T.$ $cruzi$ in mice, which suggests that trypanosomes share with $Crithidia$ the ability to synthesize nucleic acid purines from one of the imidazole precursors. Inability to synthesize purines de $novo$ from glycine is emerging as a general property of the Trypanosomatidae, the block being somewhere between glycine and synthesis of the last imidazole precursor.

None of the trypanosomatids growing in defined media (Tables I and II) require pyrimidines. Thus one expects a full complement of pyrimidine biosynthesis enzymes in these parasites. The questions remaining open are: (a) Is ability to synthesize pyrimidine de $novo$ a property of the whole family? (b) In places where alternate pathways are available, is only one pathway commonly used?

Rey and Fernandes (1962) showed a preferential incorporation of orotic acid-2-C^{14} and uracil-2-C^{14} into (a) acid-soluble plus coenzyme pyrimidines and (b) nucleic acid pyrimidines. No analyses were done for thymine derivatives. Orotic acid preferentially is incorporated into fraction (a) with label in the uridylic acid fraction one-third greater than in the cytidylic acid fraction. Incorporation into fraction (b) was one-tenth of that into (a) and showed an even greater differential between uridylic and cytidylic acid incorporation. Uracil incorporation was at least 10-fold higher than orotic acid incorporation with incorporation differentials into fractions (a) and (b) following the same general pattern as did orotic acid incorporation. 5-Fluorouracil inhibited 70–90% of uracil incorporation into both fractions; propyl thiouracil only slightly inhibited incorporation into uridylic acids of both fractions but inhibited about half of the incorporation into the cytidylic acids of both fractions. Thus propyl thiouracil preferentially inhibits the uridylic → cytidylic acid conversion.

Jaffe (1961) and Rubin et $al.$ (1962) studied effects of 6-azauracil and 6-azauridine on $T.$ $equiperdum.$ 6-Azauracil but not 6-azauridine was trypanostatic for $T.$ $equiperdum$ growing in mice. Although both uracil derivatives penetrated the trypanosomes, only 6-azauracil was converted (in in $vitro$ experiments) to 6-azauridylic acid which probably accounts for the differential in inhibitory activity. Failure of 6-azauracil to be incorporated into $T.$ $equiperdum$ nucleic acids may account for the –static rather than –cidal effect of this compound: it may activate a homeostatic mechanism which stops nucleic acid synthesis before fraudulent nucleic acids can be manufactured.

Rubin *et al.* (1962) pointed out that mammalian cells convert 6-azauracil to 6-azauridine and thence to 6-azauridylic acid but that in *T. equiperdum* conversion is directly from 6-azauracil to 6-azauridylic acid. If this direct conversion is a general property of the Trypanosomatidae, it may be useful for tracing phylogenetic affinities.

References

Aaronson, S., and Nathan, H. A. (1954). *Biochim. Biophys. Acta* 15, 306.
Alexieff, A. G. (1917). *Compt. Rend. Soc. Biol.* 80, 358.
Amrein, Y. U. (1957). *J. Protozool.* 4, 67.
Amrein, Y. U., and Fulton, J. D. (1959). *J. Protozool.* 6, 120.
Biocca, E. (1938). *Ann. Igiene* 48, 532.
Boné, G. J., and Parent, G. (1963). *J. Gen. Microbiol.* 31, 261.
Boné, G. J., and Steinert, M. (1956). *Nature* 178, 308.
Braun, W. (1946). *J. Bacteriol.* 51, 327.
Bresslau, E. L., and Scremin, L. (1924). *Arch. Protistenk.* 48, 509.
Bütschli, O. (1883–1887). "Bronn's Klassen und Ordnungen des Teirreiches," Book I, Part 2. Winter'sche, Leipzig.
Castellani, O., and Fernandes, J. F. (1962). *Exptl. Parasitol.* 12, 52.
Causey, D. (1925). *Univ. Calif. (Berkeley) Publ. Zool.* 28, 19.
Citri, N., and Grossowicz, N. (1954). *Nature* 173, 1100.
Citri, N., and Grossowicz, N. (1955). *J. Gen. Microbiol.* 13, 273.
Clark, T. B. (1959). *J. Protozool.* 6, 227.
Clark, T. B., and Wallace, F. G. (1960). *J. Protozool.* 7, 115.
Cosgrove, W. B. (1959). *Can. J. Microbiol.* 5, 573.
Cosgrove, W. B. (1963). *Exptl. Parasitol.* 13, 173.
Cosgrove, W. B., and Anderson, E. (1954). *Anat. Record* 120, 813.
Cosgrove, W. B., and Kessel, R. G. (1958). *J. Protozool.* 5, 296.
Cowperthwaite, J., Weber, M. M., Packer, L., and Hutner, S. H. (1953). *Ann. N.Y. Acad. Sci.* 56, 972.
Deane, M. P., and Deane, L. M. (1961). *Rev. Inst. Med. Trop. Sao Paulo* 3, 149.
Demarchi, J., and Nicoli, J. (1960). *Ann. Inst. Pasteur* 99, 120.
Desowitz, R. S. (1959). *Nature* 184, Suppl. 13, 886.
Diamond, L. S., and Herman, C. M. (1954). *J. Parasitol.* 40, 195.
Elkeles, G. (1944). *Bol. Acad. Nacl. Cienc. (Cordoba, Rep. Arg.)* 36, 330.
Erdman, R. (1915). *Proc. Soc. Exptl. Biol. Med.* 12, 57.
Fairbairn, H., Culwick, A. F., and Gee, F. L. (1946). *Ann. Trop. Med. Parasitol.* 40, 421.
Fernandes, J. F., and Castellani, O. (1958). *Exptl. Parasitol.* 7, 224.
Fiennes, R. N. (1945). *Nature* 156, 390.
Firshein, W., and Braun, W. (1960). *J. Bacteriol.* 79, 246.
França, C. (1911). *Bull. Soc. Pathol. Exotique* 4, 534.
Fulton, J. D. (1960). *In* "Host Influence on Parasite Physiology" (L. A. Stauber, ed.), p. 11. Rutgers Univ. Press, New Brunswick, New Jersey.
Geigy, R., Huber, M., Weinman, D., and Wyatt, G. R. (1959). *Acta Trop.* 16, 255.
Geiman, Q. M. (1940). *J. Parasitol.* 26, 22.
Gill, J. W., and Vogel, H. J. (1962). *Biochim. Biophys. Acta* 56, 200.
Gill, J. W., and Vogel, H. J. (1963). *J. Protozool.* 10, 148.

Guttman, H. N. (1962). Unpublished data.

Guttman, H. N. (1963a). *Bacteriol. Proc.* p. 99.

Guttman, H. N. (1963b). *Eptl Parasitol.* 13, 129.

Guttman, H. N. (1964a). Unpublished data.

Guttman, H. N. (1964b). *In* "Third International Pteridine Symposium." Pergamon Press, New York (in press).

Hack, M. H., Yaeger, R. G., and McCaffery, T. D. (1962). *Comp. Biochem. Physiol.* 6, 247.

Halevy, S. (1962). *Bull. Res. Council Israel* E10, 65.

Hoare, C. A. (1954). *J. Protozool.* 1, 28.

Hoare, C. A., and Bennett, C. S. J. (1938). *Parasitology* 30, 529.

Inoki, S. (1957). *Proc. Intern. Genet. Symp., Tokyo & Kyoto, 1956 (Cytologia)* p. 550.

Inoki, S., and Matsushiro, A. (1960). *Biken's J.* 3, 101.

Inoki, S., Sakamoto, H., Ono, T., and Kubo, R. (1961a). *Biken's J.* 4, 67.

Inoki, S., Taniuchi, Y., Sakamoto, H., Ono, T., and Kubo, R. (1961b). *Biken's J.* 4, 111.

Jaffe, J. J. (1961). *Biochem. Pharmacol.* 8, 216.

Janicki, C. (1915). *Biol. Zentr.* 31, 321.

Jírovec, O. (1929). *Arch. Protistenk.* 68, 187.

Jones, H., Rake, G., and Hambre, D. (1944). *Am. J. Trop. Med.* 24, 381.

Kaufman, S. (1962). *In* "The Oxygenases" (O. Hayaishi, ed.), p. 129. Academic Press, New York.

Kent, W. S. (1880). "A Manual of the Infusoria." D. Bogue London.

Kidder, G. W., Dewey, V. C., and Rembold, H. (1964). *Federation Proc.* 23, 529.

Laird, M. (1959). *Can. J. Zool.* 37, 749.

Lavier, G. (1927). *Compt. Rend. Soc. Biol.* 97, 1611.

Léger, L. (1902). *Compt. Rend. Soc. Biol.* 54, 354.

Lehmann, D. L. (1960). *Ann. Trop. Med. Parasitol.* 54, 419.

Lehmann, D. L. (1962). *J. Protozool.* 9, 325.

Linnane, A. W., Vitols, E., and Noroland, P. G. (1962). *J. Cell Biol.* 13, 345.

Lwoff, M., and Lwoff, A. (1931). *Arch. Zool. Exptl. Gen.* 71, 21.

McGhee, R. B. (1957). *Science* 125, 157.

McGhee, R. B. (1959). *J. Infectious Diseases* 105, 18.

McGhee, R. B., and Hanson, W. L. (1963). *J. Protozool.* 10, 239.

Monod, J. (1942). "La Croissance des Cultures Bactériennes." Hermann, Paris.

Mühlpfordt, H. (1959). *Z. Tropenmed. Parasitol.* 10, 19.

Mühlpfordt, H. (1963a). *Z. Tropenmed. Parasitol.* 14, 357.

Mühlpfordt, H. (1963b). *Z. Tropenmed. Parasitol.* 14, 475.

Nathan, H. A. (1954). Unpublished data.

Nathan, H. A. (1958a). *J. Protozool.* 5, 194.

Nathan, H. A. (1958b). Unpublished data.

Nathan, H. A., Baker, H., and Frank, O. (1960). *Nature* 188, 35.

Nathan, H. A., and Cowperthwaite J. (1954). *Proc. Soc. Exptl. Biol. Med.* 85, 117.

Nathan, H. A., and Cowperthwaite, J. (1955). *J. Protozool.* 2, 37.

Nathan, H. A., and Funk, H. B. (1959). *Am. J. Clin. Nutr.* 7, 375.

Nathan, H. A., Levin, H. L., and Hutner, S. H. (1956). *Nature* 178, 741.

Nathan, H. A., Levin, H. L., and Hutner, S. H. (1958). *J. Protozool.* 5, 134.

Nathan, H. A., and Ziegler, I. (1961). *Z. Naturforsch.* 16b, 262.

Newton, B. A. (1957). *J. Gen. Microbiol.* 17, 708.

Noguchi, H. (1926). *J. Exptl. Med.* **44**, 327.

Noguchi, H., and Tilden, E. B. (1926). *J. Exptl. Med.* **44**, 307.

Patterson, E. L., Milstrey, R., and Stokstad, E. L. R. (1955). *J. Am. Chem. Soc.* **80**, 2018.

Patton, W. S. (1908). *Arch. Protistenk.* **12**, 131.

Pipkin, A. C. (1960). *Exptl. Parasitol.* **9**, 167.

Pizzi, T. (1961). *Bol. Chileno Parasitol.* **16**, 35.

Pyne, C. K. (1961). *Abstr. 1st Intern. Conf. Soc. Protozool., Prague, 1961* p. 172.

Rachmilewitz, M., and Grossowicz, N. (1956). *Acta Med. Scand., Suppl.* **154**, 312, 540.

Ray, H. N., and Malhotra, M. N. (1960). *Nature* **188**, 870.

Reichenow, E. (1934). *Arch. Schiffs-U Tropen-Hyg.* **38**, 292.

Reichenow, E. (1940). *Arquiv. Inst. Biol. (São Paulo).* **11**, 433.

Rey, L., and Fernandes, J. F. (1962). *Exptl. Parasitol.* **12**, 55.

Ristic, M., and Trager, W. (1958). *J. Protozool.* **5**, 146.

Robertson, M. (1927). *Parasitology* **19**, 375.

Rubin, R. J., Jaffe, J. J., and Handschumacher, R. E. (1962). *Biochem. Pharmacol.* **11**, 563.

Ryley, J. F. (1955). *Biochem. J.* **59**, 353.

Ryley, J. F. (1956). *Biochem. J.* **62**, 215.

Ryley, J. F. (1962). *Biochem. J.* **85**, 211.

Sampath, A., and Little, P. A. (1949). *J. Bacteriol.* **57**, 265.

Schueler, F. W. (1947). *J. Infectious Diseases* **81**, 139.

Seaman, G. R. (1951). *J. Biol. Chem.* **191**, 439.

Shipley, P. G. (1916). *Anat. Record* **10**, 439.

Steinert, M. (1958a). *Exptl. Cell Res.* **15**, 431.

Steinert, M. (1958b). *Exptl. Cell Res.* **15**, 560.

Steinert, M., and Boné, G. J. (1956). *Nature* **178**, 362.

Stephen, L. E. (1962). *J. Protozool.* **9**, 450.

Streissle, G., and Maramorosch, K. (1963). *Science* **140**, 996.

Tietz, A., Lindberg, M., and Kennedy, E. P. (1963). *Federation Proc.* **22**, 296.

Tobie, E. J. (1958). *J. Parasitol.* **44**, 241.

Tobie, E. J., von Brand, T., and Mehlman, B. (1950). *J. Parasitol.* **36**, 48.

Trager, W. (1953). *J. Exptl. Med.* **97**, 177.

Trager, W. (1957). *J. Protozool.* **4**, 269.

Trager, W. (1959a). *Nature* **184**; *B. A.* **30**.

Trager, W. (1959b). *Ann. Trop. Med. Parasitol.* **53**, 473.

Trager, W., and Rudzinska, M. A. (1964). *J. Protozool.* **11**, 133.

Trejos, A., Godoy, G. A., Greenblatt, C., and Cedillos, R. (1963). *Exptl. Parasitol.* **13**, 211.

Vanderplank, F. L. (1944). *Nature* **154**, 19.

Vanderplank, F. L. (1947). *Trans. Roy. Soc. Trop. Med. Hyg.* **41**, 15.

Vickerman, K. (1962). *J. Protozool.* **9**, 26.

Vogel, H. (1963). Personal communication.

von Brand, T. (1951). *In* "Biochemistry and Physiology of Protozoa" (A. Lwoff, ed.), Vol. 1, p. 177. Academic Press, New York.

von Brand, T., McMahon, P., Tobie, E. J., Thompson, N. J., and Mosetting, E. (1959). *Exptl. Parasitol.* **8**, 171.

Wacker, A., Lochman, E.-R., and Kirschfeld, S. (1959). *Z. Naturforsch.* **14b**, 150.

Wallace, F. G. (1943). *J. Parasitol.* **29**, 196.

Wallace, F. G. (1956). *J. Protozool.* 3, 47.
Wallace, F. G., and Clark, T. B. (1959). *J. Protozool.* 6, 58.
Wallace, F. G., and Clark, T. B. (1959). *J. Protozool.* 6, Suppl., 7.
Wallace, F. G., and Johnson, A. (1961). *J. Insect Pathol.* 3, 75.
Warren, L. G. (1960). *J. Parasitol.* 46, 529.
Webber, H. J. (1898). *Botan. Gaz.* 24, 32.
Weinman, D. (1953). *Ann. N.Y. Acad. Sci.* 56, 995.
Weinman, D. (1960). *Trans. Roy. Soc. Trop. Med. Hyg.* 54, 180.
Wenrich, D. H. (1954). *In* "Sex in Microorganisms" (D. H. Wenrich, I. F. Lewis, and J. R. Raper, eds.), p. 134. Am. Assoc. Advance. Sci., Washington, D.C.
Wenyon, C. M. (1926). "Protozoology." Wm. Wood & Co., New York.
Werbitzki, F. W. (1910). *Zentr. Bakteriol., Parasitenk., Abt. I. Orig.* 53, 303.
Wertlieb, D. M. and Guttman, H. N. (1963). *J. Protozool.* 10, 109.
Wildman, S. G., Hongladarom, T., and Honda, S. I. (1962). *Science* 138, 434.
Williamson, J., and Desowitz, R. S. (1961). *Exptl. Parasitol.* 11, 161.
Williamson, J., and Rollo, I. M. (1952). *Nature* 170, 376.
Woodcock, H. M. (1914). *Zool. Anz.* 44, 26.
Yarmolinsky, M. B., and Haba, G. L. (1959). *Proc. Natl. Acad. Sci. U.S.* 45, 1711.
Ziegler, I., and Nathan, H. A. (1961). *Z. Naturforsch.* 16b, 260.
Ziegler-Gunder, I. (1956). *Z. Naturforsch.* 11b, 493.

The Chemotherapy of Trypanosomiasis

L. G. GOODWIN

The Wellcome Laboratories of Tropical Medicine, London, England

		Page
I.	Introduction	495
II.	New Trypanocidal Drugs	497
	A. Human Trypanosomiasis	497
	B. Bovine Trypanosomiasis in Africa	502
III.	Drug Resistance	506
IV.	Trypanocides and the Metabolism of Trypanosomes	509
	A. Physical Properties of Trypanocides	509
	B. Action on Enzyme Systems	510
V.	Immunity	517
	References	520

I. Introduction

Trypanosomiasis of man and animals continues to exert its influence in Africa and in South America. Control of the vectors, where it is possible, is effective in reducing the incidence of the infection, but in Africa the tsetse fly still has a firm hold on the territory and eradication by existing methods is impracticable. The achievements of the campaign against human sleeping sickness in Northern Nigeria, and the dangers that remain, have been described by Duggan (1962). The effects of bovine trypanosomiasis in Africa can sometimes be kept within bounds by the selection of suitable stock and by carefully supervised chemotherapy. But in a continent of many peoples with differing customs and languages, in which communications are inadequate and in which cattle frequently represent a taxable capital investment, it is logistically impossible to exercise control over most of the bovine population. As the peoples of Africa gain their independence, these difficulties are likely, for a time, to increase;

there are as yet too few trained African doctors, veterinarians, and administrators to maintain and extend control.

In the words of Morris (1960)—"Meanwhile the generations of a trypanosome are measured in hours, not years; epidemic diseases are no more respecters of time than of international frontiers. If the return of possibly disastrous epidemics is to be avoided, the solution must lie in the action of a body, such as the World Health Organization, with the vision and status to put forward a realistic programme of eradication on international lines."

Research in the chemotherapy of trypanosomiasis has yielded few new drugs during the past 10 years. The antibiotics which, it was hoped, would prove a source of new and potent trypanocides, have so far been disappointing. With the exception of stylomycin, which has been a useful tool in the investigation of nucleotide synthesis in trypanosomes, the search has been singularly unrewarding. Perhaps the right class of antibiotic still remains to be discovered; perhaps, as suggested by Hutner *et al.* (1958), the protozoa are more closely related metabolically to the metazoa than to the bacteria, thus making it difficult to find an antibiotic which kills the parasite without also doing serious damage to the cells of the host. Existing antibiotics are not devoid of activity against trypanosomes, but they are too toxic and too expensive to be useful (Woolfe, 1962).

Our understanding of host-parasite relationships, immunity, and the mode of action of trypanocidal drugs has notably increased. This is largely the result of the application of new techniques in biochemistry, immunology, and electron microscopy. The electron microscope has provided a new viewpoint for the causes of morphological and metabolic changes which occur when a trypanosome is transferred from the mammalian host to the arthropod vector. Metabolic studies have given indications of where to look for the sites of action of trypanocides. New immunological techniques have yielded valuable information which may possibly lead to the development of effective vaccines, in spite of the fact that the trypanosome has a protean ability to vary its antigenic characteristics.

The stretch of No-Man's-Land in the pathology of infectious disease which exists between the frontiers of biochemistry, pharmacology, parasitology, and immunology is still in need of exploration. The cause of death from trypanosomiasis in man and animals is still something of a mystery; the nature and properties of the metabolic by-products of parasites are largely unknown. Few attempts have been made to study the changes in the physiology of the host which are caused by the physical presence of the parasites in the blood stream, or by the pharmacological activity of their metabolites, or to study what happens when the parasites are killed by a trypanocidal drug.

Knowledge of these factors might be hoped to suggest means whereby the host could be protected against the chemical effects of parasitism and against the damage inflicted by the by-products of his own tissues.

II. New Trypanocidal Drugs

A. Human Trypanosomiasis

1. african trypanosomiasis

There have been very few additions to the drugs available for the treatment of human trypanosomiasis in Africa during the last 10 years. Political changes in the African continent have brought a temporary loosening of public health controls for this potentially dangerous disease and the demonstration of Heisch *et al.* (1958) that a trypanosome from a bushbuck was capable of causing typical *Trypanosoma rhodesiense* infections in human volunteers has underlined the importance of animal reservoirs. The migrant nature of some of the peoples at risk, the large-scale population movements which are now taking place in the developing countries, and the impracticability of eradication of trypanosomiasis by vector destruction, make the disease a continual threat to Africa. The drugs at present available are expensive and their regular administration is difficult. There is a requirement for a new, cheap, well tolerated drug which is easy to administer and is effective against all stages of the infection—but there is little promise that such a drug is likely to appear in the near future.

a. Aromatic Diamidines. Prophylaxis with pentamidine has had a wide measure of success in the reduction of incidence of *Trypanosoma gambiense* infection. Berenil, used in animal trypanosomiasis, is effective against the early stages of *T. gambiense* infection in man but the drug appears to have little advantage over pentamidine (Fussgänger and Bauer, 1958; Hutchinson and Watson, 1962). The use of diamidines for prophylaxis carries the danger of masking infections which have already involved nervous tissue and which are then unaffected by this class of compound.

b. Melaminyl Arsenicals. Melarsoprol (Mel B; I) now occupies an important place among trypanocidal drugs for the treatment of central nervous infections. Its activity against tryparsamide-fast strains of *T. gambiense,* which have for many years been common is the Congo basin, is of very great value. In the hands of experienced workers such as Richet *et al.* (1959) melarsoprol does not cause fatalities, but the avoidance of serious toxic reactions is dependent upon rigorous precautions and the careful selection of cases.

Standardized samples of the related pentavalent melaminyl arsenical, melarsen (II), have been reexamined in West Africa (Butler *et al.,* 1957). Melarsen appears to be as active as melarsoprol against tryparsamide-resistant strains of

T. gambiense; it is less toxic and, being water-soluble, is easier to administer. The high cost of the drug makes it at present uneconomical for use except in selected patients.

Melarsoprol

(I)

Melarsen

(II)

Mel W

(III)

Mel W (trimelarsen; pentylthiarsaphenylmelamine; III) is the latest member of this series to be introduced by its originator, Ernst Friedheim. Like melarsen, it is soluble in water and it may be given intramuscularly. Good results have been reported against *T. gambiense* (Friedheim and De Jongh, 1959; De Jongh and Friedheim, 1959; Schneider *et al.*, 1961; Watson, 1962) but against *T. rhodesiense* it was found by Robertson (1963) to be less effective than melarsoprol. A larger proportion of patients treated with Mel W relapsed, and toxic side effects were more prominent. This drug has not yet been fully evaluated.

c. Nitrofurans. Nitrofuran derivatives have a chemical structure which is entirely different from the established trypanocides and they appear to be active against both diamidine and arsenic-resistant strains. Evens *et al.* (1957) showed that nitrofurazone (IV) penetrated the blood-brain barrier to the cerebrospinal fluid when given by mouth and was of assistance in the treatment of advanced human trypanosomiasis. Apted (1960) and Fierlafyn (1960) found that oral nitrofurazone was of value in advanced *T. rhodesiense* infections which had relapsed after treatment with melarsoprol. It apparently cured some otherwise hopeless cases and prolonged the lives of others.

$$O_2N \diagdown \underset{O}{\diagup\diagdown} CH{:}N{\cdot}NH{\cdot}CONH_2$$

Nitrofurazone

(IV)

Nitrofuran derivatives apparently owe their activity to the easily reducible 5-nitro substituent; they do not generally react with thiol groups. Von Brand *et al.* (1953) made the interesting observation that an arsenic-fast strain of *T. gambiense* was more sensitive than the parent strain to nitrofurazone. Williamson (1962) suggests that this may be evidence for the development of an alteration of oxidative metabolism in the resistant strain, perhaps associated with the glycerophosphate-DPNH oxidase system of Grant and Sargent (1960). Williamson himself (1953) found some evidence of oxidative changes in a melarsen-resistant strain of *T. rhodesiense* and Williamson and Rollo (1959) have suggested that such changes may explain the curious cross-resistance which occurs between the aromatic arsenicals and acriflavine.

Nitrofurazone interferes with pyruvate metabolism and when used in human trypanosomiasis the blood pyruvate level rises. Peripheral neuritis of the beriberi type and other neuropathies frequently occur (Fierlafyn, 1960; Robertson, 1961a,b). Thiamine has been given to counteract this effect but it is not known whether the vitamin interferes with the trypanocidal activity of the drug as well as with its toxicity to the host. Bauchop (1962) has observed that the trypanosomid flagellates *Crithidia (Strigomonas) oncopelti* and *Crithidia fasciculata* possess thiamine-dependent pyruvate decarboxylase and alcohol dehydrogenase; it is possible that thiamine might antagonize the action of nitrofuran derivatives against the related human parasites, even though the oxidation of pyruvate is not a characteristic of the blood-stream form of the trypanosome. Further studies in this interesting area of biochemical pharmacology are needed.

A much more serious toxic side effect of nitrofurazone, also linked with its oxidizing power, is the production of hemolysis in individuals with a genetic deficiency of glucose-6-phosphate dehydrogenase. About 15 to 20% of Africans have this deficiency and "oxidizing" drugs such as primaquine, *p*-aminosalicylate, and nitrofurazone may bring about acute hemolysis in sensitive individuals. With the dosage of nitrofurazone required for the treatment of advanced trypanosomiasis, hemolysis is an important hazard (Robertson, 1961a,b).

2. SOUTH AMERICAN TRYPANOSOMIASIS

The treatment of Chagas' diseases is still one of the most difficult problems of protozoal chemotherapy. Although many thousands of new compounds have been tested against experimental *Trypanosoma cruzi* infections, none has yet been discovered which gives much hope of eradicating the tissue forms of the parasite without danger to the human host from drug toxicity. However, new biochemical techniques have yielded important information on the metabolism of the parasite and have given some indications of the directions in which further work should proceed. Useful reviews of the chemical composition of the parasite have been given by von Brand *et al.* (1959) and von Brand (1962).

a. 8-Aminoquinolines. This series of drugs has been extensively studied by Goble, who recently summarized the position (Goble, 1961). De Lucena (1961) has since reported that WIN 5037 [6-methoxy-8(5-propylaminoamylamino) quinoline] which has also been used as an antimalarial drug, had a curative effect in mice infected with *Trypanosoma cruzi*. The new series of leishmanicidal 8-aminoquinolines (V) described by Beveridge *et al.* (1958) contains com-

CH₃O $\cdots$

NH·[CH₂]ₙ — N ⟨ ⟩ N—R

(V)

pounds with considerable activity against the tissue forms of *T. cruzi* in mice; no results of clinical trials in man have so far been reported.

Among other drugs which are effective against *Leishmania donovani*, amphotericin B (fungizone) has only slight activity against *T. cruzi* (Botafogo Gonçalves and Gonçalves, 1961), and surface-active polyoxyethylene ethers have none at all (Goble *et al.*, 1960).

b. Nitro Compounds. Packchanian (1957) and Brener (1961) showed that nitrofuran derivatives had some action in experimental *Trypanosoma cruzi*, and Moon and Coleman (1962) observed that the D- and L-isomers of furaltadone had different degrees of activity; the L-isomer was considerably more effective than the D-isomer. Brener and Pellegrino (1958) found some activity in 2-acetamido-5-nitrothiazole. Brener (1961) reported that, as with infections by African trypanosomes, chronic *T. cruzi* infections responded less well to drugs than acute infections, probably because of the development of an immunological host-parasite relationship. Flagyl (1,β-hydroxyethyl-2-methyl-5-nitroindazole) which is given orally in the treatment of human *Trichomonas vaginalis* infections is reported by Pizzi (1961) to have a transient suppressive action on *Trypanosoma cruzi* in mice.

  c. Stylomycin. The studies of Nakamura and James (1953) on the effect *in vitro* of purine derivatives on *Trypanosoma cruzi* formed the starting point of a series of interesting investigations which are still in progress. The antibiotic stylomycin (puromycin) has considerable activity against African trypanosomes in experimental animals (Porter *et al.*, 1952; Hewitt *et al.*, 1953; Tobie, 1954) but clinical trials were disappointing. Hewitt *et al.* (1954) and Agosin and von Brand (1954) showed that its action on *Trypanosoma equiperdum* was selectively antagonized by adenine; stylomycin aminonucleoside (VI), which is

Stylomycin
aminonucleoside
(VI)

formed from the antibiotic by removal of the terminal phenylalanyl group, was more trypanocidal than the original substance. Stylomycin is also active against *T. cruzi* in mice, and Pizzi *et al.* (1953) tried it together with primaquine, with promising results. Investigations of the action of stylomycin aminonucleoside have been extended by J. F. Fernandes and his colleagues in São Paulo and it is clearly a useful tool in the study of nucleotide and polynucleotide synthesis in *T. cruzi* (Fernandes and Castellani, 1958, 1959; Silva *et al.*, 1959; Fernandes *et al.*, 1959; Moraes *et al.*, 1960; Castellani and Fernandes, 1962; Rey and Fernandes, 1962).

  Culture forms of *T. cruzi* cannot make the purine ring and are dependent upon preformed purine bases for the synthesis of nucleotides and polynucleotides. Stylomycin aminonucleoside inhibits this synthesis in *T. cruzi* flagellates and apparently also in the dividing tissue leishmania forms, which rapidly degenerate in the presence of the drug. The 6-*N*-diethyl analog and 6-*N*-dimethyladenine are inactive, indicating that the *N*-methyl group and the pentoseamine portions of the molecule are essential to the activity of the compound.

  Stylomycin bears a striking structural resemblance to the terminal adenylic acid-amino acid "tail" of transfer ribonucleic acid, and Yarmolinsky and Haba (1959) have suggested that the drug may inhibit the transfer mechanism in protein synthesis.

  Stylomycin aminonucleoside is less effective than carbidium against *T. cruzi* in tissue culture (Silva and Kirchner, 1962) and its unfortunate toxicity to the kidney makes it difficult to use in the treatment of human infections. Nevertheless it is evident that this is a promising field for further research.

The immunology of Chagas' disease has been reviewed by Pizzi (1957) and by Garnham (1963) and much work still needs to be done to elucidate the host-parasite relationship and the causes of tissue damage in the infected host.

B. Bovine Trypanosomiasis in Africa

1. aromatic diamidines

The aromatic diamidines have until recently been much more successful in the treatment of *Trypanosoma gambiense* infections in man than in *T. congolense* and *T. vivax* infections in cattle. Speculative chemical synthesis has now provided several drugs of this class which have high activity in bovine trypanosomiasis.

The active compounds have resulted from what Williamson (1962) calls "hybrid" synthesis, in which fragments of trypanocidal structures of different types have been linked together. The bis 4-aminoquinaldine derivative, surfen C (Jensch, 1937; VII) was long ago found to be active in bovine trypanosomi-

Surfen C

(VII)

asis but was discarded because of local and general toxicity to the host. The central melamine nucleus of surfen C found its way into organic arsenicals such as melarsoprol used in human trypanosomiasis, and Ashley *et al.* (1960) showed that when melamine formed the link between two amidinophenyl groups, the substance (M & B 2242; VIII) had activity against *T. congolense*.

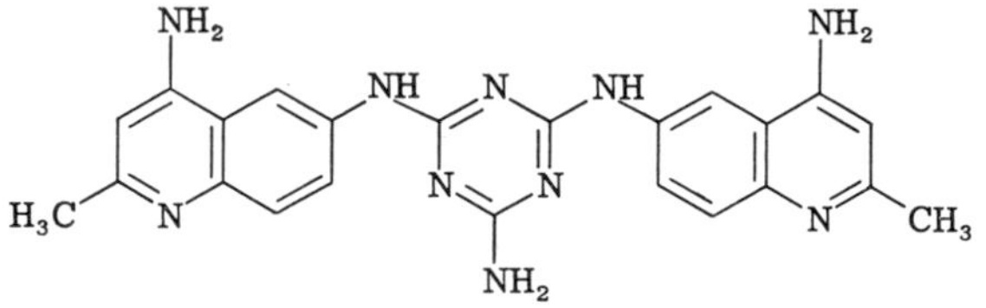

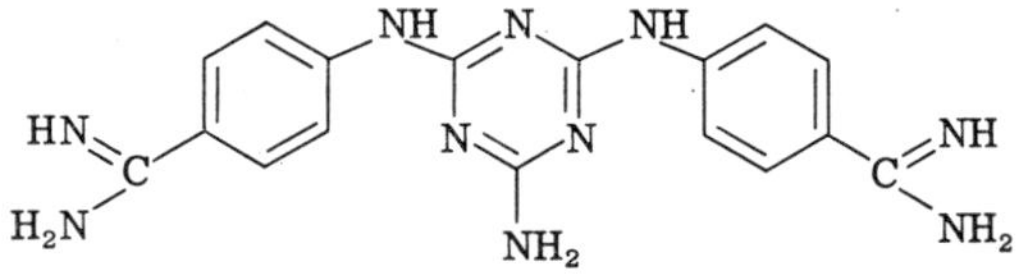

M & B 2242

(VIII)

The compound known as M & B 2242 is less active than another diamidine, "berenil" (IX), in which the melamine bridge is replaced by the simpler

Berenil

(IX)

triazene linkage. Berenil was synthesized by Jensch (1955) in the course of a systematic investigation of the parts of the molecule of surfen C which were essential to trypanocidal activity. Berenil has high activity against *T. congolense* and *T. vivax* in cattle and is also effective against *Babesia* infections. Its use in veterinary medicine is reviewed by Fussgänger and Bauer (1958).

Berenil is a useful curative drug which, being totally unlike the quaternary ammonium trypanocides in structure and action, is effective against strains of parasite which are resistant to treatment with phenanthridinium and quinaldinium compounds. It is destroyed and excreted very rapidly in the body of the host and is useless as a prophylactic. Bauer (1958) has shown that berenil is quickly and irreversibly bound by *T. congolense* both *in vitro* and *in vivo* but several hours elapse before the trypanosomes die.

Barber and Berg (1962) point out that in diamidine molecules with activity against *T. congolense,* the amidine groups are 12 to 15 A. apart; the linkage between the two aromatic amidine moieties confers a measure of rigidity by double bonds and steric hindrance, and the whole system linking the amidine groups is conjugated. There are, however, many homologs and analogs which fulfill these criteria and yet have no trypanocidal activity. In studies of the mode of action of these drugs, far too little attention has yet been paid to inactive compounds which are seemingly close relatives of the active ones.

2. QUATERNARY AMMONIUM COMPOUNDS

In Volume II of "Biochemistry and Physiology of Protozoa" (Goodwin and Rollo, 1955) it was suggested that of the large number of phenanthridinium compounds synthesized and tested against bovine trypanosomiasis, homidium (ethidium; X) might become the drug of choice. Homidium is now used ex-

Homidium

(X)

tensively and has proved to be considerably less toxic than the 10-methyl homolog, dimidium. Watkins, who synthesized ethidium, later turned his attention to "hybrid" compounds in which the pyrimidyl fragment of quinapyramine (antrycide) was linked with a variety of aminophenanthridinium derivatives. The most active compound of this series, prothidium (RD 2801; XI) had high curative and prophylactic potency (Watkins and Woolfe, 1956;

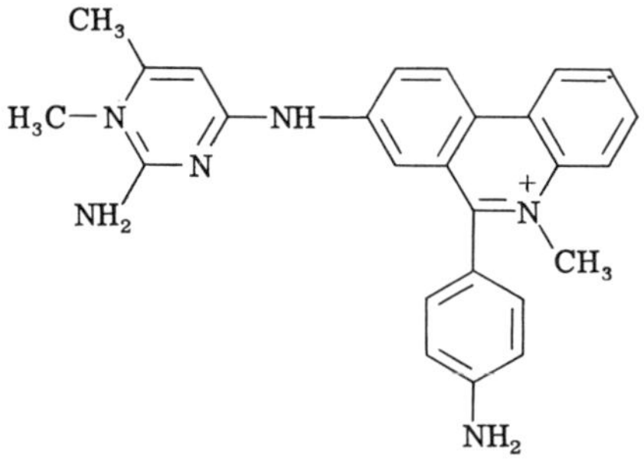

Prothidium

(XI)

Watkins, 1958; Robson, 1958, 1961; Lyttle, 1960; Smith and Brown, 1960). An injection of 2 mg./kg. of prothidium protects cattle for 4 months in areas of moderate intensity of transmission by the tsetse fly. The prophylactic action of prothidium may be due to the fact that it is bound in the liver and at the site of injection (Taylor, 1960).

In another laboratory, Wragg et al. (1958) synthesized and tested "hybrids" based upon the linkage of a diazotized portion of the berenil molecule with 7-aminophenanthridinium compounds. This gave rise to mixtures of red diazoamino and purple aminoazo isomers (Berg, 1960; Barber and Berg, 1962). The red diazoamino compounds (XII) were up to 10 times as active,

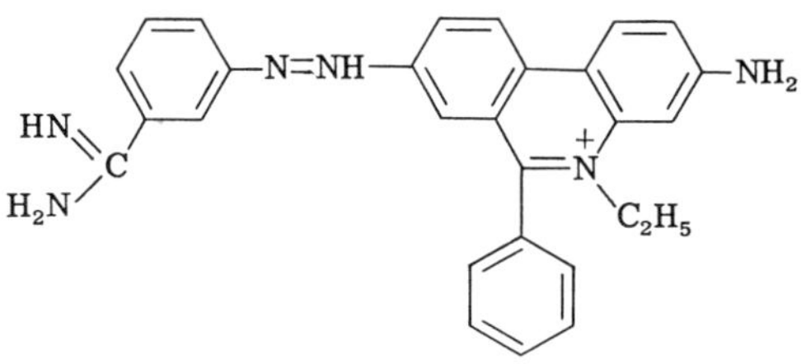

Isometamidium
(red isomer)

(XII)

both curatively and prophylactically as the purple aminoazo isomers (XIII).

Purple isomer

(XIII)

Brown *et al.* (1961) showed that, as with the parent phenanthridinium analogs, quaternary methyl compounds were less active than the corresponding ethyl derivatives. In contrast to earlier experience with aromatic amidines, the *meta* position for the amidino-group was more favorable for activity than the *para* position. The most active member of the series of red isomers was iso-metamidium (M & B 4180; XII). The addition of a second *m*-amidinophenyl-diazoamino group to the isometamidium molecule gave a compound of lower curative but longer prophylactic activity (Berg *et al.*, 1961). The activity of isometamidium in the treatment and prophylaxis of *T. congolense* and *T. vivax* infections in cattle has been amply confirmed in the field (Smith and Brown, 1960; Stephen, 1960; Whiteside, 1960).

Like dimidium these new phenanthridinium derivatives cause damage to the liver, but the margin of safety is much greater and delayed toxic effects and photosensitization do not seem to occur. Apart from considerations of drug re-sistance, the major disadvantage is that the drugs cause tissue necrosis if given subcutaneously; this problem has not yet been solved.

Tozocide (XIV) is a bis-quinaldinium derivative allied to surfen C (Austin

Tozocide

(XIV)

et al., 1957). It is effective against *T. congolense* infections in the laboratory but has proved disappointing in the field (Marshall, 1958).

3. SURAMIN SALTS

Guimaraes and Lourie (1951) showed that pentamidine formed an insoluble complex with the anionic trypanocidal substance, suramin, and that the complex was less toxic and more effective than the pentamidine it contained. Suramin also forms insoluble salts with the cationic derivatives used against cattle trypanosomiasis (Williamson and Desowitz, 1956; Wragg *et al.*, 1958). A molecule of suramin with 6 anionic groups will combine with 6 molecules of dimidium or ethidium, or with 3 molecules of quinapyramine, berenil, prothidium, or metamidium.

The insoluble suramin salts are less toxic and are better prophylactics than equivalent doses of the cationic drugs they contain (Williamson, 1957; Williamson and Desowitz, 1956; Desowitz, 1957). However, they also cause severe local irritation and the depot of drug upon which continued prophylaxis depends is frequently sloughed. Attempts to reduce local toxicity have so far failed. Irritant activity is associated with the size of particles of insoluble drug that are injected; Smith and Brown (1960) showed that metamidium suraminate with a particle size of 10 to 100 μ was less toxic, and a less effective prophylactic than material with a particle size of 3 μ.

4. DITHIOBIURET DERIVATIVES

A series of dithiobiuret derivatives was found by Woolfe (1953) to have considerable activity against *T. congolense* in laboratory animals. In view of its novel structure, one of these, 1-methyl-1-phenyldithiobiuret (XV) was tested

$$\langle \rangle \!\!-\!\! \underset{\underset{CH_3}{|}}{N} \!\!-\!\! CS \cdot NH \cdot CS \cdot NH_2$$

1-Methyl-1-phenyl
dithiobiuret

(XV)

in Nigeria, but was inactive against *T. vivax* and disappointing against *T. congolense* in cattle (Nash, 1955).

III. Drug Resistance

Reviews of drug resistance in trypanosomiasis have been provided by Schnitzer and Grunberg (1957), Davey (1958), Bishop (1959), and Williamson (1962). The practical problem of drug resistance in Kenya from the veterinary viewpoint is summarized by Whiteside (1962):

(a) Cattle trypanosomes readily become resistant to all existing drugs except berenil.

(b) Resistance develops in the treated host. With one doubtful exception (Smith and Scott, 1961), strains naturally resistant to normal dosages have not yet been observed.

(c) Resistant strains can be transmitted by tsetse flies, though this usually happens some time after they have arisen in cattle.

(d) Resistant strains carried by tsetse flies disappear after 6 to 12 months provided the sources of infection (the cattle) are removed.

(e) Most resistant infections in cattle can be eliminated by "sanative" treatment. [A "sanative" (Whiteside, 1958) is defined as any drug that cures infections resistant to any other drug.]

(f) There is no way of directly eliminating resistant strains that are being transmitted throughout an area by tsetse flies.

Whiteside studied the development of the patterns of cross-resistance to various *T. congolense* drugs in experimental syringe-transmitted infections in cattle. He found that the spectrum of cross-resistance depended on the degree of direct resistance which had been developed to a drug. Thus, a strain of *T. congolense* made just resistant to the normal curative dose of quinapyramine (antrycide; XVI) was susceptible to normal doses of homidium and berenil.

Quinapyramine
(antrycide)

(XVI)

After two more exposures to the normal dosage of quinapyramine, it became resistant to homidium but not to berenil. After a further two exposures to quinapyramine it was also resistant to berenil. During this sequence it was not possible to measure the rising resistance to quinapyramine itself, because it had long passed the limit of dosage tolerated by the cattle. Whiteside prepared a set of strains very highly resistant to each drug and then determined the degree of resistance shown by each of these strains to all the other compounds. The results of this study are summarized in Table I.

Cross-resistance occurred between all the quinaldinium and phenanthridinium compounds; differences in structure affected the degree of cross-resistance, but only in the instance of isometamidium was the difference great enough to be of practical value. Quinapyramine was the only quaternary drug of the series tested which induced cross-resistance to berenil.

Table I

SUMMARY OF PRINCIPAL CROSS-RESISTANCE TESTS WITH *Trypanosoma vivax* AND *T. congolense* IN LABORATORY CATTLE [a]

No. of strains examined	Resistant to	Test drug and dosage (mg./kg.)								
		Homidium 1	Homidium 2	Metamidium 0.5	Metamidium 2	Prothidium 1	Prothidium 2	Tozocide 4.5	Quinapyramine 4.5	Berenil 3.5–5.0
4	Homidium	+[b]	+	±[c]		±	O[d]	±	±	O
3	Metamidium	+	±	+	+	+	O		±	O
2	Prothidium	+	+	+	O	+	+		±	O
1	Tozocide	+	+			+	±	+	±	O
10	Quinapyramine	±	±	O		+	±	±	+	±
4	Homidium and Quinapyramine	+	+	+	±	±	±	±	+	±
4	Prothidium and Quinapyramine	+	±	+	O	+	+	+	+	±
1	Berenil	O	O	O	O	O	O		O	+

[a] After Whiteside, 1962.
[b] + = Resistant
[c] ± = Partially resistant
[d] O = Sensitive

As a result of these studies Whiteside devised a practical system of curative treatment in the field, in which two drugs, homidium and berenil are used. Neither of these drugs will produce strains of trypanosome cross-resistant to the other. Homidium is used to treat infected cattle over a wide area until signs of resistance appear somewhere. The drug is then withdrawn from the whole area and berenil is used instead for a year. Berenil cures the cattle whether or not the trypanosomes are homidium resistant, and whether or not a resistant strain is being transmitted by tsetse flies. At the end of the year, all such resistant strains are killed or have died out naturally—homidium is resumed and the cycle begins again. It is theoretically possible for berenil resistance to develop during the year in which it is used; in practice it does not seem to do so and, in any event, the return to homidium would deal with it. Homidium and berenil form a "sanative pair" and in areas in which treatment can be controlled by an effective central authority their alternating use has so far been successful.

The position for prophylactics is more difficult. Apart from isometamidium suraminate, which is too new to have provided much experience in the field, the only two good prophylactics are prothidium and quinapyramine chloride. These have a diaminopyrimidinium group in common, they produce reciprocal cross-resistance and therefore cannot be alternated. The only available "sanative" at present is berenil, which has no prophylactic activity and is not always effective against quinapyramine-resistant strains.

Soltys (1959) suggested that relapsing, drug-resistant trypanosomes in laboratory animals also become antibody resistant. If this were to occur in the field, drug-resistant strains would be expected to be more than usually virulent, but Whiteside (1962) points out that the opposite is observed. Resistant infections often pass unnoticed because of their relative lack of pathogenicity. In one district of Kenya, a balance was achieved; the cattle remained infected with resistant strains but became very fit and no drugs were required to maintain the balance.

The technique of giving two drugs of different type and mode of action at the same time, which has proved so valuable in the avoidance of drug resistance in *Mycobacterium tuberculosis* infections, has not yet been seriously applied to trypanosomiasis. The careful work necessary to evaluate such treatment is difficult and time consuming but it would be of great interest to know whether the principle applies.

IV. Trypanocides and the Metabolism of Trypanosomes

A. PHYSICAL PROPERTIES OF TRYPANOCIDES

Williamson (1959a,b) has made an extensive analysis of the structurally determined physical properties of trypanocidal drugs and has classified them on the basis of their neutral, cationic, or anionic characters at blood pH. A relationship can be traced between this ionic classification and cross-resistance patterns (Williamson and Rollo, 1959), activity against human or animal species of trypanosome, and the ability of the drug to pass from the blood into the cerebrospinal fluid. The relationship is incomplete and it is not yet possible to forecast the degree of activity of a new compound from either its chemical structure or its physical characteristics. Nevertheless there are useful lessons to be learned from the information already collected.

The only drugs which are effective in late-stage human sleeping sickness are arsenicals with neutral or partially ionized substituents, and lipid-soluble furan compounds (Brodie and Hogben, 1957). It is likely that the lipid solubility of un-ionized fractions of trypanocides may have an important bearing upon activity; for example, it has been suggested that the entry of homidium into trypanosomes may be assisted by the formation, at blood pH, of lipid-soluble pseudo-base and that this may be the form in which the drug exerts its lethal effect (Williamson, 1962).

B. ACTION ON ENZYME SYSTEMS

Trypanocidal drugs and compounds related to them have from time to time been examined for their action on enzyme systems. The enzymes have been derived from many sources—mammalian tissues, yeasts, bacteria, and parasitic helminths—and relatively few investigations have been made on enzyme systems extracted from trypanosomes. One good reason for this is that pathogenic trypanosomes in the form in which they occur in the mammalian host are difficult to obtain in adequate quantities. Selective toxicity, upon which chemotherapeutic action depends, is related to differences in the sensitivity of metabolic processes in parasite and host to the action of the drug. This is clearly demonstrated in a parallel field by the studies of Bueding and Mansour (1957); trivalent antimony inhibits phosphofructokinase and the enzyme extracted from schistosomes is ten times as sensitive to the action of antimony as the analogous enzyme extracted from mammalian muscle. The difference could account for the action of organic antimonials in the treatment of schistosomiasis.

Nevertheless, it is useful to survey the trypanocidal drugs in their general relation to enzyme inhibition and a table (Table II) collected from many sources has been prepared by Williamson (1962).

1. GLYCOLYSIS

The blood-stream forms of African trypanosomes of the *Trypanosoma brucei* group show a high rate of aerobic glycolysis which is incomplete; the full tricarboxylic acid cycle is wanting (Marshall, 1948; Ryley, 1956). However, our knowledge of trypanosome respiratory enzymes is not sufficient to indicate the mode of action even of the organometallic trypanocides which inhibit thiol enzymes. African trypanosomes in their mammalian hosts also lack a cytochrome system. Fulton and Spooner (1959) and Grant and Sargent (1960) have shown that an alternative system which reacts with molecular oxygen exists in homogenates of *T. rhodesiense*. This system consists of a thiol-containing DPN-linked L-α-glycerophosphate dehydrogenase and a particulate oxidase, and it is not dependent upon pyridine nucleotide coenzymes. There is no evidence that the system is coupled to phosphorylation; conventional oxidative phosphorylation does not apparently occur.

On the other hand, insect or culture forms of trypanosomes of the *T. brucei* subgroup have a typically aerobic respiration. They utilize intermediates of the

Table II

THE ACTION OF TRYPANOCIDES ON ENZYMES[a]

Enzyme system[b]	Trypanocidal drug group						
	Aromatic arsenicals, antimonials[b] (Oxophenarsine)*	Acridines[b] (Acriflavine)	Diguanidines, diamidines[b] (Pentamidine)	Aminoquinaldines[b] (Antrycide)	Triphenylmethane dyes[b] (Pararosaniline)	Sulfonated naphthylamines[b] (Suramin)	Nitrofurans (Furacin)
Cytochrome oxidase	−		+			−	−
Cytochrome oxidase synthesis		+					
Succinoxidase (T)			+				
Diaphorase							?
DPN oxido-reduction (T)					+		?
"Flavoprotein"	−						?
Catalase	−					−	
Oxidative phosphorylation			+				
Glucose oxidation	+	+	$\left\{\begin{array}{l}+B\\-L\end{array}\right.$		+		
Hexokinase (T)	[+]		−			+	
Hexosediphosphate dehydrogenase		+	−				
Phosphofructokinase	+						
3-Phosphoglyceraldehyde dehydrogenase (T)	[+]						
Diphosphoglyceraldehyde dehydrogenase			[+]				
Triosephosphate dehydrogenase (T)	[+]						−
L-α-Glycerophosphate oxidase	[+]						+
Glycerol dehydrogenase (T)	+	−	−				
Citrate oxidase	−						
Oxoglutarate oxidase (T)	+						
Succinate dehydrogenase (T)	+		$\left\{\begin{array}{l}-B\\+L\end{array}\right.$	−	+	+	+
Fumarase (T)	+	−			+	+	
Malate oxidase (T)	+		$\left\{\begin{array}{l}+\\-\end{array}\right.$				−
Citrate formation from oxaloacetate (T)						+	
Carboxylase (T)	+		[+]				−
Pyruvate oxidase (T)	+		+				$\left\{\begin{array}{l}-\\-A\\+An\end{array}\right.$

Table II (Continued)

Enzyme system[b]	Trypanocidal drug group						
	Aromatic arsenicals, antimonials[b] (Oxophenarsine)*	Acridines[b] (Acriflavine)	Diguanidines, diamidines[b] (Pentamidine)	Aminoquinaldines[b] (Antrycide)	Triphenylmethane dyes[b] (Pararosaniline)	Sulfonated naphthylamines[b] (Suramin)	Nitrofurans (Furacin)
Lipoic acid function (T)	+						
Acetyl coenzyme A formation (T)	+						+
Lactate dehydrogenase	−	−	{ − / + }		+		+
Alcohol dehydrogenase (T)	+	+	−		+		
Pasteur effect		+	+	+			
Invertase	−					−	
Hyaluronidase						+	
Pepsin	−					−	
Trypsin				−		+	
"Protease"							−
Urease (T)	+			−		{ − / + }	?
Protein synthesis from pyruvate			[+]				
Phosphoprotein metabolism	[+]						
Transaminase (T)	+		+				−
Arginase	−		−				
Monoamine oxidase	+		+				
Diamine oxidase	−		+				
Leucine diaminase			+				
Alanine deaminase			+				
Glutamate oxidation (T)	+		{ + / − }				
Glutamate utilization			+				
Alanine oxidation			+				
Asparagine oxidation			+				
D-Proline oxidation			+				
D-Amino acid oxidase (T)	+		−			−	
Tyrosinase						−	
Decarboxylase							−
Xanthine oxidase	?		−				+
Protein catabolism			?				
Papain (T)	+						−
Lipase (T)	+						
Esterase (T)	+						

Table II (Continued)

Enzyme system[b]	Trypanocidal drug group						
	Aromatic arsenicals, antimonials[b] (Oxophenarsine)*	Acridines[b] (Acriflavine)	Diguanidines, diamidines[b] (Pentamidine)	Aminoquinaldines[b] (Antrycide)	Triphenylmethane dyes[b] (Pararosaniline)	Sulfonated naphthylamines[b] (Suramin)	Nitrofurans (Furacin)
Cholinesterase (T)	+					−	
Acetylcholinesterase (T)	+		+	+			
Choline dehydrogenase (T)	+		{− / +}			+	
Stearate oxidation (T)	+						
β-Hydroxybutyrate oxidation (T)	+						
Phospholipid metabolism	[+]		?				
Adenosine triphosphatase (T)	[+]						
Uridine and cytidine nucleotide metabolism					+		
Adenine incorporation into nucleic acid				+			
Guanine incorporation into nucleic acid				+			
Uracil incorporation into nucleic acid				−			
Glycine incorporation into nucleic acid				−			
Adenine incorporation into acid-soluble nucleotides				−			
Adenylic acid utilization		+					
Adenosine triphosphate utilization		+				[+]	
"Nucleic acid function"		+	+	+	+	+	

[a] For references to original papers, see Williamson (1962).

[b] Key to symbols:

    * = Representative trypanocide shown in brackets   (T) = Thiol enzyme
    + = Inhibition   B = Bacterial enzyme
    − = No inhibition   L = Liver enzyme
    ? = Suggestive or doubtful effect   A = Aerobic
    [ ] = Observation on trypanosome   An = Anaerobic

Krebs cycle (Ryley, 1961) and possess a cytochrome system (von Brand and Johnson, 1947; von Brand, 1951; Ryley, 1956; Fulton and Spooner, 1959). Cytochromes are structural components of the walls of the mitochondria and Krebs-cycle enzymes are believed to be located in the mitochondrial lumen. Vickerman (1962) as a result of electron microscope studies of *T. brucei* and *T. rhodesiense* has correlated these biochemical findings with the structural differences between blood-stream and culture forms of the trypanosome. The blood-stream form possesses a single, simple anterior mitochondrion which originates in the kinetoplast. In culture, the anterior mitochondrion undergoes extensive proliferation; one or more prominent evaginations ramify through the cytoplasm and cristae become prominent. An additional contorted mitochondrion arising from the kinetoplast extends into the posterior end of the flagellate and this structure may well be responsible for the morphological differ-

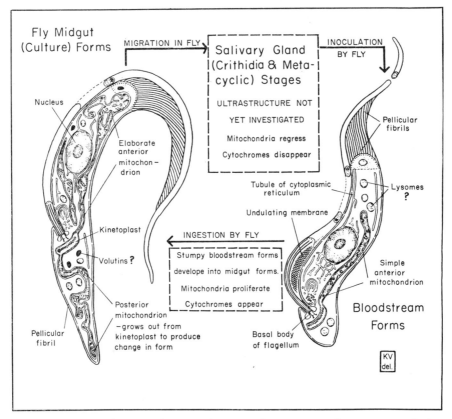

Fig. 1. Diagram showing schematic change in ultrastructure of trypanosome during its life cycle. The trypanosomes are shown partly in sagittal section. (Vickerman, 1962.)

ences between blood-stream and culture forms (Fig. 1). The consumption of O_2 and glucose by culture forms is one-tenth that of blood-stream trypanosomes (von Brand *et al.*, 1955), and it is reasonable to suppose that less O_2 and glucose are available to the parasite in the insect gut than in the mammalian circulation. Vickerman suggests that on entering the fly the trypanosome has to assume a more economical way of living and that the development of the mitochondria with the respiratory enzyme systems they contain is an adaptive change to meet the rigors of the changed environment. Studies of the correlation between morphogenesis and respiratory behavior of the *T. congolense-vivax* group of trypanosomes have not yet been made.

With increasing knowledge of the glycolytic processes of the trypanosome in the mammalian host, it may well be possible to shed light upon the mode of action of trypanocides which affect glycolytic enzyme systems.

2. NUCLEOPROTEIN METABOLISM

Trypanosoma rhodesiense is apparently unable to synthesize purines and is dependent upon preformed adenine (Williamson and Rollo, 1952). Ormerod (1951) showed that exposure of trypanosomes to quaternary ammonium compounds such as quinapyramine caused the formation of cytoplasmic granules containing ribonucleic acid and bound drug, and he suggested that the drug might prevent growth and cell division by combining with cytoplasmic ribonucleoprotein.

The trypanosomid flagellate *Crithidia (Strigomonas) oncopelti,* which occurs in the digestive tract of Hemiptera, can be grown in a simple chemically defined medium and is very sensitive to quaternary ammonium trypanocides (Newton, 1956). Like *T. rhodesiense,* it also requires adenine or other purines.

In view of the differences in metabolism of blood-stream and cultural forms of trypanosomes, the use of an insect parasite in culture for the study of drug action could be misleading, but Newton (1962) points out that parallel studies in bacterial chemotherapy have shown that if the growth of a number of different microorganisms is inhibited by a drug, the mode of action may well be the same in spite of differences of intermediary metabolism of the organisms. The results of Newton's studies on *C. oncopelti* have given a valuable clue to the probable modes of action of homidium and quinapyramine (Newton, 1957, 1958, 1960, 1962).

In the presence of homidium, *C. oncopelti* multiplied for a time and then ceased to do so; multiplication was not resumed on removal of the organisms to drug-free medium. With quinapyramine on the other hand, multiplication did not cease but the pattern of growth was changed from an exponential to a linear form; multiplication returned rapidly to an exponential pattern on removal to drug-free medium. Studies of the nucleic acid content of organisms grown in the presence of the drugs showed that homidium inhibited the synthesis of deoxyribonucleic acid (DNA) but ribonucleic acid (RNA) synthesis was un-affected for several hours. Quinapyramine had no detectable effect on DNA synthesis but caused progressive inhibition of the synthesis of RNA (Fig. 2).

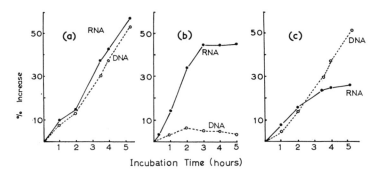

Incubation Time (hours)

FIG. 2. Effect of quaternary ammonium trypanocides on RNA and DNA synthesis by washed cell suspensions of *Crithidia* (*Strigomonas*) *oncopelti*. Washed organisms suspended in buffered salts solution containing glucose, 18 amino acids, purines, and pyrimidines (a), and with addition of 20 μg./ml. homidium (b), or of 30 μg./ml. quinapyramine (c). (Newton, 1962.)

This effect was further analyzed by the use of C^{14}-labeled metabolites. Quina-pyramine rapidly inhibited adenine or guanine incorporation, but the incorpora-tion of glycine was almost unaffected by concentrations which markedly in-hibited purine incorporation.

Newton studied 18 compounds structurally related to quinapyramine and showed that selective activity depended upon the intact quinoline-pyrimidine conjugate. The drug acted at a point in the synthesis between acid-soluble nucleotides and the formation of acid-precipitable nucleic acid. By disintegration of treated organisms in a bacterial press and differential centrifugation, it was shown that quinapyramine inhibited C^{14}-adenine incorporation into material which sedimented at 100,000 g to a much greater extent than other fractions. The particles of the 100,000 g fraction had a sedimentation constant of 78 S and resembled ribosomes isolated from other sources. After 20 hr. of growth in the presence of quinapyramine, organisms contained only 10% of their normal ribosome content; the loss was due to aggregation of particles, and nucleic acid normally found in the ribosome fraction appeared in fractions which separated at lower rates of centrifugation. Ability of *C. oncopelti* to incorporate C^{14}-leucine was lost at the same rate as the loss of ribosomes in the presence of quinapyra-mine; this suggests that aggregation of the ribosomes also results in a loss of their biological activity in protein synthesis. Microscopic examination of *C. oncopelti* grown with quinapyramine showed the formation of basophilic granules in the cytoplasm at the same rate as the aggregation of the ribosomes and Newton thinks that Ormerod's "chemotherapy granules," which contain ribonucleoprotein and bound drug, may represent aggregates of ribosomes.

During recovery in drug-free medium, new ribosomes were synthesized, but there was little disaggregation of quinapyramine-bound ribosomes. The relative insensitivity of DNA synthesis in intact organisms might be due to inability of quinapyramine to penetrate the nucleus. In contrast, homidium is clearly able to reach the site of DNA synthesis.

Chemotherapeutic effect depends upon selective action; experiments have not yet been made with pathogenic trypanosomes to see if quinapyramine aggregation of their ribosomes occurs more readily than in host tissues. Differences certainly exist between *Crithidia oncopelti* and other organisms (*Bacterium megaterium* and *Escherichia coli*) in the ease with which quinapyramine causes aggregation of ribosomal material.

Newton's studies clearly show the importance of studying the "host-parasite unit" and the need for knowledge of factors affecting the permeability of cellular and intracellular membranes to drugs. *Crithidia oncopelti* is now thought to harbor an endosymbiote; it is as yet too early to assess the effect this might have on Newton's conclusions.

V. Immunity

Evidence for the importance of the immune response of the host in bovine trypanosomiasis has been growing steadily. The naturally resistant "Ndama" born and bred outside the tsetse belt is as susceptible to trypanosome infection as the zebu, but its antibody response is much more efficient (Desowitz, 1959). Grade cattle (crosses between indigenous and exotic breeds) do not readily produce antibodies to trypanosomes; they are difficult to maintain in fly-belts and always get shorter periods of protection from prophylactic drugs. "Natural resistance" is the result of a number of influences—genetic, environmental, and acquired.

Fiennes (1950) found evidence that cryptic trypanosome infections provided premunition in animals treated with quinapyramine, and Soltys (1955) suggested that part of the prophylactic action of this drug depended upon an immune response. Stephen (1963) found that trypanosomes which appeared in the blood of cattle at the end of a period of protection with prothidium had low pathogenicity and that the cattle survived in spite of continued challenge. Hill (1963), working with another phenanthridinium prophylactic, showed that the low pathogenicity of *T. congolense* which relapsed in mice after a period of protection was due to the immune response of the host and not to any change of virulence of the parasite. The reticuloendothelial system is also of importance as a defense mechanism (Goble and Singer, 1960) and when its activity is modified by anti-organ sera, blockade, splenectomy, or corticosteroids the effects of trypanocidal drugs are also modified.

Whiteside (1962) has shown that the length of protection afforded to cattle by prophylactic drugs is related to the natural incidence of infections (transmission rate) in the area—the higher the transmission rate, the shorter the period of prophylaxis. By an ingenious analysis of the results of treating cattle exposed to different degrees of fly challenge, he has confirmed that there is an immune response in addition to the effect of the drug and has shown that this varies with the drug and with the intensity of fly challenge. Berenil, which has no prophylactic action, is associated with less immunity than quinapyramine or homidium which persist for longer periods in the body of the host.

Calves born of cows which are heavily protected by prophylactic drugs develop less immunity than those from mothers which are given just sufficient protection to keep them healthy.

The detailed analysis of the immune response has now begun; advance has been made possible by the application of new techniques. Desowitz (1956) incubated *T. vivax* with sera from infected cattle in a Warburg respirometer and showed that the development of immunity in the animal was accompanied by an inhibitory effect on the respiration of the trypanosomes. Similar results were obtained by Thurston (1958) with *T. brucei* in experimentally infected mice, and by Masseyeff and Gombert (1963) in human *T. gambiense* infections. Weitz (1960) used gel-diffusion and immune electrophoresis to study the antigen-antibody relationships of *T. brucei,* and Gray (1960) used gel-diffusion to identify trypanosome antibodies in the sera of cattle and other animals. Cunningham and Vickerman (1962) devised an improved agglutination technique for the study of antigenic variation in *T. brucei* and their method was used by Gray (1962) and by Brown (1963) to identify the variant strains which arise in the course of *T. brucei* infections in rabbits. This work stems from the original observations of Broom and Brown (1940), who described group and variant antigens in this trypanosome and showed that serological differences between variants of a strain tend to disappear after cyclical passage through *Glossina morsitans*. These observations have been confirmed and the work has been made very much easier and more reliable by the technique of freezing down the variant strains at −70°C. as they arise. The serological types can now be kept alive for reference indefinitely, without modification of antigenic structure by further animal passage. Weitz (1962) summarizes recent work in this field. During an infection of the rabbit with a monomorphic strain or a clone of *T. brucei,* the serum shows a series of antibody peaks which coincide with the development of new variants. The appearance of each new antibody is accompanied by changes in the proportions of morphologically distinct types of trypanosomes; "stumpy" forms and cytoplasmic volutin granules increase in numbers as the antibody titer rises. Ormerod (1959) showed that antibodies producing the initial crisis are stimulated more by trypanosomes containing multiple volutin granules than by those which contain a single granule; he thinks that the appearance of the granules stimulates the formation of antibody, which is responsible for the control of the infection (Ormerod, 1961). When variants are injected into new rabbits, a similar set of variant-specific antibodies occur. "There appears to be no end to the number of variants and the consequent antibodies which can be produced from a single strain of trypanosome . . . trypanosomes have an enormous potentiality for antigenic mutation" (Weitz, 1962).

Cunningham and Vickerman (1962) have been able to classify strains of *T. brucei* and *T. rhodesiense* into antigenic groups by cross-agglutination tests with rabbit sera; field studies of naturally occurring trypanosome infections should yield valuable information. The development of an effective vaccine against trypanosomiasis will not be easy—but it is not at all impossible.

Tobie and von Brand (1953) found that acquired arsenic resistance in *T. gambiense* was associated with lower pathogenicity, perhaps as a result of changed antigenic response. On the other hand, Cantrell and his colleagues in a study of the relation between antigenic type and resistance to oxophenarsine or tartar emetic in *T. equiperdum* infections of mice, have shown that a selective process among variants leads to strains which are both drug resistant and antibody resistant (Cantrell, 1958). The simultaneous appearance of drug resistance and antibody resistance in experimental infections has also been described by Soltys (1959).

Williamson (1962) makes the interesting suggestion that in human sleeping sickness, the naturally occurring tryparsamide-fast *T. rhodesiense* may in fact be an antibody-fast form of *T. gambiense,* developed by sojourn in an animal reservoir.

Nevertheless, the possibility that fly-transmission may persuade trypanosome variants to revert to their original antigenic (and perhaps metabolic) structure is an important one and merits much more extensive study. If it is true, it could account for the relatively rare occurrence of drug-fast strains in nature, in spite of the frequent misuse of the chemotherapy available.

The interrelations between drug, parasite, and host are very complex. They are well summarized by Whiteside (1962), as they apply to cattle trypanosomiasis in the field; Fig. 3 "illustrates the surprising nexus of events that is set going when we try to kill a trypanosome with a drug. The toxic action of the drug (arrow 1) is countered by the ability of the trypanosome to become drug resistant (2), which means that the chemotherapeutic attack has to be varied (3). The virulence of the trypanosome to the host (4) provokes an immune response (5) influenced by the breed of host and the drug used for treatment, which in turn is countered by antigenic variation on the part of the trypanosome (6), and perhaps by antibody-resistance (7). At the same time inter-

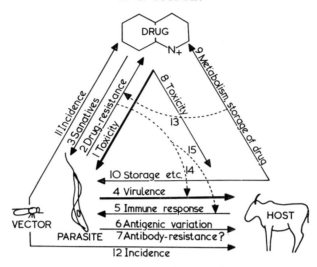

Fig. 3. Diagram representing interactions between drugs, trypanosomes, and cattle observed in the field. The arrows point toward what is inimically affected, e.g., immune response works against the parasite. (After Whiteside, 1962.)

actions develop between the *drug* and the host, for the drug is usually toxic to some extent (8) and the host responds by metabolizing it, storing it, and so on. These processes may work against the drug (9), reducing its effect on the trypanosome, or with the drug (10)—for instance storage enhances the prophylactic effect. Meanwhile the tsetse fly adds two complications because it is responsible for natural incidence, and a rising natural incidence works against the drug by shortening prophylaxis (11) and also very probably against the host by swamping the immune response (12). Finally, some of these processes themselves interact, and there is evidence that the metabolic fate of the drug influences the development of drug resistance (13), while the development of drug resistance in turn has peculiar effects on both virulence (14) and immune response (15)."

References

Agosin, M., and von Brand, T. (1954). *Antibiot. Chemotherapy* 4, 624.

Apted, F. I. C. (1960). *Trans. Roy. Soc. Trop. Med. Hyg.* 54, 225.

Ashley, J. N., Berg, S. S., and MacDonald, R. D. (1960). *J. Chem. Soc.* p. 4525.

Austin, W. C., Collier, H. O. J., Potter, M. D., Smith, G. K. A., and Taylor, E. P. (1957). *Nature* 179, 143.

Barber, H. J., and Berg, S. S. (1962). *In* "Drugs, Parasites and Hosts" (L. G. Goodwin and R. H. Nimmo-Smith, eds.), p. 165. Churchill, London.

Bauchop, T. (1962). *Biochim. Biophys. Acta* 59, 742.

Bauer, F. (1958). *Zentr. Bakteriol., Parasitenk., Abt. I. Orig.* 172, 605.

Berg, S. S. (1960). *Nature* 188, 1106.

Berg, S. S., Brown, K. N., Hill, J., and Wragg, W. R. (1961). *Nature* 192, 367.

Beveridge, E., Goodwin, L. G., and Walls, L. P. (1958). *Nature* 182, 316.

Bishop, A. (1959). *Biol. Rev. Cambridge Phil. Soc.* 34, 445.

Botafogo Gonçalves, N., and Gonçalves, F. L. (1961). *Anais Congr. Intern. Doença de Chagas, Rio de Janeiro, 1959,* 2, 645.

Brener, Z. (1961). "Contribuiçao ao Estudo da Terapêutica Experimental da Doença de Chagas." Thesis, Univ. of Minas Gerais, Belo Horizonte.

Brener, Z., and Pellegrino, J. (1958). *Rev. Brasil. Malariol Doenças Trop, Publ; Avulsas* 10, 327.

Brodie, B. B., and Hogben, C. A. M. (1957). *J. Pharm. Pharmacol.* 9, 345.

Broom, J. C., and Brown, H. C. (1940). *Trans. Roy. Soc. Trop. Med. Hyg.* 34, 53.

Brown, K. N. (1963). *In* "Immunity to Protozoa" (P. C. C. Garnham, A. E. Pierce, and I. M. Roitt, eds.), p. 204. Blackwell, Oxford.

Brown, K. N., Hill, J., and Holland, A. E. (1961). *Brit. J. Pharmacol.* 17, 396.

Bueding, E., and Mansour, J. M. (1957). *Brit. J. Pharmacol.* 12, 159.

Butler, G. C., Duggan, A. J., and Hutchinson, M. P. (1957). *Trans. Roy. Soc. Trop. Med. Hyg.* 51, 69.

Cantrell, W. (1958). *Trans. Kentucky Acad. Sci.* 19, 54.

Castellani, O., and Fernandes, J. F. (1962). *Exptl. Parasitol.* 12, 52.

Cunningham, M. P., and Vickerman, K. (1962). *Trans. Roy. Soc. Trop. Med. Hyg.* 56, 48.

Davey, D. G. (1958). *Am. J. Trop. Med. Hyg.* 7, 546.

De Jongh, R. T., and Friedheim, E. A. H. (1959). *Bull. Soc. Pathol. Exotique* 52, 769.

De Lucena, D. T. (1961). *Hospital (Rio de Janeiro)* 60, 143.

Desowitz, R. S. (1956). *Nature* 177, 132.

Desowitz, R. S. (1957). *Ann. Trop. Med. Parasitol.* 51, 457.

Desowitz, R. S. (1959). *Ann. Trop. Med. Parasitol.* 53, 293.

Duggan, A. J. (1962). *Trans. Roy. Soc. Trop. Med. Hyg.* 55, 439.

Evens, F., Niemegeers, K., and Packchanian, A. (1957). *Am. J. Trop. Med. Hyg.* 6, 665.

Fernandes, J. F., and Castellani, O. (1958). *Exptl. Parasitol.* 7, 224.

Fernandes, J. F., and Castellani, O. (1959). *Exptl. Parasitol.* 8, 480.

Fernandes, J. F., Pereira, J. P. M., and Silva, L. H. P. (1959). *Exptl. Parasitol.* 8, 496.

Fiennes, R. N. T.-W. (1950). *Ann. Trop. Med. Parasitol.* 44, 222.

Fierlafyn, E. (1960). *Ann. Soc. Belge Med. Trop.* 40, 469.

Friedheim, E. A. H., and De Jongh, R. T. (1959). *Trans. Roy. Soc. Trop. Med. Hyg.* 53, 262.

Fulton, J. D., and Spooner, D. F. (1959). *Exptl. Parasitol.* 8, 137.

Fussgänger, R., and Bauer, F. (1958). *Med. Chem., Abhandl. Med.-Chem. Forschungsstaetten Farbwerke Hoechst A. G.* 6, 504.

Garnham, P. C. C. (1963). *In* "Immunity to Protozoa" (P. C. C. Garnham, A. E. Pierce, and I. M. Roitt, eds.), p. 3. Blackwell, Oxford.

Goble, F. C. (1961). *Anais Congr. Intern. Doença de Chagas, Rio de Janeiro, 1959* 2, 613.

Goble, F. C., and Singer, I. (1960). *Ann. N.Y. Acad. Sci.* 88, 149.

Goble, F. C., Boyd, J. L., and Fulton, J. D. (1960). *J. Protozool.* 7, 384.

Goodwin, L. G., and Rollo, I. M. (1955). *In* "Biochemistry and Physiology of Protozoa" (S. H. Hutner and A. Lwoff, eds.), Vol. 2, p. 225. Academic Press, New York.

Grant, P. T., and Sargent, J. R. (1960). *Biochem. J.* 76, 229.

Gray, A. R. (1960). *Nature* 186, 1058.

Gray, A. R. (1962). *Ann. Trop. Med. Parasitol.* 56, 4.

Guimaraes, J. L., and Lourie, E. M. (1951). *Brit. J. Pharmacol.* 6, 514.

Heisch, R. B., McMahon, J. P., and Manson-Bahr, P. E. C. (1958). *Brit. Med. J.* II, 1203.

Hewitt, R. I., Wallace, W. S., Gumble, A. R., Gill, E. R., and Williams, J. H. (1953). *Am. J. Trop. Med. Hyg.* 2, 254.

Hewitt, R. I., Gumble, A. R., Wallace, W. S., and Williams, J. H. (1954). *Antibiot. Chemotherapy* 4, 1222.

Hill, J. (1963). *Ann. Trop. Med. Parasitol.* 56, 426.

Hutchinson, M. P., and Watson, H. J. C. (1962). *Trans. Roy. Soc. Trop. Med. Hyg.* 56, 227.

Hutner, S. H., Nathan, H. A., Aaronson, S., Baker, H., and Scher, S. (1958). *Ann. N.Y. Acad. Sci.* 76, 457.

Jensch, H. (1937). *Angew. Chem.* 50, 891.

Jensch, H. (1955). *Arzneimittel-Forsch.* 5, 634.

Lyttle, C. N. (1960). *J. Comp. Pathol. Therap.* 70, 18.

Marshall, P. B. (1948). *Brit. J. Pharmacol.* 3, 8.

Marshall, R. S. (1958). *Proc. 7th Intern. Sci. Committee Trypanosomiasis Res., Brussels, 1958* p. 13.

Masseyeff, R., and Gombert, J. (1963). *Ann. Inst. Pasteur* 104, 115.

Moon, A. P., and Coleman, J. F. (1962). *Bol. Chileno Parasitol.* 17, 63.

Moraes, G. E. S., Lopes Faria, J., and Fernandes, J. F. (1960). *Rev. Inst. Med. Trop. Sao Paulo* 2, 147.

Morris, K. R. S. (1960). *Science* 132, 652.

Nakamura, M., and James, M. B. (1953). *Exptl. Parasitol.* 2, 19.

Nash, T. A. M. (1955). *Ann. Rept. West African Inst. for Trypanosomiasis Research* p. 28.

Newton, B. A. (1956). *Nature* 177, 279.

Newton, B. A. (1957). *J. Gen. Microbiol.* 17, 718.

Newton, B. A. (1958). *J. Gen. Microbiol.* 19, ii.

Newton, B. A. (1960). *Biochem. J.* 77, 12P.

Newton, B. A. (1962). *In* "Drugs, Parasites and Hosts" (L. G. Goodwin and R. H. Nimmo-Smith, eds.), p. 142. Churchill, London.

Ormerod, W. E. (1951). *Brit. J. Pharmacol.* 6, 334.

Ormerod, W. E. (1959). *J. Gen. Microbiol.* 21, 287.

Ormerod, W. E. (1961). *Trans. Roy. Soc. Trop. Med. Hyg.* 55, 313.

Packchanian, A. (1957). *Antibiot. Chemotherapy* 7, 13.

Pizzi, T. (1957). "Immunologia de la Enfermedad de Chagas." Univ. de Chile, Santiago.

Pizzi, T. (1961). *Bol. Chileno Parasitol.* 16, 35.

Pizzi, T., Prager, R., and Kuierim, R. (1953). *Bol. Chileno Parasitol.* 8, 77.

Porter, J. N., Hewitt, R. I., Hesseltine, C. W., Krupka, G., Lowery, J. A., Wallace, W. C., Bohonos, N. and Williams, J. H. (1952). *Antibiot. Chemotherapy* 2, 409.

Rey, L., and Fernandes, J. F. (1962). *Exptl. Parasitol.* 12, 55.

Richet, P., Lotte, M., and Foucher, G. (1959). *Med. Trop.* 19, 253.

Robertson, D. H. H. (1961a). *Ann. Trop. Med. Parasitol.* 55, 49.

Robertson, D. H. H. (1961b). *Ann. Trop. Med. Parasitol.* 55, 278.

Robertson, D. H. H. (1963). *Trans. Roy. Soc. Trop. Med. Hyg.* 57, 274.

Robson, J. (1958). *Vet. Record* 70, 925.

Robson, J. (1961). *Vet. Record* 73, 641.

Ryley, J. F. (1956). *Biochem. J.* 62, 215.

Ryley, J. F. (1961). *Ann. Trop. Med. Parasitol.* 55, 149.

Schneider, J., Leveuf, J.-J., and Tangara, S. (1961). *Bull. Soc. Pathol. Exotique* 54, 345.

Schnitzer, R. J., and Grunberg, E. (1957). "Drug Resistance of Micro-organisms." Academic Press, New York.

Silva, L. H. P., and Kirchner, E. (1962). *Rev. Inst. Med. Trop. Sao Paulo* 4, 16.

Silva, L. H. P., Yoneda, S., and Fernandes, J. F. (1959). *Exptl. Parasitol.* 8, 486.

Smith, I. M., and Brown, K. N. (1960). *J. Comp. Pathol. Therap.* 70, 161.

Smith, I. M., and Scott, W. N. (1961). *J. Comp. Pathol. Therap.* 71, 325.

Soltys, M. A. (1955). *Ann. Trop. Med. Parasitol.* 49, 1.

Soltys, M. A. (1959). *Parasitology* 49, 143.

Stephen, L. E. (1960). *Vet. Record* 72, 80.

Stephen, L. E. (1963). *Ann. Trop. Med. Parasitol.* 56, 415.

Taylor, A. E. R. (1960). *Brit. J. Pharmacol.* 15, 235.

Thurston, J. P. (1958). *Parasitology* 48, 463.

Tobie, E. J. (1954). *Am. J. Trop. Med. Hyg.* 3, 852.

Tobie, E. J., and von Brand, T. (1953). *J. Infect. Diseases* 92, 132.

Vickerman, K. (1962). *Trans. Roy. Soc. Trop. Med. Hyg.* 56, 487.

von Brand, T. (1951). *In* "Biochemistry and Physiology of Protozoa" (A. Lwoff, ed.), Vol. 1, p. 177. Academic Press, New York.

von Brand, T. (1962). *Rev. Inst. Med. Trop. Sao Paulo* 4, 53.

von Brand, T., and Johnson, E. M. (1947). *J. Cellular Comp. Physiol.* 29, 33.

von Brand, T., Tobie, E. J., Mehlman, B., and Weinbach, E. C. (1953). *J. Cellular Comp. Physiol.* 41, 1.

von Brand, T., Weinbach, E. C., and Tobie, E. J. (1955). *J. Cellular Comp. Physiol.* 45, 421.

von Brand, T., McMahon, P., Tobie, E. J., Thompson, M. J., and Mosettig, E. (1959). *Exptl. Parasitol.* 8, 171.

Watkins, T. I. (1958). *J. Chem. Soc.* p. 1443.

Watkins, T. I., and Woolfe, G. (1956). *Nature* 178, 368.

Watson, H. J. C. (1962). *Trans. Roy. Soc. Trop. Med. Hyg.* 56, 231.

Weitz, B. (1960). *J. Gen. Microbiol.* 23, 589.

Weitz, B. (1962). *In* "Drugs, Parasites and Hosts" (L. G. Goodwin and R. H. Nimmo-Smith, eds.), p. 180. Churchill, London.

Whiteside, E. F. (1958). *Proc. 7th Intern. Sci. Committee Trypanosomiasis Res., Brussels, 1958* p. 83.

Whiteside, E. F. (1960). *Proc. 8th Intern. Sci. Committee Trypanosomiasis Res., Jos, 1960* p. 141.

Whiteside, E. F. (1962). *In* "Drugs, Parasites and Hosts" (L. G. Goodwin and R. H. Nimmo-Smith, eds.), p. 116. Churchill, London.

Williamson, J. (1953). *Exptl. Parasitol.* 2, 348.

Williamson, J. (1957). *Ann. Trop. Med. Parasitol.* 51, 440.

Williamson, J. (1959a). *Brit. J. Pharmacol.* 14, 431.

Williamson, J. (1959b). *Brit. J. Pharmacol.* 14, 443.

Williamson, J. (1962). *Exptl. Parasitol.* 12, 274.

Williamson, J., and Desowitz, R. S. (1956). *Nature* 177, 1074.

Williamson, J., and Rollo, I. M. (1952). *Nature* 170, 376.

Williamson, J., and Rollo, I. M. (1959). *Brit. J. Pharmacol.* 14, 423.

Woolfe, G. (1953). *Brit. J. Pharmacol.* 8, 420.

Woolfe, G. (1962). *In* "Antibiotics in Agriculture" (M. Woodbine, ed.), p. 58. Butterworths, London.

Wragg, W. R., Washbourn, K., Brown, K. N., and Hill, J. (1958). *Nature* 182, 1005.

Yarmolinsky, M. B., and Haba, G. L. (1959). *Proc. Natl. Acad. Sci. U.S.* 45, 1711.

The Chemotherapy of Malaria

I. M. ROLLO

Department of Pharmacology and Therapeutics, University of Manitoba Medical College, Winnipeg, Manitoba, Canada

	Page
I. Introduction	525
II. Malaria and the Host	526
A. Metabolic Activity of Plasmodia	528
B. How Plasmodia Affect the Host Cell	530
C. Dietary Factors and Malaria Infection	531
D. Influence of Factors Other Than Diet on Malaria Infection	533
E. Influence of Infection on Host Tissues	535
III. The Chemotherapy of Malaria	536
A. Mechanisms of Antimalarial Action	536
B. Development of Drug-Resistant Strains	542
C. Effect of Drugs on Sexual Stages	547
D. New Antimalarials	547
E. Fate of Antimalarials in the Body	551
F. Primaquine Sensitivity	553
G. Combined Therapy	554
References	558

I. Introduction

Complete chemotherapeutic control of malaria is now feasible. Through empiricism and intelligent guesswork, antimalarials have been developed which, properly used, can safely cure the overt attack, provide prophylaxis and, in conjunction with persistent insecticides, make economically possible the clearance of large tracts of the world where the disease is endemic.

Most of the mysteries still surrounding the pathogenic plasmodium are academic. Its life cycle has been laid bare. The classic studies of Shortt and his colleagues provided the final link in the chain of events representing the parasite's stay in the human body. Nevertheless the most fundamental and, in many respects, most interesting work has still to be done. The questions are obvious; the answers are far from complete.

II. Malaria and the Host

If we consider the life cycle of *Plasmodium vivax* (Fig. 1) we ·may ask—

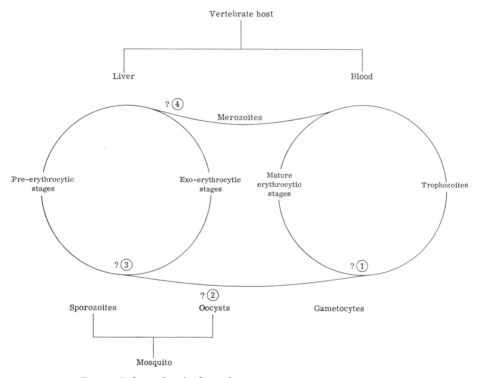

Fig. 1. Life cycle of *Plasmodium vivax* in man and mosquito.

"what environmental changes are responsible for the metamorphoses that occur in the various phases of developments?" Four main changes in form occur and at these points the questions are:

1. Why do some trophozoites, previously undifferentiated, mature as gametocytes?

2. What factors are responsible for exflagellation?

3. Why are the parenchyma cells of the liver peculiarly suited for the intracellular development of a previously extracellular stage?

4. What changes in the parasite or in the tissue microclimate occur to induce merozoites to enter erythrocytes and initiate the blood cycle?

No answer has been attempted to the first question, although it may be the most interesting in respect to sudden differentiation of cell type. Are we to look for clues in the variation in proportion of gametocytes to asexual parasites between initial infection and relapse, and between infection in children and adults? Perhaps the answer lies in an enforced change in metabolic patterns in response to a changing environment; perhaps it is a reflection of the development of immune processes. An enforced change in environment, provided by the presence of certain antimalarial drugs, is certainly known to increase markedly the numbers of gametocytes in the blood of chicks infected with *Plasmodium gallinaceum* (Bishop, 1954a).

Clues may be provided by the work of Deegan and Maegraith (1956). In considering the nature of malarial pigment it was concluded that previous methods of extraction gave rise to artifacts. If this were the case, the pigment present in the cells is not simply hematin as had been thought. Evidence for a more complex structure was afforded by the fact that succinic dehydrogenase, which appears to play an important part in the metabolism of plasmodia, is inhibited by hematin but not by hematin in combination with a nitrogenous compound. This material exhibited distinctly different properties from acid hematin obtained from extracts described by other workers. The properties of the extracted material could not be explained on the basis of its hematin nature alone, but were more probably due to a hematin-denatured protein complex. Interesting comparisons might be made between the nature of pigment from asexual parasites and that from gametocytes.

Some evidence has been provided for the second. Bishop and McConnachie (1956) studied what factors may be responsible for emergence of gametocytes from red cells and the exflagellation of male gametocytes of *P. gallinaceum*. Carbon dioxide had an inhibitory effect. Exposure to 100% CO_2 was completely inhibitory, while after exposure to lower concentrations emergence and exflagellation took place only after return to an atmosphere of air. Oxygen was not necessary since exflagellation occurred normally in blood exposed to pure nitrogen.

The time of emergence and exflagellation was not correlated with pH in the range 7 to 9, although lowering the pH partially inhibited gametocyte development. Experiments with washed cells showed that plasma played a part but there was no confirmation of earlier suggestions that mosquito salivary gland secretions were necessary. It was suggested that a factor or factors may be present in plasma which are activated possibly by diffusion of CO_2 from blood when drawn.

Later work showed that horse serum was satisfactory for both emergence and sexual development. Immune factors played no part, for emergence and exflagellation occurred just as readily in plasma from hyperimmune birds as in normal plasma (Bishop and McConnachie, 1960).

As for the third and fourth questions, we have as yet no shred of evidence to essay an answer.

A. METABOLIC ACTIVITY OF PLASMODIA

The volume of work on the biochemistry and physiology of the malaria parasite has decreased considerably over the past 10 years. Now is the time for consolidation; finer detail can be looked for in the light of the earlier, rather empirical, discoveries.

Much attention has been focused on *Plasmodium berghei*. Quite naturally this parasite of mammalian erythrocytes lends itself to studies which in the final analysis must be applied to the species infecting man. The main advantages are: the host cell is nonnucleated and a high degree of parasitemia is produced in a host which is a common, easily handled, laboratory animal. In contrast it has a predilection for reticulocytes which have appreciable metabolic activity of their own, the response of infection to various drugs is somewhat different from the responses of other species, and transmission by sporozoites has not yet been accomplished.

Early work showed that the purine and pyrimidine bases present in nucleic acids of *P. berghei* were the same as those described for ribonucleic acid (RNA; yeast) and deoxyribonucleic acid (DNA; thymus) (Whitfeld, 1953a). As might be expected, the proportions of the bases present differed. The DNA belonged to what has been described as the "AT" type in which the concentration of adenine and thymine exceeded that of guanine and cytosine; 5-methylcytosine was not detected.

In studies on the uptake of P^{32} by *P. berghei in vivo*, the highest content of P^{32} was in the lipid fraction of free parasites (Whitfeld, 1953b). However, the greatest incorporation of P^{32} during the period 2 to 48 hr. after the injection of the radioisotope into the host, was in the DNA fraction. In the RNA fraction the content of P^{32} remained fairly constant over the experimental period. A suggestion by the author that interesting results might be forthcoming in a comparison of the P^{32} content in the nucleotides of nucleic acids isolated from normal and drug-resistant strains has not been followed up so far.

Glycolysis in *P. berghei* has been investigated by Bowman *et al.* (1960). Parasites freed from the host cell had low infectivity compared with intact infected erythrocytes. These isolated parasites did not contain endogenous substrate and their rate of glucose catabolism was low. Glucose catabolism was enhanced, however, by the addition of saline with a Na:K ratio of 1:7 as is found in red cells. Glucose catabolism by free parasites in an extract of normal reticulocytes was similar to that in an intact cell but respiration was lower.

Later work (Bowman *et al.*, 1961) showed that lactic acid and hexose-6-

phosphates, mainly glucose-6-phosphate, were the major products of glucose metabolism by the parasite. The amounts of $C^{14}O_2$ and the distribution of the isotope in lactate formed from $[1 - C^{14}]$- and $[6 - C^{14}]$- glucose indicated that almost all of the glucose was metabolized by the Embden-Meyerhof glycolytic pathway. The small conversion of $[U - C^{14}]$- glucose into $C^{14}O_2$ by both free parasites and intact parasitized reticulocytes indicated that only minor amounts of glucose are oxidized by the tricarboxylic acid cycle. In this respect *P. berghei* differs from the parasites of avian and simian malaria, both of which readily oxidize lactate or intermediates of the tricarboxylic acid cycle.

Mepacrine (quinacrine) markedly inhibited utilization of glucose by free parasites (Fig. 2); this effect appeared selective for the parasites since an

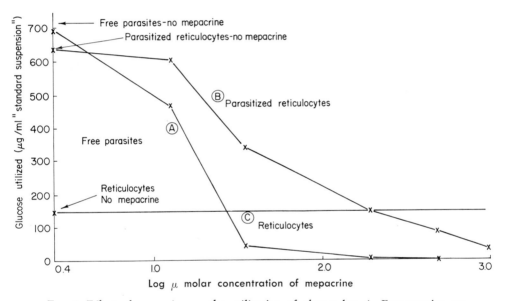

FIG. 2. Effect of mepacrine on the utilization of glucose by; A. Free-parasite suspension, parasites originally present in 2×10^9 infected reticulocytes. B. Parasitized reticulocytes, 1.6×10^9 cells of which 72% were infected. C. Normal reticulocytes, 10^9 cells of which 87% were reticulocytes. (After Bowman *et al.*, 1961.)

equivalent number of reticulocytes was unaffected by the drug at much higher concentrations. The ratio of $C^{14}O_2$ obtained from $[1 - C^{14}]$- and $[6 - C^{14}]$- glucose was not significantly altered by the presence of mepacrine; thus the contribution of the alternative pathway involving pentose phosphate to the amount of glucose metabolized was unaffected by the drug. At the same time, mepacrine did not significantly alter the percentage of $[U - C^{14}]$-glucose which was converted to $C^{14}O_2$ and hence the inhibitory effect of the drug most probably is located at some step in the conversion of glucose to lactate. From further consideration it was concluded that the enzyme involved may be 6-phosphofructokinase.

Following the early work of Moulder and Evans (1946) who showed that hemoglobin was split slowly or not at all by cell-free extracts of *P. gallinaceum*, but that the acid-denatured globins were rapidly hydrolyzed, Cook *et al.* (1961) have investigated the proteolytic enzymes of *P. berghei* and *P. knowlesi*. With monkey urea-denatured globin and mouse globin as substrates, proteinases were found in the parasites freed from the host cells. These enzymes were not inhibited by thiol-group reagents but were inhibited by metal-chelating agents. It was suggested that the digestion of hemoglobin *in vivo* was not necessarily effected by release of these enzymes into the cytoplasm of the host cell, but rather that the process occurred in the cytoplasm of the parasite. They envisaged hemoglobin molecules ingested by a process of pinocytosis followed by digestion in the vacuole and retention of the residual material as malarial pigment.

Previous work by Fulton and Grant (1956) using *P. knowlesi in vivo* and monkey cells labeled with S^{35}-methionine showed in fact that 80% of the methionine in parasite protein was obtained from the globin of the red cell. It was well known that of the amino acids only methionine had to be added to the medium for the growth *in vitro*, of *P. knowlesi* (McKee *et al.*, 1947); this implied that essentially all the parasite's requirements for other amino acids are obtained from the intracellular constituents of the erythrocytes. Fulton and Grant also found that S^{35}-cysteine injected into an infected monkey appeared in parasite protein. A comparison was therefore made of the uptake of S^{35}-cysteine and S^{35}-methionine by parasitized erythrocytes *in vitro*. There was a very low uptake of cysteine compared to that of methionine. This fact together with the estimate made *in vivo* that only about 20% of the methionine in parasite protein is obtained from free amino acid in the plasma, would indicate that free cysteine in the plasma is a minor source of cysteine to the parasite. It may be that the small utilization of plasma cysteine by the parasite is a function of restricted penetration into host erythrocyte. There is some evidence (Johnson and Bergeim, 1951) which suggests that human erythrocytes are freely permeable to methionine but not to cystine and presumably not to cysteine.

B. How Plasmodia Affect the Host Cell

Although it is generally accepted that the malaria parasites are situated inside the erythrocytes, it has been argued that they are attached to the outer surface of the host cells. Shute and Maryon (1956) firmly supported this view, quoting in evidence the microscopic appearance of stained blood films. Fulton and Flewett (1956), however, examined red cells infected with *P. berghei* and *P. knowlesi* using phase-contrast and electron microscopy and did not note "any appearance to suggest that a parasite was on the surface of a cell." Further work by Wolcott *et al.* (1958) using phase-contrast microscopy showed that immature parasites in a cover-slip preparation could readily escape from the host cell without rupturing it but that mature parasites did rupture the cell. Pseudopodia of *P. vivax* could be seen moving about in three dimensions but always within the confines of the cell membrane. Good evidence for the presence of *P. relictum* within pigeon red cells is furnished by the displacement of the host cell nucleus.

Electron microscopy of *P. lophurae*-infected blood cells by Rudzinska and Trager (1957) also demonstrated the intracellular locus of the parasite, but perhaps of greater importance was the discovery of a large food vacuole. This was shown to be about 2μ long and was of the same consistency as the cytoplasm of the erythrocyte. It had a fine limiting membrane on which were attached the granules of malarial pigment. The vacuole was formed from the cytoplasm of the host cell by invagination of the parasite's limiting membrane: intracellular phagotrophy had occurred.

C. Dietary Factors and Malaria Infection

1. milk and malaria

Since the original observation that a milk diet can have a suppressive effect on malaria of experimental animals (Maegraith *et al.*, 1952), a voluminous literature has appeared on the subject.

a. Avian Malaria (P. gallinaceum). In adult fowls, a milk diet appeared to cause a more intense parasitemia which was invariably fatal (Ramakrishnan *et al.*, 1953b). In young chicks, parasitemia after sporozoite inoculation was delayed by a significant period (Greenberg *et al.*, 1954) whereas in chicks on a purified diet and inoculated with asexual forms there was as rapid multiplication as in chicks on a stock diet (D. J. Taylor and Greenberg, 1955).

b. Rodent Malaria (P. berghei). In suckling mice, the resultant parasitemia was low if the inoculum was sufficiently high to suppress the incubation period and normal if a small number of parasites was inoculated. This difference disappeared when the mice were weaned (Fabiani and Orfila, 1956). In young mice, infection was prolonged but all eventually died when the animals were left on a milk diet, while in adult animals some which recovered relapsed and died when returned to a stock diet (Carrescia, 1955). Schneider and Montézin (1953), Durard and Mathis (1955), and Fulton (1954) were unable to demonstrate any protective effect of a milk diet on adult mice although the first-mentioned used a heavy inoculum of parasites; variable results were obtained by Fabiani and Orfila (1954). Raffaele and Carrescia (1954) found a marked effect in that nearly half of the infected mice recovered spontaneously after a marked prolongation of infection when compared with control mice on stock diet. Several of the recovered mice, with noninfective blood, were challenged by reinoculation and showed a certain, but variable, degree of immunity. The development of immunity therefore seemed favored by a prolongation of the duration of infection under the influence of the milk diet.

The administration of p-aminobenzoic acid (PAB) caused a notable increase in parasitemia with P. berghei in suckling rats (Hawking, 1954). There was no regularity of supression in adult rats kept on a milk diet but more promising results were obtained by using suckling mice fed by mothers kept on a deficient diet (Hawking and Terry, 1957). Complete lack of effect was observed by Corradetti et al. (1955), a milder infection by Ramakrishnan et al. (1953c), and suppression by Mackerras (1953) in adult rats on a milk diet. Fulton (1954) obtained incomplete suppression in adult rats, although 150-g. rats on a milk diet were insusceptible to infection. Using a diet of amino acids, fats, and carbohydrates he found that the addition of methionine resulted in parasitemia in 6 out of 6 rats; the addition of p-hydroxybenzoic acid resulted in parasitemia in 4 out of 5. Only 3 out of 6 rats given PAB showed parasites.

c. Simian Malaria. The effect of PAB on P. cynomolgi and P. knowlesi infection of suckling monkeys was observed to be similar to that on P. berghei infection of suckling rats (Hawking, 1954). Suppression of P. knowlesi infection was obtained in adult rhesus monkeys left on a milk diet 7 days before inoculation (Jaswant Singh et al., 1953).

d. Human Malaria. A milk and sugar diet given to African children had no effect on P. vivax, P. falciparum, or P. malariae infection (Miller, 1954); Chaudhuri and Dutta, 1955). Gilles (1957) commenting on the marked increase in parasite rate in Gambian children from the first to the sixth month of life, observed that this bore an inverse relationship to the amount of fetal hemoglobin in the red cells and might be correlated with the decay of an as yet hypothetical maternal antibody. On the other hand the developing flora of the gut might make available increasing amounts of PAB: it is known that the concentration of this metabolite in the breast milk of Gambian mothers is low.

It is obvious that no satisfactory conclusions can be drawn from this work on the suppression of malaria infection by milk. In many of the studies uncontrolled variables permit of no direct correlation between species and between hosts. It should be obvious that nutritional requirements of the various species may differ in important details. The various hosts may differ in ability to supply deficiencies provided by the dietary regimes. There may be differences not only between hosts but within hosts from laboratory to laboratory and from age group to age group. In addition the diets may vary quite considerably in their ability to supply the factor or factors essential for the well-being not only of the parasite but also of the host.

2. OTHER DIETARY FACTORS

Feeding mice inoculated with P. *berghei* with a synthetic diet supplemented with 5% cod liver oil resulted in complete suppression which could be reversed by the concomitant administration of vitamin E, ascorbic acid, and tetraethylthiuram disulfide (disulfiram; Godfrey, 1957). Suppression of P. *galinaceum* infection in chicks was observed after feeding a diet rich in cod liver oil (A. E. R. Taylor, 1958). Administration of vitamin E reversed the effect. It was concluded that unsaturated fatty acids in the oil were oxidized by the host to give peroxides, the presence of which was unfavorable to the parasite. The production of inhibitory peroxides was readily prevented by the potent antioxidants.

A wholly meat diet given to mice eventually results in a severe anemia, characterized in its terminal stages by a striking anisocytosis, which can be prevented or reversed by the feeding of liver. In mice thus treated the inoculation of P. *vinckei*, which normally results in 100% mortality, produced few deaths even after splenectomy. When 2 µg./day PAB was given, however, the infection developed normally (Adler, 1958a,b).

In a series of experiments on the effect of diet on P. *berghei*-infected rats, Ramakrishnan (1954) demonstrated that a pyridoxine-deficient diet decreased parasitemia, probably by a direct effect on the parasite. A ketogenic and inadequate diet resulted in weight loss of the host and reduced parasitemia, probably an effect mediated by the metabolism of the host. Coatney and Greenberg (1961) fed mice a diet known to produce multiple necrotic degeneration of various organs because of deficiencies of Factor 3, cystine, and vitamin E. The mean survival period of P. *berghei*-infected mice was 23 days in a control group and 15 days in a deficient group. The fact that deficient mice died a week earlier than would have been expected from malaria alone would imply that the dietary deficiency placed an additional strain on the infected mice.

D. INFLUENCE OF FACTORS OTHER THAN DIET ON MALARIA INFECTION

In addition to its effect on parasitemia in milk-fed hosts, the effect of PAB itself has been investigated. Feeding PAB to starving rats increased parasitemia to control levels from a suppressed level. Methionine produced a similar effect while glucose and biotin did not (Ramakrishnan *et al.*, 1953a). An increase in parasitemia in P. *gallinaceum*-infected chicks occurred after the addition of either PAB or *p*-hydroxybenzoic acid to a basal diet (A. E. R. Taylor, 1957). A decrease in the blood level of PAB was shown to occur during patent infection (Rama Rao and Sirsi, 1956a). There seems little doubt from this and previous work that PAB is an essential metabolite for mammalian and avian parasites. The high activity of sulfadiazine as an antimalarial agent against these infections lends support to this view. The same may well hold true for the human malarial parasites. Although a milk diet has been shown to have no effect on the course of infection, no determinations have been carried out of the PAB content either of the plasma or of the erythrocytes. This may well be sufficiently high to make insignificant any alteration due to dietary intake. In any event the relative inactivity of sulfonamides as antimalarials in the human suggests that more than adequate amounts of PAB are available to the parasite.

A deficiency of riboflavin was shown by A. E. R. Taylor (1957) to result in a decreased parasitemia in chicks infected with *P. gallinaceum*. Since the blood level of riboflavin decreased during progression of infection (Rama Rao and Sirsi, 1956b), it seems probable that this vitamin is utilized by the plasmodium. The fact that the parenteral administration of riboflavin during the course of infection resulted in increased parasitemia and in some cases earlier death of the host, lends further support to this premise.

A deficiency of vitamin A on the other hand resulted in increased parasitemia and deaths in rats infected with *P. berghei* (Bouisset and Ruffié, 1958a,b). The acute course of infection was probably due to the absence of the vitamin in the diet and not to the physical deterioration of the host since the administration of a preparation containing vitamins A and D to the infected, deficient animals resulted in parasitemia similar to that of control animals. It had previously been shown that rats on a vitamin A-deficient diet suffered aggravated signs of deficiency on infection with *P. berghei* but there was no great effect on parasitemia (Fabiani and Grellet, 1952). However, it is probable that the degree of deficiency in these experiments was not so great as that obtained by Bouisset and Ruffié.

Early work had shown the importance of coenzyme A to *P. lophurae* and that depletion of the coenzyme in the livers of infected chicks appeared to be correlated with its appearance in the parasites (Trager, 1952, 1954). During the course of *P. berghei* infection the coenzyme concentration in the liver decreased while the size increased so that the total amount present was unaltered. In the spleen the concentration remained unaltered and the total amount present was increased (Singer and Trager, 1956). In considering the differences found between rats which succumbed and those which recovered, and the results of previous studies, they put forward the view that the ability to produce coenzyme A may rank as one of those factors of innate immunity which determine the ultimate death or survival of the host. If the animal can maintain the coenzyme supply to its own tissues then the forces of acquired immunity will control the infection.

The early studies also showed the beneficial effect of pyruvate on survival of *P. lophurae in vitro*. However, commercial samples had no such effect due to the presence of a lactone of a dimer of pyruvic acid, parapyruvic acid. This substance was found to have a detrimental effect on development *in vitro* of both freed and intact parasites, possibly due to interference with the utilization of α-ketoglutarate in the Krebs cycle.

A marked increase in parasitemia occurred under conditions leading to hypoxia in canaries infected with *P. cathemerium* (Hughes and Tatum, 1955) and in rats infected with *P. berghei* (Hughes and Tatum, 1956). The increase in parasitemia appeared similar to that occurring after the administration of cortisone. The effects suggested an interference with cellular reaction to infection. In the case of *P. cathemerium* infection there was a striking increase in the amount of primaquine required for the cure of hypoxic birds. While this may be bound up with reduction in host protective mechanisms, alteration of parasite metabolism or reduction in the formation of active metabolite of primaquine by the host may also be significant factors.

A puzzling effect was observed by Tolbert and McGhee (1960). In rats made diabetic by the administration of alloxan, infection with *P. berghei* was inhibited with a resultant lower parasitemia. In these rats the blood glucose was greater than 340 mg./100 ml. Alloxan itself was without effect at doses which did not produce any damage to the β-cells of the pancreas. It is known that in rats the ED_{50} and LD_{50} are almost identical and an explanation may lie in an indirect effect mediated by kidney damage due to the nephrotoxic action of alloxan.

E. INFLUENCE OF INFECTION ON HOST TISSUES

Rats infected with *P. berghei* showed a decrease in liver glycogen which progressed with increase in parasitemia (Mercado and von Brand, 1954). A decrease in carcass glycogen also occurred but became apparent only in highly parasitized animals. This decrease in carcass glycogen was found to be due to decreased food intake by the sick animals, however this factor explained only part of the loss in liver glycogen. A true disturbance of liver function was assumed in addition to the effect of semistarvation. This was substantiated by the lesser deposition of glycogen in the liver of parasitized rats compared with normal rats after oral or intravenous administration of glucose. Later work showed evidence that the reduction of glycogen synthesis was due to adrenal dysfunction in combination with centrilobular damage to the liver due to anoxia (Mercado and von Brand, 1957).

In contrast, infection with *P. knowlesi* in monkeys caused a considerable reduction in liver and muscle glycogen but this could be increased markedly by intravenous injection of glucose. There was no apparent fault in glycogenesis. Blood sugar was reduced during infection and this became very marked on approaching death. Calculation indicated a possible competition between host and parasite for available glucose.

Appreciable alterations in duck erythrocytes infected with *P. lophurae* were found by Trager (1959). While uninfected erythrocytes contained minimal amounts (1 mμg./ml.), infected cells contained 20–60 mμg./ml. folic acid and 10–20 mμg./ml. folinic acid. Calculation of the amount present in parasite material showed that each parasite contained 2–4 $\times$ 10^{-9} mμg. folic acid and 0.5–1.5 $\times$ 10^{-9} mμg. folinic acid, while each infected erythrocyte contained 12 $\times$ 10^{-9} mμg. folic acid and 2–4 $\times$ 10^{-9} mμg. folinic acid. It was presumed that the difference was contained within the components of the erythrocytes. From this it was thought that the metabolism of the host cell had been markedly altered by the presence within itself of the parasite. This conclusion is supported by evidence from earlier work (Trager, 1958) where it was shown that folic acid was beneficial to the growth *in vitro* of P. *lophurae* intracellularly but not when the parasite was maintained extracellularly. Presumably the mediation of the erythrocyte was required for the conversion of folic acid to the usable folinic acid. Folinic acid itself had a favorable effect *in vitro* on the extracellular forms. Further evidence was also provided by the effect of antimalarial drugs on the concentrations of the metabolites; this will be discussed later.

Studies on erythrocytes and their invasion by plasmodia were carried out by Sergent (1958). There was a rapid mobilization of polychromatophils and reticulocytes 24 hr. after the inoculation of mice with P. *berghei*. This was due to the destruction of mature erythrocytes. It was supposed that polychromatophils differ from mature cells in having a "soft" cytoplasm and in being invested in a fragile membrane and suggested that these properties might facilitate penetration. However, the environment provided did not seem to be favorable since many parasites underwent degenerate changes and disintegrated.

III. The Chemotherapy of Malaria

A. Mechanisms of Antimalarial Action

Even now, many years after their discovery, the mode of action of most antimalarial drugs is incompletely understood. The reason for this is our sketchy knowledge of the metabolic pathways, and less still of the comparative biochemistry of the several species of plasmodia infecting man and experimental animals. During the last 10 years or so a considerable amount of attention has been focused on those antimalarials whose action has been considered to be concerned with interference with the synthesis of purines and pyrimidines via the PAB $\rightarrow$ folic acid $\rightarrow$ folinic acid system.

Using *Lactobacillus casei* as indicator organism, Ryley (1953) found that in a medium containing a minimal amount of either folic acid or thymine for maximal growth, inhibition of growth was caused by proguanil, a dichloro

analog of proguanil, triazine metabolites of these two drugs, and pyrimethamine
(Fig. 3).

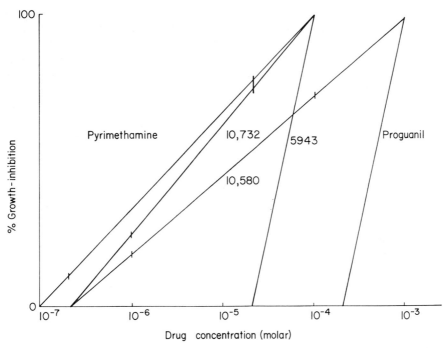

Fig. 3. Inhibition of folic acid- and thymine-stimulated growth of *Lactobacillus
casei* by:
    Proguanil; N_1-(4-chlorophenyl)-N_5-*iso*propylbiguanide
    Pyrimethamine; 2,4-diamino-5-(4-chlorophenyl)-6-ethyl pyrimidine
    5943; N_1-(3,4-dichlorophenyl)-N_5-*iso*propylbiguanide
    10,580; 2,4-diamino-1-(4-chlorophenyl)-1,6-dihydro-6,6-dimethyl-1,3,5-triazine
    10,732; 2,4-diamino-1-(3,4-dichlorophenyl)-1,6-dihydro-6,6-dimethyl-1,3,5-tria-
zine
The sections between vertical bars indicate the range of concentrations over which
competitive inhibition was observed. Proguanil and 5943 produced an "all or none"
inhibition which could not be reversed by folic acid and thymine. (After Ryley,
1953.)

The two biguanides caused an "all or none" inhibition and in neither case
could this inhibition be reversed by the addition of folic acid or thymine. In
contrast the addition of increasing amounts of any of the other three substances produced a graded response which could be reversed by the addition
of either folic acid or thymine. In all these cases the reversal of growth inhibition was competitive. With pyrimethamine or the triazines, one molecule of

folic acid reversed the toxic action of several thousand molecules of drug, whereas there was a more nearly equimolar relationship between these compounds and thymine. Ryley considered therefore that the drugs may produce their antimalarial effect not by antagonizing folic acid but rather by interfering with reactions involving thymine or its derivatives. This being so, folic acid would exert an antagonistic action, not by competing directly with the drug, but by acting catalytically in the synthesis of increased amounts of thymine.

Unfortunately growth of *L. casei* in the absence of folic acid is limited if thymine (and adenine) is present; maximal growth is only about one-half that obtained in the presence of optimal amounts of folic acid. It would be difficult therefore to draw hard and fast conclusions from experiments in which the organism was growing atypically.

Further experiments carried out *in vitro* with chick erythrocytes infected with *P. gallinaceum,* showed that proguanil and compound 10,732 produced typical effects on both morphology and viability, but on no occasion was the antimalarial action antagonized by the presence of folic acid, folinic acid, adenosine, or a mixture of adenine, guanine, and thymine. It was suggested that the parasites are possibly unable to use folic acid as such, but require a "higher" form of folic acid, and rather than use free purines or pyrimidines, prefer to use the corresponding nucleosides or nucleotides.

Working with chicks infected with *P. gallinaceum,* Bishop (1954b) confirmed earlier work in showing that PAB antagonized the antimalarial action of sulfadiazine and that the antagonism was competitive. In addition her data showing the antagonistic effect of folic acid on sulfadiazine were suggestive of a competitive antagonism. When tested with proguanil, PAB showed no antagonistic effect. At the doses used, however, PAB itself had a depressing effect on parasitemia. Folic acid, used at very high doses, was slightly antagonistic.

Competitive antagonism of the antimalarial effect of sulfadiazine has been demonstrated using folic acid and several analogs of folic acid (Greenberg, 1954). Both aminopterin and amethopterin were tried but proved to be toxic to the host at doses below that at which folic acid produced significant reversal of the action of sulfadiazine. Chick blood was analyzed for diazotizable amines after giving 200 mg./kg. folic acid but none could be detected. It seemed therefore as if the administered material was itself responsible for the antagonism, not a metabolic product such as PAB. However while no amine was present in the blood at a concentration detectable by the method used, effective concentrations may have been present at intracellular sites. So far, we have no direct evidence of any such degradative mechanism existing within the plasmodial cell; it may be well worth looking for.

Thurston (1954), using *P. berghei* infection in mice, has also investigated antagonism by PAB and folic acid. She found that the antimalarial action of

sulfadiazine, proguanil, and pyrimethamine was antagonized by both metabolites but that no antagonistic effect was shown by a series of amino acids and
purine and pyrimidine derivatives.

An attempt has been made by Rollo (1955a) to unravel the complicated
and sometimes apparently contradictory facts brought to light in experiments
with the agents discussed above. The behavior of combinations of proguanil
and pyrimethamine and of sulfadiazine and pyrimethamine were first studied.
As can be seen from Fig. 4 no potentiation was observed with proguanil-

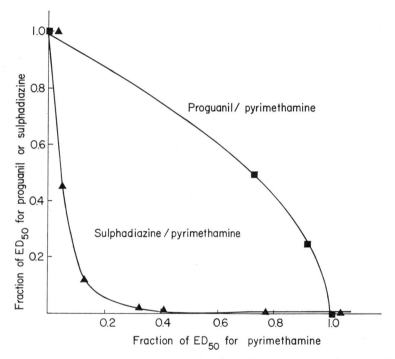

Fig. 4. E.D.$_{50}$-isobols of the antimalarial effect of combinations of proguanil and
pyrimethamine (■) and of sulfadiazine (sulphadiazine) and pyrimethamine (▲)
against *Plasmodium gallinaceum* infection of chicks. (After Rollo, 1955a.)

pyrimethamine combinations, but a very marked degree of potentiation occurred with sulfadiazine-pyrimethamine combinations. Potentiation between
proguanil and sulfadiazine had previously been observed (Greenberg, 1949).

Studies were made also of the development of resistance to the three drugs
and of the occurrence of cross-resistance. The relationship may be summarized
thus: (a) strains resistant to sulfonamides are usually resistant to proguanil
and to pyrimethamine; (b) strains resistant to proguanil are usually resistant
to pyrimethamine and *vice versa*; (c) strains resistant to proguanil and to

pyrimethamine are not usually resistant to sulfonamides. It was further observed that pyrimethamine resistance appears to develop less readily and to be more labile in character than resistance to proguanil.

Rollo assumed that the system upon which these antimalarials act is as follows:

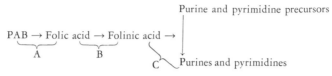

and that the pertinent facts are: (a) strains resistant to proguanil and pyrimethamine retain full sensitivity to sulfonamides; (b) sulfonamide-resistant strains are cross-resistant to proguanil and to pyrimethamine; (c) sulfadiazine potentiates the action of proguanil and pyrimethamine. Facts (a) and (c) suggest that there is no common locus of action for sulfonamides and proguanil-pyrimethamine; fact (b) suggests a common locus.

The effect of sulfonamides on plasmodia is presumably due to interference with the utilization of PAB in reaction A. The other drugs may, however, act quite differently. The results of cross-resistance tests and the lack of complete antagonism by PAB and folic acid indicate that their action may be more than simple competition with a metabolite. Previous evidence on the differing ability of folic and folinic acids to reverse the effects of pyrimethamine favors a blockage of reaction B; and if resistance to proguanil and to pyrimethamine involved interference with their action at point B only, this would leave reactions A and C vulnerable to other drugs—for example, to the action of sulfonamides at A.

The experimental findings could be explained by a two-point mode of action for proguanil and pyrimethamine. This would involve (1) an acceptor mechanism whereby the drugs are made available to interfere with the metabolic reactions and (2) a "lethal" point of action within the metabolic pathway. There may thus be cell receptors responsible for making PAB available to reaction A. Sulfonamides would also be accepted, thus making possible the blocking of reaction A.

Sulfonamide resistance may involve a decrease in cell permeability to the sulfonamide molecule, or a change in distribution or orientation of the receptors, so that, although PAB is still accepted, the sulfonamide molecule is rejected. If pyrimethamine and the active metabolite of proguanil are accepted or rejected by the same mechanism as sulfonamides, sulfonamide-resistance would be accompanied by resistance to these drugs, perhaps before the resistance to sulfonamides became evident, as has been observed.

Resistance to proguanil and pyrimethamine could involve a by-pass of their effects on reaction B, leaving unchanged the sensitivity of the strain to sulfonamides acting at A. On the other hand, a reorientation of PAB receptors, insufficient in extent to cause rejection of sulfonamide molecules, might yet be sufficient to cause rejection of the proguanil-metabolite and pyrimethamine. This would also explain the observation that a strain treated with proguanil soon acquired a high degree of resistance to proguanil but only a slight cross-resistance to pyrimethamine. A strain treated under the same conditions with pyrimethamine, on the other hand, remained indistinguishable from the parent strain in sensitivity to either drug. Bishop (1954b) has shown that a strain treated with 2,4-diamino-6,7-di-*iso*-propylpteridine became resistant to pyrimethamine but only after resistance had developed first to the pteridine and then to proguanil. Here we must assume that pyrimethamine has a firmer "foothold" upon the receptors than has the proguanil metabolite.

Little change would be required in the distribution or orientation of the receptors for the complete rejection of the proguanil metabolite, the smallness of the change being reflected in the ease with which resistance can be induced. Pyrimethamine resistance on the other hand may involve a greater change. Further evidence of the effects of small changes of structure in molecules of the pyrimethamine type upon their action against resistant strains was given by Greenberg and Bond (1956). They found that, in a strain made 800-fold resistant to pyrimethamine and tested during the development of resistance with a series of pyrimethamine analogs, the slopes of the curves of degree of resistance against time varied markedly from one substance to another. The analogs, resembling pyrimethamine closely in structure, would be expected to act at the same point in the metabolic reactions; differences in activity upon resistant strains would best be accounted for by differences in degrees of acceptance resulting from differences in spatial structure.

Pyrimethamine and the metabolite of proguanil may enter the metabolic pathway concerned with the uptake and utilization of PAB by the same acceptor mechanism as PAB; the drugs then kill the parasite by interfering with the conversion of folic acid to folinic acid.

Trager's observations on the metabolism of duck erythrocytes infected with *P. lophurae* stemmed from the many observations that the antimalarial effect of proguanil and pyrimethamine can be antagonized by PAB, folic acid, and folinic acid and that this antagonism does not seem to follow any consistent pattern. Although if we consider that folic and folinic acids may be degraded to a greater or lesser extent to PAB or PAB-like compounds, and that their antagonistic effect depends largely on the relative permeabilities to the parent and degraded products and the sites of degradation, then it does not need too great a stretch of the imagination to make order out of disorder. The conception of alteration in host cell metabolism in response to invasion by a parasite has not been considered before with respect to malaria. However, caution must be exercised in the interpretation of results of such experiments, for in the preparation of freed parasite suspension for assay of folic and folinic acids inevitable losses of these substances may occur. If the cell membrane of the parasite is more or less freely permeable to both factors, an appreciable proportion of the parasite's content might be lost in the procedure for lysing the erythrocyte and purifying the parasite suspension.

The action of sulfadiazine and pyrimethamine on infected erythrocytes resulted in a reduction of both factors by the former and only of folinic acid by the latter (Trager, 1961). This is consistent with previous work on the mode of action of these two substances. However if a strain made resistant to sulfadiazine, and cross-resistant to pyrimethamine, was similarly treated the same results were obtained. This would seem to provide further evidence that the synthetic mechanism may reside in the infected cells rather than in the parasite and to suggest that resistance to sulfadiazine and pyrimethamine depends on a decreased requirement for the products of the reactions inhibited by these drugs.

These observations are extremely interesting and offer much speculation for further work. The strain used in the experiments was, however, not fully resistant to the two drugs tested and at the concentrations used showed appreciable reduction in parasitemia compared to untreated controls. Another interesting facet was the apparent increase in both folic and folinic acid content of erythrocytes containing parasites of a sulfadiazine-treated strain compared with the normal untreated strain. Although there was an appreciable spread in the figures given, they appear to be sufficiently significant to warrant further investigation.

Hitchings (1963) points out that the plasmodium might well be synthesizing folic acid in excess and excreting it into the erythrocyte. Folic acid synthesis appears to be a function which was lost in the lower orders of the animal tree and it is difficult to visualize the plasmodium contributing the missing elements of this biosynthetic pathway to the erythrocyte of a species as highly evolved as the duck. The ultimate resolution will come from the demonstration of folic acid synthesis by plasmodia *in vitro* and of their inability to take up pre-existing folic acid.

B. DEVELOPMENT OF DRUG-RESISTANT STRAINS

1. RESISTANCE IN THE LABORATORY

Bishop (1958) has studied the development of resistance to metachloridine (2-metanilamido-5-chloropyrimidine) in two clones of *P. gallinaceum* each derived from a single erythrocytic parasite and maintained in young chicks by serial inoculation of infected blood. In many of the strains an enhancement of resistance was obtained after 3 to 5 courses of treatment. It was not always possible to relate the rate of development of resistance to the drug to the number of parasites exposed to its action, but with an inoculum of 10^9 parasites, resistance developed after the shortest period of contact with the drug. With an inoculum of 2.5×10^7 parasites, resistance failed to develop although treatment with the drug was prolonged. The rate of development of resistance did not appear to be related to the size of dose of the drug; however all doses within the range used markedly reduced the parasitemia.

A mutational origin for resistance is suggested on the basis of the suddenness of its development and the stability of resistance when once developed. Although the rate of development of resistance to this compound was extremely high compared with other antimalarials there was no evidence that it was mutagenic.

This work was extended into an examination of the development of resistance to proguanil and to pyrimethamine (Bishop, 1962). With proguanil, the rate of development of resistance was compared in strains maintained by inocula of 5×10^7, 1×10^8, and 1×10^9 parasites. There was some evidence that the rate was related to the numbers of parasites in the inocula. In the case of pyrimethamine, resistance developed sporadically and there seemed to be no correlation between the rate and the size of the population exposed to the drug. There was, however, a greater variability in the rate in strains maintained by a smaller than by a larger inoculum. As was the case with metachloridine, there was no evidence that pyrimethamine could produce resistance more readily in small doses than in large doses, but again all doses within the range used produced a marked reduction in parasitemia.

In many of the strains, treated with either drug, resistance appeared to develop quite suddenly; in others it developed more gradually. Altogether it appeared that the development of resistance in strains treated with either of these drugs could be explained by the selection of spontaneously occurring mutants. It appeared also that the degree of resistance differed among the mutants.

It is generally considered that inadequate dosing together with significant parasitemia provide the conditions which lead to the development of drug resistance in the field (Covell et al., 1955). While there can be no argument on the importance of large numbers regardless of the mechanism of development of resistance, evidence for the necessity of gross mismanagement, in treatment or suppression, in such development seems false. Young (1957) has described the rapid development of resistance to pyrimethamine in a strain of P. *malariae* not previously exposed to its action. Resistance was observed first in a patient undergoing malaria therapy for neurosyphilis. The strain had responded well to the drug in 14 patients treated previously, but thereafter showed varying degrees of resistance—usually of a high order—in 6 others.

This evidence, together with Bishop's work, suggests that regardless of the dose used, so long as it is not a sterilizing dose, mutations occurring in a sufficiently large population of parasites will eventually give rise to resistant strains. In addition, as shown by Bishop (1958) and Jaswant Singh (1952) for P. *gallinaceum,* the property resides not only in the asexual blood forms but also in the sexual and exoerythrocytic forms. It has been suggested that hybridization between strains may also occur (Greenberg and Trembley, 1954). When two strains of *P. gallinaceum*, each producing a characteristic infection in chicks were mixed and then passaged by mosquito, the resulting infection eventually produced the characteristics of one of them but only after the appearance of mixed characteristics. The inoculation of one strain which resulted in death from late exoerythrocytic forms before the appearance of blood forms and was resistant to pyrimethamine, when mixed with a pyrimethamine-sensitive benign strain, resulted, after mosquito passage, in a strain with the benign character of one but the high degree of pyrimethamine resistance of the other. This suggests that a genetic transfer of drug resistance had occurred.

2. RESISTANCE IN HUMAN INFECTION

Since the publication of Volume II of "Biochemistry and Physiology of Protozoa," resistance of malaria parasites to the action of antimalarial substances has become of some considerable importance in the field. This has undoubtedly been due to the greatly increased scope of schemes for mass prophylaxis and for eradication.

a. Proguanil. Proguanil resistance was first reported from Malaya. For some time it had been suspected that not only the asexual blood forms but all stages of the life cycle possessed this property. This might be expected since all investigations on laboratory strains have shown that resistance persists after mosquito passage. Walker and Reid (1953) provided proof of this in showing that volunteers bitten by mosquitoes infected with a resistant strain of *P. falciparum* developed malaria despite the administration of proguanil before, during, and up to the appearance of parasitemia. In addition the donor received proguanil before and during the infection of mosquitoes.

Further evidence was given by Laing (1956) who fed mosquitoes on patients suffering from proguanil-resistant *P. falciparum* infection who were being treated daily with large doses of the drug. Positive gland infections were found in some mosquitoes of every batch.

b. Pyrimethamine. Mass prophylactic schemes in East Africa have been the origin of many reported cases of resistance to pyrimethamine. Resistant strains of *P. falciparum* occurred in Tanganyika after 6 months of monthly administration of 100 mg. of the drug (Clyde and Shute, 1954); it was suggested that resistant strains may be induced by single doses of pyrimethamine given at intervals of greater than 14 days. A regime involving widely spaced doses has been criticized by Bray (1955) and Rollo (1955b) on the grounds that a single dose may not entirely eradicate the blood forms of *P. falciparum* and that, since resistance can readily be acquired in the laboratory by giving subcurative doses at widely spaced intervals, the interval between doses should not exceed 1 week.

The development of resistance by *P. falciparum* to pyrimethamine due to an entirely different cause has been described by Grounds (1954). This strain appeared in Europeans undergoing apparently adequate prophylaxis with pyrimethamine. Previous to this proguanil had been used and it was suggested that the irregular use of this agent by African workers had encouraged the emergence of a strain resistant to proguanil with concurrent cross-resistance to pyrimethamine.

The technique of clearing out patent infection with a potent schizonticide before undertaking mass prophylaxis with pyrimethamine was practiced by Clyde and Shute (1957). At the end of 5 months, however, *P. falciparum* persisted in a few cases although all other species appeared to have been eradicated. Full courses of treatment with pyrimethamine failed to dislodge the parasites even at doses considerably in excess of those normally effective, but the strain remained sensitive to proguanil. One may speculate here on the possible occurrence of an insensitive as opposed to a resistant strain previously swamped by a preponderance of sensitive individuals. Infected mosquitoes would provide a reservoir if mosquito clearance was not practiced. It is interesting that the resistant parasites showed minor morphological differences from normal, but these differences were not constant. A preliminary survey of the sensitivity of the parasites suggested that a small proportion was considerably less sensitive than the main bulk.

Further evidence of the part played by a small reservoir of insensitive individuals in the eventual appearance of a resistant population was provided by Jones (1958). A field trial of mass prophylaxis resulted in a preponderance of *P. falciparum* infection insensitive to the drug and also insensitive to proguanil. Insensitive parasites were known to be present at the start of the trial. It was concluded that the rapid spread of insensitive *P. falciparum* was chiefly due to the selective action of pyrimethamine in the presence of existing insensitive infection.

A question of semantics now arises. It is obvious that the appearance of a strain of malaria parasites which will not respond to normally effective doses of administered antimalarial can have two causes; it may have been normally sensitive to the doses used but due to mutation and selection has become unresponsive, or as a natural characteristic it may not respond to the doses used. A strain such as the latter, present as a small proportion of the total population, would have no appreciable effect on, say, parasite rate in short-term antimalarial studies.

That the first process occurs is beyond doubt. Many laboratory studies have shown that initially sensitive strains can be made resistant to high concentrations of a drug; more particularly strains arising from clones can be made resistant just as readily as those from a heterogeneous population. The term "resistant" must be reserved for these strains.

As evidence accumulates, it is becoming obvious that the second process may also occur. Previously it had been of no account; no selective process acted to bring to the surface the small proportion of insensitive parasites swamped in a preponderance of sensitive individuals. With the advent of schemes of mass prophylaxis, however, the population pressure is reversed and these strains may become preponderant. If, in preliminary survey, it is shown that such strains exist in a community and if, after a period of prophylaxis, they become predominant, the term "insensitive" must be used.

The dangers of inadequate dosing must always be kept in mind, particularly in the use of pyrimethamine where, as will be shown later, the amount absorbed from the gastrointestinal tract may be small in relation to the dose. This has been demonstrated in recent attempts to carry out mass prophylaxis in Netherlands New Guinea by incorporating pyrimethamine in cooking salt (Meuwissen, 1961). At best, adults received daily amounts sufficient to total 25 mg. per week. Three months after the start of the trial, strains of *P. falciparum* showed signs of resistance to pyrimethamine and cross-resistance to proguanil. It seems probable that in this case, cumulative levels of pyrimethamine in the blood would be ineffective in eliminating parasitemia, the more so since preliminary survey showed that some infections reacted only moderately to pyrimethamine therapy. In this instance, initial "clear out" with chloroquine seems to have been ineffective.

Pyrimethamine resistance in *P. vivax* has also been observed. Infections with the Chesson strain were deliberately treated with subcurative doses. The development of resistance was slow and gradual but eventually a 25-fold increase in resistance with cross-resistance to proguanil was attained (Hernandez *et al.*, 1953). Similarly, pyrimethamine resistance in *P. vivax* was developed by treating neurosyphilitics undergoing malaria therapy with subcurative doses during the acute stage of infection (Young and Burgess, 1959).

c. Primaquine. It was stated in Volume II of this work that it was unlikely that a high degree of resistance could be induced to quinine, mepacrine, and the 4- and 8-aminoquinolines. This prediction has proved to be too optimistic. Ramakrishnan and Satya Prakash (1961) developed a strain of *P. knowlesi* resistant to primaquine by treating highly parasitized monkeys with subcurative doses of the drug. The strain was less than one-thirteenth as sensitive as the parent strain. A primaquine-resistant strain of *P. vivax* was obtained by Arnold *et al.* (1961) by treating partially immune volunteers with subcurative doses of the drug. The asexual blood forms became resistant to the maximum tolerated dose of the drug after 36 passages. Gametocytes could be transmitted to mosquitoes and developed to the stage of mature and apparently viable sporozoites. These however did not infect man.

d. Chloroquine. Laboratory studies have shown that a very slight and slow increase in resistance could be developed to chloroquine in a strain of *P. gal-*

linaceum (Ray and Sharma, 1956). A slow but very marked development of resistance in *P. berghei* was also obtained by Ramakrishnan *et al* (1957). No report of chloroquine resistance in the field was made until 1961 despite the widespread use of the drug. In 1961 Moore and Lanier described *P. falciparum* infections in Colombia which relapsed after adequate courses of treatment with chloroquine. The strain was normally sensitive to quinine. Further investigation showed that the insensitivity remained after mosquito passage (Young and Moore, 1961). The strain was also insensitive to amodiaquine and hydroxy-chloroquine but remained sensitive to quinine, mepacrine, and pyrimethamine. It seems likely that this strain is naturally insensitive to 4-aminoquinolines. More recently chloroquine-insensitive strains have been reported from Venezuela, Brazil, Cambodia, and Thailand.

C. Effect of Drugs on Sexual Stages

In the battle against malaria some alteration in tactics may be called for. Whereas until recently the main emphasis has been on clearance of existing infection, now the prevention of transmission may occupy an important role side by side with programs of mosquito eradication. It has been known for many years that the 8-aminoquinoline antimalarials were effective as gametocyticidal agents but their toxic potentialities precluded their uncontrolled use. Investigation for this property in other antimalarials seemed warranted.

Using the Chesson strain of *P. vivax*, Jeffery (1958) showed that gametocytes became noninfective after chloroquine treatment. This was in marked contrast to *P. falciparum* infection where, after treatment with chloroquine, gametocytes were found to be infective for as long as they were present in sufficient density in the blood (Jeffery *et al.*, 1958). From this it would appear that the addition of another gametocyticidal drug, necessary for the rapid elimination of viable gametocytes of *P. falciparum*, might not be so important in *P. vivax* infections.

Pyrimethamine has also been shown to possess gametocyticidal properties against *P. vivax* (Young and Burgess, 1957) but, in contrast to chloroquine, is also active in this respect against *P. falciparum*. This appears to be a direct effect on the gametocyte and not due to the ingestion by the mosquito of circulating drug along with infected erythrocytes (Bray *et al.*, 1959).

D. New Antimalarials

Within the last 10 years several new antimalarial compounds have been described. With only one exception all are near relatives of drugs already in the clinical armamentarium.

1. RELATIVES OF PROGUANIL

a. Chlorproguanil. This is proguanil with an additional chlorine atom in position 3 of the terminal phenyl ring. It has been found to be more active and more persistent in the body than proguanil. In prophylaxis, a weekly dose of 15 mg. is regarded as adequate for protection against *P. falciparum.* Like proguanil, it clears parasitemia and reduces fever only slowly, from 2 to 4 days being required. It also prevents the development of oocysts in mosquitoes fed on treated patients (Davey and Robertson, 1957).

b. New Guanidines. These have the general formula:

$$X - \langle\!\!\langle \;\rangle\!\!\rangle - NH \cdot \underset{\substack{\| \\ O}}{C} \cdot NH \cdot \underset{\substack{\| \\ NH}}{C} \cdot NH_3^+ \cdot Cl^-$$

$$\text{Where } X = NO_2, \ NH_3^+Cl^-,$$
$$\text{or other groups}$$

When tested against *P. gallinaceum,* the nitro compound proved to be only one-quarter as active as proguanil (Chin *et al.,* 1960).

c. Dihydrotriazines. Interest in these substances was aroused by the identification of the metabolic product of proguanil as a triazine derivative. Hewitt *et al.* (1954) have described the testing of 28 substituted dihydrotriazines. When tested against *P. lophurae,* 4,6-diamino-1-(4-chlorophenyl)-1,2-dihydro-2,2-dimethyl-*s*-triazine was found to be the most active with a proguanil equivalent of greater than one. Two others, 4,6-diamino-1-(3,4-dichlorophenyl)-1,2-dihydro-2-methyl-*s*-triazine and its 2,2-dimethyl analog, were found to be more active than all the other antimalarials tested against *P. berghei,* with the exception of pyrimethamine.

2. 4-AMINOQUINOLINES

a. Hydroxychloroquine. This is a close relative of chloroquine and is reputed to be less toxic, to give higher blood levels after oral administration and to persist in the body for a longer period of time than the parent compound. It has been tested in partial immunes against *P. vivax* and *P. falciparum* infections; the results compared favorably with those obtained with other 4-aminoquinoline antimalarials (Hoekenga, 1955). When tested against *P. vivax* infection it was found to control rapidly both parasitemia and fever (Nieto-Caicedo, 1956).

b. Propoquine. This is very similar in structure to amodiaquine as shown in the formulas:

$$CH_2 \cdot CH_3$$
$$R \equiv N$$
$$CH_2 \cdot CH_3$$

$$CH_2 \cdot R$$
$$OH$$
$$HN$$
$$Cl \qquad N$$

Amodiaquine

$$CH_2 \cdot CH_2$$
$$N$$
$$CH_2 \cdot CH_2$$

Propoquine

In the laboratory this compound was shown to have a quinine equivalent of 37 compared to 30 for amodiaquine, against *P. lophurae* infection (P. E. Thompson *et al.*, 1958). In 70 patients treated intramuscularly, parasitemia and fever disappeared after 48 hr.; side effects, which were trivial, developed only in 3 (Rathscheck, 1959). Similar success in the use of this compound both orally and intramuscularly in *P. falciparum* and *P. vivax* infections was reported from South America by Hoekenga (1957).

3. ACRIDINE DERIVATIVES

a. Azacrine. This substance, 2-methoxy-6-chloro-9-(5'-diethylamino-2-pentyl)-amino-3-aza-acridine hydrochloride, was mentioned briefly in Volume II of this work. Subsequent investigation in West Kenya showed it to be an effective schizonticide in acute *P. falciparum* infection; it was perhaps slightly more rapid in action than either chloroquine or mepacrine (Ang'Awa and Fendall, 1954). In Malaya it was found to be about as effective as mepacrine in treating semi-immunes but was not reliable when given as a single dose. In this respect it is therefore inferior to both chloroquine and amodiaquine. It was found to have no action on the gametocytes of *P. falciparum* nor did it prevent their development in the mosquito (Edeson, 1954). The general impression seems to be that it is no more effective than mepacrine and is certainly more unpleasant in taste.

b. Compound CI-423. This compound, 3-chloro-9-(4-diethylamino-1-methylbutylamino) acridine, 10-oxide 2HCl, was described by P. E. Thompson *et al.* (1961) as being 16 times as effective as quinine, 4 times as effective as quinacrine and one-half as active as amodiaquine against *P. lophurae*. It effected more cures and suppressed parasitemia more rapidly than either amodiaquine or quinacrine.

4. 8-AMINOQUINOLINES

a. Compound WIN 5037. This is a close relative of pentaquine and has the formula, 6-methoxy-8-(5-propylaminoamylamino)quinoline phosphate. It was claimed (Berberian *et al.*, 1962) to be comparable to primaquine with respect to tolerance and to be distinguished from other 8-aminoquinoline antimalarials by its greater schizonticidal activity. In experiments on sporozoite-induced *P. cynomolgi* infection, as the initial dose was increased within tolerated limits, the schizonticidal activity approached that of chloroquine. When the loading dose was followed by fractional daily doses to complete 14 days treatment, the compound produced radical cure. Hoekenga (1962) tested this substance in Panama against both *P. vivax* and *P. falciparum* infection of non- and semi-immunes and found that, while it was not equally effective with standard treatment with 4-aminoquinoline antimalarials, it nevertheless produced decreased parasitemia after 1 day and disappearance of asexual parasites within 2 days. It produced radical cure and was approximately equal in this respect to combinations of an effective 4-aminoquinoline with primaquine or pyrimethamine at the dosage used.

b. Quinocide. Quinocide [6-methoxy-8(4'-amino-4'-methylbutylamino) quinoline] is an isomer of primaquine and differs only in the position of the methyl group on the butylamino side chain. It was synthesized and tested in Russia (Lysenko, 1960) and, as expected, had similar properties to primaquine. Alving *et al.* (1960) found it to have more pronounced hemolytic activity than primaquine in infected human volunteers.

5. SYNTHETIC QUINAZOLONES

Although these substances are interesting in the laboratory (Volume II of this work) they proved to be rather inactive in trials against human malaria and to be emetic in many cases (Edeson and Wilson, 1955).

6. DIAMINODIPHENYLSULFONE (DDS)

Following up the observation that DDS had some beneficial effect on lepers suffering from malaria, Archibald and Ross (1960) showed that the drug could clear the blood of trophozoites of *P. falciparum* and *P. malariae* in infected patients. Although this occurred at a much slower rate than that achieved by chloroquine, its cheapness compared to the latter might merit serious consideration of its use in the event of a mass-treatment campaign against malaria in West Africa.

7. COMPOUND 377C54

This substance is one of a series of substituted naphthalene compounds described by Duffin and Rollo (1957) and is the only new antimalarial of completely novel structure. Its formula is 1,6-dihydroxy-2,5-bis(cyclohexylaminomethyl)naphthalene dihydrochloride. A high degree of antimalarial activity was shown against *P. gallinaceum, P. berghei, P. cathemerium,* and *P. knowlesi.* It acted rapidly against parasitemia of *P. gallinaceum* and *P. knowlesi:* parasiticidal activity remained in the blood of chicks for a long time after a single oral dose. Clinical trials in Nigeria showed it to have a pronounced schizonticidal effect against *P. falciparum* and *P. ovale.* It was less active however than 4-aminoquinoline antimalarials when given in single doses of 200–300 mg., and showed no evidence of gametocyticidal or sporonticidal activity on *P. falciparum* (Bruce-Chwatt and Charles, 1957). Single dose treatment with 600 mg. in India, however, produced a clearance of both *P. vivax* and *P. falciparum* parasitemia very similar to that produced by 4-aminoquinolines at the same dose. Its action against gametocytes was very slow (Ray *et al.,* 1959). It is relatively inactive against chloroquine-insensitive human malaria (Young *et al.,* 1963).

E. FATE OF ANTIMALARIALS IN THE BODY

After the discovery that proguanil and pamaquin were degraded in the body to compounds with greater antimalarial activity than the parent substances there has been more interest than previously on the physiological disposition and fate of antimalarial drugs.

1. PROGUANIL AND ITS CONGENERS

Robertson (1957) investigated the antimalarial activity of the triazine metabolite of proguanil and its dichloro analog; both were considerably more active than the parent compounds against *P. gallinaceum.* However, trials with African volunteers infected with *P. falciparum, P. vivax,* and *P. malariae* were disappointing. Although the substances acted qualitatively like the parent compounds, the antimalarial action was less persistent than that of proguanil. It seems probable that these substances are either rapidly metabolized or rapidly excreted.

These findings prompted further investigation on the physiological disposition of proguanil and its triazine metabolite. In monkeys 60–80% of proguanil given parenterally was recovered in the urine; about one-third was triazine. In man total recovery in urine after oral administration ranged from 56 to 66%; of this, about 60% was parent compound and 30% triazine. Thus when proguanil was given, substantial amounts of triazine were formed.

There was considerable persistence of triazine when the substance itself was administered; levels in serum after intramuscular injection were consistently higher than the corresponding levels when proguanil was injected. When tested for antimalarial activity, however, proguanil was found to be 2 to 4 times as active as the triazine. This suggested strongly that the superior antimalarial activity of proguanil must be due in part to intrinsic activity of the parent substance (Smith *et al.*, 1961). The apparent lack of activity of proguanil *in vitro* on the one hand and these findings on the other, therefore provide a fertile field for future controversy. The observation by Ray *et al.*, (1954) that the triazine metabolite of bromoguanide, the bromo analog of proguanil, is about twice as active as the parent substance against *P. cynomolgi* infection will also have to be explained.

2. PYRIMETHAMINE

The remarkable persistence of this antimalarial substance in the body after oral administration, as made evident by its success in prophylactic schemes when doses are widely spaced, has been demonstrated by Smith and Ihrig (1959). In studying excretion of pyrimethamine in man it was found that, 30 days after a single dose of 100 mg., about 1 mg. still remained in the body. This is all the more remarkable since more recent experiments with H^3-labeled drug have shown that the greater part of an oral dose is not absorbed by monkeys, but is eliminated unchanged in the feces (Gaudette *et al.*, 1961). Smith and his colleagues (1963), however, have disputed these findings and present data which show that C^{14}-labeled pyrimethamine is almost completely absorbed when administered orally to rhesus monkeys.

3. CHLOROQUINE AND HYDROXYCHLOROQUINE

The main advantage claimed for the use of hydroxychloroquine is in the higher levels produced in the blood after single oral doses and hence the possibility of using smaller doses. After single oral doses of 200 mg., 25% appeared in the feces but the drug continued to be excreted in the urine for more than 10 days. Comparison with chloroquine showed that the daily excretion of the latter was about 3 times greater than that of the hydroxy derivative (McChesney and McAuliff, 1961). Hydroxychloroquine is not widely employed as an antimalarial; its chief use is in the treatment of arthritis when large doses are given over long periods.

Since little chloroquine is excreted unchanged in man, one factor limiting its antimalarial effectiveness is the metabolic transformations undergone in the body. Experiments carried out in rabbits have shown that SKF 525A, a substance which inhibits many enzymes concerned with detoxification, prolongs the stay of unchanged chloroquine in the plasma. This effect lasts only for 24 hrs. and is thus of little practical application. Some antimalarial substances, however, were also found to interfere with the detoxification of chloroquine. The most effective were amodiaquine, hydroxychloroquine, and pamaquin in equal concentration with chloroquine. With these, elevated and prolonged plasma levels of chloroquine were obtained (Gaudette and Coatney, 1961). These inhibitors have the additional advantage of themselves possessing antimalarial properties.

4. PENTAQUINE

Smith (1956) has studied the metabolism of pentaquine in rhesus monkeys using material labeled with C^{14} either in the 6-methoxy or in the terminal isopropyl group. Pentaquine is degraded rapidly in the monkey with production of at least 6 metabolic derivatives. The methoxy group is cleaved very rapidly: the terminal isopropyl group is more resistant to oxidation.

F. PRIMAQUINE SENSITIVITY

Although all drugs are potentially toxic, particularly if taken in overdosage, the 8-aminoquinoline antimalarials have a particularly bad reputation in this respect. The introduction of primaquine helped to improve this, but like pamaquin it causes intravascular hemolysis in some races. The hemolytic action is also shown by several other drugs and the ingestion of partially cooked or uncooked broad beans (favism). The phenomenon was found to be due to an inborn error of metabolism which is inheritable. The defect is common in dark-skinned peoples and certain other racial and ethnic groups. Its incidence, in general, follows the same geographical pattern as the distribution of malaria. Hemolysis is caused by daily doses of 30 mg. of primaquine.

The erythrocytes of primaquine-sensitive individuals have many intrinsic biochemical abnormalities. A decrease of glucose-6-phosphate dehydrogenase (G-6-PD) activity, first shown to be characteristic of primaquine sensitivity by Carson et al. (1956), may represent the major enzymatic deficiency of the erythrocytes. Previously, Beutler et al., (1955) had shown that erythrocytes from primaquine-sensitive individuals contained less reduced glutathione than normal erythrocytes; this substance appears to protect erythrocytes against a variety of physical and chemical agents. Glutathione is maintained in the reduced state by the enzyme glutathione reductase, with reduced triphosphopyridine nucleotide (TPNH) as coenzyme. In mature erythrocytes, reduction of TPN requires the oxidation of glucose via the pentose-phosphate pathway. The first enzyme in this pathway is G-6-PD a deficiency of which will lead through the chain of interrelated biochemical events to an inability to maintain a protective level of reduced glutathione in the erythrocyte.

The first step in the metabolism of primaquine is the removal of a methyl group to form a 6-hydroxy compound which has a powerful oxidizing capacity. Such a substance would be expected to affect adversely erythrocytes deficient in reduced glutathione.

Energy for the specific enzymatic reduction of methemoglobin (Met Hb) is derived from glucose metabolism in the mature human erythrocyte. At least two routes are known to be involved: the glycolytic pathway, through which approximately 90% of glucose is normally channeled, and which supplies energy for reduced diphosphopyridine nucleotide (DPNH)/Met Hb reductase, and the pentose phosphate pathway, which yields energy for TPNH/Met Hb reductase. Under physiological conditions, tthe conversion of Met Hb to Hb seems to be almost entirely catalyzed by DPNH/Met Hb reductase. However, when the activity of the pentose phosphate pathway is markedly accelerated by an artificial electron carrier, such as methylene blue, the rate of reduction of Met Hb by TPNH/Met Hb reductase is greatly increased, while the activity of the former main pathway is only slightly increased.

This is the basis for a simple *in vitro* test devised by Brewer *et al.* (1960) since erythrocytes from primaquine-sensitive individuals are deficient in G-6-PD and hence TPNH. Most primaquine-sensitive males are fully susceptible to drug-induced hemolysis, and this and other tests can distinguish them successfully from normal males. Most affected females, however, have an intermediate susceptibility to hemolysis, have extremely variable biochemical changes in their erythrocytes, and are difficult, if not impossible, to distinguish by currently available tests (Brewer *et al.*, 1960). A schematic diagram of the biochemical pathways discussed is shown in Fig. 5.

Older red cells appear to be more susceptible to hemolysis than those that have recently left the bone marrow, and if the treatment of a sensitive patient with large doses of primaquine is continued in spite of hemolysis, there is a brisk reticulocytosis (Dern *et al.*, 1954). The lysed, older cells are soon replaced by less sensitive younger cells and the blood picture returns to normal. The resistance of the younger cells is, however, less than that of normal erythrocytes, and excessive dosage with primaquine causes a chronic hemolytic anemia of great severity.

G. COMBINED THERAPY

There is an increasing tendency nowadays to give antimalarial drugs in combination, in order to obtain the benefit of their different types of activity against the various stages of the malaria parasite.

1. PRIMAQUINE–4-AMINOQUINOLINE COMBINATIONS

Partly because of the side effects described above and partly because of the impracticability of relying on a return voyage from the tropics which lasts for the 15 days necessary for the curative treatment of *P. vivax* infection with fairly low doses of primaquine, Alving *et al.* (1960) tried primaquine together with chloroquine at weekly intervals in members of the American forces. Using the Chesson strain of *P. vivax*, which requires double the standard dose of

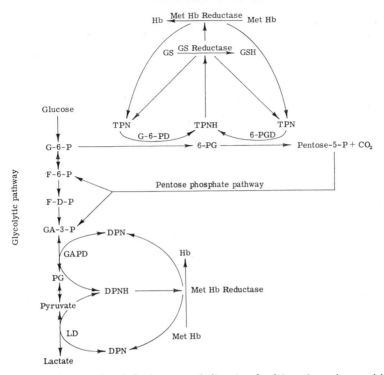

F<small>IG</small>. 5. Pathways of carbohydrate metabolism involved in primaquine sensitivity and its detection. (Many details in both pathways have been excluded in the interest of simplicity.)

K<small>EY TO</small> A<small>BBREVIATIONS</small>: DPN, diphosphopyridine nucleotide; DPNH, reduced DPN; F-D-P, fructose diphosphate; F-6-P, fructose-6-phosphate; G-6-P, glucose-6-phosphate; G-6-PD, G-6-P dehydrogenase; GAPD, glyceraldehyde phosphate dehydrogenase; GA-3-P, glyceraldehyde-3-phosphate; GS, glutathione; GSH, reduced GS; Hb, hemoglobin; Met Hb, methemoglobin; 6-PG, 6-phosphogluconate; 6-PGD, 6-PG dehydrogenase; PG, phosphoglycerate; LD, lactic dehydrogenase; TPN, triphosphopyridine nucleotide; TPNH, reduced TPN.

primaquine for its cure, it was determined that 60 mg. primaquine together with 300 mg. chloroquine given weekly for 8 weeks resulted in 6% failure compared with about 30% failure resulting from 15 mg. primaquine alone daily for 14 days. The use of combinations containing 45 mg. primaquine resulted in 10% failure, and 30 mg. in 55% failure. The highest dose regime had a negligible hemolytic effect upon the red cells of primaquine-sensitive individuals. It was recommended that, for well-disciplined population groups or military personnel, a weekly dose of 60 mg. primaquine plus 300 mg. chloroquine (or other 4-aminoquinoline antimalarial) for 8 weeks should cause radical cure of most *P. vivax* infections. Where strict surveillance could not be maintained the primaquine component should be reduced to 45 mg. Courtney *et al.* (1960) have conducted similar studies using primaquine and amodiaquin. Previous studies have shown that chloroquine (and quinine) seem to potentiate the curative action of primaquine despite lack of evidence of any effect on the tissue stages of the parasite (Alving *et al.*, 1955).

2. CHLOROQUINE–PYRIMETHAMINE COMBINATIONS

Chloroquine is given with pyrimethamine (or chlorproguanil) so that the combination will exert a 3-fold action on the asexual blood parasites, the tissue forms in the liver and the gametocytes. Such combinations are often used during malaria eradication schemes and in areas where such campaigns have been carried out. Facilities may not always be available for complete investigation and treatment, and people with fever must be presumed to be infected with the malaria parasite. A dose of a schizonticide plus a sporonticide will help to insure that such people will not act as foci from which the spread of malaria may begin again.

In a trial of Daraclor (30 mg. pyrimethamine + 300 mg. chloroquine) with groups of semi-immunes, G. R. Thompson and Carter (1961) found that, in untreated cases the incidence of infection was 6.3%, while in cases treated fortnightly for a period of 2 months the incidence was nil.

Prolonged use of antimalarial drugs necessitates the keeping of careful watch for the development and propagation of resistant strains in the treated population. This applies also where such agents are used in combination.

For example the presence of one agent in a mixture in such concentration as to provide, if considered alone, a suboptimal dose might result in the development of resistance. Some evidence for this was provided in the trial of a pyrimethamine-chloroquine combination in small doses, as a mass prophylactic in young children in the Northern Cameroons (Schneider *et al.*, 1957). The parasite index decreased from 67% to nil over 3.5 months after weekly treatment but thereafter showed a progressive rise, until after a further 2 months the index had reached 27%. The strain proved on testing to be resistant to pyrimethamine but retained its sensitivity to chloroquine. Further work in the same area (Schneider *et al.*, 1958) showed that during the rainy season, weekly doses of 75 mg. of chloroquine together with 6.25 mg. of pyrimethamine given to school children allowed the parasite rate to rise to 35%. However, when weekly doses of 300 mg. of chloroquine alone were given to another group of the same children during the same season, the parasite rate rose to 13%. This would indicate either that the parasites were resistant to this large dose of chloroquine, or, which is more likely, that the doses were not being taken regularly by the children.

3. SULFONAMIDE–PYRIMETHAMINE COMBINATIONS

As outlined above the rationale for using combinations of antimalarials is to obtain the benefit of their different types of activity, and as in the successful use of drug combinations in tuberculosis, to minimize the development of resistance. It is also logical to apply the principle of true potentiation as demonstrated in laboratory malaria infection, using sulfonamides with pyrimethamine (Rollo, 1955a). Hurly (1959) tested this principle by treating children infected with *P. falciparum* and *P. malariae* with pyrimethamine and sulfadiazine, alone and in combination. The results he obtained are shown in Fig. 6; this

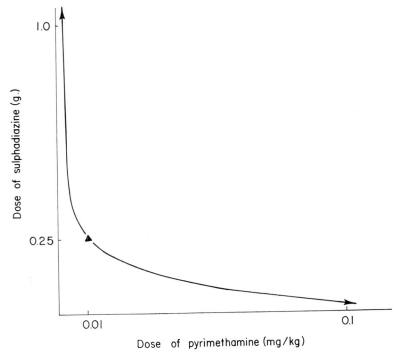

FIG. 6. Isobol for curative effect of combination of pyrimethamine and sulfadiazine (sulphadiazine) in *Plasmodium falciparum* and/or *P. malariae* infection in Gambian children. (Note: curative dose of sulfadiazine is greater than 1 g. and of pyrimethamine is greater than 0.1 mg./kg., when each is given alone.) (After Hurly, 1959.)

isobol closely resembles that obtained when pyrimethamine and sulfadiazine were tested against *P. gallinaceum*. It can be seen that cure was obtained by a combination of less than one-tenth of the curative dose of pyrimethamine when given alone plus less than one-quarter of the curative dose of sulfadiazine when given alone.

More recently, Basu *et al.* (1962) have shown that a combination of pyrimethamine and diaminodiphenyl-sulfone is also more effective than pyrimethamine alone in human malaria in India.

REFERENCES

Adler, S. (1958a). *Harefuah* 54, 63.
Adler, S. (1958b). *Bull. Res. Council Israel* E7, 9.
Alving, A. S., Arnold, J., Hockwald, R. S., Clayman, C. B., Dern, R. J., Beutler, E., and Flanagan, C. L. (1955). *J. Lab. Clin. Med.* 46, 301.
Alving, A. S., Johnson, C. F., Tarlov, A. R., Brewer, G, J., Kellermeyer, R. W., and Carson, P. E. (1960). *Bull. World Health Organ.* 22, 621.
Ang'Awa, J. O. W., and Fendall, N. R. E. (1954). *J. Trop. Med. Hyg.* 57, 59.
Archibald, H. M., and Ross, C. M. (1960). *J. Trop. Med. Hyg.* 63, 25.
Arnold, J., Alving, A. S., Clayman, C. B., and Hockwald, R. S. (1961). *Trans. Roy. Soc. Trop. Med. Hyg.* 55, 345.
Basu, P. C., Mondal, M. M., and Chakrabarti, S. C. (1962). *Indian J. Malariol.* 16, 157.
Berberian, D. A., Coulston, F., Drobeck, H. P., Freele, H. W., and Dennis, E. W. (1962). *Antibiot. & Chemotherapy* 12, 103.
Beutler, E., Dern, R. J., Flanagan, C. L., and Alving, A. S. (1955). *J. Lab. Clin. Med.* 45, 286.
Bishop, A. (1954a). *Parasitology* 44, 120.
Bishop, A. (1954b). *Parasitology* 44, 450.
Bishop, A. (1958). *Parasitology* 48, 210.
Bishop, A. (1962). *Parasitology* 52, 495.
Bishop, A., and McConnachie, E. (1956). *Parasitology* 46, 192.
Bishop, A., and McConnachie, E. (1960). *Parasitology* 50, 431.
Bouisset, L., and Ruffié, J. (1958a). *Compt. Rend. Soc. Biol.* 152, 168.
Bouisset, L., and Ruffié, J. (1958b). *Ann. Parasitol. Humaine Comp.* 33, 209.
Bowman, I. B. R., Grant, P. T., and Kermack, W. O. (1960). *Exptl. Parasitol.* 9, 131.
Bowman, I. B. R., Grant, P. T., Kermack, W. O., and Ogston, D. (1961). *Biochem. J.* 78, 472.
Bray, R. S. (1955). *Trans. Roy. Soc. Trop. Med. Hyg.* 49, 93.
Bray, R. S., Burgess, R. W., Fox, R. M., and Miller, M. J. (1959). *Bull. World Health Organ.* 21, 233.
Brewer, G. G., Tarlov, A. R., and Alving, A. S. (1960). *Bull. World Health Organ.* 22, 633.
Bruce-Chwatt, L. J., and Charles, L. J. (1957). *Brit. Med. J.* II, 23.
Carrescia, P. M. (1955). *Riv. Malariol.* 34, 93.
Carson, P., Flanagan, C., Ickes, C., and Alving, A. (1956). *Science* 124, 484.
Chaudhuri, R. N., and Dutta, B. N. (1955). *Indian J. Med. Sci.* 9, 297.
Chin, Y. C., Wu, Y. Y., Skowronska-Serafin, B., Urbanski, T., and Venulet, J. (1960). *Nature* 186, 170.
Clyde, D. F., and Shute, G. T. (1954). *Trans. Roy. Soc. Trop. Med. Hyg.* 48, 495.
Clyde, D. F., and Shute, G. T. (1957). *Trans. Roy. Soc. Trop. Med. Hyg.* 51, 505.
Coatney, G. R., and Greenberg, J. (1961). *J. Parasitol.* 47, 601.
Cook, L., Grant, P. T., and Kermack, W. O. (1961). *Exptl. Parasitol.* 11, 372.
Corradetti, A., Tentori, L., and Verolini, F. (1955). *Rend. Ist. Super. Sanita* 18, 256.

Courtney, K. O., Hodgkinson, R., Ramsey, R., and Haggerty, M. (1960). *Am. J. Trop. Med. Hyg.* 9, 149.

Covell, G., Coatney, G. R., Field, J. W., and Jaswant Singh (1955). *Chemotherapy of Malaria,* Monograph Ser. No. 27. World Health Organization, Geneva.

Davey, D. G., and Robertson, G. I. (1957). *Trans. Roy. Soc. Trop. Med. Hyg,* 51, 457.

Deegan, T., and Maegraith, B. G. (1956). *Ann. Trop. Med. Parasitol.* 50, 194.

Dern, R. J., Beutler, E., and Alving, A. S. (1954). *J. Lab. Clin. Med.* 44, 171.

Duffin, W. M., and Rollo, I. M. (1957). *Brit. J. Pharmacol.* 12, 171.

Durard, P., and Mathis, M. (1955). *Arch. Inst. Pasteur Tunis.* 32, 313.

Edeson, J. F. B. (1954). *Ann. Trop. Med. Parasitol.* 48, 160.

Edeson, J. F. B., and Wilson, T. (1955). *Trans. Roy. Soc. Trop. Med. Hyg.* 49, 543.

Fabiani, G., and Grellet, P. (1952). *Compt. Rend. Soc. Biol.* 146, 441.

Fabiani, G., and Orfila, J. (1954). *Compt. Rend. Soc. Biol.* 148, 1239.

Fabiani, G., and Orfila, J. (1956). *Bull. Soc. Pathol. Exotique* 49, 705.

Fulton, J. D. (1954). *Lancet* I, 162.

Fulton, J. D., and Flewett, T. H. (1956). *Trans. Roy. Soc. Trop. Med. Hyg.* 50, 150.

Fulton, J. D., and Grant, P. T. (1956). *Biochem. J.* 63, 274.

Gaudette, L. E., and Coatney, G. R. (1961). *Am. J. Trop. Med. Hyg.* 10, 321.

Gaudette, L. E., Titus, E. D., and Coatney, G. R. (1961). *Exptl. Parasitol.* 11, 152.

Gilles, H. M. (1957). *Ann. Trop. Med. Parasitol.* 51, 58.

Godfrey, D. G. (1957). *Exptl. Parasitol.* 6, 555.

Greenberg, J. (1949). *J. Pharmacol. Exptl. Therap.* 97, 238.

Greenberg, J. (1954). *Exptl. Parasitol.* 3, 351.

Greenberg, J., and Bond, H. W. (1956). *Am. J. Trop. Med. Hyg.* 5, 14.

Greenberg, J., and Trembley, H. L. (1954). *J. Parasitol.* 40, 667.

Greenberg, J., Taylor, D. J., and Trembley, H. L. (1954). *Am. J. Hyg.* 600, 99.

Grounds, J. G. (1954). *E. African Med. J.* 31, 51.

Hawking, F. (1954). *Brit. Med. J.* I, 425.

Hawking, F., and Terry, R. J. (1957). *Z. Tropenmed. Parasitol.* 8, 151.

Hernandez, T., Myatt, A. V., Coatney, G. R., and Jeffery, G. M. (1953). *Am. J. Trop. Med. Hyg.* 2, 797.

Hewitt, R. I., Wallace, W. S., Gumble, A., White, E., and Williams, J. H. (1954). *Am. J. Trop. Med. Hyg.* 3, 225.

Hitchings, G. H. (1963). *In* "Drugs, Parasites and Hosts" (L. G. Goodwin, and R. H. Nimmo-Smith, eds.), p. 241. Churchill, London.

Hoekenga, M. T. (1955). *Am. J. Trop. Med. Hyg.* 4, 221.

Hoekenga, M. T. (1957). *Am. J. Trop. Med. Hyg.* 6, 987.

Hoekenga, M. T. (1962). *Antibiot. & Chemotherapy* 12, 525.

Hughes, F. W., and Tatum, A. L. (1955). *J. Infect. Diseases* 97, 231.

Hughes, F. W., and Tatum, A. L. (1956). *J. Infect. Diseases* 99, 38.

Hurly, M. G. D. (1959). *Trans. Roy. Soc. Trop. Med. Hyg.* 53, 412.

Jaswant Singh (1952). *Indian J. Malariol.* 6, 457.

Jaswant Singh, Nair, C. P., Ramakrishnan, S. P., and Ray, A. P. (1953). *Indian J. Malariol.* 7, 253.

Jeffery, G. M. (1958). *Am. J. Trop. Med. Hyg.* 7, 207.

Jeffery, G. M., Young, M. D., and Eyles, D. (1958). *Am. J. Hyg.* 64, 1.

Johnson, C. A., and Bergeim, O. (1951). *J. Biol. Chem.* 188, 833.

Jones, S. A. (1958). *Trans. Roy. Soc. Trop. Med. Hyg.* 52, 547.

Laing, A. B. G. (1956). *Trans. Roy. Soc. Trop. Med. Hyg.* 50, 496.

Lysenko, A. Y. (1960). *Bull. World Health Organ.* 22, 641.

McChesney, E. W., and McAuliff, J. P. (1961). *Antibiot. & Chemotherapy* 11, 800.

McKee, R. W., Geiman, Q. M., and Cobby, T. S. Jr. (1947). *Federation Proc.* 6, 276.

Maegraith, B. G., Deegan, T., and Sherwood Jones, E. (1952). *Brit. Med. J.* II, 1389.

Mackerras, M. J. (1953). *Australian J. Sci.* 16, 24.

Mercado, T. I., and von Brand, T. (1954). *Exptl. Parasitol.* 3, 259.

Mercado, T. I., and von Brand, T. (1957). *Am. J. Hyg.* 66, 20.

Meuwissen, J. H. E. T. (1961). *Am. J. Trop. Med. Hyg.* 10, 135.

Miller, M. J. (1954). *Am. J. Trop. Med. Hyg.* 3, 825.

Moore, D. V., and Lanier, J. E. (1961). *Am. J. Trop. Med. Hyg.* 10, 5.

Moulder, J. W., and Evans, E. A., Jr. (1946). *J. Biol. Chem.* 164, 145.

Nieto-Caicedo, M. (1956). *Am. J. Trop. Med. Hyg.* 5, 681.

Raffaele, G., and Carrescia, P. M. (1954). *Riv. Malariol.* 33, 47.

Ramakrishnan, S. P. (1954). *Indian J. Malariol.* 8, 85, 89, 97, 107.

Ramakrishnan, S. P., and Satya Prakash. (1961). *Bull. Natl. Soc. India Malaria Other Mosquito-borne Diseases* 9, 261.

Ramakrishnan, S. P., Bhatnagar, V. N., Satya Prakash, and Misra, B. G. (1953a). *Indian J. Malariol.* 7, 261.

Ramakrishnan, S. P., Satya Prakash, Krishnaswami, A. K., and Chanan Singh. (1953b). *Indian J. Malariol.* 7, 61.

Ramakrishnan, S. P., Satya Prakash, Krishnaswami, A. K., and Chanan Singh. (1953c). *Indian J. Malariol.* 7, 225.

Ramakrishnan, S. P., Satya Prakash, and Choudhury, D. S. (1957). *Indian J. Malariol.* 11, 213.

Rama Rao, R., and Sirsi, M. (1956a). *J. Indian Inst. Sci.* 38, 224.

Rama Rao, R., and Sirsi, M. (1956b). *J. Indian Inst. Sci.* 38, 186.

Rathscheck, H. J. (1959). *Z. Tropenmed. Parasitol.* 10, 36.

Ray, A. P., and Sharma, G. K. (1956). *Nature* 178, 1291.

Ray, A. P., Nair, C. P., Menon, M. K., and Misra, B. G. (1954). *Indian J. Malariol.* 8, 209.

Ray, A. P., Singh, N., Sen Gupta, G. P., and Misra, B. G. (1959). *J. Indian Med. Assoc.* 32, 398.

Robertson, G. I. (1957). *Trans. Roy. Soc. Trop. Med. Hyg.* 51, 488.

Rollo, I. M. (1955a). *Brit. J. Pharmacol.* 10, 208.

Rollo, I. M. (1955b). *Trans. Roy. Soc. Trop. Med. Hyg.* 49, 94.

Rudzinska, M. A., and Trager, W. (1957). *J. Protozool.* 4, 190.

Ryley, J. F. (1953). *Brit. J. Pharmacol.* 8, 424.

Schneider, J., and Montézin, G. (1953). *Bull. Soc. Pathol. Exotique* 46, 947.

Schneider, J., Languillon, J., and Delas, A. (1957). *Bull. Soc. Pathol. Exotique* 50, 295.

Schneider, J., Languillon, J., and Delas A. (1958). *Bull. Soc. Pathol. Exotique* 51, 316.

Sergent, E. (1958). *Arch. Inst. Pasteur Algerie* 36, 1.

Shute, P. G., and Maryon, M. (1956). *Trans. Roy. Soc. Trop. Med. Hyg.* 50, 139.

Singer, I., and Trager, W. (1956). *Proc. Soc. Exptl. Biol. Med.* 91, 315.

Smith, C. C. (1956). *J. Pharmacol. Exptl. Therap.* 116, 67.

Smith, C. C., and Ihrig, J. (1959). *Am. J. Trop. Med. Hyg.* 8, 60.

Smith, C. C., Ihrig, J., and Menne, R. (1961). *Am. J. Trop. Med. Hyg.* 10, 694.

Smith, C. C., Schmidt, L. H., Robinson, N., Faulkner, A., and Simmons, D. (1963). *Exptl. Parasitol.* 13, 178.

Taylor, A. E. R. (1957). *Trans. Roy. Soc. Trop. Med. Hyg.* 51, 241.

Taylor, A. E. R. (1958). *Ann. Trop. Med. Parasitol.* 52, 139.

Taylor, D. J., and Greenberg, J. (1955). *Proc. Soc. Exptl. Biol. Med.* 90, 551.

Thompson, P. E., Weston, K., Glazko, A. J. Fisken, R. A., Reutner, T. F., Bayles, A., and Weston, J. K. (1958). *Antibiot. & Chemotherapy*, 8, 450.

Thompson, P. E., Meisenhelder, J. E., Najarian, H. H., and Bayles, A. (1961). *Am. J. Trop. Med. Hyg.* 10, 335.

Thompson, G. R., and Carter, S. B. (1961). *W. African Med. J.* 10, 93.

Thurston, J. P. (1954). *Parasitology* 44, 99.

Tolbert, M. G., and McGhee, R. B. (1960). *J. Parasitol.* 46, 552.

Trager, W. (1952). *J. Exptl. Med.* 96, 465.

Trager, W. (1954). *J. Protozool.* 1, 231.

Trager, W. (1958). *J. Exptl. Med.* 108, 753.

Trager, W. (1959). *Exptl. Parasitol.* 8, 265.

Trager, W. (1961). *Exptl. Parasitol.* 11, 298.

Walker, A. J., and Reid, J. A. (1953). *Trans. Roy. Soc. Trop. Med. Hyg.* 47, 580.

Whitfeld, P. R. (1953a). *Australian J. Biol. Sci.* 6, 234.

Whitfeld, P. R. (1953b). *Australian J. Biol. Sci.* 6, 591.

Wolcott, G. B., Young, M. D., and Ferguson, M. S. (1958). *Trans. Roy. Soc. Trop. Med. Hyg.* 52, 87.

Young, M. D. (1957). *Am. J. Trop. Med. Hyg.* 6, 621.

Young, M. D., and Burgess, R. W. (1957). *Am. J. Trop. Med. Hyg.* 6, 805.

Young, M. D., and Burgess, R. W. (1959). *Bull. World Health Organ.* 20, 27.

Young, M. D., and Moore, D. V. (1961). *Am. J. Trop. Med. Hyg.* 10, 317.

Young, M. D., Contacos, P. G., Stitcher, J. E., and Millar, J. W. (1963). *Am. J. Trop. Med. Hyg.* 12, 305.

Author Index

Aaronson, S., 52, 56, 209, 210, 211, 213, 214, 217, 220, 221, 222, 223, 231, 232, 233, 235, 236, 237, 330, 331, 337, 423, 453, 464, 491, 496, 522
Abé, S., 64, 80, 81, 124
Abé, T. H., 66, 70, 71, 72, 119
Abelson, P. H., 355, 381
Abou Akkada, A. R., 203, 224, 227, 229, 233
Abrahamsen, N. S. B., 230, 237
Adams, M. S., 76, 77, 120
Addison, M. A., 202, 204, 205, 206, 235
Adler, S., 533, 558, 410, 430, 450
Afzelius, B. A., 89, 119, 133, 135, 140, 192
Agosin, M., 233, 501, 520
Airth, R. L., 334, 337
Ajl, S., 224, 239
Akatov, V. A., 434, 450
Akita, Y. K., 216, 233
Alexander, J. B., 150, 151, 192
Alexandrov, V. Y., 149, 152, 192
Alexieff, A. G., 460, 491
Allegre, C. F., 116, 119
Allen, K. W., 395, 415, 417, 418, 456
Allen, M. B., 233, 321, 322, 323, 324, 329, 331, 332, 334, 335, 336, 337
Allen, P., 77, 126
Allen, R. D., 66, 67, 68, 69, 70, 72, 81, 84, 85, 119
Allen, R. S., 210, 236
Allen, S. L., 218, 219, 233, 247, 261, 262, 269, 272
Alverdes, F., 100, 120
Alving, A. S., 546, 550, 553, 554, 556, 558, 559
Ambrose, E. J., 75, 120

Amesz, J., 322, 337
Amino, E., 432, 435, 454
Amrein, Y. U., 486, 491
Andersen, F. L., 432, 438, 444, 450, 453
Anderson, E., 63, 115, 120, 144, 192, 460, 491
Anderson, J. D., 77, 83, 120
Anderson, M. E., 202, 233
Anderson, M. L., 347, 349, 350, 355, 356, 358, 360, 361, 362, 363, 364, 365, 366, 381
André, J., 135, 138, 192, 193, 197, 259, 269
Andresen, N., 77, 120
Andrews, J., 388, 450
Andrus, W. DeW., 216, 233
Ang'Awa, J. O. W., 549, 558
Apted, F. I. C., 499, 520
Archibald, A. R., 227, 233
Archibald, H. M., 550, 558
Arnold, J., 546, 556, 558
Arronet, N. I., 149, 152, 192
Asami, K., 432, 435, 441, 450
Ashburn, L. L., 443, 455
Ashkenazi, Y., 300, 302, 317
Ashley, J. N., 502, 520
Astbury, W. T., 98, 99, 101, 102, 120
Austin, M. L., 257, 269
Austin, W. C., 505, 520

Baba, T., 401, 402, 406, 450
Bacharach, T., 441, 456
Back, A., 430, 450
Baernstein, H. D., 405, 406, 407, 410, 411, 412, 413, 451
Bailey, R. W., 227, 233
Bak, I. J., 25, 29, 55, 218, 233

Baker, H., 3, 7, 211, 220, 221, 222, 223, 233, *235*, *237*, *239*, *423*, *453*, *465*, 470, 474, *492*, 496, *522*
Baker, H. G., 111, *124*
Balamuth, W., 172, *193*
Balbinder, E., 257, 264, *269*
Ball, G. H., 425, *457*
Bancroft, F. W., 107, *120*
Barber, H. J., 503, 504, *520*
Barbera, P. W., 223, *241*, 437, *457*
Bard, S., 349, 350, 361, 371, *381*
Barka, T., 245, 246, *271*
Barnes, E. C., 208, *234*
Barnett, A., 260, 261, *269*, *274*
Baronowsky, P., 231, *233*
Barretto, M., 432, 440, *451*
Basu, P. C., *558*, *558*
Batra, P. P., 330, *337*
Bauchop, T., 499, *520*
Bauer, F., 497, 503, *520*, *521*
Bayles, A., *549*, *561*
Beale, G. H., 218, *237*, 244, 256, 257, 260, 263, 264, 265, *269*, *270*, *271*
Beamer, P., 444, *454*
Beams, H. W., 63, 115, *120*, 144, *192*
Beattie, H. E. R., 438, *451*
Beevers, H., 365, *379*
Beighton, E., 98, 99, 101, 102, *120*
Beil, E. A., 434, *455*
Bělař, K., 84, 87, *120*, 173, *193*
Bell, L. G. E., 70, *120*
Bendix, S. W., 280, 283, *295*
Benitez, A., *339*
Bennet-Clarke, T. A., 290, *295*
Bennett, C. S. J., 488, *492*
Bennett, G. H., 438, *453*
Bennett, H. S., 217, *233*
Bensky, B., 211, 223, *233*, 330, 331, *337*
Berberian, D. A., *550*, *558*
Berech, J., Jr., 204, 223, 228, *233*, *241*, 252, *269*
Berg, S. S., 502, 503, 504, 505, *520*, *521*
Bergeim, O., 530, *559*
Bergendahl, J. C., 19, *55*
Bergmann, W., 337, *338*
Bernhard, W., 138, *193*
Bernstein, E., 330, *338*
Bernstein, F., 11, 54, *55*
Berrend, R. E., 84, 87, *120*
Berthrong, M., 441, *455*

Beutler, E., *553*, *554*, *556*, *558*, *559*
Beveridge, E., *500*, *521*
Beyer, G., 180, *193*
Bhagavan, N. Y., 33, 55
Bhatnagar, V. N., *533*, *560*
Bidder, G. P., 101, *120*
Biegeleisen, J. Z., *456*
Bingley, M. S., 65, 68, 70, *120*
Binns, V. M., 223, *235*
Biocca, E., 484, *491*
Bishop, A., *506*, *521*, *527*, *528*, *538*, *541*, *543*, *558*
Bishop, D. W., 90, *120*, 148, 159, *193*
Bishop, J., 256, *269*
Bishop, J. O., 256, *269*
Bishop, N. I., 312, *318*
Björkman, N., 144, *194*
Blackshaw, A. W., 438, *451*
Blanckart, S., 170, *193*
Blinks, L. R., 334, *337*
Bloch, K., 209, 210, 211, 213, 220, 230, 231, *233*, *234*, *235*, *236*
Bloom, B., 349, 350, 372, 373, 374, 376, *379*, *381*
Blum, H. F., 282, *295*
Blum, J. J., 15, 17, 53, 55
Blumenthal, L. K., 53, 55
Bogorad, L., 321, *337*
Bohonos, N., *501*, *522*
Bolton, E. T., 355, *381*
Bond, H. W., 541, *559*
Boné, G. J., 479, 480, 483, 489, *491*, *493*
Bonner, J., 77, 80, *128*
Bonner, J. T., 72, 73, 75, 76, 77, *120*, 343, 347, 356, 357, 363, *379*, *381*
Borgers, J. A., 98, *120*
Botafogo Gonçalves, N., *500*, *521*
Bouisset, L., *534*, *558*
Bovee, E. C., 18, *55*, 63, 65, 66, 68, 69, 70, 72, 73, 74, 84, 87, 88, 89, 90, 91, 95, 96, *120*, *123*
Bowman, I. B. R., *528*, *529*, *558*
Boyd, J. L., *500*, *521*
Boyd, W. C., 354, *379*
Boyle, J. V., 44, *58*
Braarud, T., 10, 55
Brachet, J., 70, *127*
Brachon, S., 167, *193*
Bradfield, J. R. G., 99, 102, *120*, 134, 160, 161, *193*

Bradley, S. G., 347, *379*
Brault, J., 81, *119*
Braun, R., 225, *233*
Braun, W., 482, *491*
Braunitzer, G., *317*
Braunthal, S. D., 431, 442, *453*
Brawerman, G., 326, 327, *337*
Bray, R. S., 544, 547, *558*
Brefeld, O., 358, 361, *380*
Brener, Z., 500, *521*
Bresslau, E. L., 460, 436, *491*
Bretscher, M. S., 302, *316*
Brewer, G. J., 550, 554, *558*
Briggs, R., 263, *270*
Brion, A., 444, *451*
Britt, J. J., 209, 210, 211, 213, 220, *236*
Brittain, M. S., 19, *55*
Britten, R. J., 355, *381*
Brodie, B. B., 509, *521*
Brodsky, A., 114, *120*
Brokaw, C. J., 64, 90, 98, *120*, 147, 148, 150, 151, 152, 162, *193*, 282, *295*
Bronsweig, R. D., 357, 361, *380*
Broom, J. C., 518, *521*
Brown, A., 28, *58*
Brown, F. A., Jr., 114, *126*
Brown, G. W., 229, *233*
Brown, H., 217, *233*
Brown, H. C., 518, *521*
Brown, H. P., 92, 99, *120*
Brown, J. S., 321, 322, 323, 324, 325, 326, 336, *337*
Brown, K. N., 504, 505, 506, 518, *521*, *523*, *524*
Brown, L. H., 264, *270*
Brown, M., 64, 81, 110, 111, *123*
Brown, M. B., 378, *381*
Browning, C. H., 448, *451*
Browning, I., 19, *55*
Bruce, V. G., 10, *55*, 285, *295*
Bruce-Chwatt, L. J., 551, *558*
Brucker, W., 282, *295*
Brühmüller, M., 358, 360, 361, 369, 370, 374, 375, *380*, *381*
Buck, R. E., 223, *239*
Buder, J., 278, 283, *295*
Bücher, T., 32, *56*
Bueding, E., 510, *521*
Bülbring, E., 180, *193*
Bünning, E., 279, 281, 286, 287, 291, *295*

Bütschli, O., 90, *121*, 461, *491*
Buffaloe, N. D., 299, *316*
Buhse, H. E., 222, *234*
Bullock, T. H., 181, *193*
Buretz, K. M., 162, *196*
Burger, R. M., 330, *339*
Burgess, R. W., 546, 547, 558, *561*
Burns, V. W., 10, 53, *55*
Burroughs, M., 209, 222, *235*
Burroughs, W., 220, 221, *239*
Burt, J. C., 414, *452*
Burt, R. L., 204, *234*
Butler, G. C., 497, *521*
Buttrey, B. W., 444, *451*, *456*
Butzel, H. M., Jr., 204, 228, 229, *234*, 260, 264, 265, *270*
Byfield, J. E., 33, 34, *58*

Calkins, G. N., 89, *121*
Calvin, M., 224, *238*
Camp, W. G., 77, 83, *121*
Campbell, A., 10, *55*
Campbell, D. H., *380*
Canella, M. F., 117, *121*
Cantrell, W., 519, *521*
Carasso, N., 138, 141, 147, *193*
Carey, S. E., 202, 204, 205, 206, *235*
Carlson, L., 249, *271*
Carrescia, P. M., 531, 558, *560*
Carrier, R. F., 228, *239*, 245, *273*
Carrow, L. A., 427, *451*
Carson, P. E., 550, 553, 554, *558*
Carter, G. S., 101, 102, *121*, 161, *193*
Carter, L., 216, *234*
Carter, S. B., 556, *561*
Caskey, F. H., 444, *452*
Caspersson, T. O., 248, 249, *271*
Castellani, O., 489, 490, *491*, 501, *521*
Castrejon, R. N., 52, *55*, 211, *234*
Caughey, P. A., 253, 261, *272*
Causey, D., 460, *491*
Cavalieri, L. F., 229, *233*
Cedillos, R., 483, *493*
Celliers, P. G., 202, *234*
Cerroni, R. E., 28, 29, 31, *55*
Chadwick, C. S., 447, *454*
Chaix, P., 225, *234*
Chakrabarti, S. C., 558, *558*
Chambers, R., 103, *121*
Chanan Singh, 531, 532, *560*

Chance, B., 309, *316,* 320, *337*
Chandler, A. C., 446, *456*
Chapman, D. J., 332, *337*
Chapman-Andresen, C., 218, 219, *234*
Chargaff, E., 326, 327, *337*
Charles, L. J., *551, 558*
Chatton, E., 102, 103, *121,* 134, 143, 166, 167, *193*
Chaudhuri, R. N., *532, 558*
Chauvet, J., 225, *234*
Cheldelin, V. H., 374, *380*
Child, F. M., 26, *55,* 64, 89, *121,* 148, 149, 150, 151, 154, 161, 182, 189, *193, 196,* 216, *235*
Chin, Y. C., *548, 558*
Chiquoine, A. D., *356, 357, 363, 379*
Chou, S. C., 33, 34, 35, 36, *55, 58*
Choudhury, D. S., *547, 560*
Christensen, A. K., 145, *193*
Christensen, E., 257, *271*
Christensson, E., 26, 27, *55,* 226, *238*
Christiansen, E. R., 166, *194*
Christiansen, W. C., 220, 221, *239*
Chuma, E., 444, *453*
Chun-Hoon, H., 447, *451*
Cinter, E., 225, *240*
Cirillo, V. P., 216, 219, *234*
Citri, N., 477, 478, 479, 481, *491*
Claff, C. L., 222, *234*
Claparède, E., 116, *121*
Clark, A. M., 105, *121*
Clark, G. M., 202, 205, *235, 265, 270*
Clark, T. B., 460, 461, 463, 484, *491, 494*
Clarke, B., 140, 141, 171, *195, 196*
Clarke, R. T. J., 227, *233*
Clausen, R. K., 426, *451*
Clayman, C. B., *546, 556, 558*
Clayton, R. B., 211, *234*
Clegg, J., *359,* 361, *380*
Cleveland, L. R., 106, *121,* 144, *193*
Cloyd, W. J., 113, *121*
Clyde, D. F., *544, 545, 558*
Coatney, G. R., *533, 543, 546, 552, 553, 558, 559*
Cobby, T. S., Jr., *530, 560*
Cohen, A. I., 218, *234*
Cohen, L. W., 148, *197,* 253, 255, 259, *270, 274*
Cohn, F., 277, 281, *295*
Cole, A., 86, *121*

Cole, B. A., 385, 387, 388, *451*
Coleman, J. F., *500, 522*
Collier, H. O., *505, 520*
Collin, B., 117, *121*
Collins, F. I., 230, *237*
Concannon, J. N., 396, 401, 402, 433, *451*
Conger, N., 204, *235*
Conner, R. L., 14, *52, 56, 57,* 211, 213, 214, 230, *234, 238, 239*
Contacos, P. G., *551, 561*
Cook, J. R., 12, 13, 16, 18, *54, 55*
Cook, L., *530, 558*
Cooledge, J. W., 67, *119*
Coon, M. J., 225, *234, 240*
Corbett, J. J., 20, *55*
Cordray, D., 444, 449, *455*
Corliss, J. O., 102, *121,* 200, 202, 220, *234*
Corradetti, A., *532, 558*
Cottereau, P., 444, *451*
Couillard, P., 64, 65, *127*
Cosgrove, W. B., 460, 461, 475, 477, *491*
Coulston, F., *550, 558*
Courtney, K. O., *556, 559*
Covell, G., *543, 559*
Cowie, D. B., *355, 381*
Cowperthwaite, J., 464, 465, 469, 476, *491, 492*
Craig, M. F., *255, 275*
Crane, F. L., 225, *234*
Crawley, H., 115, *121*
Cristofalo, V. J., 11, *54, 55*
Cuckler, A. C., 449, *451*
Culwick, A. F., 486, *491*
Cunningham, B., 229, *234*
Cunningham, M. P., *518, 519, 521*
Cury, A., 220, 222, *237*

Dabrowska, J., 293, *295*
Dales, R. P., 321, 331, *337*
Danielli, J. F., 109, *121*
Datta, N., 90, *129*
Dauchy, S., 344, *380*
Daugherty, K., 282, *295*
Davern, C. I., 248, *270*
Davey, D. G., *506, 521, 548, 559*
Davidoff, F., 361, *380*
Davies, B. H., 329, *337*
Davis, R. E., 203, 220, 224, 232, *236, 242*
Davis, R. J., 203, 207, 221, *236*

Dawson, J. A., 18, *55*, 103, 121, 251, *270*
Deane, L. M., 480, 483, *491*
Deane, M. P., 480, 483, *491*
De Bary, A., 77, *121*
de Carneri, I., 431, 433, 440, *451*
Deegan, T., *527*, 531, *559*, *560*
DeHaan, R. I., 77, *121*
de Haller, G., 114, *121*, 187, 190, *993*
de Harven, E., 138, *193*
De Jongh, R. T., 498, *521*
Dekker, E. E., 225, *234*
Delas, A., *556*, *560*
De Lucena, D. T., 500, *521*
Demain, A. L., 208, *234*
Demarchi, J., 486, *491*
Den, H., 225, *234*
Dendy, P. O., 53, *58*
Dennis, E. W., *550*, *558*
de Oliveira, P. V., 432, 440, *451*
De Pinto, S., 262, *272*
Dern, R. J., *553*, *554*, *556*, *558*, *559*
DeSaedeleer, H., 87, *121*
Desowitz, R. S., 488, *491*, *494*, *506*, *517*, *578*, *521*, *523*
Devaney, B. M., 444, *455*
Devine, R. L., 115, *120*
Dewey, V. C., 28, *56*, 201, 202, 203, 204, 205, 206, 207, 209, 213, 215, 223, 225, 228, 229, 230, *233*, *234*, *235*, *236*, *238*, *239*, 241, *425*, *453*, *470*, *492*
Diamond, L. S., 384, 431, 439, *451*, 481, 482, *491*
Dickie, N., 203, *235*
Dierks, K., 113, *121*
Dippell, R. V., 169, 186, *193*, *197*, 251, *254*, *255*, *263*, *266*, *270*, *274*, *275*
Dirksen, E. R., 187, *193*
Diskus, A., 114, *121*
Doetsch, R. N., 203, 224, 232, *242*
Doran, D. J., 116, *121*, 391, 392, 393, *395*, 396, 397, 398, 399, 401, 402, 403, 405, 406, 407, 410, 411, *451*
Doroszewski, M., 103, 105, *121*, 157, 172, *193*
Doscher, G. E., 388, 399, 407, 410, 412, 419, *451*, *457*
Dougherty, E. C., 334, 335, *337*
Dragesco, J., 168, *193*
Drobeck, H. P., 115, *125*, *550*, *558*
Druga, A. 218, *239*

Dryl, S., 257, *270*
Dubert, J. M., 261, 262, *272*
Dubnau, D. A., 188, *193*
Ducoff, H. S., 43, *55*
Duffin, W. M., *551*, *559*
Duggan, A. J., 495, 497, *521*
Dujardin, F., 63, *121*
Dunham, P. B., 182, *193*, 216, *235*
Dunn, M. S., 202, *235*, *240*
Durard, P., 531, *559*
Dutcher, J. D., 211, *238*
Dutta, B. N., 532, *558*
Duysens, L. M. N., 322, *337*
Dysart, M. P., 246, *270*

Eagle, H., 223, *235*, 363, *380*
Ebersold, W. T., 298, 299, 300, 311, *317*
Ebert, J. D., 354, *380*
Edeson, J. F. B., 549, *550*, *559*
Edström, J.-E., 247, *273*
Edwards, A. M., 211, *234*
Eggman, L., 64, 77, 80, *128*
Ehrenberg, C. G., 63, *121*
Ehret, C. F., 137, 167, 187, 190, *193*, 250, *252*, *270*
Eichel, H. J., 37, 40, *55*, 204, 225, 226, 228, 230, *235*, *240*
Eiler, J. J., 27, 33, 40, 47, 48, 50, 51, *55*, *57*, *58*
Eismond, J., 117, *121*
Elkeles, G., 486, *491*
Elliott, A. M., 25, 29, 40, *55*, 202, 204, 205, 206, 215, 218, *233*, *235*, 265, *270*
Elliott, R. F., 321, *338*
Elsbach, P., 210, *235*
Engelberg, J., 53, *56*
Engelmann, T. W., 279, 280, *295*
Engleman, M., 228, *235*
English, A. E., 444, *454*
Ennis, H. L., *75*, *128*, 346, 347, *379*, *380*
Ephrussi, B., 303, *317*
Epstein, H. T., 325, *338*
Epstein, S. S., 209, 222, *235*
Erdman, R., 485, *491*
Erhard J., 90, *121*
Erwin, J., 52, *56*, 202, 203, 204, 205, 206, 207, 208, 209, 210, 211, 213, 214, 215, 217, 220, 221, 223, 226, 230, 231, 232, *235*, *236*, 237, 241, 430, *452*
Eugere, E., 426, *451*

Evans, E. A., Jr., 530, *560*
Evens, F. 498, *521*
Ewart, J. A., 81, *121*
Eyles, D., 547, *559*

Fabiani, G., 531, 534, *559*
Fairbairn, H., 486, *491*
Faulkner, A., 552, *561*
Fauré-Fremiet, E., 63, 116, *121, 127,* 133, 134, 138, 141, 143, 147, 150, 153, 170, 171, *193, 196, 235, 250, 251, 254, 270*
Faust, R. G., 350, *380*
Favard, P., 138, 141, 147, *193*
Fawcett D. W., 63, 89, 100, 102, *121,* 133, 134, 140, 144, 145, 149, 156, 159, *193*
Feinberg, F. G., 413, 415, 434, *451*
Fendall, N. R. E., 549, *558*
Fennell, D. I., 358, 361, *381*
Fennell, R. A., 40, *56*
Ferguson, M. S., 531, *561*
Fernandes, J. F., 489, 490, *491, 493,* 501, *521, 522, 523*
Fernell, W. R., 202, 203, *235, 240*
Field, J. W., 543, *559*
Fiennes, R. N., 486, *491*
Fiennes, R. N. T.-W., 517, *521*
Fierlafyn, E., 499, *521*
Figueroa, E., 204, *235*
Filadoro, F., *451*
Filho, H. Z., 432, 440, *451*
Filosa, M. F., 350, 359, 361, *380*
Finch, H., 282, *295*
Finger, I., 151, *194, 256, 270*
Firshein, W., 482, *491*
Fisken, R. A., 549, *561*
Fitton-Jackson, S. F., 252, *273*
Fitzgerald, P. R., 432, 437, 438, 444, *452*
Flanagan, C. L., 553, 556, *558*
Flavin, M., 228, *235*
Fleischman, R., 363, *380*
Flewett, T. H., 530, *559*
Flick, E. W., 449, *452*
Foley, G. E., 223, *235*
Folger, H. T., 291, *295*
Folk, K. G., 365, *381*
Folkers, K., 225, *241*
Folsom, C. E., 299, *317*
Fonseca, J. R. C., 90, 91, 93, 94, 95, 96, 100, 101, *120, 123*

Fork, D. C., 321, 332, 334, *338*
Forster, H., 298, *317*
Forsyth, G., 227, *235*
Fortner, J., 435, *452*
Foucher, G., 497, *522*
Fox, D. L., 282, *295,* 329, *338*
Fox, H. M., 293, *295*
Fox, R. M., 547, *558*
França, C., 482, *491*
Frank, H. G., 427, *452*
Frank, O., 223, *235,* 465, 470, 474, *492*
Frank, S. R., 321, *338*
Frankel, J., 26, *56,* 220, *235*
Fredricsson, B., 144, *194*
Freele, H. W., 550, *558*
French, C. S., 321, 322, 323, 324, 336, *337, 338, 339*
Fresco, J. R., 302, *318*
Frey-Wyssling, A., 81, 84, *121*
Fridhandler, L., 374, *380*
Frieden, E., 378, *381*
Friedheim, E. A. H., 498, *521*
Friedkin, M., 230, *235*
Friedman, W., 223, *236, 239*
Friend, A., 444, *455*
Fries, L., 332, 336, *337*
Fritsch, 337, *338*
Fromageot, C., 225, *234*
Frost, J. K., 441, 442, 443, *452, 453*
Fu, F. L., 76, *128*
Fujiwara, J., 444, *453*
Fuller, R. C., 201, 202, 205, 206, *238*
Fulton, J. D., 486, *491,* 500, 510, 514, *521,* 530, 531, 532, *559*
Funk, H. B., 465, 470, 474, *492*
Fussgänger, R., 497, 503, *521*

Gabel, J. R., 432, *452*
Gaither, N., 247, 255, 259, 266, 267, *271*
Gall, J. G. 135, 138, 186, *194,* 204, 228, *236,* 248, 252, *270*
Galuszka, J., 432, *452*
Garnham, P. C. C., 502, *521*
Garnjobst, L., 204, 205, *236*
Gauchery, M., 63, 116, *121, 127,* 171, *196*
Gaudetle, L. E., 552, 553, *559*
Geckler, R. P., 247, 266, *270*
Geddes, M., 223, *236*
Gee, F. L., 486, *491*

Geigy, R., 485, *491*
Geiman, Q. M., *491*, 530, *560*
Gelber, B., 20, 54, 58, 245, 249, *275*, 292, 295
Gellerman, J. L., 231, *236*
George, P., 226, *241*
Gerisch, G., 347, *380*
Gezelius, K., 349, 358, 361, 366, 367, *380*
Gibbons I. R., 134, 135, 137, 138, 140, 145, 160, *194*
Gibbons, R. J., 225, *236*
Gibbs, S. P., 114, *122*, 143, 162, *194*, 306, 307, *317*
Gibson, I., 218, *237*, 264, 265, *270*
Giese, A. C., 31, 40, 41, 56, 216, *233*
Gilbert, L. I., 231, *240*
Gill, E. R., 501, *522*
Gill, J. W., 464, *491*
Gilles, H. M., 532, *559*
Gillham, N. W., 299, 304, 305, *317*
Gimesi, N. I., 81, *122*
Ginel, W., 448, *452*
Glaser, L., 360, 365, *380*
Glazko, A., 549, *561*
Goble, F. C., 500, 517, *521*
Godfrey, D. G., 533, *559*
Godoy, G. A., 483, *493*
Gössel, I., 280, 281, 286, 287, *295*
Goldacre, R. J., 63, 64, 66, 68, 69, 70, *122*, 291, *295*
Goldberg, R., 214, *234*, 423, 424, 425, 426, *456*
Goldfine, H., 231, *233*
Goldsmith, T. H., 288, *295*, 329, 330, 336, *338*
Goldwasser, E., 228, *236*
Gombert, J., 518, *522*
Gonçalves, F. L., 500, *521*
Goodgal, S. H., 266, *273*
Goodwin, L. G., 500, 503, *521*
Goodwin, T. W., 289, *295*, 328, 329, 330, 331, 332, 335, 336, *337*, *338*
Gordon, J. I., 52, 57, 214, *239*
Goreau, T. F., 144, *194*
Gosselin, R. E., 106, *122*
Gottlieb, S., 154, *197*
Gough, L. H., 10, *56*
Graff, S., 228, *235*
Graham, J. R., 323, *338*
Granick, S., 226, *236*, *240*, 298, *317*, *338*

Grant, P. T., 499, 510, 522, 528, 529, 530, 558, 559
Grassé, P. P., 132, 171, *194*
Gray, A. R., 518, *522*
Gray, J., 97, 98, 99, 100, 101, *122*, 156, 159, 174, 178, 183, 184, *194*
Gray, R. A., 330, *338*
Gray, W. D., 83, *122*
Grebecki, A., 188, *194*, 217, *236*
Green, A., 256, *270*
Green, L., 229, *241*
Green, L. W., 414, *452*
Greenberg, J., 531, 533, 538, 539, 541, 544, 558, 559, 561
Greenblatt, C. L., 326, *338*, 483, *493*
Greenwood, A. D., 141, *195*
Gregg, J. H., 76, *122*, 346, 350, 354, 355, 356, 357, 361, *380*
Grellet, P., 534, *559*
Grimstone, A. V., 89, 106, *121*, *122*, 133, 134, 137, 140, 144, 147, 160, *194*, 250, 252, *270*
Gross, D., 228, *236*
Gross, J. A., 289, *295*, 329, 330, 331, *338*
Grossowicz, N., 474, 477, 478, 479, 481, 491, 493
Grounds, J. G., 545, *559*
Groupé, V., 211, 217, *236*, *238*
Greenberg, E., 506, *523*
Grunberg-Manago, M., 302, *316*
Günther, F., 114, *122*
Guida, H. G., 440, *452*
Guimaraes, J. L., 432, 440, *451*, 506, *522*
Guirard, B. M., 223, *235*
Gulbransen, R., 448, *451*
Gumble, A. R., 501, *522*, 548, *559*
Gurin, S., 333, 334, *339*
Gurski, D. R., 423, 424, 425, 426, 428, 451
Guthrie, R., 426, *452*
Gutierrez, J., 203, 220, 224, 227, 232, *236*, 242
Guttes, E., 83, *122*
Guttes, S., 83, *122*
Guttman, H. N., 223, *236*, 467, 470, 472, 474, 475, 476, *492*, *494*
Guttman, R., 23, *57*

Haba, G. L., 489, *494*, 501, *524*

Hack, M. H., 231, *236*, 488, *492*
Hackney, A. L., 350, 355, 361, *380*
Hagen-Seyfferth, M., 188, *194*
Haggerty, M., *556*, *559*
Hahnert, W. F., 69, *129*
Haines, T. H., 231, *236*
Halberg, F., 14, *56*
Halevy, S., 417, *452*, 489, *492*
Hall, C. E., 63, 114, *123*, 149, *194*
Hall, P. J., 67, *119*
Halldal, P., 278, 280, 281, 282, 283, 284, 285, 286, 288, 289, 290, 291, *295*
Halvorson, H., 356, *380*
Hamada, Y., 416, 444, *452*, *453*
Hambre, D., 484, *492*
Hamburger, K., 22, 24, 27, 34, 35, 40, 44, 45, 46, 51, *56*
Hamilton, J. G., 52, 55, 211, *234*
Hammarsten, E., 229, *236*
Hammond, D. M., 432, 437, 444, *450*, *452*, *453*
Hammond, J. C., 103, *122*, 172, *194*
Hancock, G. J., 99, *122*
Handschumacher, R. E., 490, 491, *493*
Hanson, E. D., 245, 250, *270*
Hanson, J., 84, 86, *123*, 160, *194*
Hanson, W. L., 463, 475, 476, *492*
Hardin, G., 322, 331, 332, *339*
Harmon, W., 91, 97, *123*
Harrington, J. D., 31, 42, *56*
Harrington, N. R., 292, *295*
Harris, J. E., 101, *122*, 160, 161, *194*
Harris, P., 145, *194*
Hartman, E., 432, 446, *452*, *455*
Hartshorne, J. N., 307, *317*
Hase, E., 10, *58*
Hastings, J. W., 13, 14, 54, *56*, *58*
Hatano, S., 64, 80, 90, *125*, *128*
Haupt, W., 280, 282, 283, 284, 287, *295*
Havinga, E., 336, 337, *338*
Hawking, F., 532, *559*
Haxo, F. T., 321, 332, 334, *337*, *338*
Hayes, B. S., 448, *452*
Hayes, R. E., 72, *126*
Heald, P. J., 224, 227, *236*
Hearon, J. Z., 266, *270*, *271*
Heckmann, K., 259, *270*
Heftmann, E., 343, 344, 345, 346, *380*
Heilbron, I. M., 330, 331, *338*
Heilbrunn, L. V., 67, *122*, 282, *295*

Heinrich, M. R., 209, 213, 228, 229, *234*, *236*, *238*
Heinrikson, R. L., 228, *236*
Heisch, R. B., 497, *522*
Heller, C., 256, *270*
Hendlin, D., 208, *234*, 330, *338*
Heppel, L. A., 230, *236*
Herman, C. M., 431, *451*, 481, 482, *491*
Hernandez, T., *546*, *559*
Herriot, R. M., 266, *273*
Herrman, E. C., Jr., 217, *236*
Hershenov, B. R., 140, 145, *197*
Hertwig, R., 84, 87, 116, *122*
Hesseltine, C. W., 501, *522*
Hesseltine, H. C., 414, *452*
Hewitt, R. I., 501, *522*, 548, *559*
Hibler, C. P., 444, *452*
Hill, A. V., 65, *122*
Hill, C. H., 444, *456*
Hill, F. D., 210, *236*
Hill, J., 504, 505, 506, 517, 521, 522, 524
Hilmoe, B. L., 230, *236*
Hirschberg, E., 347, *380*
Hirshfield, H. I., 70, *122*
Hirst, E. L., 227, *235*
Hitchcock, L., Jr., 292, *295*
Hitchings, G. H., 542, *559*
Hiwatashi, K., 254, 259, 261, *270*
Hoare, C. A., 486, 487, 488, *492*
Hockwald, R. S., *546*, *556*, *558*
Hodge, A. J., 99, *122*
Hodgkinson, R., *556*, *559*
Hoekenga, M. T., 548, 549, 550, *559*
Hoffmann-Berling, H., 64, 65, 84, 89, 113, 114, *122*, 151, 191, *194*, 281, 291, *295*
Hogben, C. A. M., 509, *521*
Hogg, J. F., 26, 37, 38, 39, 56, *58*, 223, 224, 229, *236*, *242*
Hogue, M. J., 445, *452*
Hollaender, A., 266, *270*, *271*
Holland, A. E., 505, *521*
Holland, J., 223, *236*
Holley, E. C., 444, *454*
Holtzer, M., 282, *295*
Holz, G. G., Jr., 23, 29, 43, 49, 51, 52, 56, 202, 203, 204, 205, 206, 207, 208, 209, 210, 211, 213, 214, 215, 217, 220, 221, 223, 226, 228, 232, *235*, *236*, *237*, *240*, 429, 430, *452*, *453*

Holzman, H. E., 263, *271*
Hoyle, F., 4, *7*
Honda, S. I., 488, *494*
Hongladarom, T., 488, *494*
Honigberg, B. M., 384, 429, 431, 433, 434, 439, 440, 441, 442, 443, 445, 449, *452, 453, 455*
Hoogasian, A. C., 445, *453*
Hopkins, J. M., 64, 89, *129*, 141, 148, 150, *196, 197*
Horecker, B. L., 230, *241*
Hosoi, T., 81, *122*
Hostak, M. B., 344, *380*
Hotchkiss, R. D., 10, *56*
Houlahan, D. A., 438, *454*
Houlihan, R. K., 90, *127*, 180, *197*
Howard, B. H., 203, 224, 227, 229, *233, 237*
Howell, R., 230, *237*
Huber, M., 485, *491*
Hughes, F. W., 535, *559*
Hughes, W. L., 300, *318*
Hull, R. W., 64, 116, 117, *122*, 222, *237*
Humphrey, G. F., 223, *236*
Hunter, N. W., 89, *122*, 225, 227, 230, *237*
Hunter, R., Jr., 225, *237*
Hurly, M. G. D., 557, *559*
Hutchens, J. O., 15, *56*
Hutchinson, M. P., 497, *521, 522*
Hutner, S. H., 1, 3, 5, 7, 208, 215, 220, 221, 222, 223, *233, 235, 237, 239*, 330, *338, 339*, 385, 423, 424, 425, 426, 428, 429, *453, 454*, 464, 465, 470, 475, 476, 483, *491, 492, 496, 522*
Huxley, A. F., 84, *122*
Huxley, H. E., 84, 86, *123*, 160, *194*
Huzisige, H., 325, 326, 330, *338*
Hyman, L. H., 132, *194*

Ibsen, K. H., 224, *237*
Ickes, C., 553, *558*
Ihrig, J., 552, *560*
Ikeda, T., 414, *453*
Imparato, A. M., 223, *239*
Ingraham, J. L., 230, *239*
Inoki, S., 257, *271*, 444, *453*, 486, 487, *492*
Inoué, S., 102, *123*
Irving, L., 230, *237*

Ishida, M. R., 298, 312, 313, *317*
Iverson, R. M., 31, 40, 41, *56*
Ivey, M. H., 435, *453*
Iwai, S., 443, *453*
Iwamura, T., 10, *58*

Jackson, S. F., 63, *126*, 153, 170, *196*
Jacob, F., 257, 258, 263, *271, 272*
Jacobs, L., 443, *455*
Jacobsen, I., 105, *123*, 173, *194*
Jacobson, N. L., 210, *236*
Jacobson, W. E., 223, *241*
Jaffee, J. J., 490, 491, 492, *493*
Jahn, F., *453*
Jahn, F. F., 92, *123*
Jahn, T. L., 23, 24, 25, 26, 27, 28, 29, 31, *58*, 64, 65, 66, 67, 68, 69, 70, 78, 79, 80, 81, 82, 84, 85, 86, 87, 88, 89, 90, 91, 92, 93, 94, 95, 96, 97, 100, 101, 106, 107, 108, 109, 110, 111, 112, 114, 115, 116, *120, 121, 123, 125, 126*, 155, 176, *194*, 246, 249, *273*, 330, *338*, 388, 398, 401, 402, 406, 407, 410, 411, 433, *457*
Jakus, M. A., 63, 114, *123*, 149, *194*
James, M. B., 501, *522*
James, T. W., 12, 13, 14, 15, 16, 17, 18, 23, 26, 27, 53, 54, 55, 56, 57, *58*
Jamieson, C., 105, *124*, 172, *194*
Jamikorn, M., 328, 329, 330, 331, 332, *338*
Janicki, C., 166, *194*, 460, *492*
Jaquette, D. S., 441, *453*
Jarosch, R., 64, 81, 84, 86, 115, *123*
Jaśkowski, L., 432, *453*
Jasmin, R., 213, 223, *237*
Jaswant Singh, 543, *559*
Jeffery, G. M., 546, 547, *559*
Jeffrey, S. W., 320, 321, 322, 328, 329, 331, 332, *338*
Jeffries, W. B., 223, *241*
Jenkins, M. M., 217, *233*
Jennings, H. S., 70, 100, 101, 103, 105, *123, 124*, 172, *194*, 281, *295*
Jensch, H., 502, 503, *522*
Jensen, E. A., 432, *453*
Jensen, P., 178, *194*
Jepps, M. W., 84, 87, *124*
Jerlov, N. G., 294, *295*

Jibbs, J., 282, *295*
Jírovec, O., 223, *237*, 487, *492*
Jörgensen, E., 10, *56*
Johnson, A., 488, *494*
Johnson, A. E., 417, 418, 419, 444, *452, 453*
Johnson, C. A., *530, 559*
Johnson, C. F., *550, 554, 558*
Johnson, D. F., 344, 345, 346, *380*
Johnson, E. M., *514, 523*
Johnson, J. G., 385, 388, 389, 433, *453*
Johnson, W. H., 201, 202, 203, 204, 205, 206, 210, 216, *237, 239*
Johnson, W. J., 213, 223, *237*
Jones, A. S., 229, *237*
Jones, A. W., 113, *121*
Jones, H., 222, *235*, 484, *492*
Jones, I., 424, *453*
Jones, I. G., 256, *271*
Jones, K. M., 202, *237*
Jones, P. F., 64, 111, *124*
Jones, R., 298, *318*
Jones, R. F., 148, 150, *194*, 282, *295*
Jones, S. A., *545, 559*
Joyner, L. P., 437, 438, *453*
Jurand, A., 217, 218, *237*, 263, *269*

Kaback, M., 256, *270*
Kabat, E. A., 414, *457*
Kacser, H., 256, *269*
Käppner, W., 291, *295*
Kafig, E., 439, *451*
Kahl, A., 117, *124*
Kalckar, A. M., 230, *237*
Kamada, T., 106, 107, 108, 109, *124*, 174, 175, *194*
Kamen, M. D., 224, *241*
Kamf, B. M., 322, *337*
Kamiya, N., 64, 65, 68, 77, 78, 79, 80, 81, 82, 83, 86, 112, 114, *124*
Kamiya, T., 31, 32, 35, 37, *56, 58*
Karakashian, M. W., 14, *56*
Karakashian, S. J., 220, *237*
Karnovsky, M. L., 219, *237*
Katashima, R., 259, *271*
Kato, T., 435, *453*
Katsurai, T., 334, *339*
Katz, J., 373, *380*
Kaudewitz, F., 248, *271*

Kaufman, S., 207, *237*, 473, 475, *492*
Kavanau, J. L., 67, 81, *124*
Kayser, F., 344, *380*
Kean, B. H., 444, *453, 457*
Keane, M., 330, *339*
Keilin, D., 226, *237*
Kellermeyer, R. W., *550, 554, 558*
Kelly, D. R., 444, 448, *455*
Kennedy, E. P., 207, *241*, 473, *493*
Kennedy, J. R., Jr., 25, 29, *55*
Kent, W. S., 463, *492*
Kermack, W. O., *528, 529, 530, 558*
Kerr, N. S., 216, 219, *241*, 343, *381*
Kessel, J. F., 440, *453*
Kessel, R. G., 461, *491*
Kessler, D., 202, 203, 204, 205, 206, 207, 208, 209, 210, 215, 217, 220, *236, 237*, 430, *452*
Kessler, W. R., 18, *55*
Kidder, G. W., 28, *56*, 201, 202, 203, 204, 205, 206, 207, 209, 213, 215, 218, 223, 225, 228, 229, 230, *233, 234, 235, 236, 237, 238, 239, 241*, 425, *453*, 470, *492*
Kihara, H., 202, *238*
Kihara, J. T., 440, *456*
Kikuchi, S., 32, *58*
Killian, J. R., Jr., 2, *7*
Kimball, R. F., 204, 218, 228, *238, 239*, 245, 246, 247, 248, 249, 252, 255, 259, 264, 265, 266, 267, *270, 271, 273*
King, K. W., 53, *58*
King, T. J., 263, *270*
King, V. M., 439, *453*
Kinosita, H., 98, 107, 108, 109, *124*, 173, 174, 175, 181, 182, 185, *194*
Kirby, H., Jr., 166, *194*, 219, *238*
Kirchner, E., 501, *523*
Kirk, J. T. O., 321, 326, 330, 331, *338*
Kirk, P. L., 229, *234*
Kirschfield, S., *493*
Kiseleva, M. L., 432, *453*
Kitching, J. A., 63, 77, 87, 98, 116, 117, *120, 124*, 217, *238*
Kittner, P., 256, *270*
Klamer, B., 40, *56*
Klebs, G., 114, *124*
Klein, B. M., 102, *124*, 166, *194*
Klein, H. P., 337, *339*
Klein, R. L., 64, *124*
Klingenberg, H. L., 32, *56*

Klosek, R. C., 202, 203, 204, 205, 206, 208, 209, 238
Klosty, M., 337, 338
Knight-Jones, E. W., 163, 164, 195
Koch, M., 115, 124
Kofoid, C. A., 166, 195
Koizumi, S., 257, 271
Kolar, J. R., 223, 241, 437, 457
Kolderie, M. Q., 356, 357, 363, 379
Konijn, T. M., 75, 77, 124
Koplan, J., 222, 235
Kormos, J., 117, 124
Korn, E. D., 361, 362, 380
Kornacker, M. S., 214, 234
Kornberg, H. L., 38, 39, 56, 224, 225, 236, 238
Kosloff, E., 115, 123
Koss, L. G., 442, 453
Kostellow, A., 347, 380
Kotcher, E., 445, 448, 452, 453
Kozloff, E. N., 222, 238
Kozłowska, D., 432, 453
Kradolfer, F., 427, 445, 453, 457
Kraft, H., 106, 124
Krahl, M. E., 374, 380
Kramer, C. Y., 53, 58
Krebs, H. A., 38, 56, 225, 238
Krezanoski, J. Z., 40, 55
Krichevsky, M. I., 347, 352, 353, 367, 368, 380
Krijgsman, B. J., 97, 124, 156, 195
Krinsky, N. I., 288, 295, 329, 330, 336, 338
Krishnaswami, A. K., 531, 532, 560
Kriszat, G., 64, 124
Krivanek, J. O., 348, 350, 355, 356, 361, 363, 364, 366, 369, 380
Krivanek, R. C., 348, 355, 356, 363, 369, 380
Kruger, F., 63, 129
Krupka, K., 501, 522
Kubo, R., 486, 487, 492
Kucker, S., 423, 424, 425, 426, 456
Kuczyniska, K., 433, 453
Kudo, R. R., 18, 56, 57
Kümmel, G., 115, 124, 144, 195
Kuhn, R., 330, 338
Kuierim, R., 501, 522
Kunitake, G., 385, 389, 407, 410, 411, 415, 418, 419, 453

Kupferberg, A. B., 384, 388, 390, 394, 399, 405, 406, 407, 410, 411, 412, 419, 449, 451, 453, 457
Kuroda, K., 112, 124
Kuznicki, L., 188, 194
Kylin, H., 332, 338

Lacaillade, C., 433, 451
Lachmann, J., 116, 121
Laing, A. B. G., 544, 560
Laird, M., 462, 492
Lampson, G., 388, 390, 394, 399, 405, 406, 410, 453
Lamy, F., 135, 144, 195
Landau, J. V., 64, 69, 70, 80, 82, 124, 129
Landman, M., 90, 91, 93, 95, 96, 97, 100, 120, 123
Lang, N. J., 306, 317
Languillon, J., 556, 560
Lanier, J. E., 547, 560
Lansing, A. I., 135, 144, 195
Larison, L. L., 253, 259, 271, 274
Lascelles, J., 226, 238
Lash, J. J., 432, 454
Lavier, G., 487, 492
Lawlis, J. F., Jr., 432, 454
Leaming, E., 292, 295
Leboy, P. S., 230, 238
Lederberg, S., 29, 57
Lee, F., 343, 381
Lee, J. J., 385, 387, 417, 423, 424, 425, 426, 428, 429, 431, 433, 453, 454
Lee, J. W., 98, 124
Lee, K. H., 23, 27, 40, 50, 51, 55, 57, 58
Leedale G. F., 11, 12, 57
Leevy, C. M., 223, 235
Léger, L., 461, 462, 492
Lehman, F. E., 124
Lehmann, D. L., 480, 492
Leidl, W., 438, 444, 452, 454
Leidy, J., 84, 87, 124
Leiwant, B., 444, 455
Lennarz, W. J., 231, 233
Lepşi, J., 105, 125
LeTourneau, N. W., 248, 273
Leveuf, J. -J., 498, 523
Levin, H. L., 470, 475, 476, 483, 492
Levine, E. E., 298, 300, 317
Levine, L., 113, 125

Levine, N. D., 418, 419, 432, 438, 444, 450, 452, 453, 455
Levine, R. P., 298, 299, 300, 304, 311, 312, 317
Levisohn, S., 229, 240, 356, 381
Levy, L., 388, 390, 394, 399, 405, 406, 410, 453
Levy, M., 19, 27, 30, 37, 57, 58
Lewin, R. A., 6, 7, 64, 90, 91, 124, 125, 148, 149, 150, 162, 188, 194, 195, 282, 295
Lewis, W. H., 66, 125
Liddel, G. U., 343, 348, 351, 352, 358, 361, 380
Liener, I. E., 203, 235, 241
Liesche, W., 18, 57
Light, R., 231, 233
Lilly, D. M., 202, 203, 204, 205, 206, 208, 209, 220, 238, 239
Lindberg, M., 207, 241, 473, 493
Lindblom, G. P., 388, 391, 392, 393, 395, 398, 399, 401, 402, 403, 405, 406, 407, 410, 411, 412, 454
Lindh, N. O., 226, 238
Ling, G. N., 110, 125
Links, J., 281, 295, 336, 337, 338
Linnane, A. W., 488, 492
Lipmann, F., 154, 195, 228, 238
Litman, R., 256, 275
Little, P. A., 481, 493
Lochman, E. -R., 470, 493
Lockwood, S., 221, 237, 423, 453
Loefer, J. B., 110, 111, 125, 126, 215, 228, 238, 257, 271, 272
Loewy, A. G., 64, 77, 80, 81, 84, 125
Lom, J., 431, 454
Lopes Faria, J., 501, 522
Loquin, M., 83, 125
Lorch, I. J., 63, 64, 122, 291, 295
Losch, M. B., 438, 454
Lotte, M., 497, 522
Louderback, A. L., 24, 25, 27, 28, 29, 31, 58, 246, 249, 273
Louloudes, S. J., 238
Lourie, E. M., 180, 193, 506, 522
Lowenstein, J. M., 32, 57
Lowery, J. A., 501, 522
Lowndes, A. G., 90, 91, 92, 93, 96, 97, 99, 100, 125, 155, 195
Lowy, R. S., 423, 424, 456

Ludloff, K., 106, 125
Ludwig, W., 101, 106, 125
Lund, E. E., 102, 103, 104, 125, 166, 167, 169, 195
Lund, P. G., 200, 215, 225, 232, 238, 239, 240, 385, 423, 424, 425, 426, 427, 428, 429, 430, 449, 454, 456
Luntz, A., 280, 286, 295
Lwoff, A., 3, 4, 7, 102, 103, 121, 134, 167, 190, 193, 195, 250, 252, 271, 460, 462, 492
Lwoff, M., 167, 193, 384, 385, 387, 414, 419, 426, 429, 454, 460, 462, 492
Lyman, H., 325, 338
Lynch, J. E., 444, 454
Lynch, V., 426, 451
Lynch, V. H., 224, 238
Lysenko, A. Y., 550, 560
Lyttle, C. N., 504, 522
Lyttleton, J. W., 228, 238

McAuliff, J. P., 552, 560
McCaffery, T. D., 231, 236, 488, 492
McCarthy, R. E., 223, 235
McCaul, W. E., 438, 454
McChesney, E. W., 552, 560
McConnachie, E., 527, 528, 558
McDaniel, M. R., 215, 238
McDonald, B. B., 57, 245, 246, 247, 272
MacDonald, J. B., 225, 236
MacDonald, R. D., 502, 520
McDowell, S. J., 433, 454
McEntegart, M. G., 434, 439, 446, 447, 454
McEwen, W. K., 48, 55
McGhee, R. B., 463, 475, 476, 484, 492, 535, 561
Machin, K. E., 99, 125
McKee, C. M., 211, 238
McKee, R. W., 530, 560
Mackerras, M. J., 532, 560
McKibben, W. R., 114, 123
McLaughlan, J. M., 223, 240
McLaughlin, J. J. A., 334, 337
McLoughlin, D. K., 440, 441, 454
McLure, M. T., 441, 442, 445, 452, 453
McMahon, J. P., 497, 522
McMahon, P., 489, 493, 500, 523
McManus, M. A., 83, 125
McWade, D. H., 438, 454

Madsen, N. B., 38, *56*
Maegraith, B. G., *527, 531, 559, 560*
Magara M., 432, 435, *454*
Mager, J., 154, *195*, 228, *238*
Mahrla, A., 438, *454*
Mainz, F., 336, *338*
Malhotra, M. N., 488, *493*
Mallory, F. B., 52, *57*, 214, *239*
Maly, R., 251, *272*
Mandel, M., 229, *240, 356, 381*, 429, 431, *453, 455*
Mandelstam, J., 356, 362, 363, *380, 381*
Manners, D. J., 37, *57*, 226, 227, *233, 239*, 398, 415, *455*
Manning, W. M., 322, 331, 332, *339*
Manson-Bahr, P. E. C., 497, *522*
Mansour, J. M., 510, *521*
Mantel, N., 222, *235*
Manten, A., 278, *295*
Manton, I., 93, 98, *125*, 140, 141, 143, 149, 171, *195, 196*
Manwell, R. D., 115, *125*
Maramorosch, K., 463, *493*
Margison, J. E., 444, *454*
Margolin, P., 256, 257, *272*
Mark, M. F., 223, *239*
Markees, D. G., 213, *234, 239*
Marmur, J., 229, *241, 356, 381*
Marquardt, W. C., 438, 444, *454*
Marques, W., 432, 440, *451*
Marquis, D., 2, *7*
Marr, A. G., 230, *239*
Marsh, G., 68, *125*
Marshall, P. B., 505, 510, *522*
Marshall, R. S., *522*
Marsland, D. A., 64, 68, 82, *124, 125, 129*
Martin, W. B., Jr., 264, *270*
Maryon, M., 530, *560*
Masseyeff, R., 518, *522*
Mast, S. O., 66, 67, 69, 82, 98, 107, *125*, 280, 283, 284, 286, 287, 290, 291, 292, 293, *295, 296*
Mathis, M., 531, *559*
Matsushiro, A., 257, *271*, 486, *492*
Matthaei, J. H., 300, *317*
Maupas, E., 116, *125*
Maven, I., 444, *454*
Mayer, A. M., 282, 283, 284, 285, *296*
Mazia, D., 17, 18, 28, 29, *57*, 149, 154, 187, *193, 195*

Medeiros, P. M., 440, *452*
Mefferd, R. B., Jr., 110, 111, *125, 126*
Mehlman, B., 482, *493*, 499, *523*
Mehra, K. N., 418, 419, 438, *454, 455*
Mehta, R. K., 48, *57*
Meier, R., 427, *457*
Meinhart, J. O., 149, *195*
Meisenhelder, J. E., *549, 561*
Mellentin, R. W., 449, *456*
Mendonca, J., 432, 440, *451*
Menne, R., *552, 560*
Menolasino, N. J., 446, *455*
Menon, M. K., *552, 560*
Mercado, T. I., *535, 560*
Meryman, H. T., 439, *451*
Mesa, C. P., 441, *455*
Meselson, M., 248, *270*, 300, *317*
Metz, C. B., 137, *195, 259, 272*
Metzner, P., 280, *296*
Meuwissen, J. H. E. T., *546, 560*
Michaels, R. M., 415, 429, 448, *455*
Millar, J. W., *551, 561*
Millar, P. G., 437, *453*
Miller, C. A., 202, 203, 204, 205, 206, 208, 209, 210, 216, *237, 239*
Miller, M. J., *532, 547, 558, 560*
Miller, W. H., 181, *197*
Millman, N., 449, *451*
Milne, L. J., 280, *296*
Milne, M. L., 280, *296*
Milstrey, R., 465, *493*
Miner, M. L., 437, *452*
Minick, O. T., *57*
Mintz, R. H., 162, *195*
Misch, M. S., 218, 219, *233*, 262, *269*
Misra, B. G., *533, 551, 552, 560*
Mita, T., 23, 27, 28, 31, *57, 58*
Mitchell, H. K., 303, *317*
Mitchell, M. B., 303, *317*
Mitchison, J. M., 70, *125*, 245, *275*
Mitchison, N. A., 254, 266, *272*
Mitropolitanskaya, R. L., 181, *195*
Miyake, A., 247, *259, 272*
Mizell, M., 438, *454*
Mjaaland, G., 280, *296*
Molinari, V., *455*
Mondal, M. M., *558, 558*
Monod, J., 257, *258, 263, 271, 272*, 477, *492*
Monroe, R. E., *238*

Montezin, G., 531, 560
Moog, F., 354, 381
Moon, A. P., 500, 522
Moore, D. V., 547, 560, 561
Moore, M., 211, 238
Moore, W. E. C., 53, 58
Moraes, G. E. S., 501, 522
Morales, M. F., 15, 56
Mordarski, M., 449, 455
Morgan, W. T. J., 413, 415, 451, 456, 457
Morris, K. R. S., 496, 522
Morrison, B. M., 218, 219, 233, 262, 269
Morrison, J., 444, 454
Mosetting, E., 489, 493, 500, 523
Mott, M. R., 256, 269, 272
Mould, D. L., 227, 239
Moulder, J. W., 530, 560
Mühl, D., 115, 125
Mühlethaler, K., 358, 361, 381
Mühlpfordt, H., 487, 492
Mueller, J. A., 263, 264, 272, 273, 274, 275
Müller, M., 176, 196, 203, 217, 218, 219, 239
Muller, A., 322, 339
Murrell, C. B., 223, 241, 437, 457
Myatt, A. V., 546, 559
Myers, J., 323, 338

Nachmansohn, D., 181, 193, 195
Nachtwey, D. S., 52, 57
Nagata, R., 401, 402, 406, 450
Nagel, J., 262, 272
Nair, C. P., 532, 552, 559, 560
Nairn, R. C., 447, 454
Naitoh, Y., 98, 104, 107, 125, 174, 180, 195
Najarian, H. H., 549, 561
Nakajima, H., 64, 80, 81, 90, 124, 125
Nakajima, T., 401, 402, 406, 450
Nakamura, M., 431, 441, 447, 450, 455, 501, 522
Nakatani, M., 213, 234
Nanney, D. L., 245, 247, 253, 255, 256, 257, 258, 260, 261, 262, 263, 269, 272
Naschke, M. D., 240
Nash, T. A. M., 506, 522
Nathan, H. A., 220, 221, 222, 223, 237,

239, 240, 423, 453, 464, 465, 467, 469, 470, 472, 474, 475, 476, 483, 489, 491, 492, 494, 496, 522
Nauss, R. N., 84, 87, 125
Nelson, L., 89, 90, 125
Neresheimer, E. R., 113, 126
Nettleton, R. M., Jr., 110, 126
Newton, B. A., 492, 515, 516, 522
Nicander, L., 145, 195
Nicoli, J., 486, 491
Niedergerke, R., 84, 122
Niemegiers, K., 498, 521
Nieto-Caicedo, M., 548, 560
Nihei, T., 10, 58
Nijenhuis, L. E., 296
Ninomiya, H., 390, 394, 397, 398, 401, 402, 405, 406, 407, 410, 411, 412, 455
Nirenberg, M. W., 300, 317
Nishi, A., 32, 33, 37, 39, 40, 45, 57, 225, 239
Nishimura, M., 325, 326, 330, 338
Nobili, R., 245, 246, 247, 254, 263, 264, 272, 273
Noble, A. E., 116, 126
Nodake, Y., 435, 450
Noguchi, H., 462, 463, 475, 476, 481, 492, 493
Noirot-Timothée, C., 169, 195
Noland, L. E., 68, 77, 84, 126
Nordli, E., 280, 296
Norman, J. O., 225, 239
Noroland, P. G., 488, 492
Norris, A. T., 231, 233
Norris, P., 334, 338
Notzold, R. A., 438, 454
Novikoff, A. B., 217, 239
Noyes, H. M., 365, 381

O'Brien, J. E., 427, 455
Odell, L. D., 414, 452
Ogston, D., 528, 529, 558
ÓhEocha, C., 334, 338
Okajima, A., 98, 103, 104, 107, 116, 126, 165, 174, 195
Oliphant, J. F., 107, 126
Olmstead, M. A., 298, 300, 317
Ono, T., 23, 27, 28, 31, 57, 58, 486, 487, 492
Oosawa, F., 64, 65, 80, 126

Orfila, J., 531, 559
Orias, E., 265, 273
Orlowska, V., 449, 455
Ormerod, W. E., 515, 518, 519, 522
Orsi, N., 451
Osterhout, W. J. V., 81, 126
Otey, M. C., 230, 239
Outka, D. E., 215, 235
Owen, R. D., 257, 271, 272
Oxford, A. E., 224, 227, 235, 236

Packchanian, A., 498, 500, 521, 522
Packer, L., 464, 465, 491
Padilla, G. M., 13, 14, 15, 16, 17, 53, 54, 55, 56, 57
Pagliara, A., 264, 270
Palade, G. E., 306, 317
Papa, M., 224, 239
Pappas, J., 10, 55
Pardoe, V., 180, 193
Parducz, B., 100, 126, 138, 157, 165, 167, 169, 171, 176, 177, 180, 181, 182, 183, 188, 195, 196
Parent, G., 479, 491
Parisis, N. G., 113, 126
Parke, M., 141, 171, 195
Parke, R. R., Jr., 228, 238
Patterson, E. L., 465, 493
Patterson, K., 202, 204, 205, 206, 237
Patton, W. S., 461, 493
Pautard, F. G. E., 65, 126
Pavlova, E., 433, 455
Pellegrino, J., 500, 521
Penard, E., 87, 113, 116, 117, 126
Perdue, S. W., 204, 228, 238, 247, 248, 249, 252, 264, 267, 271
Pereira, J. P. M., 501, 521
Perry, S. V., 63, 126
Petersen, R. A., 221, 237, 423, 453
Petrovic, Z., 431, 455
Phagpolngarm, S., 329, 331, 332, 337
Philpott, D. E., 144, 162, 194
Pierce, S., 385, 387, 423, 424, 425, 426, 428, 429, 454
Piette, L. H., 312, 317
Piez, K. A., 363, 380
Pigoń, A., 177, 196, 247, 273
Pilcher, H. L., 203, 239

Pipkin, A. C., 94, 126, 485, 493
Pirenne, M. H., 77, 124
Pitelka, D. R., 63, 89, 93, 100, 102, 104, 105, 113, 126, 133, 137, 138, 141, 144, 145, 147, 170, 183, 188, 195, 196
Pittendrigh, C. S., 285, 295
Pitts, W. R., Jr., 81, 119
Pizelli, G. N., 440, 452
Pizzi, T., 490, 493, 501, 502, 522
Plastridge, W. N., 455
Plate, L., 117, 126
Plaut, W., 312, 317
Pleaner, P., 230, 239
Plentyl, A. A., 229, 233, 239
Plesner, P., 23, 32, 33, 57, 228, 239
Plowman, K., 90, 125
Podolsky, B., 15, 56
Pogo, A. O., 326, 327, 337
Pohl, R. Z., 285, 296
Polgár, M., 218, 239
Poljakoff-Mayber, A., 278, 284, 296
Pollack, B. M., 77, 120
Pollard, W. O., 232, 239
Porter, J. N., 501, 522
Porter, K. R., 63, 100, 121, 127, 134, 137, 140, 149, 193, 197
Pottage, R. H., 116, 126
Potter, M. D., 505, 520
Powers, E. L., 137, 167, 193, 250, 251, 252, 266, 270, 273
Pozsár, B. I., 81, 122
Prager, R., 501, 522
Pray, E. G., 432, 455
Preer, J. R., 148, 149, 151, 196, 220, 226, 239, 241, 252, 253, 256, 257, 265, 269, 273
Preer, L. B., 148, 149, 151, 196, 256, 273
Prell, H., 115, 126
Prescott, D. M., 18, 20, 54, 57, 204, 218, 221, 228, 238, 239, 245, 246, 247, 248, 249, 250, 271, 273
Price, E. V., 230, 239
Price, K. E., 223, 239
Price, W., 77, 126
Pringsheim, E. G., 330, 336, 338
Pringsheim, O., 330, 338
Prosser, C. L., 114, 126
Provasoli, L., 1, 7, 330, 338, 384, 424, 426, 453

de Puytorac, P., 171, *196*
Pyne, C. K., 464, *493*

Quinn, L. Y., 220, 221, *239*

Rabinowitch, E. I., 294, *296*
Rachmilewitz, M., 474, *493*
Raffaele, G., 531, *560*
Raftery, M., 334, *338*
Rake, G., 484, *492*
Ramakrishnan, S. P., 531, 532, 533, 546, 547, 559, *560*
Ramanis, Z., 303, 304, *317*
Rama Rao, R., 533, 534, *560*
Rampton, V. W., 153, *196*, 252, *273*
Ramsey, R., 556, *559*
Rånby, B. G., 358, 361, *380*
Randall, J. T., 63, *126*, 141, 148, 153, 170, *196*, *197*, 252, *273*
Raper, K. B., 75, 77, *124*, *129*, 344, 358, 361, *380*, *381*
Rashevsky, N., 78, *126*
Rasmussen, L., 23, 24, 48, 49, 50, 51, 52, 53, 56, 57, 211, *237*
Rathscheck, H. J., 549, *560*
Rauscher, F. J., 217, *236*
Ray, A. P., 532, 547, 551, 552, 559, *560*
Ray, D. L., 72, *126*
Ray, H. N., 488, *493*
Read, C. P., 385, 387, 388, 389, 390, 391, 394, 398, 399, 401, 403, 405, 407, 410, 411, 412, 442, 449, *453*, *455*
Reardon, L. V., 443, *455*
Reber, E. F., 418, 419, *455*
Rees, C. W., 103, *126*
Reeve, E. C. R., 264, *273*
Reeve, S. J., 262, *272*
Reeves, H., 224, *239*
Reichard, P., 229, *236*
Reichenow, E., 482, 486, *493*
Reid, J. A., 544, *561*
Reilly, S. M., 220, *239*
Reiner, L., 427, *452*
Reisner, A., 256, *275*
Rem, L. T., 37, 40, 55, 225, *235*
Rembold, H., 470, *492*
Remo, J. W., 444, *456*
Rendina, G., 225, *240*
Reutner, T. F., 549, *561*

Rey, L., 490, *493*, 501, *522*
Reynolds, H., 215, 228, *240*
Rhoades, M. M., 303, 315, *317*
Richards, O. W., 249, *273*
Richet, P., 497, *522*
Richter, J. E., 115, *126*
Rickes, E. L., 208, *234*
Rikmenspoel, R., 98, *126*
Rinaldi, R. A., 64, 65, 66, 67, 69, 70, 81, 84, 85, 86, 88, 116, *121*, *123*, *126*
Ris, H., 312, *317*
Ristic, M., 480, *493*
Rivera, J. A., 98, *126*, 133, *196*
Robbins, W. E., *238*
Robbins, W. J., 110, *126*
Roberts, R. B., 355, *381*
Robertson, D. H. H., 498, 499, *522*
Robertson, G. I., 548, 551, 559, *560*
Robertson, M., 460, *493*
Robertson, R. N., 285, *296*
Robinson, N., 552, *561*
Robinson, W. G., 225, *240*
Robson, J., 504, *523*
Rockland, L. B., 202, 235, *240*
Rodriguez, E., 221, *237*, 423, *453*
Röhlich, P., 218, 219, *239*
Roll, P. W., 229, *233*
Rollo, I. M., 489, *494*, 499, 503, 509, 515, 521, *523*, 524, 539, 544, 551, 557, 559, *560*
Romano, A. H., 388, 390, 394, 399, 405, 406, 410, *453*
Ron, A., 23, *57*
Ronkin, R. R., 162, *196*
Rosen, G. D., 202, 203, 235, *240*
Rosen, G. I., 203, *241*
Rosenbaum, J. L., 228, 232, *240*
Rosenbaum, N., 52, 56, 202, 203, 204, 205, 206, 207, 208, 209, 210, 211, 213, 214, 215, 217, 220, 221, 223, *236*, *237*, *240*
Rosenbaum, R. M., 217, 218, *240*
Rosenberg, L. E., 104, 105, *126*
Rosenberg, T., 216, *241*
Roslansky, J. D., 66, 68, 69, 70, *119*
Ross, C. M., 550, *558*
Ross, G. J. S., 264, *273*
Rosselet, J. P., Jr., 415, 429, *455*
Roth, J. S., 225, *240*
Roth, L. E., 57, 63, 104, 105, 114, *127*,

141, 145, 169, 170, 171, 180, 188, *196,* 217, *240*

Rothman, A. H., 389, 390, 394, 398, 399, 401, 403, 405, 410, *455*

Rothschild, L., 98, *127*

Rouiller, C., 63, 116, *121, 127,* 143, 147, 170, 171, *193, 196*

Rubens, S., 224, *241*

Rubin, R., 444, 449, *455*

Rubin, R. J., 490, 491, *493*

Rudzinska, M. A., 63, *127,* 171, *196,* 226, *240, 245, 256, 263, 272,* 487, *493, 531, 560*

Ruffié, J., *534, 558*

Rumberg, A., 322, *339*

Rumberg, B., *339*

Rupert, C. S., 266, *273, 275*

Rusch, H. P., 83, *122,* 347, *380*

Ryley, J. F., 37, *57,* 223, 224, 225, 226, *237, 239, 240,* 389, 391, 392, 395, 398, 399, 401, 402, 403, 405, 406, 407, 410, 411, 412, 415, 416, *455,* 477, *493,* 510, 514, *523, 536, 537, 560*

Sachs, T., 282, 283, 284, *296*

Sadovsky, A., 430, *450*

Sager, R., 298, 299, 300, 302, 303, 304, 305, 307, 309, 312, 313, *316, 317, 318,* 320, 321, 328, 329, *337, 338*

Sakamoto, H., 486, 487, *492*

Salisbury, G. W., 65, 98, *127*

Saltman, P., 385, 389, 398, 401, 402, 406, 407, 410, 411, 415, 418, 419, *453, 457*

Saluste, E., 229, *236*

Sampath, A., 481, *493*

Samuel, E. M., *75, 76, 127*

Samuels, R., 385, 428, 430, 433, 434, 435, 436, 447, 449, 450, *451, 454, 455*

Sanborn, W. R., 446, *455*

Sanders, M., 221, 223, *237, 240*

Sanders, M., 423, 425, 427, *453, 455*

Sandon, H., 84, *127*

Sargent, J. R., 499, 510, *522*

Sargent, M. C., 329, *338*

Saquis, J., 432, 440, *451*

Satir, P. G., 18, *57,* 141, 149, 161, 181, *196, 197*

Sato, H., 40, *57,* 221, *240*

Sato, T., 226, *240*

Satti, M. H., *439, 455*

Satya Prakash, *531, 532, 533, 546, 547, 560*

Saunders, J. T., 113, *127*

Saxe, L. H., 444, *455*

Saylor, J. H., 210, *236*

Schäfer, E. A., 101, *127*

Schaeffer, A. A., 65, 69, 70, *127,* 292, *296*

Schatz, A., 330, *338*

Schensted, I. V., 261, *273*

Scher, S., 220, 223, *237,* 330, *337,* 496, *522*

Scherbaum, O. H., 10, 19, 21, 22, 23, 24, 25, 26, 27, 28, 29, 30, 31, 32, 33, 34, 35, 36, 37, 39, 40, 43, 44, 45, 53, 54, 55, 56, 57, 58, 59, 220, 225, 228, *236, 238, 239, 242,* 246, 249, *273*

Scheurbrandt, G., 231, *233*

Schewiakoff, W., 84, 87, 115, *127*

Schiff, J. A., 325, 326, 337, *338, 339*

Schildkraut, C. L., 229, *240,* 356, *381*

Schimke, R. T., 378, *381*

Schlein, A., 223, *239*

Schlenk, H., 231, *236*

Schlesinger, M. J., 225, *234*

Schmidt, L. H., *552, 561*

Schmidt, R. R., 53, *58*

Schmidt, W. J., 113, *127*

Schmidt-Nielsen, K., 230, *237*

Schneider, J., 498, *523,* 531, *556, 560*

Schneider, K. C., 84, *127*

Schneider, L., 171, *197*

Schneiderhöhn, G., 281, 286, 287, 291, *295*

Schneiderman, H. A., 231, *240*

Schneller, M. V., 254, 255, 263, 264, 266, *273, 274, 275*

Schnitzer, R. J., 444, 448, *455, 506, 523*

Schoenheimer, R., 229, *239*

Schoenherr, K. E., 446, *455*

Schooley, C. N., 93, *126,* 141, 144, *196*

Schuberg, A., 102, *127*

Schueler, F. W., 488, *493*

Schultze, M., 84, 115, *127*

Schulze, F. E., 63, *127*

Schuster, F. L., 137, 144, 145, 187, 189, *197*

Schuster, G. L., 23, *58*

Scott, J. F., 248, *273*

Scott, W. N., 507, *523*

Scremin, L., 460, 486, *491*

Seaman, G. R., 90, *127*, 154, 180, 181, *197*, 201, 202, 204, 206, 217, 218, 219, 223, 224, 225, 226, 229, 230, *239, 240*, *252, 273, 274*, 406, 410, *455, 493*

Sebek, O. K., 415, 429, *455*

Sedar, A. W., 137, *197*

Seifriz, W., 77, *127*

Sells, B. H., 70, *127*

Sen Gupta, G. P., 551, *560*

Seravin, L. N., 103, *127*, 152, 178, *197*

Seraydarian, K. H., 33, 34, *58*

Sergent, E., 536, *560*

Settow, J. K., 266, *274*

Settow, R. B., 266, *274, 275*

Shaffer, B. M., 74, 75, 76, 77, *127*, 343, *381*

Shaffer, J. G., *456*

Shapiro, J. E., 140, 145, *197*

Sharma, G. K., 547, *560*

Sharp, R. G., 166, *197*

Sharpey, W., 63, *127*

Shaw, R. F., 202, 215, 222, *240*, 444, *456*

Shenoy, K. G., 223, *240*

Sherwood Jones, E., 531, *560*

Shibata, K., 10, *58*

Shifrine, M., 211, 223, *233*

Shigenaka, Y., 188, *196*

Shin, E., 284, 291, *296*

Shipley, P. G., 488, *493*

Shorb, D. A., 444, *456*

Shorb, M. S., 200, 215, 225, 231, 232, *238, 239, 240*, 385, 417, 423, 424, 425, 426, 427, 428, 429, 430, 449, *454, 456*

Short, R. B., 18, *58*

Shupe, J. L., 432, 444, *452*

Shute, G. T., 544, 545, *558*

Shute, P. G., 530, *560*

Siegel, R. W., 148, *197*, 220, *240*, 253, 255, 259, 264, *270, 271, 274*

Silberstein, T. K., 18, *55*

Silva, L. H. P., 501, *521, 523*

Silvester, N. R., 150, 151, *192*

Simard-Duquesne, N., 64, 65, *127*

Siminoff, P., 223, *239*

Simmons, D., 552, *561*

Singer, I., 517, *521*, 534, *560*

Singer, S., 201, *240*

Singer, W., 27, *58*

Singh, N., 551, *560*

Singher, H. O., 388, 390, 394, 399, 405, 406, 410, *453*

Sirsi, M., 533, 534, *560*

Six, N., 70, *127*

Skaar, P. D., 257, *274*

Skowronska-Serafin, B., 548, *558*

Sleigh, M. A., 89, 90, 91, 96, 99, 100, 101, 102, 103, *127, 128*, 156, 157, 160, 172, 178, 179, 182, 183, 184, *197*

Slifkin, M. K., 347, *381*

Small, E. B., 65, 66, 84, 88, *123*

Small, M., 209, 222, *235*

Smallman, E. T., 378, *381*

Smillie, R., 311, *317*

Smith, B. F., 424, 426, *453, 456*

Smith, B. J., 417, 418, 423, 424, 425, 426, 428, 429, *454*

Smith, C. C., 552, 553, *560, 561*

Smith, C. L., 53, *58*

Smith, G. K. A., 505, *520*

Smith, H., 203, *241*

Smith, I. M., 504, 505, 506, 507, *523*

Smith, J. E., 264, *274*

Smith, J. H. C., 322, 325, *339*

Smith, J. P., 256, *270*

Smith, M. H., 226, *241*

Smith-Sonneborn, J. E., 229, *240, 241*, 356, *381*

Snell, E. E., 202, 223, *235, 238*, 426, *452*

Snyder, R. L., 44, *58*

Sobels, F. H., 266, *274*

Sobotka, H., 3, 7, 221, 222, *233, 237*

Sörensen, N. A., 330, *338*

Soldo, A. T., 219, 223, 228, 229, 230, *241*

Solomon, J. M., 396, 410, 411, 431, *456*

Soltys, M. A., 509, 517, 519, *523*

Sonneborn, D. R., 245, 260, *274*

Sonneborn, T. M., 186, *197*, 219, *241*, 244, 247, 250, 251, 252, 253, 254, 255, 256, 257, 258, 259, 260, 261, 263, 264, 266, *272, 273, 274, 275*, 316, *317*

Sorel, C., 432, *456*

Sorokin, S., 188, *197*

Sotelo, J. R., 188, *197*

Sparks, J. T., 43, *58*

Speir, D., 81, *119*

Spencer, H. T., 53, *58*

Spindler, L. A., 444, *456*

Spooner, D. F., 510, 514, *521*

Spriggs, A. S., 417, 418, *456*
Sprince, H., 385, 388, 423, 424, 425, 426, *453, 456*
Stabler, R. M., 440, 441, 449, *455, 456*
Stahl, F. W., 300, *317*
Stahler, N., 292, *296*
Steele, W. J., 333, 334, *339*
Steers, E., 256, *275*
Steinert, M., 480, 483, 489, *491, 493*
Stene, J., 330, *338*
Stephen, L. E., 486, *493*, 505, 517, *523*
Stephens, G. C., 216, 219, *241*
Stern, A. I., 337, *339*
Stewart, B. T., 77, 78, 80, 81, *128*
Stewart, P. A., 77, 78, 80, 81, 82, *128*
Stitcher, J. E., 551, *561*
Stitt, C., 385, 389, 407, 410, 411, 415, 418, 419, *453*
Stock, C. C., 223, *241*
Stokstad, E. L. R., 465, *493*
Stone, G. E., 222, *241*
Stott, J. A., 203, *241*
Stoucler, D. J., 436, 450, *455*
Strain, H. H., 320, 322, 328, 329, 331, 332, 336, *339*
Strasburger, E., 280, *296*
Streissle, G., 463, *493*
Strother, G. K., 288, *296*
Subak-Sharpe, H., 303, *317*
Sueoka, N., 229, *241*, 300, *317*
Sugimura, T., 23, 27, 28, 31, *57, 58*
Sullivan, W. D., 43, 44, *58*
Sussman, M., 73, 75, 76, *128*, 343, 345, 347, 348, 354, 356, 357, 358, 359, 361, *378, 381*
Sussman, R. R., 76, *128*, 345, *381*
Suzcioki, T., 388, 391, 394, 395, 397, 401, 403, 410, 412, *456*
Suzuoki, Z., 388, 390, 391, 394, 395, 397, 398, 401, 402, 403, 405, 406, 407, 410, 411, 412, *455, 456*
Svedberg, T., 334, *339*
Svensson, G., 249, *271*
Sweeney, B. M., 13, 14, 54, *58*
Swenson, P. A., 418, 419, *456*
Swezy, O., 166, *197*
Swift, H., 20, 54, *58*, 245, 249, *275*
Switzer, W. P., 444, 446, *456*
Szarski, H., 177, *196*
Szent-Györgyi, A., 63, 65, 68, 80, *128*

Taft, E. B., 248, *273*
Tahmisian, T. N., 115, *120*
Takagi, Y., 230, *241*
Takahaski, T., 32, 37, 56, 58
Takata, M., 64, *128*
Taketomi, T., 211, 225, 231, *241*
Takeuichi, I., 64, 76, 80, *128*, 355, 363, 364, *381*
Tallan, I., 264, 266, *274, 275*
Tamiyo, H., 10, *58*
Tamiyo, H., 226, *240*
Tanabe, T., 435, *453*
Tangara, S., 498, *523*
Taniuchi, Y., 486, *492*
Tarantola, V. A., 203, 204, *241*
Tarlov, A. R., 550, 554, *558*
Tartar, V., 113, *128, 170, 182, 186, 197,* 246, 250, 251, 252, *275*, 293, *296*
Tarver, H., 228, *236*
Tatum, A. L., 535, *559*
Tatum, E. L., 204, 205, *236*
Taub, S. R., 260, *275*
Tauc, L., 77, *128*
Taylor, A. E. R., 504, *523*, 533, 534, *561*
Taylor, C. V., 103, 104, *128*, 167, 168, 170, 172, *197*, 204, 205, *236*
Taylor, D. J., 531, *559, 561*
Taylor, E. P., 505, *520*
Taylor, G. I., 93, 99, 100, *128*
Taylor, J. H., 300, *318*
Tazawa, M., 279, 287, *295*
Tefankjian, A., 261, *272*
Telford, S. R., Jr., 91, 96, *120*
Tentori, L., 532, *558*
Terada, T., 63, *128*, 326, 330, *338*
Teras, J., 388, 443, *456*
Terry, O. P., 284, *296*
Terry, R. J., 532, *559*
Thayer, P. S., 223, *235*
Thomas, D. M., 332, 336, *337, 339*
Thomas, E. W., 337, *339*
Thomas, G. J., *239*
Thomas, J. B., 278, *296*
Thomas, J. O., 224, 227, *241*
Thompson, C. F., 440, *453*
Thompson, C. M., 65, 68, 70, *120*
Thompson, D'A. W., 101, *128*
Thompson, G. R., 556, *561*
Thompson, J. C., Jr., 220, *241*
Thompson, M. J., *238*, 500, *523*

Thompson, N. J., 489, *493*
Thompson, P. E., 549, *561*
Thompson, T. W., 229, *237*
Thompson, W. D., 225, *241*
Thoms, R. K., 426, 427, *451*, *455*
Thormar, H., 46, *58*, 220, *241*
Thorne, J. L., 444, *452*
Thurston, J. P., 518, *523*, 538, *561*
Tibbs, J., 64, 89, *128*, 147, 150, 181, *197*
Tietz, A. M., 207, *241*, 473, *493*
Tilden, E. B., 462, 463, 481, *493*
Tischer, J., 329, 330, *339*
Titus, E. D., 552, *559*
Tobie, E. J., 482, 489, *493*, 499, 500, 501, 515, 519, *523*
Törő, I., 203, 217, 218, 219, *239*
Tokuyasu, K., 188, *197*
Tollert, M. G., 535, *561*
Tollin, G., 330, *337*
Tomkins, G., 369, *381*
Tóth, J., 218, 219, *238*
Trager, W., 219, 222, *241*, 465, 468, 480, 485, 487, *493*, 531, 534, 536, 542, 560, *561*
Trégouboff, G., 89, *128*
Trejos, A., 483, *493*
Trembley, H. L., 531, 544, *559*
Trujillo-Cenoz, O., 188, *197*
Trussell, M. H., *453*
Trussell, R. E., 384, 389, 433, *453*
Trygstad, C. W., 346, *380*
Ts'O, P. O. P., 64, 77, 80, *128*
Tsubo, Y., 283, *296*, 298, 304, 305, 307, *317, 318*
Tucker, P. A., 396, 434, *456*
Tuffrau, M., 168, *197*, 293, *296*
Tulloch, G. S., 140, 145, *197*
Tunka, A. F., 444, *456*
Twichell, J. B., 245, *270*
Twohy, D. W., 385, 387, 388, 396, 434, *456*
Tyler, H. M., 414, *456*

Ueda, K., 174, *197*
Uemura, T., 326, 330, *338*
Ueno, T., 435, *450*
Uhlig, G., 250, 251, *275*
Ulehla, V., 100, *128*
Ungar, F., 214, *234*

Urbá, R. C., 363, *381*
Urbanski, T., 548, *558*
Ussing, H. H., 68, *128*

Vakirtzi-Lemonias, C., 225, *241*
Vanderplank, F. L., 486, *493*
van Eys, J., 223, 224, *241*
van Niel, C. B., 224, *241*
van Tÿn, B., 256, *275*
van Tubergen, R. P., 248, *275*
van Wagtendonk, W. J., 64, *128*, 201, 202, 203, 204, 205, 206, 211, 213, 223, 228, 229, 230, *233, 234, 239, 241, 252*, 256, 264, 269, *270, 275*, 419, 429, *456*
Varga, A., 433, *456*
Vasaitis, V., 232, *239*
Vávra, J., 280, *296*
Vegotsky, A., 378, *381*
Vennes, J. W., 23, *58*
Venulet, J., 548, *558*
Verloop, A., 336, 337, *338*
Verolini, F., 532, *558*
Verworn, M., 87, 100, 106, *128*, 172, 183, *197*
Vickerman, K., 463, *493*, 514, 518, 519, 521, *523*
Vila, E., 432, 440, *451*
Villeneuve-Brachon, S., 168, *197*
Vinciguerra, B., 265, *270*
Vinograd, J., 64, 77, 80, *128*
Vivier, E., 259, *269*
Visscher, J. P., 113, *128*
Viswanatha, T., 203, *241*
Vitols, E., 488, *492*
Vivier, E., 138, *193, 197*
Vloedman, D. A., Jr., 64, *128*, 223, *241*
Vogel, H. J., 464, 467, *491, 493*
Vogt-Köhne, L., 247, 248, 249, *271*
Volkmann, D., 311, *317*
von Brand, T., 223, *233, 241*, 385, 387, 388, 419, *450, 456*, 477, 482, 489, *493*, 499, 500, 501, 514, 515, 519, 520, *523*, 535, *560*
von Gelei, G., 167, 169, *194*
von Gelei, J., 102, 105, *129*, 166, *194*
Voskresenskaya, G. V., 432, *453*
Vouk, V., 77, *129*

Wacker, A., 470, *493*

Wagner, A. F., *241*

Wagner, B., 202, 203, 204, 205, 206, 207, 208, 209, 210, 211, 213, 214, 215, 220, 225, 226, *235, 236, 241*, 430, *452*

Wagner, C., 38, *56, 58*

Walker, A. J., *544, 561*

Walker, D. A., 365, *379*

Walker, L. M., 245, 257, *269*

Walker, P. M. B., *275*

Wallace, F. G., 460, 461, 463, 480, 481, 484, 488, *491, 493, 494*

Wallace, W. S., 501, *522*, 548, *559*

Walls, L. P., 500, *521*

Walton, B. C., 441, *456*

Wang, H., 222, *241*

Wantland, E. M., 416, 417, 444, *456*

Wantland, W. W., 416, 417, 444, *456*

Ward, C., 358, 360, 361, *381*

Warnock, L. G., 223, 224, *241*

Warren, L. G., 395, 415, 417, 418, 446, *456*, 481, *494*

Warwick, E. J., 232, *236*

Washbourn, K., 504, 506, *524*

Watanabe, I., 107, *129*

Watkins, T. I., 504, *523*

Watkins, W. M., 413, 414, *456, 457*

Watson, H. J. C., 497, 498, *522, 523*

Watson, M., 115, *129*

Watson, M. R., 64, 89, *129*, 148, 150, 151, *192, 197*

Watters, C. D., 115, *129*

Watts, T., 202, 204, 205, 206, *237*

Weaver, E. C., 312, *318*

Webber, H. J., 460, *494*

Weber, H. H., 63, 65, 84, 85, *129*, 161, *197*, 282, *296*

Weber, M. M., 464, 465, *491*

Wedmayer, D., 257, 264, *269, 275*

Weeks, D. C., 285, *296*

Wegner, Z., 431, *457*

Weibull, C., 98, 99, 101, 102, *120*

Weidman, T. A., 416, 417, 444, *456*

Weinbach, E. C., 499, 515, *523*

Weinman, D., 481, 482, 485, *491, 494*

Weinstein, I. B., 300, 302, *317, 318*

Weinstein, M., 231, *240*

Weiss, E. D., 425, *457*

Weisz, P., 218, *241*

Weitz, B., 518, 519, *523*

West, R. A., Jr., 223, *241*

Weld, J. T., 444, *453, 457*

Wellerson, R., 388, 399, 407, 410, 411, 412, 419, *457*

Wellerson, R., Jr., 405, 406, 407, 410, 411, *457*

Wells, C., 248, *275*

Wenrich, D. H., 486, *494*

Wense, T., 180, *193*

Wenyon, C. M., 460, 461, 486, *494*

Werbitzki, F. W., 487, *494*

Wertlieb, D. M., 476, *494*

West, R. A., Jr., 437, *457*

Westfall, J. A., 137, 144, *195, 198*

Weston, J. K., 549, *561*

Wheeler, W. M., 7

White, E., 548, *559*

White, G. J., 348, 354, 356, 357, 358, 359, 361, *381*

Whiteside, E. F., 505, 506, 507, 508, 509, 518, 519, 520, *523*

Whitfeld, P. R., 528, *561*

Whittingham, W. F., 77, *129*

Whittington, M. J., 440, *457*

Wichterman, R., 103, 106, 113, *129*, 167, *198*

Wiese, L., 298, *317, 318*

Wilbrandt, W., 216, *241*

Wildman, S. G., 488, *494*

Wilkins, M. J., 285, *296*

Wilkinson, J. F., 256, *269*

Williams, D. B., 249, *275*

Williams, H. H., 202, 203, *233, 239*

Williams, J. A., 438, *454*

Williams, J. H., 501, *522*, 548, *559*

Williams, N. E., 23, 25, 26, 29, 43, *56, 58*, 202, 215, 220, *236, 240, 241, 242*, 257, *275*

Williams, P. P., 203, 224, 232, *236, 242*

Williams, R. P., 225, *239*

Williamson, J., 489, *494*, 499, *502*, 506, 509, 510, 513, 515, 519, *523, 524*

Williamson, M., 223, *241*

Wilson, B. W., 17, *58*

Wilson, D. E., 87, *120*

Wilson, I. B., 181, *195*

Wilson, S. M., 247, 259, 266, 267, *271*

Wilson, T., 550, *559*

Winet, H., 111, *123*

Wingo, W. J., 225, *241*
Winquist, D. L., 444, *456*
Wirtschafter, S. K., 388, 398, 401, 402, 406, 407, 410, 411, 432, 449, *457*
Witt, H. T., 322, *339*
Wittner, M., 217, 218, *240*
Wohlfarth-Bottermann, K. E., 63, 85, 113, 114, *129*
Wolcott, G. B., 531, *561*
Wolinska, W. H., 442, *453*
Wolken, J. J., 99, *129,* 284, 288, 291, *296,* 324, 325, 330, *339*
Wood, H. G., 373, *380*
Woodcock, H. M., 461, *494*
Woods, P. S., 300, *318*
Woodward, J., 20, 54, 58, 245, 249, *275*
Woolfe, G., 496, 504, 506, 523, *524*
Woolley, D. W., 202, *237*
Worley, L. G., 103, 105, 107, *129,* 172, 174, *198*
Wragg, J. B., 215, 228, *240*
Wragg, W. R., 504, 505, 506, 521, *524*
Wright, B. E., 76, *129,* 343, 344, 345, 346, 347, 348, 349, 350, 351, 352, 353, 355, 356, 358, 360, 361, 362, 363, 364, 365, 366, 367, 368, 369, 370, 371, 372, 373, 374, 375, 376, 378, *380, 381*
Wright, D. E., 227, 232, *233, 242*
Wu, C., 26, *58,* 229, *242*
Wu, Y. Y., 548, *558*
Wulff, D. L., 266, *275*
Wyatt, G. R., 485, *491*

Wyss, W., 427, *457*

Yaeger, R. G., 231, *236,* 488, *492*
Yamada, E., 188, *197*
Yamaguchi, T., 174, 175, 182, *198*
Yarmolinsky, M. B., 489, *494,* 501, *524*
Yocom, H. B., 166, 168, 170, *198*
Yokouchi, K., 432, 435, *454*
Yokouti, E., 432, *454*
Yoneda, M., 161, *198*
Yoneda, S., 501, *523*
Young, M. D., 531, 543, 546, 547, 551, *559, 561*
Young, M. L., 256, *275*
Yuzuriha, Y. O., 27, 50, 51, 57

Zago, H., 432, *451*
Zahalsky, A. C., 330, *339*
Zahler, S. A., 53, 55
Zalokar, M., 309, *317,* 320, 321, 328, 329, *338*
Zarnitz, M. L., 414, *457*
Zayicek, J., 90, *129*
Zerahn, K., 68, *128*
Zeuthen, E., 10, 18, 21, 22, 23, 24, 25, 27, 28, 29, 31, 34, 35, 40, 44, 45, 46, 49, 50, 51, 52, 53, 54, 55, 56, 57, 58, 59, 211, *237, 249, 275*
Ziegler-Gunder, I., 3, 7, 469, 472, 492, *494*
Ziffer, H., 223, *235*
Zimmerman, A. M., 64, 82, *124, 129*

Subject Index

Acanthamoeba, locomotion, 64, 72, 74
Acetabularia, protoplasmic movement, 64
2-Acetamido-5-nitropyridine, in antitrichomonad therapy, 448
2-Acetamido-5-nitrothiazole, in experimental *Trypanosoma cruzi* infections, 500
Acetate
 antimetabolites, effect on *Tetrahymena*, 213
 in carotenoid biosynthesis, 333
 in ciliate nutrition, 207, 208, 216, 225
 incorporation in trypanosomatids, 489
 and O_2 uptake in trichomonads, 400
 as sterol precursor in trichomonads, 417
 in *Tetrahymena*, induction of isocitrate lyase, 38
 required by *Trichomonas gallinae*, 385
 stimulation of metaboly in *Euglena*, 114
Acetate-requiring mutants in *Chlamydomonas*, 301, 305, 311
Acetic acid production by trichomonads, 394, 399, 411
Acetoacetate, formation by *Tetrahymena*, 40
Acetylcholine in *Trypanosoma*, 180
Acetylcholinesterase
 absence in flagellates, 181
 in ciliates, 90, 180–181
 effect of trypanocides, 513
 in trypanosomes, 513
Acetarsone, resistance in trichomonads, 443
Acid phosphatase
 in food vacuoles, 217, 218
 in *Tetrahymena*, 40
 genetics, 262
Acineta, tentacular movement, 116

Aconitase, in trichomonads, 409
Acrasiae
 aggregation, 75, 76, 77
 locomotion, 72–75, 88
Acrasin, 343–346
 general properties, 75, 76
Acridine antimalarials, 549–550
Acridones, effect on enzymes of trypanosomes, 511–513
Acriflavine
 antagonism of pararosaniline in trichomonal infections, 448
 effect on enzymes of trypanosomes, 511–513
 induction of akinetoplasty, 487
Actidione resistance, as genetic marker in *Chlamydomonas*, 301
Actin
 in muscle, 63, 84, 90
 action, 160
 resemblances to isolated cilia, 150
Actinomycin D, effect on timing in *Gonyaulax*, 13
Actomyosin, in muscle, 63–65, 68, 70, 80, 81, 89, 113, 118, 150, 281
Acytostelium, acrasin assay, 344
Adenine
 annuller of 6-methylpurine inhibition in *Tetrahymena*, 213
 antagonism of puromycin, 501
 incorporation by trypanosomes, 513, 516
 in *Tetrahymena* cilia, 150
 uptake in trypanosomatids, 466, 467, 489–490
Adenopterin, 51
Adenosine, contamination with *Crithidia* factor, 465

Adenosine diphosphate
   dephosphorylation by isolated cilia, 151
   effect on cilia models, 153
Adenosine monophosphate, inability to re-
      place ATP for reactivation cilia
      models, 153
Adenosine triphosphate or pyrophosphate,
      see ATP
Adenylate kinase, in isolated cilia, 151
Adenylic acid, utilization in trypanosomes,
      513
Alanine-α-ketoglutaric transaminase, in
      Dictyostelium, 364, 366, 368
Alcohol dehydrogenase
   effect of trypanocides, 512
   thiamine-dependent, relation to nitro-
      furan therapy, 499
Aldolase, in trichomonads, 406, 408
Algae
   nutrition, 1
   phylogeny, 132
Alkaline phosphatase, in Dictyostelium,
      363, 364, 366–368
Alkaloids, acrasin activity, 344
Allogromia, filopodia, 63, 85
Allophycocyanin, in algae, 334
Alloxan, induction of diabetes by, and
      rat malaria, 535
Alpha particles, as mutagen in ciliates, 267
Ameba-to-flagellate transformation, see
      Naegleria
Amebae
   growth oscillations in, 18
   locomotion, 63–74, 79, 80, 81, 84, 118
Amebo-flagellates, see Naegleria
Amethopterin, antimalarial activity, 538
Amine oxidase, in Dictyostelium, 363
Aminitrazole, in antitrichomonad therapy,
      449
Amino acid(s)
   analogs, inhibition of Tetrahymena, 49,
      52
   in cilia, 150–151
   free in Tetrahymena, 26
   in flagella, 148
   incorporation in proteins, see Genetic
      Code
   pool
      in ciliates, 228

in Dictyostelium differentiation, 348–
      349, 361
   requirements
      of ciliates, 201–203
      in trichomonads, 425–426
   in trypanosomatids, 488
   uptake
      by Paramecium, 248, 249
      by Tetrahymena, 26, 201–203
p-Aminobenzoic acid
   effect on malarial infections, 532–534
   and folic nutrition in ciliates, 207
   genetic marker in Chlamydomonas, 300
   as target antimalaria drugs, 536, 538–
      542
γ-Aminobutyric acid, formation in tricho-
      monads, 395
2-Amino-4-hydroxy-6,7-dimethyl tetra-
      hydropteridine, in phenylalanine
      hydroxylation, 473, 475
4-Amino-5-imidazole carboxamidine, pu-
      rine precursor in Crithidia, 464,
      467, 489
2-Amino-5-nitropyrimidine, in antitricho-
      monad therapy, 448, 449
2-Amino-5-nitrothiazole (Enheptin), in
      antitrichomonad therapy, 449
7-Aminophenanthridium compounds, in
      anti-trypanosome therapy, 504
Aminopterin, antimalarial activity, 538
Aminoquinaldines, see Quinapyramine
4-Aminoquinoline antimalarials, 546–556,
      see also Amodiaquine, Chloroquine,
      and Hydroxychloroquine
8-Aminoquinoline antimalarials, 536, 546,
      550, 553–556, see also Pamaquin,
      Pentaquine, Primaquine
8-Aminoquinolines, in Chagas' disease, 500
p-Aminosalicylic acid, induction of acute
      hemolysis by, 499
3-Amino-1,2,4-triazole, bleaching of Eu-
      glena, 330, 331
Ammonia
   effect on pattern swimming, 111
   production by ciliates, 229–230
Amodiaquine
   comparison with propoquin against Plas-
      modium lophurae, 549
   effect of SKF 525A on detoxication, 553

Amodiaquine-resistant *Plasmodium falciparum,* 547
Amoeba carolinensis, diurnal variation in reproduction rate, 18
Amoeba proteus
actomycin-like protein, 64
cold shock, 18
diurnal variations in reproductive rate, 18
phototaxis, 279, 291–292
synchronization index, 54
Amphotericin B, in *T. cruzi* infections, 500
Amylase
in *Entodinium,* 227
in *Stylonychia,* 227
in trichomonads, 408
Anaerobiosis
inhibition of pattern formation, 111
Anodonta, see Molluscs
Antheroxanthin, in *Euglena,* 329
Antibiotics
in isolating trichomonads, 431, 433–437, 440
screening with ciliates, 222, 223
in treatment of trypanosomiasis, 496
Antihistamines, bleaching of *Euglena,* 330
Antimonials
effect on trypanosome enzymes, 511–513
inhibition of phosphofructokinase, 510–511
resistance in trypanosomes, 519
Antioxidants, in trichomonad nutrition, 419, 422, 424–430, 434, 437
Antithyroid drugs, effect on protozoa, 223
Antrycide, *see* Quinapyramine
Apistonema, carotenoids, 331
L-Arabinose, *see also* Carbohydrates.
in permeability studies in *Tetrahymena,* 216
Arachidic acid, in nutrition of *T. cruzi,* 480
Arachidonic acid
absence in ciliates, 209, 230
in nutrition of *T. cruzi,* 480
occurrence in nature, 231, 232
Arcella, 6
Arginine, genetic marker in *Chlamydomonas,* 300

Aromatic diamidines,
effect on trypanosome enzymes, 511–512
in treatment of trypanosomiasis, 497, 502–503
Arsenate, inhibition of trichomonads, 403–405
Arsenical-resistant trypanosomes, 498, 499, 519
Arsenicals
effect on trypanosome enzymes, 511–512
treatment
bovine trypanosomiasis, 502
human trypanosomiasis, 497–498, 509–510
Arsenite
inhibition
of phototaxis, 285
of trichomonads, 403–406
Arsenoacetate, inhibition of trichomonads, 404–406
Ascorbic acid, effect on malarial infections, 533
Ascorbyl palmitate, in trichomonad nutrition, 423
Aspartate, in *Tetrahymena,* possible conversion to glycogen, 38
Aspergillus, nonchromosomal factors, 303
Astasia
ATP formation, 17
flagellar movement, 96
growth oscillations in, 14–17
metaboly, 114
O₂ consumption, 17
synchronization index, 54
Astasia ocellata, α-carotene in, 337
Astaxanthin, in *Englena,* 330
Atabrine, *see* Quinacrine
ATP
in ciliary and flagellar contraction, 161, 291
effect
on glycinated *Vorticella* stalks, 191
on suctorian feeding, 117
formation in *Astasia,* 17
impairment synthesis by antisterols, 214
in locomotion, 63–65, 68, 70, 80–81, 84, 113–114, 116, 118, 284–285, *see also* other entries under ATP.
in motility, 281

in muscle, 63, 281
reactivation of cilia and flagella models, 152–153, 159, 161, 165, 178–179, 182, 191
in *Tetrahymena*, 33
ATPase
action on fibrillar proteins of protozoa, 64, 70, 114
in flagella
of *Chlamydomonas*, 148, 162
of *Polytoma*, 147–148, 282
in muscle, 281
in trypanosomes, 513
Autogamy, in *Paramecium*, 253–255, 258, 266
Axoneme(s), 460
definition, 139–140
function, 160–162
morphology
in ciliates, 139–143, 149
in flagellates, 140, 188–189
in metazoa, 188
sheath, 141–143
Axopods, 63
Axosome, in cilia of *Paramecium*, 135, 138–139, 146–147
Azacrine, as schizonticide in *Plasmodium falciparum*, infection, 549
8-Azaguanine
antagonism by guanine, guanosine, adenine, 51
inhibition
Astasia division, 17
Tetrahymena division, 51
and *Paramecium* symbionts, 265
Azapurines, effect on *Tetrahymena*, 230
Azaserine, 51
inhibition purine synthesis in *Trypanosoma cruzi*, 489
Azathymine, 51
6-Azauracil, effect on *Trypanosoma equiperdum*, 490–491
Azide
inhibition ion exchange in *Tetrahymena*, 216
inhibition of trichomonad metabolism, 403–406
In *Tetrahymena*, effect on growth, 45

Ba^{++}, reversal ciliary beat, 107, 108

Babesia infections, effect of berenil, 503
Bacteria
complexity of, 3
phylogenetic relations to algae, 335
Balantidium, glycolysis in, 223
Behenic acid, in nutrition *T. cruzi*, 480
Benzpyrene, ciliate assays, 222
Berenil
immunity in animals treated by, 518
in treatment bovine trypanosomiasis, 502–504, 507–508
in *Trypanosoma gambiense* infections, 497
Bicarbonate, uptake by trichomonads, 388
Biliproteins, in flagellates, 334
Biochemistry, unity of, 3
Biomyxa, movement in, 87
Biopterin, 465, 469–473, 475
assay of, 6
folic-sparing in *Tetrahymena*, 207
Biotin
in nutrition of ciliates, 205
requirement in trichomonads, 424
Bis-quinaldinium drugs, *see* Tozocide
Blastocrithidia
lipids, 488, 489
nutrition, 464, 466, 474, 475, 477, 484
taxonomy, 461, 462
Blepharoplast, *see also* Kinetoplast, Kinetosome
in trichomonads, 166
Blood-group substances, decomposition by trichomonad enzymes, 413–414
Bodo
axosome, absence of, 139
flagellar movement, 155
kinetosome, 137–138, 145
paraxial rods, 143
root fibrils of flagella, 145
Brassicasterol
in nutrition of ciliates, 213
in trichomonad nutrition, 429
5-Bromouracil, 51
Bryopsis, ϵ-carotene in, 332
Butyrate, oxidation by trichomonads, 401
Butyric acid, oxidation by *Tetrahymena*, 225

Ca++ and acrasian aggregation, 77
  detachment of cilia by, 148
  effect
    on glycerinated *Vorticella* stalks, 191
    on movements, 64, 108–110, 112–113, 116, 174–176, 282, 285
    lack of effect on cilia models, 153
CaCl₂
  effect on ciliate myonemes, 113
    on suctorian tentacles, 116
Caffeine, 113
Calcium ion, *see* Ca++
Calcium requirement in trichomonads, 424, 425
Campanella, filamentous tracts, 147
Campesterol, in nutrition of ciliates, 212
Canavarine, cause of delayed division in *Tetrahymena*, 49
Carbohydrates
  in cilia of *Tetrahymena*, 150
  in ciliate metabolism, 207–208, 215–216, 223–227
  in Crithidia-factor synthesis, 470, 472
  in flagella of *Polytoma*, 147
  in kinetosomes, 154
  in *Tetrahymena*, 35–36
  in trypanosomatid nutrition, 475–477
Carbohydrate metabolism, in trichomonads, 385–411
Carbon dioxide
  fixation in trichomonads, 399, 411
  formation in *Dictyostelium*, 369–375, 378
  inhibition of malarial gametocytes, 527
  in isolating trichomonads, 432, 435, 436, 439
  metabolism in ciliates, 223–232
  and pattern swimming, 111
  and phototaxis, 282–284, 290
  production by *Plasmodium berghei*, 529
    by trichomonads, 388–396, 411, 412
  reversal of ciliary beat by, 107
Carbon monoxide
  chemotactic effect on *Chlamydomonas* gametes, 298
  inhibition of trichomonads, 403–406
5-carboxyuracil, in ciliate nutrition, 204, 207
Carcinogens, ciliate assays for, 222
Cardiolipid, in trypanosomatids, 489

α-Carotene
  in chlorophytes, 327–329
  in chrysophytes, 331
  in cryptomonads, 332
  as phyletic marker, 335
β-Carotene
  in chlorophytes, 327–329
  in chrysomonads, 331
  in chrysophytes, 331
  in cryptomonads, 332
  in dinoflagellates, 332
  in *Englena*, 329–330, 333, 334
  extraplastidic pigment in *Dunaliella*, 329
  in eyespots, 330
  as phyletic marker, 335
  in *Polytoma*, 336
ε-Carotene, in *Cryptomonas*, 332
γ-Carotene, in *Englena*, 329
ζ-Carotene, in *Englena*, 330, 331
Carotenoid(s)
  biosynthesis, 332–334
  eyespot, 288–289, 329–330
  mutants in *Chlamydomonas*, 307, 309–311
  in phototaxis, 278, 281, 288–289, 294
  as phyletic markers, 335–336
  plastid, 327–334
Catalase
  effect of trypanocides, 511
  in trichomonads, 397, 409
  in trypanosomatids, 476
Cell membrane, effect of ions on, 109, 110
Cellulose, in *Dictyostelium*, 342, 357–358, 360, 361, 378–379
Centrifugation, effect on division in *Tetrahymena*, 20
Centrioles
  in metazoa, 153, 159, 186–188, 252
  in *Naegleria*, 187
Ceratium
  flagellar movement, 90–92, 97
  growth oscillations in, 10
  photoreceptor, 280
Cetyltrimethylammonium Cl, trichocyst extrusion by, 114
Chagas' disease, 500–502, *see also Trypanosoma cruzi*
  immunity in, 502
  treatment with amphotericin B, 500

Chaos chaos
  growth oscillations, 18
  locomotion, 69
Chara, streaming in, 86
Chlamydomonas
  ATPase, 64
  carotenoids, 328, 329
  chlorophylls, 320, 321
  flagella
    chemical composition of, 150
    growth, 188, 189
    isolation of, 148
    movement, 90–92, 96, 101, 162
Chlamydomonas
  mutants with impaired motility, 162
  phototaxis, 283–285
  relation to *Polytoma*, 337
  xanthophylls, 328, 329
Chlamydomonas moewusii
  growth oscillations in, 10, 11
  synchronization index, 54
Chlamydomonas reinhardi
  genetics of, 298–316
  morphology, 298–302, 306–307
  sexuality, 5
  zygotes, 6
Chloral hydrate, effect on cilia, 188
Chloramphenical, *Tetrahymena*, inhibition
  of, 49, 50
Chlorella
  carotenoids, 328, 329
  chlorophylls, 320
  growth oscillations in, 10
  steroids, 337
  symbiotic, *see Paramecium bursaria*
3-Chloro-9-(4-diethylamino-1-methylibu-
  tylamino) acridine, 10-oxide 2HCl,
  protection against *Plasmodium lophurae*, 549–550
Chloromonads, ignorance about, 322
Chlorophenyldimethylurea, effect on phototaxis, 284, 285
Chlorophyll(s)
  in flagellates, description, 319–327
  mutants in *Chlamydomonas*, 307, 309–
    311
  as phyletic markers, 336
  and phototaxis, 294
Chlorophyta, chlorophylls, 320–321

Chlorophytes, phylogeny based on pigments, 335–336
Chlorpromazine, effect on *Tetrahymena*,
  223
Chloroquine
  in combined antimalarial therapy, 554–
    556
  comparison, with compound WIN 5037
    against malaria, 550
  in *Plasmodium falciparum* infection,
    with azacrine, 549
    with diaminodiphenylsulfone, 550
  fate in body, 552–553
Chloroquine-resistant
  Plasmodium berghei, 547
  Plasmodium falciparum, 547
  Plasmodium gallinaceum, 546–547
Chlorproguanil
  in combined therapy, 556
  protection against *Plasmodium falci-
    parum*, 548
Cholestanol, in trichomonad nutrition,
  429, 430
Δ^5-Cholestenol, in trichomonad nutrition,
  430
Δ^7-Cholestenol, in nutrition ciliates, 211,
  212
Cholesterol
  in nutrition of ciliates, 211, 212, 214
  in trichomonad nutrition, 417, 419, 424,
    426–430
Choline
  in ciliate nutrition, 205, 210
  requirement in *Trichomonas*, 424, 427
  in trypanosomatids, 488
Choline dehydrogenase
  in trypanosomes, effect of trypanocides,
    513
Choline requirement, *Leishmania tarentolae*, 465, 468
Cholinesterase, in trypanosomes, effect of
  trypanocides, 513
Chromulina
  flagellar movement, 93
  rhizoplasts, 143
Chrysochromulina
  carotenoids, 331
Chrysochromulina
  chlorophylls, 321

Chrysomonads
carotenoids, 331–332
chlorophylls, 321
flagella, morphology, mastigonemes, 141
movements, 90, 92–94, 96, 98, 100,
156
Cilia
antigenic analysis of, 151
chemical composition of, 150–155
enzymes in, 151
function, 63–65, 84, 100–107, 118–119,
131, 155–162, 172–185
coordination, 163–185, 191–192
growth and regeneration, 188, 190, 268
isolated, 147–148, 259
mating substances in, 148, 259
models, 149–153, 159, 178–179, 182,
184, 191
morphology, 89, 102–103, 133–137,
146, 148–149, see also Cilia, models
in ciliates, 132–149
in ctenophores, 135
in molluscs, see ciliated epithelium
in opalinids, 132
in rotifers, 135
relation to pellicular structures in ciliates, 168–171
Ciliated epithelium
glycerinated models, 152, 161
isolation of cilia, 148
morphology, 132–134, 140, 144
movement, 156–157, 159, 182
Ciliates, see also Colpidium, Euplotes,
Glaucoma Paramecium, Stentor
Tetrahymena, etc.
aging, 254–256
amino acid degradation, 229–230
requirements, 201–202
B vitamin requirements, 204–207
carbohydrate utilization, 207, 208
caryonidal inheritance, 260–262
cilia in, evolution, 132, 133
comparative biochemistry, 232–233
control of cell size, 249–250
fatty acid nutrition, 208–211, 214, 215,
232
synthesis, 230–232
glyoxylic acid cycle, 37–39, 224, 225,
233

growth during cell cycle, 249
oscillations in, 19–53, 249
gullet, self-duplication, 250
high temperatures and nutrition, 220–
221
immobilization antigens, 148, 256–258,
261–263, 268
lipid nutrition, 207–215, 230–233
mating types, 259–263
nuclear differentiation, 258–262, 268,
see also Macronuclei and Micronuclei
nucleotide synthesis, 228–229
oral primordia, 25–26
organic acid and alcohol requirements,
207–208
oxidative metabolism, 223–226
pattern inheritance, 250–253
phototaxis in, 279, 292–293
protein synthesis, 227–228
purine and pyrimidine catabolism, 230
requirements, 203–204, 233
RNA synthesis, 247–249, 265
sterol requirements, 210–215
symbiosis and parasitism in, 219–220,
263–265, 268–269
vitamin B_{12} in, 206, 207, 233
Circadian rhythms
in ciliate conjugation, 14, 260, 261
definition and examples, 14
Cirri
associated fibers, 168, 170
movement, 101, 157, 179, 184
saponin models, 153
Citrate, oxidation by trichomonads, 401
Citric acid, inhibition O_2 uptake by trichomonads, 406
Citric-synthetase, in Tetrahymena, 38
Citrostadienol, in nutrition ciliates, 212
Clionasterol, in nutrition of ciliates, 212
Cobaltous ion, effect on aldolase in Trichomonas, 406, 407
Coccolithophorids, 6
phototaxis in, 280
Cod liver oil, effect on malarial infections,
533
utilization by ciliates, 206
Coenzyme A
in malaria infections, 534
utilization by ciliates, 206

Coenzyme Q
in *Tetrahymena,* 225
in trichomonad nutrition, 424–425, 449
Colchicine, growth inhibition of *Tetrahymena,* 213
Colpidium
kinetosome, 137
nutrition, 201, 204–206, 215
root fibrils, 145
Colpidium campylum
effect of cooling, 21
nutrition, 201, 204, 205
Colpidium steinii, nutrition, 204, 205
Compound Cl–423, *see* 3-chloro-9-(4-diethylamino-1-methylbutylamino) acridine, 10-oxide 2HCl
Compound 377C54, antimalarial activity, 551
Compound 5943 (antimalarial biguanide), effect on *Lactobacillus casei,* 537
Compound 10,580 and 10,732 (antimalarial triazines), effect on *Lactobacillus casei,* 537, 538
Compound WIN 5037, effect on *Plasmodium* infections, 550
Condylostoma, fibrils in, 105, 113
Contractile vacuoles
morphology in ciliates, 171
movements, 112
in suctorial feeding, 117
in trypanosomatids, 461, 462
Cooling
see Temperature changes
Coproporphyrin, in *Tetrahymena,* 226
Corals, flagella, morphology, 144
Cortisone, growth inhibition of *Tetrahymena,* 213
Costa, definition, 144
Coumarin, inhibition of phototaxis, 285
Crabtree effect, in *Tetrahymena,* 222, 223
Crithidia
for biopterin assay, 6
taxonomy, 461–463, 475–477
Crithidia factor, 465, 469–474, 478
Crithidia fasciculata
alcohol dehydrogenase, 499
lipids, 488, 489
nutrition, 464–466, 469–479, 484
pyruvate decarboxylase, 499

Crithidia luciliae
lipids, 488, 489
nutrition, 474, 475, 484
Crithidia oncopelti, 462–464, 466, 467, 473, 474, 488, 489
adenine requirement in relation to chemotherapy, 515, 516
effect of quaternary ammonium trypanocides, 515
leucine uptake, effect of quinapyramine, 516
pyruvate decarboxylase, 499
Crithidia sp., growth in eggs, 484
Cryptochrysis, biliproteins, 334
Cryptomonads
biliproteins, 334
carotenoids, 332
chlorophylls, 321–322
phylogeny based on pigments, 335, 336
Cryptomonas
biliproteins, 334–336
carotenoids, 332
chlorophylls, 321, 322
Cryptoxanthin, in eyespots, 330
Ctenophores, cilia, 135
Curare, 113
Cyanide
inhibition of phototaxis, 285
of trichomonads, 403–406
Cyanocobalamin, *see* Vitamin B_{12}
Cyanophyceae, biliproteins, 334–336
Cyclidium, movement, 112
Cyclosis, 64, 68, 112, 118
Cyphoderia, movement in, 87
Cysteine
stimulation of *Euglena* and *Astasia* in dark, 16
uptake by *Plasmodium knowlesi,* 530
Cytidine
dephosphorylation by isolated cilia, 151
non-uptake by kinetosomes, 153
uptake by ciliates, 228
Cytidine nucleotide metabolism, in trypanosomes, 513
Cytochromes
absence from African trypanosomes in mammalian hosts, 510–511
in ciliates, 226
and trichomonads, 409, 412
in trypanosomes, 514

Cytochrome oxidase
  absence in blood forms in trypanosomes, 510–511
  in *Dictyostelium,* 363, 364
  in *Tetrahymena,* 226
  in trichomonads, 409

Dasytricha, carbohydrate fermentation, 224
Dasytrichs, carbohydrases, 227
7-Dehydrocholesterol
  in ciliate nutrition, 211
  in trichomonad nutrition, 429, 430
Deoxyadenine, effect on *Tetrahymena,* 29, 31
Deoxyguanine, effect on *Tetrahymena,* 29
Dephosphorylases, in isolated cilia, 151
Desmosterol, in ciliate nutrition, 211–213
Detergents, use in dispersing cilia, 150–153
Dextrin, in nutrition of *Tetrahymena,* 215
Diadinoxanthin, in chrysophytes, 331, 336
Diamidines, *see* Aromatic diamidines
Diamine oxidase, in trypanosomes, effect of trypanocides, 512
Diaminodiphenylsulfone, with pyrimethamine in malaria, 558
2,6-Diamino-4-isoamyloxypyridine, growth inhibition of *Tetrahymena,* 213
Diaminophenylsulfone, effect on human malaria, 550
2,4-Diamino-6,7-*iso*-propylpteridine, cross-resistance with pyrimethamine in malaria, 541
2,6-Diaminopurine, effect on kappa, 223
Diamond's medium, 384, 431–436, 438, 482
Diatoms, phylogeny based on pigments, 335–336
Diatoxanthin
  in chrysophytes, 331
  in *Cryptomonas,* 332
Dicrateria
  carotenoids, 331
  chlorophylls, 321
Dictyostelium, 6, 75, *see also* Acrasiales
  aggregation, 342–350
  differentiation
    amino acid pool in, 348, 349, 361
    antigenic changes in, 354–355

  carbohydrates in, 356–361
  nitrogenous compounds in, 355
  enzymes in, 363–379
  fatty acid synthesis, 360–362
  glucose metabolism, 373–377
  protein synthesis, 362–363
  respiration, 350–354, 361
  life cycle, diagram, 342
Digitoxin, effect on ciliary beat, 178
Diguanidines, effect on trypanosome enzymes, 511–513
Dihydrocholesterol, in trichomonad nutrition, 429
Dihydrolanosterol, in ciliate nutrition, 211, 212
Dihydrostreptomycin, bleaching of *Euglena,* 330
Diisopropylfluorophosphate, effect on *Tetrahymena* motility, 180
Dileptus, ciliary beat, 105
4,4'-Dimethyl-Δ^8-cholesterol, in nutrition of ciliates, 212
Dimidium, in treatment bovine trypanosomiasis, 504
Dimorpha, movement in, 87
2,4-Dinitrophenol
  effect on phototaxis, 284, 285
  inhibition phenylalanine uptake by *Tetrahymena,* 216
  Inhibition of *Tetrahymena,* 44, 45, 49, 52, 53
  sterol antagonism, 213, 214
  inhibition of aggregation in *Dictyostelium,* 347
  inhibition of trichomonad metabolism, 403–405, 449
Dinoflagellates
  carotenoids, 332
  chlorophylls, 322
  flagellar movement, 90–92, 97
  growth oscillations, 10, 13, 14, (*see also Ceratium*)
  luminescence, 13
  phototaxis in, 280, 283, 288, 289
  phylogeny inferred from pigments, 335–336
Dinoxanthin, in chrysophytes, 331
Diplodinium, motility, 166, 188
2,2'-Dipyridyl, effect on trichomonads, 404–406

Distigma, metaboly, 114
Dithiobiuret derivatives
  action on *Tryptosomia congolense,* 506
    Trypanosoma vivax, 506
DNA, *see also* Nucleic acids
  in akinetroplasty, 487, 488
  in *Chlamydomonas* gametes, 298
  in chloroplasts, 312–316
  composition in ciliates, 229
  formation, inhibition by quinapyramine
    in *Crithidia oncopelti,* 515–517
  in kinetosomes, 153–155
  synthesis in ciliates, 244–249
  in trichomonads, 416–417
DPN-isocitric acid dehydrogenase, in *Dictyostelium,* 364–366
DPN-malic dehydrogenase, in *Dictyostelium,* 364
Drosophila, eye pigments, 3
Drosopterin, *Crithidia*-factor activity, 472
Dunaliella
  carotenoids, 328, 329
  chlorophylls, 320
  phototaxis, 282

Echinenone
  in *Euglena* eyespots, 288, 329, 330
  in *Polytoma,* 336
Ecology
  and phototaxis, 293–294
  and protozoological biochemistry, 5, 6
EDTA
  aldolase, inhibition in *Trichomonas,* 406
  dehiscence of cilia by, 148
  inhibitor of aggregation in *Dictyostelium,* 347
  prevention of aggregation in acrasiae, 77
Eimeria, swimming by sporozoites, 116
Elaidic acid, in trichomonad nutrition, 427
Electric current, effect on ciliary beat, 106–108
Electron-spin resonance, in *Chlamydomonas,* 311–312
Elliptio, ciliary beat in gill epithelium, 161–162
Endoplasmic reticulum, 67
Energid, definition, 166
Enheptin, in antitrichomonad therapy, 449
Enolase, in trichomonads, 408

Entodinium
  carbohydrases, 227
  nitrogen excretion, 229
  uptake fatty acids, 232
  uptake starch, 227
Entosiphon, flagellar movement, 91, 95, 96
Enzymes, *see also* under specific enzymes
  in action of trypanocides, 510–517
  in *Dictyostelium* differentiation, 363–379
  in food vacuoles, 217–219
  hexose monophosphate shunt in *Dictyostelium,* 373–377
  in kinetosomes, 154
Ephelota, morphology of tentacles, 116
Epidinium
  uptake amino acids and proteins, 203
  uptake starch, 227
Epistylis
  filamentous reticulum in, 147
Epistylis
  kinetosome in, 138, 147
  in ciliate nutrition, 213
Ergosterol
  in *Euglena,* 337
  in *Polytoma,* 337
  in trichomonad nutrition, 429
  in trypanosomatids, 489
Escherichia coli
  complexity of, 3, 4
  genetic code in, 300
  and mevalonic acid, as sterol precursor, 344–346
Eserine, effect on *Tetrahymena* motility, 180, 181
Esterases, genetic control in ciliates, 262
Estradiol, acrasin activity, 76
Ethane, chemotactic effect on *Chlamydomonas* gametes, 298
Ethanol
  in ciliate nutrition, 201, 208
  detachment of flagella by, 188
  oxidation by trichomonads, 401
  requirement by *Tetrahymena setifera,* 208
Ethidium, *see also* Homidium
  incorporation into *Tetrahymena* protein, 228
  Tetrahymena, delayed division, 49

Ethylene, chemotactic effect on *Chlamydomonas* gametes, 298
Ethylenediaminetetraacetate, *see* EDTA
Euglena
  chlorophylls, 321–327
  flagellar movement, 91–92, 99–100
  growth oscillations in, 11, 13, 14, 16, 18, *see also E. gracilis*
  kinetosomes, 145
  metaboly, 114
  paraxial swelling, 143
  phobo-phototaxis, 278–279
  photoreceptor, 280
  phototaxis, 278–280, 285–288
  protochlorophyll, 325–327
  RNA in chloroplasts, 327
  root fibrils, 145
  sterols, 337
  topo-phototaxis, 278–279, 286–288
  use in B_{12} assay, 473, 474
  vitamin B_{12} requirement, 206
Euglena gracilis
  bleaching by chemicals, 330–331
  carotenoids, 288–289, 332–34, *see also Euglena*
  ecology, 5
  sex, 5
  synchronization index, 54
Euglena heliorubescens, red pigment in, 330
Euglenarhodone, as eyespot pigment, 288, 329
Euglenoids
  chlorophylls, 321–327, 336
  flagella, function, 155–156, 159, *see also Peranema*
    morphology, 141
  mastigonemes, 141
  morphology, reservoir, 139
  movements, 112, 114–115
  phylogeny, based on pigments, 335–336
Euglypha, movement in, 87
Euplotes
  cilia, models by saponin technique, 152–153, 165, 178–180
  fibrillar system, 104, 166, 168, 170–173, 178–179, *see also* Silver-impregnated structures
  food vacuoles, 217, 218

mating types, 259
nuclear behavior, 245–248
nucleosides, penetration of, 204, 218
Europhthalmus, as host of trypanosomatids, 464, 474, 475, 484
Eyespot
  in *Chlamydomonas*, 306, 307
  pigments in *Euglena*, 329, 330
  and phototaxis, 279–281, 286

Fast green
  binding by *Tetrahymena*, 27
Fats, in *Tetrahymena*, conversion to glycogen, 37
Fatty acid(s)
  in *Dictyostelium* differentiation, 360–362
  and nutrition of ciliates, 208–211, 213–215
  requirements in trichomonads, 419, 423–430
    in *Trypanosoma cruzi*, 477–479
  synthesis in ciliates, 230–232
Fe^{++}, effect on *Trichomonas* aldolase, 406
Feeding
  in ciliates, 216–219
Feulgen reaction
  in trypanosome kinetoplasts, 460, 486
Feulgen staining
  in ciliates, 244–245, 252
Fibrillar systems, *see also* Root fibrils
  in ciliates, 165–171, 190–192
  in *Euplotes*, 170
  in *Opalina*, 170
  in *Stentor*, 170
Flagella
  chemical composition, 147, 150–155
  emergence, 139
  growth and regeneration, 188–190
  isolation of, 147–148
  lipid in, 148
  models, 151–153, 159, 191
  morphology, 89, 132–141, 143–144, 149, 190–192
    in algae, 140
    in brown algae, scales, 141
    in corals, 144
    in flatworms, 144
    of root fibrils, 143–145, 189–190

movement, 63–65, 90–99, 118–119, 131–133, 155–185
nucleotide phosphatase activity in, 148
protein in, 147
in trypanosomatids, 460–463
Flagellates
  chlorophylls, 320–327
  chloroplast pigments, 319–339
  growth oscillations in, 10–18
  locomotion, 63, 64
  marine, review, 1
  photosynthesis in, 1, 5, 6
Flagyl, in treatment *Trypanosoma cruzi* infections, 500–501
Flamella, diurnal variations in reproductive rate, 18
Flatworms
  morphology of cilia, 144
Flavin protein terminal oxidase, in trichomonads, 409
Fluorescent antibodies, to trichomonads, 447–448
Fluoride
  inhibition phosphatase in *Tetrahymena,* 45
  inhibition of phototaxis, 285
  of trichomonads, 403–407
Fluoroacetate
  inhibition phosphatase in *Tetrahymena,* 45
5-Fluoro-2'-deoxyuridine, effect on DNA synthesis in *Tetrahymena,* 28, 29, 51
p-Fluorophenylalanine, 26, 52
  effect on *Tetrahymena* growth oscillations, 49, 50, 53
5-Fluorouracil, 51
  inhibition uracil uptake in *T. cruzi,* 490
Folic acid
  in ciliate metabolism, 201, 205–207
  in malaria infections, 535, 536
  requirement in trichomonads, 424
  in trypanosomatids, 465, 470–475
  as target antimalarial drugs, 536–542
Folinic acid, *see also* Folic acid
  in *Crithidia* nutrition, 472
  food vacuoles, in ciliates, 217–219
Foraminifera, locomotion, 63, 84–86, 88, 118
Formalin, effect on cilia models, 153

Formate
  and H_2 production in trichomonads, 395, 396
  and O_2 uptake in trichomonads, 400
  in purine synthesis, 229
Formic dehydrogenase, in trichomonads, 410
Formic hydrogenlyase, in trichomonads, 410
Fucosterol, in nutrition of ciliates, 212, 213, 215
Fucoxanthin
  in Chrysophyta, 331
  as phyletic marker, 336
Fucus, flagellar movements, 98
Fumarase
  in *Tetrahymena,* after X-irradiation, 44
  in trichomonads, 409
Fumarate, effect on O_2 uptake by trichomonads, 401, 406
Furacin, effect on trypanosome enzymes, 511–513
Furaltadone, in *Trypanosoma cruzi* infections, 500

Gamma rays, effect on mycetozoan locomotion, 83
Genetic code, in *Chlamydomonas,* 300–302, 315, 316
Geotropism, in *Paramecium,* 293
Giardia, fibrillar system or "neuromotor apparatus," 166
Gibbs-Donnan ratio, 108–110, 113
Glaucoma chattoni
  effect of cooling, 21
  fatty acids in, 230
  nutrition, 202–206, 208–210
Gloeschrysis, carotenoids, 331
Gluconic acid, inhibition O_2 uptake by trichomonads, 406
Glucose, *see also* Carbohydrates, Glycolysis
  in *Dictyostelium* differentiation, 347, 351–353, 358–361, 372–377
  effect on malarial infections, 533
  incorporation in *Trichomonas,* 385
  in nutrition of ciliates, 215, 216
  oxidation by trichomonads, 397, 398, 400, 402
    by trypanosomes, 511, 515

utilization, in *Plasmodium berghei*, inhibition by quinacrine, 529
by *Tetrahymena*, 38
by trypanosomes, 511, 515
Glucose dehydrogenase
in trichomonads, 408
Glucose-6-phosphate
in *Dictyostelium*, 377, 379
Glucose-6-phosphate dehydrogenase
deficiency and hemolysis induced by nitrofurazone, 499
by primaquine and other 8-aminoquinolines, 553–555
in *Dictyostelium*, 364–366
in trichomonads, 407, 408
β-Glucuronidase, in trichomonads, 414
Glutamate
and gas production in trichomonads, 395, 415
oxidation by trichomonads, 401
by trypanosomes, 512
Glutamic acid
in *Dictyostelium*, 369–372
requirement in trypanosomatida, 464, 466–468, 476
Glutamic acid dehydrogenase
in *Dictyostelium*, 364, 366, 368–372, 379
Glutamine, utilization by *Tetrahymena*, 39
Glutathione, in drug-induced hemolysis, 553–555
Glyceraldehyde
effect on *Dictyostelium*, 377
and trichomonads, 404, 405
Glyceraldehyde phosphate dehydrogenase
in *Dictyostelium*, 364, 366
Glycerides, in ciliate nutrition, 210
Glycerol
in freezing trichomonads, 437–439
in *Tetrahymena*, conversion to glycogen, 38
Glycerol dehydrogenase
in trichomonads, 408
Glycerophosphate
in ciliate nutrition, 210
in trichomonad nutrition, 424, 427
α-Glycerophosphate dehydrogenase, in trichomonads, 408

L-α-Glycerophosphate dehydrogenase, in *Trypanosoma rhodesiense*, 510–511
L-α-Glycerophosphate-NADH (DPNH)-oxidase, in relation to nitrofurazone sensitivity in trypanosomes, 499
Glyceryl ethers, and unconjugated steridines, 473
Glycinamide ribotide, block in purine synthesis in ciliates, 229
Glycine
as precursor of porphyrins in *Tetrahymena*, 226
in purine synthesis, 229
uptake by *Tetrahymena*, 38
Glycogen
metabolism in *Tetrahymena*, 36–38, 224, 226–227
in trichomonads, 389–391, 394, 398–400, 411, 415–416
Glycolysis
in ciliates, 223–224
in *Dictyostelium*, 373–377
in *Plasmodium berghei*, 528–530
role in drug sensitivity, 553–555
in trichomonads, 385–397, 402–413
in trypanosomes, 510–511, 515
Glyconeogenesis
in *Tetrahymena*, 37–39, 223, 226
Glyoxylic acid cycle, in *Tetrahymena*, 37–39, 224–225, 233
Golgi apparatus, definition, 143
Gonyaulax (or *Goniaulax*)
growth oscillations in, 13, 14
phototaxis, 289
synchronization index, 54
Gregarines, movements, 112, 114, 115
Guanine, incorporation in trypanosomes, 513
Guanosine
contamination with *Crithidia* factor, 465
dephosphorylation by isolated cilia, 151
Gymnodinium
carotenoids, 332
chlorophylls, 322

H₂ production by trichomonads, 388, 390–397, 410–413

H_2O_2
  inhibition of trichomonads, 403–405
  and mutagenesis in ciliates, 266
H^3, as mutagen in ciliates, 266
Haematococcus, carotenoids, 328, 329
Haematoloechus, axonemes in spermato-
    zoon, 140–141
Halteria, movement, 112
Haptonema, in chrysomonads, 171
Haptophrya, contractile vacuole, 112
Hartmannella, locomotion, 72, 73
Heat shock, *see* Temperature changes
Heliozoa
  locomotor mechanisms, 63, 84, 86, 87,
    112
  taxonomic significance of movement, 88
Hematin
  in culture media for trypanosomatids,
    466–468, 478–480
  in pathogenesis trypanosomiasis, 486
  relation to malarial pigment, 527
Hemiselmis
  biliproteins, 334
  carotenoids, 332
  chlorophylls, 321
Hemoflagellates, *see* Trypanosomatids
Hemoglobin
  in ciliates, 226
  digestion by plasmodia, 530–531
Hemolysis
  drug-induced, 553–555
  acute
    in primaquine therapy, 553
    relation to glucose-6-phosphate de-
      hydrogenase, 499
Herpetomonas, bionomics, 461–463, 465
Herpetomonas culicidarum, bionomics, 476
Herpetomonas muscidarum, lipids, 489
Heterokonts, phyletic position from pig-
    ments, 335, 336
Heteronema, metaboly, 114
Hexokinase
  in trichomonads, 407, 408
  in trypanosomes, 511
Hexose monophosphate shunt
  in ciliates, 223
  in *Dictyostelium,* 373–378
  in trichomonads, 407, 408, 411–412
Hill reaction, in *Chlamydomonas*, 311–312

Histidine, *see also* Amino acids
  stimulation of morphogenesis in *Dictyo-
    stelium,* 347
  uptake by *Tetrahymena*, 27
Histones, in *Tetrahymena*, 27
Homidium
  effect on *Crithidia oncopelti*, 515–517
  immunity in animals treated by, 518
  in treatment bovine trypanosomiasis,
    503–504, 507–509
Hyaluronidase, effect of trypanocides, 512
β-Hydroxybutyrate
  and O_2 uptake by trichomonads, 402
  oxidation by *Tetrahymena* homogenates,
    40
  by trypanosomes, 513
Hydroxychloroquine
  fate in body, 552, 553
  protection against *Plasmodium falci-
    parum* and *P. vivax,* 548
Hydroxychloroquine-resistant *Plasmodium
    falciparum,* 547
Hydroxyechinenone, as eyespot pigment,
    288–289, 329
1-(2-Hydroxyethyl)-2-methyl-5-nitroim-
    idazole, in antitrichomonad ther-
    apy, 449
1-β-Hydroxyethyl-2-methyl-5-nitroimid-
    azole, inhibition of *T. cruzi*, 490
1,β-Hydroxyethyl-2-methyl-5-nitroinda-
    zole, *see* Flagyl
β-Hydroxyisobutyric acid, oxidation by
    Tetrahymena, 225
Hydroxylamine, inhibition of trichomon-
    ads, 404–406
β-Hydroxy-β-methyl glutaryl CoA, de-
    acylation by *Tetrahymena* extracts,
    225
5-Hydroxymethyluracil, in ciliate nutri-
    tion, 204, 207
Hydroxyproline, absence from *Tetra-
    hymena* cilia, 150
β-Hydroxypropionic acid, oxidation by
    Tetrahymena, 225
8-Hydroxyquinoline, inhibition of tri-
    chomonad metabolism, 403–405,
    407
Hymenomonas
  carotenoids, 331
  chlorophylls, 321

Hypermastigotes, kinetids, 134, 139
Hypocholesteremic agents, effect on flagellates, 223, *see also* Triparanol
Hypotrichomonas acosta, 386–387, 425, 426, 428, 433
Hypoxanthine, excretion by *Paramecium*, 230

Immobilization antigens
  in ciliates, 148, 151, 256–258, 261–263, 268
  in *Paramecium*, 148
  in *Tetrahymena*, 151
Inositides
  as lipid source for *T. cruzi* and *T. mega*, 479, 480
  in trypanosomatids, 488
Invert soaps, trichocyst extrusion by, 114
Iodoacetamide, inhibition of trichomonads, 404–406
Iodoacetate
  inhibition of phototaxis, 285
  of trichomonads, 403–406
  inhibitor ionic exchange in codoacetate, 216
Isochrysis
  carotenoids, 331
  chlorophylls, 321
Isocitrate dehydrogenase, in trichomonads, 409
Isocitrate lyase, in *Tetrahymena*, 38, 39, 224
Isodrosopterin, *Crithidia*-factor activity, 472
Isometamidium, in treatment of bovine trypanosomiasis, 504–505, 507–509
Isotricha
  carbohydrate fermentation, 224
  ciliary beat, 165
  uptake of fatty acids, 232
Isotrichs, carbohydrases, 227

Janus green, staining of trypanosomes, 488
Juvenile hormone, in *Tetrahymena*, 231

K+
  effect, on cilia models, 153
    on movements, 64, 108–110, 116, 162, 175–176, 281–282, 285

exchangeable, in flagella, 162
  uptake by *Tetrahymena*, 216
Kappa
  effect of antibiotics on, 222, 223
  genetics, 263
Karyomastigont, definition, 166
KCl, effect on myonemes, 113
α-Ketoglutarate, CO_2 precursor in *Dictyostelium*, 369–370
α-Ketoglutaric acid, effect on O_2 uptake in trichomonads, 401, 406
α-Ketoglutaric dehydrogenase, in trichomonads, 409
Kinetid(s), *see also* Flagella *and* Cilia
  definition, 134, 166
  morphology, 134–149, 166
  in *Naegleria*, 189–190
  of *Paramecium*, 135–136, 142–143, 145–147
  of *Trichnympha*, 138, 147
  definition, 102, 134
  effect of parasitism on number, 222
  and kinetodesmos, 167
  and kinetosomes and trichocysts in *Paramecium*, 167
  in *Opalina*, 170
Kinetin, effect on synchrony in *Tetrahymena*, 23
Kinetodesmal fibrils
  in ciliates, 143, 168–171, 190
  definition, 102, 134, 167
  in *Euplotes*, 170
  in *Paramecium*, 135–138, 142–147, 167, 169, 190
Kinetome, definition, 134
Kinetoplast, *see also* Kinetosomes
  in trypanosomatids, 460–463, 486–488, 514
Kinetosomes
  in *Bodo*, 137, 138
  in ciliary function, 102, 134
  in ciliate morphogenesis, 25, 26
  composition, 153–155, 252
    RNA and DNA in ciliate kinetosomes, 153–155, 252
  isolation of, 154–155
  in molluscs, 137, 138, 145, 186
  morphological relations, in *Euplotes*, 170
    in *Stentor*, 170–171

morphology, general, 134, 190–191
in ciliated epithelium, 134, 144, 186
in ciliates, 134–139, 143–147
relation to pellicular morphology, 169–171
in *Epistylis*, 138
in hypermastigotes, 137
in *Naegleria*, 137, 144
in *Paramecium*, 135, 137, 138, 167
phylogenetic significance, 166
replication, 166, 186–187, 252–253
Kl, anesthesia of myonemes, 113
Krebs cycle, *see* Tricarboxylic acid cycle

Labyrinthula, sterol requirement, 211
Lactate
as CO_2 fixation product in trichomonads, 399, 411
in nutrition of ciliates, 201, 225
oxidation in trichomonad cultures, 400, 402
Lactate dehydrogenase, effect of trypanocides, 512
Lactic acid, in anaerobic *Trichomonas* cultures, 388–397, 399, 403
Lactic acid dehydrogenase, in *Dictyostelium*, 364, 366
Lactic dehydrogenase, in trichomonads, 406, 407, 409
Lactobacillus casei, effect of antifolics, 536–538
Lactobacillus heterohiochi, stimulation by ethanol, 208
Lactobacillus leichmannii, vitamin B_{12} requirement, 206
Lambda, effect of antibiotics on, 222, 223
Lanosterol, in nutrition, ciliates, 211, 212
Lauric acid
in nutrition *T. cruzi*, 480
as trichomonadicide, 427
Lecithin, in nutrition trypanosomatids, 475, 479, 480
Leishmania, taxonomy, 462
Leishmania donovani
lipids, 488, 489
nutrition, 480
Leishmania tarentolae
akinetoplasty, 487
nutrition, 464, 465, 468, 484

Leishmania tropica
in avian eggs, 484
nutrition, 478, 479, 484, 489
Leishmanicides, 8-aminoquinolines, 500
Leptomonas, bionomics, 461, 463
Leucine
precursor iso acids in *Tetrahymena*, 231
uptake in *Crithidia oncopelti*, 516
Leucovorin, *see* Folinic acid
α-Levulinic acid dehydrase, in *Tetrahymena*, 226
Linoleic acid
in nutrition, ciliates, 208–210, 215
T. cruzi, 479, 480
trichomonads, 427
α-Linolenic acid, in nutrition ciliates, 209
γ-Linolenic acid, metabolism in ciliates, 230–233
Lipids
in cilia of *Tetrahymena*, 150
in flagella of *Polytoma*, 147
requirements in trypanosomatids, 475
synthesis, inhibitors, 51, 52
in trypanosomatids, 488–489
Lipoic acid, *see* Thioctic acid
Lithium salts, prevention reactivation cilia models, 153
Lophenol, in nutrition ciliates, 211–212
Ludloff phenomenon, 106
Luminescence, 14
Lutein
in chlorophytes, 327, 328
in *Cryptomonas*, 332
in eyespots, 330
Lysosomes, relation to food vacuoles, 217

M & B 2242, in treatment trypanosomiasis, 502
Macronuclei
DNA synthesis, 28–32, 42, 43, 244–249
duplication, 245–54, 258, 260, 264
RNA transfer from, 29, 30
uptake of thymidine, 218
Magnesium, *see* Mg
Malaria, *see also Plasmodium*
dietary factors, 531–533
drug resistance in, 542–547
drug sensitivity of sexual stages, 547
infections, combined therapy, 539, 554–558

folic and folinic acid in, 535–536
gametocyte induction, 526–528
Malarial parasite
  DNA type, 528
  life cycle, 525–528
Malarial pigment, 527
Malate, oxidation by trichomonads, 401, 402
Malate synthase, in *Tetrahymena,* 224
Malate synthetase, in *Tetrahymena,* 38, 39
Malic acid, production by trichomonads, 388
Malic dehydrogenase, in trichomonads, 409, 411
Malic enzyme, in trichomonads, 409, 411
Malonate, inhibition of trichomonads, 403–406
Maltase, in trichomonads, 408
Maltose, utilization by trichomonads, 388, 390–394, 396, 399–400, 402
Maltotriose, synthesis by *Tetrahymena,* 227
Manganese ions, reversal ciliary beat, 107, 108
Marine flagellates, 1
Mastigamveba, flagellar movements, 91–92, 95–97
Mastigonemes
  in chrysomonads, 141
  in euglenoids, 141
  general morphology, 93, 94, 100, 141
Mastigont, *see* Kinetids
Mastigophora, see Flagellates
Mate-killer symbiont, in *P. aurelia,* 264–265
Mating type substances, in cilia, 148
Mel W, *see* Trimelarsen
Melaminyl arsenicals, in treatment *trypanosoma gambiense,*
Melarsen, activity against tryparsamide-resistant *Trypanosoma gambiense,* 497–498
Melarsen-resistance, in *Trypanosoma rhodesiense,* effect of nitrofurazone, 499
Melarsoprol
  in treatment, bovine trypanosomiasis, 502, 506, 508
    Trypanosoma gambiense infections, 497

Menadione, *see* Vitamin K
Mepacrine, *see* Quinacrine
p-Mercuribenzoate, inhibition of trichomonads, 406
Metachloridine, resistance to in experimental malaria, 542–543
Metachrony, ciliary, 163–165, 172–185
Methane, production by trichomonads, 388
Methanol, as growth factor for *Tetrahymena setifera,* 208
Methemoglobin, in hemolytic reactions, 554–555
Methionine
  dietary, effect on *Plasmodium* infections, 532, 533
  stimulation *Euglena* and *Astasia* in dark, 16
  in trypanosomatid nutrition, 474–475
  uptake by *Plasmodium knowlesi,* 530
Methosterol, in nutrition ciliates, 211
Methylcellulose, effect on pattern swimming, 111
4α-Methyl-Δ^8-cholestenol, in nutrition of ciliates, 212
24-Methylene cholesterol, in nutrition of ciliates, 212
6-Methylpurine
  growth inhibitor of *Tetrahymena,* 51, 213
O-Methylthreonine, bleaching of *Euglena,* 330–331
Metronidazole, in antitrichomonad therapy, 449
Mevalonic acid
  in carotenoid biosynthesis, 333
  inactivity in nutrition of ciliates, 211
  as stigmastenol precursor in *E. coli,* 344–346
  in trichomonad nutrition, 430
Mg^{++}
  in contractility, 64, 108–110, 175, 178
  effect on cilia models, 153
  role in movement, 281–282, 285
  suctorian, 116
Microbiological assays, 3, 6, 202–203, 222–223
Micromonas, flagellar scales, 141
Micronuclei, after UV, 43
  function, 245, 247–248, 255, 258

Mitochondria
  in *Chlamydomonas*, 308, 309
  glyoxylate cycle enzymes in *Tetrahymena*, 38
  and kinetosomes, 488
  oxidative phosphorylation in *Tetrahymena*, 39, 40
  in temperature-inhibited *Tetrahymena*, 221
  in trypanosomes, 514–515
Mitotic apparatus, 63, 187
Molluscs, cilia in, 135, 138, 139, 141, 145, 148, 161, 162, 181, 182
Monamine oxidase, in trypanosomes, effect of trypanocides, 512
Monas, flagellar movements, 97, 156
Monocercomonas
  flagellar movement, 96
  nutrition, 385, 387, 417, 426, 428, 429
Morphine, 113
Motorium
  definitions, 104, 165–166
  in *Euplotes*, 168
  in *Paramecium*, 167, 169
Mu, 22, 263
Mucopolysaccharides
  degradation by trichomonads, 413–414
  in *Dictyostelium* differentiation, 359–361
Mycetozoa, locomotion, 77–78, 81–83, 88, 89, 118
Myonemes
  in ciliates, 63, 112, 113, 160, 171
  in gregarines, 115
  in *Stentor*, 171
Myosin, action in muscle, 160
Myristic acid
  in ciliates, 230
  in nutrition *Trypanosoma cruzi*, 480
Myxomycetes, *see Physarum*
Myxomyosin, 64, 80

Na+
  effect on cilia models, 153
  in locomotion, 65, 110
  uptake by *Tetrahymena*, 216
NAD, antagonism of thalidomide, 223
NAD oxidase, in trichomonads, 409
NADH, NADPH, *see* Pyridine nucleotides

NADH cytochrome c reductase, in *Tetrahymena*, 37
NADH nucleotide cytochrome c reductase, in *Tetrahymena*, 37, 226
NADH oxidase
  in *Tetrahymena*, 37, 225
  in trichomonads, 409
Naegleria, kinetosome, 137, 187, 189, 190
  rhizoplast, 144, 189–190
  root fibrils, 145
Na I, anesthesia of myonemes, 113
Na lauryl sulfate, as trichomonadicide, 427
Nannochloris, carotenoids, 328, 329
  chlorophylls, 320, 321
Naphthalenes, substituted as antimalarials, 551, *see also* Compound 377C54
Nassula, food vacuoles, 218
Navicula, ε-carotene in, 332
Neospongesterol, in nutrition of ciliates, 213
Neoxanthin
  in chlorophytes, 327, 328
  in *Euglena*, 329
Neuromotor apparatus, definitions, 165–166
Neurospora, nonchromosomal factors, 303
Neutral red, 68
Nickel salts, effect on cilia, 153, 188
Nicotinamide
  genetic marker in *Chlamydomonas*, 300
  requirement in *Trichomonas*, 424
Nicotine, 113
Nicotinic acid
  required by ciliates, 205
  as thalidomide antagonist, 223
Nitella, cyclosis, 64, 68, 112
Nitrate, genetic marker in *Chlamydomonas*, 301
Nitro compounds, in chemotherapy trichomonad infections, 448–449
Nitrofurans
  effect on trypanosome enzymes, 511–513
  in treatment African trypanosomiasis, 498–499
  in *Trypanosoma cruzi* infections, 500
Nitrofurazone
  action on trypanosome infections, 498–499
  interference with thiamine, 499

Novocain, reversal ciliary beat, 107
Nuclei, size in *Tetrahymena*, 24
Nucleic acid(s)
  Astasia, 17
  content of chloroplasts, 312–316
  function, in trypanosomes, effect of try-panocides, 513
  synthesis, *Tetrahymena*, inhibition by base analogs, 51, 52
  Tetrahymena, 28–32
    after UV irradiation, 42
Nucleoprotein metabolism, in trypanosomes, 513, 515–517
5-Nucleotidase, in *Dictyostelium*, 363
Nucleotide phosphatase, in flagella, 148
Nucleotides, in *Tetrahymena*, 33, 51, *see also* Purines and Pyrimidines
  cilia, 150
  synthesis, in ciliates, 228
Nystatin, in isolation of trichomonads, 432
Nyctotherus, ciliary beat, 104, 105

O_2, consumption, *Tetrahymena*, 24, 25, 45
  in trypanosomatids, 477
  and phototaxis, 282
  tension and growth oscillation in ciliates, 23–26, 47–49, 52
  and trichomonads, 397–406, 412
Ochromonas, chlorophyll *a*, 321
Ochromonas danica
  carotenoids, 331–332
  flagella, movement, 93
    regeneration, 188–189
  native chlorophyll in, 322–323
  as research tool, 1, 6
Ochromonas malhamensis
  and *Crithidia*-produced vitamin B_{12}, 473–474
  feeble photosynthesis of, 323
  flagellar movement, 93
  source of *Crithidia* factor, 465
Oleic acid, *see also* Fatty acids
  antagonism of triparanol, 52
  metabolism in ciliates, 230–232
  in nutrition, of ciliates, 209, 210
    of *Trypanosoma cruzi*, 477–480
    of trichomonads, 423, 425, 427, 429, 449

Opalina
  ciliary beat, 100, 103–104, 157, 165, 169–170, 173–174, 176, 170–182, 184–185, 191
  kinetosomes, 170
  morphology, cell surface, 169–170
Opalinids, flagellar morphology, 132
Ophryoglena, food vacuoles, 218
Ophryoscolecids, fermentation of starch, 224
Ophryoscolex
  uptake, amino acids and proteins, 203
  starch, 227
Oral membranelle, in *Stentor*, 171
Orotic acid, incorporation into *Trypanosoma cruzi*, 490
Osmium fixation, 133
Oxalate, reversal of ciliary beat, 107, 108
Oxidases, in trypanosomes, 510
Oxidative phosphorylation
  and phototaxis, 284, 285
  in *Tetrahymena*, 39, 40, 45, 48
  in trypanosomes, 510–511
Oxophenarsine
  effect on trypanosome enzymes, 511–513
  resistance in trypanosomes, 519
Oxygen consumption, *Astasia*, 17

Palmitic acid
  in ciliate nutrition, 209, 210
  in nutrition, of trichomonads, 423, 424, 449
    of *Trypanosoma cruzi*, 479
  triparanol antagonist, 52
Palmitoleic acid
  metabolism in ciliates, 230
  in nutrition of *Trypanosoma cruzi*, 480
Pamaquin, detoxication in body, 553
Panose, synthesis by *Tetrahymena*, 227
Pantothenic acid
  in nutrition of ciliates, 205, 206, 223
  requirement in trichomonads, 424
  as tolbutamide antagonist, 223
Parabasal body
  definition, 143, *see also* Golgi apparatus
  relation to rhizoplast, 144
Parabasal fibrils, 166
Paramecium
  amino acid requirements, 202

cell surface, morphology, 167–169, *see also* Silver-impregnated structures
cilia, beat, 100–108, 157–159, 165, 174–177, 180–185, 191–192
　glycerinated and saponin models of, 152–153, 191
　isolation of, 148
　mating-type substances in, 148
　morphology, 134–147
　　axosomes in, 139–141, 146–147
　　root fibrils, 144, 190
　　regeneration, 188, 190
circadian rhythms, 14
cortex, morphology, 167–169
fatty acid requirements, 208–211
fibrillar systems, 166–169, 171
food vacuoles, 217–219
geotropisin, 293
kinetids in, 134–141
mating types, 259–261
Na+ pump, 216
nutrition, 202–206, 208–213, 217–220
phasing of, 20
phototaxis, 292–293
purine and pyrimidine requirements, 203–204
in screening antibiotics, 222, 223
sterol requirements, 211–213
trichocysts, morphology, 167, 168, *see also* Trichocysts
Paramecium aurelia
　ATPase, 64
　caryonidal inheritance, 260–262
　clonal life history, 253–256
　esterases, genic control, 262
　immobilization antigens, 148, 256–258
　nuclear behavior, 245–248, 258–260
　parasite-(symbiont)-containing strains, 220, 222, 223, 263–265, 268–269
　senescence, 253–256
　synchronization index, 54
Paramecium bursaria
　aging in, 255
　chlorellae, 220, 264
　mating type substances, 148, 253–254, 259
Paramecium caudatum
　nuclear behavior, 245–248
Parapyruvate, inhibition pyruvate oxidation in *Trichomonas*, 406

Pararosaniline
　effect on trypanosome enzymes, 511–513
　induction of akinetoplasty, 487
　in trichomonad infections, 448
Pararosaniline resistance
　genetic marker, 486
Parathion, inhibition of pattern swimming, 111
Paratrichomonas marmotae, see Trichomitis marmotae
Paraxial rods, in flagellates, 143
Paraxial swelling, in *Euglena*, 143
Pasteur effect
　in *Tetrahymena*, 223, 224
　in trypanosomes, effect of trypanocides, 511
Pattern swimming, 110, 111
Pavlova
　carotenoids, 331
　chlorophylls, 321
Pelomyxa, diurnal variation in reproductive rate, 18
Pentamidine
　effect on trypanosome enzymes, 511
　in treatment, African trypanosomiasis, 497
　　bovine trypanosomiasis, 506
Pentaquine
　comparison with compound WIN 5037 as antimalarial, 550
　fate in body, 553
Pentatrichomonas hominis, 396, 408–410, 431, 433
Pentose phosphate cycle, *see* Hexose monophosphate shunt
Pentylthiarsaphenylmelamine, *see* Trimelarsen
Peptides, free in *Tetrahymena*, 225
Peranema
　flagellar movements, 91, 95–97, 115, 156, 159
　linoleate requirement, 6
　metaboly, 114
　paraxial rods, 143, 171
Peridinin, in dinoflagellates, 332
Peridinium, carotenoids, 332
　chlorophylls, 322
　growth oscillations, 10

Peritrichs
  cilia, morphology, 147
  elastic stalks in, 141–143
Peroxidase, in trichomonads, 410
Petalomonas, flagellar movement, 91, 95–96
pH
  and phototaxis, 282, 283, 290, 294
  and reproduction in *Tetrahymena*, 20
Phaeocystis, carotenoids, 331
Phaeophyceae, phylogeny based on pigments, 335
Phaeophytin-like pigment, in *Euglena*, 325, 326
Phaester
  carotenoids, 331
  chlorophylls, 321
Phagocytosis, in ciliates, 217–219
Phenanthraquinone, stimulation of pattern swimming, 111
Phenanthridinium compounds, in treatment bovine trypanosomiasis, 503–509, 517
o-Phenanthroline, inhibition of phototaxis, 285
Phenothiazine tranquilizers, effect on *Tetrahymena*, 223
Phenylalanine
  hydroxylation, role of pteridines, 207
  oxidation by *Tetrahymena*, 225
  in *Tetrahymena*, utilization for glycogen synthesis, 38
  and unconjugated pteridines, 473, 475
Phenylmercuric acetate, effect on trichomonads, 404
Phenylurethane, *Tetrahymena*, effect on division, 47, 48
Phobo-phototaxis, 278, 290–291
Phosphagen, in *Tetrahymena*, 224
Phosphate, in *Dictyostelium*, 361, 364, 367–368, 379
Phosphatidylethanolamine
  in *Tetrahymena* cilia, 150
  in trypanosomatids, 488, 489
Phosphoenolpyruvic and carboxykinase, in *Tetrahymena*, 224
Phosphofructokinase
  inhibition by antimonials, 510, 511
  possible inhibition by quinacrine, 529, 530
  in trichomonads, 408

Phosphoglucoisomerase, in trichomonads, 408
Phosphoglucomutase, in trichomonads, 408
6-Phosphogluconic dehydrogenase, in *Dictyostelium*, 364
Phosphoglyceric acid, precursor of pyruvate in trichomonads, 403
Phosphoglycerolenolase, in trichomonads, 408
Phosphoglyceromutase, in trichomonads, 408
Phospholipids
  in ciliates, composition, 231
  in Dictyostelium, 361–362
  metabolism in trypanosomes, 513
  in nutrition of ciliates, 210, 213, 214, 221, 222
  in trichomonads, 417
  in trypanosomatids, 488–489
β-Phosphonopropionate, inhibition of trichomonads, 404–406
Phosphoriboisomerase, in trichomonads, 407, 408
Phosphorus
  content of *Tetrahymena*, 34–36
  in *Tetrahymena* cilia, 150
Phosphorus-32, as mutagen in ciliates, 266
Photophosphorylation, and phototaxis, 285
Photoreactivation
  in irradiated ciliates, 266
  in *Tetrahymena*, 41
Photoreceptor
  in *Ceratium*, 280
  in *Euglena*, 280
  in *Platymonas*, 289, 290
Photosynthesis, 1, 5, 14
  and phototaxis, 294
Photosynthetic mutants, in *Chlamydomonas*, 311–312, 315
Phototaxis, 14
  action spectra, 277–279, 285–292, 294
  in *Amoeba*, 291–292
  cycles, 285
  definition, 277
  in purple bacteria, 279
  receptor in, 294
Phycocyanin, in cryptomonads and other algae, 334

Phycoerythrin, in cryptomonads and other
    algae, 334–336
Physarum
    acetylcholinesterase, 162
    contractility, 63, 64
    locomotion, 78–80, 83
Physostigmine, 113
Phytoene, in carotenoid biosynthesis,
    333
Phytoflagellates, *see also Astasia, Chlamy-
    domonas, Euglena, Polytoma,* etc.
    flagella in, 132–133, 141
    phylogeny inferred from pigments, 335–
    336
Phytofluene, in *Euglena,* 330, 331
Phytol, in chlorophyll synthesis, 325
Phytomonads, colonial, flagellar move-
    ments, 96
Phytomonas, bionomics, 463
Phytomonas elmassiani, failure to infect
    duck eggs, 484
Phytoplankton, marine, 1
Plastoquinone, 312
Pi, effect of antibiotics, 222, 223
Pinocytosis, in ciliates, 217–219
Plasmodia
    metabolism, 528–530
    pinocytosis and phagocytosis, 530
Plasmodium, pathogenesis, 530–531
    effect of hypoxia, 535
    of milk diet, 531–533
    in erythrocytes, 530, 531
    glycolysis, 528–530
    infections
        blood picture, 536
        chemotherapy by antifolics and sul-
            fonamides, 538, 539, 548
        in diabetic rats, 535
        effect of compound 377C14, 551
        effect, of diet on, 532–534
            of dihydrotriazines, 548
        of pyrimethamine, 548
            of vitamin A deficiency, 534
        host tissue pathology, 535–536
        liver function, 535
    proteinases, 530
    purine and pyrimidine content, 528
    as research tool, 528–530
    tricarboxylic acid cycle, 529
    uptake P^{32}, 528

Plasmodium cathemerium
    infections
        effect of compound 377C54, 551
        of hypoxia, 535
Plasmodium cynomolgi
    effect of WIN 5037, 550
    infections, effect of diet, 532
Plasmodium falciparum
    effect of diaminophenylsulfone, 550
    effect of diet, 532
    effect of propoquine, 549
    infections, combined therapy in, 557
        drug resistance in, 544–547
        effect of chloroquine on gametocytes,
            547
        effect of compound 377C54, 551
        effect of compound WIN 5037, 550
        effect of proguanil metabolites, 551
    pyrimethamine as gametocide, 547
Plasmodium gallinaceum
    cell-free extracts, non-digestion of
        hemoglobin, 530
    induction gametocytes by drugs, 527
    infections, chemotherapy by antifolics
        and sulfonamides, 538–541, 551
    chemotherapy by proguanil and com-
        pound, 10, 538, 732
    drug resistance, 542–544, 546
    effect of compound 377C34, 551
    effect of milk diet, 531
    effect of proguanil metabolites, 551
    effect of riboflavin deficiency, 534
    effect of sulfonamides, 538
Plasmodium knowlesi
    in erythrocytes, 530, 531
    infections, effect of compound 377C54,
        551
        effect of diet, 532
        host tissue pathology, 535
    primaquine resistance, 546
    proteinases, 530
    uptake cysteine and methionine, 530
Plasmodium lophurae
    effect of 3-chloro-9-(4-diethylamino-1-
        methylbutylamino) acridine, 10-
        oxide 2HCl, 549–550
    effect of propoquine, 549
    effect of pyrimethamine, 548
    effect of pyruvate on survival, 534,
        535

infections, folic and folinic acid in, 535–536
host pathology, 535, 536
phagocytosis in, 531
Plasmodium malariae
effect of diaminodiphenylsulfone, 550
effect of diet, 532
infections, combined therapy in, 557
effect of proguanil congeners, 551
resistance to pyrimethamine, 543
Plasmodium ovale, effect of compound 377C54, 551
Plasmodium relictum, in red cells, 531
P. vinkei, infections, effect of diet, 533
Plasmodium vivax
infections, combined therapy, 554–556
effect of chloroquine on gametocytes, 547
effect of compound 377C54, 551
effect of compound WIN 5037, 550
effect of diet, 532
effect of proguanil congeners, 551
effect of propoquine, 549
in erythrocyte, 531
life cycle, 526
primaquine resistance, 546
pyrimethamine, as gametocide, 547
and proguanil resistance, 546
Platymonas, phototaxis, 282–284, 289–291, 294
Pneumococcus (Diplococcus), growth oscillations, 10
Podophrya, tentacular activity, 117
Polyoxyethylene ethers, ineffectiveness against Trypanosoma cruzi, 500
Polysphondylium, locomotion, 75
Polytoma
carotenoids, 336–337
flagella, 90
chemical composition of, 150
glycerinated models, 152
isolation of, 147
movements, 96
flagellar ATPase, 64
Polytomaxanthin, in Polytoma, 336
Poriferasterol, in nutrition of ciliates, 213
Porphyrin synthesis, in Tetrahymena, 226
Potassium ion, see K+
Primaquine
in combined therapy, 554–556

comparison with quinocide in human malaria, 550
hemolysis by, 499
in Plasmodium cathemerium infections, 535
in treatment Trypanosoma cruzi infections in mice, 501
Primaquine-resistant
Plasmodium knowlesi and Plasmodiam vivax, 546
Primaquine sensitivity, hemolysis, 553–555
Progesterone
acrasin activity, 76
growth inhibitor of Tetrahymena, 213
Proguanil
fate in body, 551–552
mode of action as an antimalarial, 536–542
in Plasmodium lophurae infections, 548
triazine derivative, antimalarial activity, 551–552
Proguanil resistance, 538–541, 543–546
in Plasmodium falciparum, 544–546
Proline, in trichomonad nutrition, 426
Propionate, oxidation by trichomonads, 401
Propionic acid, oxidation by Tetrahymena, 225
Propoquine, protection against malarial infections, 548–549
Propylthiouracil
effect on protozoa, 223
effect on Trypanosoma cruzi, 490
Prorocentrum, phototaxis, 288, 289
Protein(s)
biological value of, assay with Tetrahymena, 202–203
in cilia of Tetrahymena, 150–151
in flagella of Polytoma, 147
in kinetosomes, 154
plastid, 316
in synchronized Tetrahymena, 27
Proteomyxans, locomotion, 84, 87
Prothidium
induction akinetoplastic Trypanosoma evansi, 488
in treatment bovine trypanosomiasis, 504, 508–509
Protochlorophyll
in Chlamydomonas, 307
in Euglena, 325–327

Protoplasmic streaming, 62, 64, 65
Protoporphyrin, in *Tetrahymena*, 226
Prymnesium
  carotenoids, 331, 332
  chlorophyll *c*, 321
Pseudopedinella
  carotenoids, 331
  chlorophylls, 321
Pteridines, 3
  requirements in trypanosomatids, 464–465, 469
  unconjugated; *see* Biopterin, *also* *Crithidia* factor
Purine(s)
  in nutrition of ciliates, 203–207, 220–221, 228–229, 233
  requirement in trypanosomatids, 464–467, 489–491
Puromycin
  and nucleic and synthesis in *Trypanosoma cruzi*, 489–490
  Tetrahymena, inhibition of, 49
  tool for studying nucleotide and polynucleotide synthesis in *Trypanosoma cruzi*, 501
  in treatment, of African Trypanosomiasis, 496
    of *Trypanosoma cruzi* infections, 501
Pusillum, 96, 97
Pyrenoid, in *Chlamydomonas*, 306–309
Pyridine nucleotides, in *Tetrahymena*, 32
Pyridoxal, *see* Vitamin B$_6$
Pyridoxine, *see* Vitamin B$_6$
Pyridoxine-deficiency, effect on malaria infections, 533
Pyrimethamine
  in combined therapy, 556–558
  fate in body, 552
  gametocide for plasmodia, 547
  mode of action as antimalarial, 537–542
  protection against *Plasmodium berghei*, 548
Pyrimethamine-resistance, 539–547
  in *Plasmodium falciparum*, 544–546
Pyrimethamine-sensitivity, of chloroqiune-resistant *Plasmodium falciparum*, 547
Pyrimidine(s)
  in ciliate nutrition, 203–207, 220–221, 228–229, 233

metabolism in trypanosomatids, 490–491
Pyrophosphate
  inability to replace ATP in cilia model reactivation, 153
  inhibition aldolase in *Trichomonas*, 406
Pyrrophyta, *see* Dinoflagellates
Pyrsonympha, axostyle, 171
Pyruvate
  in ciliate nutrition, 201, 208, 216
  and gas production by trichomonads, 395–397
  oxidation, role of thiamine in therapy with nitrofurans, 499
    by trichomonads, 401, 402
  utilization by *Tetrahymena*, 38
Pyruvate dehydrogenase, in trichomonads, 409, 411
Pyruvate kinase, in trichomonads, 408
Pyruvic acid
  effect on survival *Plasmodium lophurae*, 534, 535
  production by trichomonads, 388, 389, 403, 407

Quinacrine
  comparison with azacrine in *Plasmodium falciparum* infections, 549
  inhibition glucose utilization in *Plasmodium berghei*, 529–530
Quinacrine-sensitivity
  of chloroquine-resistant *Plasmodium falciparum*, 547
Quinaldinium compounds, in treatment bovine trypanosomiasis, 503, 506–509
Quinapyramine
  in design of aminophenanthridium drugs, 504
  drug resistance, in *Trypanosoma congolense*, 507–509
    in *Trypanosoma vivax*, 508
  effect on *Crithidia oncopelti*, 515–517
  effect on enzymes of trypanosomes, 511–513, 515–517
  immunity in animals treated by, 517, 518
  induction RNA granules in *Trypanosoma rhodesiense*, 515
Quinazolones, in human malaria, 550
Quinine, comparison with propoguine, 549

Quinine-sensitivity, of chloroquine-resistant *Plasmodium falciparum*, 547
Quinocide, antimalarial activity, 550

Radiation mutagenesis, in ciliates, 265–267
Radiolaria, locomotion, 84, 86–89, 112
Radioopaque agents, effect on *Tetrahymena*, 223
Respiration
 in *Dictyostelium* differentiation, 350–354, 361
 terminal in *Tetrahymena*, 225–226
 trypanosomes, 510–515
Reticulomyxa, movement in, 87
Reynolds' number, 99, 111
Rhabdomonas, flagellar movement, 91–93, 99
Rhizoplasts
 in *Naegleria*, 144
 in phytoflagellates, 143–145
Rhodomonas
 biliproteins, 334
 chlorophylls, 321, 322
 phylogeny, 132, 335–336
Riboflavin
 and acriflavine-induced akinetoplasty, 487
 deficiency, effect on malaria infections, 534
 required by ciliates, 205
Ribonuclease
 destruction mate-killer symbiont in *Paramecium*, 265
 liberation by ciliates, 205
 penetration into *Paramecium*, 218, 219
Ribonucleic Acid, *see also* Nucleic acids
 diminution in ribonuclease-fed *Paramecium*, 218, 219
 drug-induced cytoplasmic granules in trypanosomes, 515
 in kinetosomes, 153–155
 in plastids, 327
 synthesis in ciliates, 247–249, 264, 265, 269
 transfer, resemblance to puromycin, 501
Ribose, in *Tetrahymena cilia*, 150
Ribosomes
 in *Crithidia oncopelti*, effect of quinapyramine, 516–517
 Tetrahymena, 32

Root fibrils, of cilia and flagella, 143–147, 166, 189–190
Rosaniline
 induction akinetoplasty by, 487
 resistance as genetic marker in trypanosomes, 486
Rotifers, cilia, morphology, 135, 144
Rule of desmodexy, 167

Salgyran, trichocyst extrusion by, 114
Saponin, use in making cilia models, 152–153
Sarcocystis, movements, 115, 116
Sarcodina, taxonomic significance of movement, 88, 89, 118
Scenedesmus, photosynthetic mutants, 311
Schistosomes, effect of antimonials on phosphofructokinase, 510
Senescence, 253–256, 268
Sennia, biliproteins, 334
Serine
 genetic marker in *Tetrahymena*, 265
 requirement in *Tetrahymena*, 201, 202
Silver-impregnated structures, in ciliates, 102, 104, 166–170
β-Sitosterol
 in nutrition of ciliates, 211–213
 of *Trichomonas*, 215
 of trichomonads, 429, 430
SKF 525A, effect on detoxication of chloroquine, 552–553.
Slime molds, *see* Mycetozoa
Sodium ion, *see* Na$^+$
Sodium sulfate, effect on myonemes, 113
Sorbitol, in *Crithidia nutrition*, 470, 472
Sorocarp of *Dictyostelium*, definition, 341, *see also Dictyostelium*
Spasmonemes, 63, 112–113
Spathidium, control of size, 248, 249
Sperm
 morphology
  in brown algae, spines on flagella, 141
  in flatworm, *Haematolvicus*, axoneme structure, 140
 motility, 97–99, 159
 snail, centrioles in, 135, 186
 kinetosomes, 186
Sperm tails
 glycerinated models of, 152
 isolation flagella from, 148

in lepidoptera, 135
movement, 156
resemblance to cilia and flagella, 132–134
root fibrils, 145
Spermatocytes, centriolar asymmetry, 138
Sphaleromantis
carotenoids, 331
chlorophylls, 321, 322
Spirostomum
cila models by saponin technique, 152–153, 178
ciliary beat, 105, 178
myonemes, 113
Na^+ pump, 216
Sporozoa, movements, 112, 115, 116
Squalene
inactivity in nutrition of ciliates, 211
in trichomonad nutrition, 430
Sr^{++}, effect on suctorian movements, 116
$Sr^{89,90}$, as mutagens in ciliates, 266
Stearate oxidation, in trypanosomes, 513
Stearic acid, *see also* Fatty acids
as oleic acid precursor, 231
requirement of *Trypanosoma cruzi*, 479
Stentor
ciliary beat, 100–102, 165, 172–173, 178, 179, 182, 183, 185
fibrillar systems, 170–171
food vacuoles, 218
kinetosomes, RNA and DNA, 153, 246
morphogenesis, 250–252
myonemes, 113
nuclear behavior, 246
phototaxis, 293
Steroid(s)
acrasin-active, 343–346
content in trichomonads, 417
inhibition O_2 uptake by trichomonads, 406
interconversions by trichomonads, 415
requirements in trichomonads, 419, 422, 424, 426–430
in ciliate nutrition, 210–215
requirements in metazoa, 211
synthesis in *Tetrahymena*, 52
in trypanosomatids, 489

Stigma, *see* Eyespot
Δ^{22}-Stigmasten-3β-ol (stigmastenol), acrasin activity of, 343–345
Stigmasterol
in ciliate nutrition, 211, 213
in trichomonad nutrition, 430
Stilbamidine resistance, in *Trypanosoma rhodesiense*, 488
Streptomycin, bleaching of *Euglena*, 330, 331
Streptomycin resistance, and sensitivity as genetic marker in *Chlamydomonas*, 301, 303–305, 315
Strigomonas, bionomics, 462, 465, *see also Crithidia oncopelti*
Strigomonas oncopelti, see Crithidia oncopelti
Strychnine, 113
Stylomycin, *see* Puromycin
Stylonychia, amylase, 227
Succinic acid
incorporation in *Trichomonas*, 385
oxidation by trichomonads, 401, 402, 406, 411
production by trichomonads, 388, 394, 397, 399, 411
Succinic dehydrogenase
in *Dictyostelium*, 364
inhibition by hematin, 527
in *Tetrahymena*, 226
after UV and X-irradiation, 43
in trichomonads, 406, 409
Succinoxidase
in *Tetrahymena*, 225
in trichomonads, 409
Suctoria
locomotor mechanisms, 63
tentacles, 112, 116, 171
Sulfadiazine, *see also* Sulfonamides
antimalarial action, 538–542, 557
in combined antimalarial therapy, 557–558
in malarial infections, 533–534, 538–542, 557–558
Sulphydryl
in locomotion, 84
in *Tetrahymena*, 28
in trichocyst excretion, 114
Suramin, effect on trypanosome enzymes, 511–513

Suramin salts, with pentamidine in treatment bovine trypanosomiasis, 506, 509
Surfen C, in treatment of bovine trypanosomiasis, 502
Synchronization index, 53–55
Synchrony, of cirri and membranelles, 163
Synura, rhizoplasts, 143

Tartar emetic, resistance in trypanosomes, 519
TEM-4T
  as lipid source, 209
  for trichomonads, 423, 426–429
Temperature
  changes, effect on *Amoeba protens,* 18
  effect on *Astasia* growth, 14–16
  effect on *Tetrahymena* growth, 20–23, 44, 52
  effect on *Tetrahymena* morphogenesis, 25–26, 246, 256, 257, 261
  factors, in ciliate nutrition, 220–221
    in *Crithidia* nutrition, 474, 475, 483, 484
  sensitivity, as genetic marker in *Paramecium,* 265
Testosterone, acrasin activity, 76
Tetraethylthiuram disulfide, effect on malarial infections, 533
Tetrahymena
  acetate, induction of isocitrate lyase, 38
  acetoacetate formation, 40
  acetylcholinesterase, 162
  acid phosphatase in, 40
  acid phosphatases, genetics, 262
  adenopterin, lack of effect on division, 51
  aging, 255
  amino acid requirements, 201–203
  assay of biological value of proteins, 202–203
  ATPase, 64
  azide, effect on division, 45
  B vitamins, assay, 6
  biopterin and folic acid, 207
  5-bromouracil, inhibition by, 51
  canavarine, delayed division by, 49
  carbohydrate(s), 35–36
    utilization, 476

chloramphenical, inhibition of growth by, 49–51
cilia, beat, 100, 104
  chemical composition of, 150–151
  isolation of, 148–149
  morphology, 149
citric synthetase, 38, 39
deoxyadenosine, inhibition by, 29, 31
deoxyguanosine, inhibition by, 29, 31
dinitrophenol, 44, 49, 52
DNA synthesis, 245–247
ethionine, delay of division, 49
facultative parasitism, 220
fats, conversion to glycogen, 37
fibrillar morphology, 145, 171
fluoride, effect on phosphatase, 45
fluoroacetate inhibition of phosphatase, 45
5-fluoro-2′-desoxyuridine, effect on DNA synthesis, 28, 29
  inability to delay division, 51
  inhibition by, 28, 29
p-fluorophenylalanine, effect on growth, 49, 52
5-fluorouracil, effect on division, 51
folic acid requirement, 205–207
food vacuoles, 217–219
fumarase, after x-irradiation, 44
glucose utilization, 38
glutamine utilization, 39
glycerol, conversion to glycogen, 38
glycine utilization, 38
glycogen content, 36
glycogen formation, 38
glyoxylate cycle, 38, 39
immobilization antigens, 257
isocitrate lyase, 38, 39
kinetosomes, DNA and RNA in, 153–155
  isolation, 154–155
lipid synthesis inhibitors, 51, 52
literature on, 200–201
malate synthetase, 38, 39
mating types, 251, 261
6-methylpurine, inhibition of division, 51
micronuclei, after UV, 43
mitochondria, 38
NADH cytochrome c reductase, 37
NADH oxidase, 37

nuclear behavior, 245–248, 258–262
nucleic acid synthesis, inhibition by base
    analogs, 51
nucleic acids, after UV, 42
nutrition, 200–226, 228–229, 231–233
oxidative phosphorylation, 39, 45
phenylalanine utilization, 38
phenylurethane, effect on division, 47
phosphorus content, 34–35
photoreactivation, 41
puromycin, inhibition by, 49
pyridine nucleotides, 32
ribosomes, 32
size of nuclei, 14
sterol requirements in, 211–215
sterol synthesis, 52
succinic dehydrogenase, after UV, 45
swimming patterns, 110
β-thionylalanine, effect on division,
    49
triparanol, 52
ultraviolet light, effect on division, 40,
    45
uracil-free medium, effect on division,
    29
uridine uptake, 29
utilization of aspartate, 38
Tetrahymena corlissi
    effect of cooling, 21
    fatty acids in, 230
    nutrition, 201, 205, 206, 209–215, 220–
        221
Tetrahymena limacis
    nutrition, 203, 206, 210, 215, 220
    parasitism and ciliary meridians, 222
Tetrahymena paravorax
    fatty acids in, 230
    nutrition, 202, 209–213, 215
    polymorphism, 221
Tetrahymena patula
    nutrition, 202–204, 210, 215, 222
    polymorphism, 221, 222
Tetrahymena pyriformis
    generation time, 20
    synchronization index, 54
Tetrahymena rostrata
    effect of cooling, 21
    parasitism and ciliary meridians, 222
Tetrahymena setifera
    fatty acids in, 230
    nutrition, 202–204, 208, 215

Tetrahymena vorax
    effect of cooling, 21
    nutrition, 202–206, 222
    polymorphism, 221–222, 257
    porphyrin synthesis, 226
Tetrahymenol, 214, 233
Tetraselmis
    carotenoids, 328
    chlorophylls, 320
Tetratrichomonas buttreyi, 393, 396–402,
    405, 408–411, 431
Tetratrichomonas gallinarum, 225, 385–
    395, 398–401, 403, 405, 407–412,
    415–419, 424–431, 433, 436, 439–
    443, 445–447, 449–450
Tetratrichomonas limacis, 432
Tetratrichomonas ovis, 444
Tetratrichomonas prowazeki, 433, 434
Thalidomide, effect on *Tetrahymena*, 223
Thallochrysis, carotenoids, 331
Thecamoeba striata, 70, 71
Thiamine
    antagonism by nitrofurazone, 499
    genetic marker in *Chlamydomonas*, 301
    tritiated
        non-uptake by kinetosomes, 153
        uptake by *Tetrahymena*, 28, 31, 42,
            43
Thiamine-dependent, pyruvate decarboxy-
    lase, relation to nitrofuran therapy,
    499
Thioctic acid, in nutrition of ciliates,
    206, 207, 233
Thiolutin, resistance in trichomonads, 436,
    449
β-Thionylalanine, *Tetrahymena*, effect on
    division, 49
Thymidine
    folic-sparing in *Tetrahymena*, 206, 207
    tritiated, in *Tetrahymena*, uptake by
        Euplotes, 218
        uptake by ciliates, 228, 248, 249, 252
Thymine
    and folic acid, 470, 472
    as target of antimalarials, 536–540
Tocopherols, in nutrition of trichomonads,
    225, 424–425, 428
Tolbutamide, effect on protozoa, 223
Topo-phototaxis
    action spectrum, 286–287

definition, 278, 290
in *Englena*, 278–281
Toxoplasma, movements, 115, 116
Tozocide
  cross-resistance with *Trypanosoma congolense* and *Trypanosoma vivax*, 505
  effect on *Trypanosoma congolense*, 505
TPN-isocitric dehydrogenase, in *Dictyostelium*, 364
TPN-malic acid and dehydrogenase, in *Dictyostelium*, 364
Tractellum, definition, 96
Tradescantia, protoplasmic streaming, 86
Transaldolase, in *Tetrahymena*, 223
Transketolase, in *Tetrahymena*, 223
Transmembrane potential, 173–177, 181–183
Trehalose
  in *Dictyostelium*, 359, 361
  in *Trypanosoma* infectivity, 485
  utilization by trichomonads, 385, 386, 400, 402
2,4,5-Triamino-6-hydroxy pyrimidine, and *Crithidia* factor, 470, 472
Triazine(s)
  congeners of proguanil, antimalarial activity, 551–552
  antimalarial, effect on *Lactobacillus casei*, 537, 538
  dihydro, effect on *Plasmodium berghei* and *Plasmodium lophurae*, 548
Tricarboxylic acid cycle
  in ciliates, 223–225
  and trichomonads, 385, 400–402, 409, 411–412
  in trypanosomes, 510–511, 514
Trichites, 171
Trichocysts
  genic control, 252
  morphology, 167–169
Trichomitis batrachorum, 434
Trichomitis marmotae, 432
Trichomonads
  agar-plate colonies, 434–437
  amino acid, composition, 417–419
    requirements, 425–426
  anaerobic products, 388–397, 404–406
  bionomics, 384
  blood-group substances, effect on, 413–414

carbohydrate utilization, 385–411
culture media, defined for, 419–430
endogenous respiration, 397–400
fat-soluble vitamins, 424–430
fatty acid requirements, 419, 423–430
glycogens 415–416, *see also* Glycogen
infections, immunology, 446–448
isolation methods, 431–437
lipid composition, 417
nucleic acid composition, 416–417
pathogenicity, 414, 440–446
preservation by freezing, 438–440
proteolytic enzymes, 414–415
purine-pyrimidine requirements, 425, 449
steroid interconversions by, 415
steroid requirements, 419, 422, 424, 426–430
storage, 437–440
survival factors, 440
of termites, attached spirochetes, 106
vitamin requirements, 424–425
Trichomonas, flagellar movement, 91, 96
Trichomonas acosta, see Hypotrichomonas acosta
Trichomonas ardin-delteili, 446
Trichomonas augusta, see Tritrichomonas augusta
Trichomonas batrachorum, see Trichomitis batrachorum
Trichomonas bosi, see Trichomonas gallinae
Trichomonas buttreyi, see Tetratrichomonas buttreyi
Trichomonas columbae, see Trichomonas gallinae
Trichomonas colubrorum, see Monocercomonas
Trichomonas elongata, see Trichomonas tenax
Trichomonas enteris, see Tritrichomonas enteris
Trichomonas foetus, see Tritrichomonas foetus
Trichomonas gallinae, 205, 405, 409, 417, 419, 423–431, 433, 436, 439–443, 445–447, 449
  infections, 441–443, 445–448
Trichomonas hominis, see Pentatrichomonas hominis
Trichomonas marmotae, 432

Trichomonas ovis, see Tetratrichomonas ovis
Trichomonas pavlovi, 432
Trichomonas prowazeki, see Tetratrichomonas prowazeki
Trichomonas tenax, 416, 417, 431, 441, 443
Trichomonas termopsidis, flagellar movements, 96
Trichomonas vaginalis, 385–390, 394–395, 397–404, 406–419, 425, 426, 432–436, 439–450
  infections, 441–448
Trichonympha
  axonemes, 139
  flagellar grooves, 139
  kinetids, 134, 138–139, 147
  kinetosomes, 137–138
  parabasal fibrils, 144
Trimelarsen, action against *Trypanosoma gambiense* and *Trypanosoma rhodesiense,* 498
Triosephosphate dehydrogenase, in trichomonads, 408
Triosephosphate isomerase, in trichomonads, 407, 408, 411
Triparanol, effect on ciliates, 51, 52, 209, 211, 213, 214, 217, 232, *see also* Hypocholesteremic agents
Triphenylmethane dyes, effect on trypanosome enzymes, 511–513
Triterpenoid, in *Tetrahymena,* 214
Tritrichomonas augusta, metabolism, 385–388, 396, 400–402, 429, 431
Tritrichomonas eberthi, 431, 433
Tritrichomonas enteris, 432
Tritrichomonas foetus
  flagellar movements, 96
  infections, 444, 446, 448
  metabolism, 385–389, 391–392, 394–403, 405–419
Tritrichomonas muris, rhizoplast, 144
Tritrichomonas rotunda, 444
Tritrichomonas suis, metabolism, 389, 391, 395, 397–402, 405–411, 423, 425, 426, 429, 430, 432, 436
Trypanocides, *see also* specific trypanosomes and compounds
  action on enzyme systems, 510–517
Trypanosoma, taxonomy, 462

Trypanosoma acomys, nutrition, 478, 479
Trypanosoma brucei
  akinetoplasty, 486
  in avian eggs, 484
  culture media, 482
  in *Glossina* tissue culture, 485
  glycolysis, 510–511
  growth in vertebrate tissue, 485
  immunity and chemotherapy, 518, 519
  respiration, 510–515
Trypanasoma congolense
  cross-resistance, 508
  drug resistance, 507
  effect of berenil, 503
  effect of dithiobiuret derivatives, 506
  effect of isometamidium, 505
  effect of tozocide, 505
  in *Glossina* tissue culture, 485
  infections, immunity and phenanthridinium prophylaxis, 517
Trypanosoma conorrhini, nutrition, 480, 483
Trypanosoma cruzi
  akinetoplasty, 487
  amino acids in, 488
  effect of azaserine, 489
  flagellar movement, 94
  growth with *Trichomonas,* 431
  infections, 500–502, *see also* Chagas' disease
    in mice, treatment with 2-acetamido-5-nitrothiazole, 500
    treatment with 8-aminoquinolines, 500
    treatment by Flagyl, 500–501
    treatment with furaltadone, 500
    treatment with nitrofuranes, 500–501
    treatment by polyoxyethylene ethers, 500
    treatment by puromycin (stylomycin), 501
    treatment by WIN 5037, 500
  nucleic acid synthesis, 489–490
  nutrition, 477–479, 481
  purine metabolism, 501
  tissue cultures, effect of carbidium, 501
    effect of puromycin, 501–502
Trypanosoma equinum, amino acids in, 488

DATE DUE

Trypanosoma equiperdum
  akinetoplasty, 486, 487
  antipyrimidines, 490–491
  effect of puromycin, 501
  relation drug and antibody resistance, 519
Trypanosoma evansi, akinetoplasty, 486–488
Trypanosoma gambiense
  action of berenil, 497
  action of nitrofurazone, 499
  action of trimelarsen, 498
  akinetoplasty, 487
  culture media, 482
  immunity and chemotherapy, 518, 519
  prophylaxis with pentamidine, 497
  trehalose and infectivity, 485
  tryparsamide-fast strains, 497, 519
Trypanosoma lewisi
  amino acids in, 488
  flagellar movement, 93
Trypanosoma mega
  adenine uptake, 489
  morphogenesis, 482–483
  nutrition, 479–480
Trypanosoma ranae, nutrition, 481, 482
Trypanosoma ranarum, nutrition, 480, 481
Trypanosoma rhodesiense
  action of nitrofurazone, 499
  action of trimelarsen, 498
  animal reservoirs, 497
  culture media, 482
  dependence on preformed adenine, 515–516
  proteins in stilbamine resistant strain, 488
  respiration, 510–515
  trehalose and infectivity, 485
Trypanosoma rotatorium, polymorphisin, 482
Trypanosoma simiae, lack of sexuality, 486
Trypanosoma theileri, nutrition, 480
Trypanosoma vivax
  cross-resistance, 508
  in *Glossina* tissue culture, 485
  infections, effect of berenil, 503
    effect of dithiobiuret derivatives, 506
  effect of isometamidium, 505

Trypanosomatids
  akinetoplasty, 486–488
  chemical composition, 488
  growth, in eggs, 484–485
    in insect tissue culture, 485
    in invertebrate and vertebrate tissue, 485–486
  immunological relationships, 475–476
  lipids, 488, 489
  methionine requirement, 474–475
  nucleic acid synthesis, 489–491
  pyrimidine metabolism, 489–491
  taxonomy, 460–463
Trypanosomes, *see also* Trypanosomatids
  arsenic-resistant, action of nitrofurazone, 498–499
  blood-stream forms, lack of cytochrome oxidase, 510
    metabolic and morphological specializations, 514–515
    non-oxidation of pyruvate, 499
  diamidine-resistant strains, action of nitrofurazone, 498–499
  enzymes in, 510–515
  flagellar movements, 90, 92–97, 101
  glycerinated models of flagellum, 152
  morphology of reservoir, 139
  phenanthridinium-resistant, effect of berenil, 503
  quinaldinium-resistant, effect of berenil, 503
  sexuality, 486
Trypanosomiasis
  bovine, chemotherapy, 502–506
    immunity in, 517–520
  drug resistance, 506–509
  geography, 495–497
  immunity in, 496, 509
  pathogenesis in, 496
Tryparsamide-resistant, trypanosomes, pathogenicity of, 519
    sensitivity to melarsen, 497–498
    use of melarsoprol, 497
Tryptophan, and unconjugated pteridines, 473
Tween 60, in nutrition *Trypanosoma cruzi,* 480
Tween 80
  as fatty acid source, 478, 479